UNITED STATES DEPARTMENT OF COMMERCE

MAURICE H. STANS, *Secretary*

NATIONAL BUREAU OF STANDARDS • LEWIS M. BRANSCOMB, *Director*

Kinetic Data on Gas Phase Unimolecular Reactions

Sidney W. Benson

Stanford Research Institute
Menlo Park, California 94025

and

H. Edward O'Neal

San Diego State College
San Diego, California 92115

NSRDS–NBS 21

National Standard Reference Data Series, National Bureau of Standards (United States) 21, 645 pages (Feb. 1970)
CODEN:NSRDA

Issued February 1970

Abstract

Available rate data on thermally induced, unimolecular, homogeneous gas phase reactions of molecules and free radicals have been reviewed and critically evaluated. Introductory discussion is given of theory and assumptions used in compiling the selected data. Mechanisms of reaction are discussed. The major portion (537 out of 617 pages) of the work presents selected data, with references, in the form of data sheets (one to two pages per molecule). Preferred values are indicated and discussed.

Key words: Arrhenius parameters; chemical kinetics; critical review data; gas phase; mechanisms; molecular reactions; rate constants; reaction rates.

Library of Congress Catalog Card Number: 68-67395

The National Standard Reference Data System provides effective access to the quantitative data of physical science, critically evaluated and compiled for convenience, and readily accessible through a variety of distribution channels. The System was established in 1963 by action of the President's Office of Science and Technology and the Federal Council for Science and Technology, with responsibility to administer it assigned to the National Bureau of Standards.

The System now comprises a complex of data centers and other activities, carried on in academic institutions and other laboratories both in and out of government. The independent operational status of existing critical data projects is maintained and encouraged. Data centers that are components of the NSRDS produce compilations of critically evaluated data, critical reviews of the state of quantitative knowledge in specialized areas, and computations of useful functions derived from standard reference data. In addition, the centers and projects establish criteria for evaluation and compilation of data and make recommendations on needed improvements in experimental techniques. They are normally closely associated with active research in the relevant field.

The technical scope of the NSRDS is indicated by the principal categories of data compilation projects now active or being planned: nuclear properties, atomic and molecular properties, solid state properties, thermodynamic and transport properties, chemical kinetics, and colloid and surface properties.

The NSRDS receives advice and planning assistance from the National Research Council of the National Academy of Sciences-National Academy of Engineering. An overall Review Committee considers the program as a whole and makes recommendations on policy, long-term planning, and international collaboration. Advisory Panels, each concerned with a single technical area, meet regularly to examine major portions of the program, assign relative priorities, and identify specific key problems in need of further attention. For selected specific topics, the Advisory Panels sponsor subpanels which make detailed studies of users' needs, the present state of knowledge, and existing data resources as a basis for recommending one or more data compilation activities. This assembly of advisory services contributes greatly to the guidance of NSRDS activities.

The NSRDS–NBS series of publications is intended primarily to include evaluated reference data and critical reviews of long-term interest to the scientific and technical community.

LEWIS M. BRANSCOMB, *Director.*

III

The NBS Office of Standard Reference Data, as administrator of the National Standard Reference Data System, has officially adopted the use of SI units for all NSRDS publications, in accordance with NBS practice. This publication does not use SI units because contractual commitments with the authors predate establishment of a firm policy on their use by NBS. We urge that specialists and other users of data in this field accustom themselves to SI units as rapidly as possible.

CONTENTS

3. Isomerization Reactions (Other Than Cyclic Compound Reactions)

4. Simple Bond Fission Reactions

Alkanes:

Alkenes and aromatics:

Oxygen compounds:

Acids:

Kinetic Data on Gas Phase Unimolecular Reactions

Sidney W. Benson
Stanford Research Institute
Menlo Park, California 94025

and

H. Edward O'Neal
San Diego State College
San Diego, California 92115

I. Introduction

1.0. Purpose and Objectives

This collection of chemical rate data has been made under the auspices of the National Standard Reference Data System. The purpose of the collection is to satisfy the following needs:

a. To provide in a convenient format a listing and referencing of all available reaction rate data for first-order, unimolecular, homogeneous, gas phase reactions.

b. To provide insofar as possible a critical evaluation of the reported kinetic parameters for each reaction.

c. To compile rate constants and Arrhenius parameters for each reaction and provide as much additional information as may be necessary for the reader to make an independent decision regarding the validity of the reported data.

d. To provide a primary rate data collection to which future kinetic results pertinent to unimolecular, homogeneous gas phase reactions may be conveniently added.

e. To indicate those areas in which theories of kinetics and existing rate data are nonconcordant, and by so doing provide a background with which future experimental investigations may be both planned and compared.

2.0. Scope and Limitations

Our aim has been to review all available rate data on thermally induced unimolecular, homogeneous, gas phase reactions of molecules and free radicals, and to present as comprehensive a collection of these data as possible. Literature through December 31, 1966, has been reviewed. Reactions of special interest appearing in print between January 1, 1967, and February 1, 1968 have also been included.

Although every effort has been made to effect as thorough and complete a survey as possible, it cannot be claimed with certainty that all reactions properly belonging to this monograph have been reviewed. Nor can it be claimed that all available data for any particular reaction listed have been presented. In some instances early literature was extensive, although not particularly reliable. Such literature has been intentionally omitted, or only selectively listed. (Many pyrolysis reactions originally listed in the literature as unimolecular have been omitted without comment where, in our opinion, the reactions were clearly complex chains.)

The initial collection (date of issue February 1970) has been limited to the reaction kinetics of thermally equilibrated molecules and free radicals. Ionic species have not been included. Also absent are the reaction kinetics of vibrationally and/or electronically energetic reactive intermediates produced photochemically, by chemical activation, or by high-energy radiation. "Unimolecular" reactions which are not first-order (i.e., those in their low-pressure or pressure-dependent regions) have been reviewed only in those cases where extrapolations or calculations were made to provide estimates of the limiting high-pressure first-order rate constants.

Evaluations of the reaction rate data necessarily reflect the opinions, views, and possible prejudices of the compilers. The reader should be well aware of the assumptions and ground rules followed by the authors in making decisions on the credibility of the reported rate constants and rate constant parameters. To this end, the discussions on mechanisms relative to each "reaction type" are pertinent. (See also sections I–3 and I–4).

1

3.0. Assumptions

a. Gases are ideal.

b. The Arrhenius equation is a sufficiently accurate description of a rate constant

$$k = Ae^{-E/RT} \text{ sec}^{-1} \qquad \text{I-3.0-1}$$

$$\log k = \log A - E/\theta \qquad \text{I-3.0-2}$$

with $\theta = 2.303\,RT$ in units of kcal/mole.

c. Forward and reverse rate constants of a reaction (even though determined under conditions far from the equilibrium state) are related through the equilibrium constant by the equation,

$$K = k_f/k_r \qquad \text{I-3.0-3}$$

where k_f and k_r are the specific rate constants of a reaction in the forward and reverse directions, respectively.

d. In the high-pressure limit of a unimolecular reaction, molecules of the activated complex are in true equilibrium with reactant molecules. Transition state theory is accepted.

e. The activation energy for radical-radical recombination at 0 °K is zero (i.e., $\Delta E^{\ddagger}_{(\text{rec})} = 0$ at 0 °K).

f. The heat capacity of activation for radical-radical recombinations expressed in the concentration standard state is zero. This particular assumption is discussed in detail in the Bond Fission Reaction section (i.e., $\langle \Delta C^{\ddagger}_v \rangle_{\text{rec}} = 0$).

4.0. Thermodynamic Relations of a Unimolecular First-Order Reaction

a. The general first-order reaction stoichiometry.

$$aA \rightleftharpoons bB + cC \qquad \text{I-4.0-1}$$

b. Thermodynamic relations.

$$\Delta H° = \Sigma \Delta H°_f \text{ (products)} - \Sigma \Delta H°_f \text{ (reactants)} \qquad \text{I-4.0-2}$$

$$\Delta H° = b\overline{\Delta H°_f}(B) + c\overline{\Delta H°_f}(C) - a\overline{\Delta H°_f}(A) \qquad \text{I-4.0-3}$$

$$\Delta S° = \Sigma S° \text{ (products)} - \Sigma S° \text{ (reactants)} \qquad \text{I-4.0-4}$$

$$\Delta S° = b\bar{S}°(B) + c\bar{S}°(C) - a\bar{S}°(A) \qquad \text{I-4.0-5}$$

and finally,

$$\Delta G° = \Delta H° - T\Delta S° = -RT \ln K_p \qquad \text{I-4.0-6}$$

c. The 1 atm standard state is assumed throughout.

4.1. Thermodynamics of the Transition State

a. General activation reaction.

$$\Sigma a_i A_i \rightleftharpoons (T^{\ddagger}) \longrightarrow \text{products} \qquad \text{I-4.1-1}$$

b. Thermodynamic relations.

$$\Delta H^{\ddagger} = \overline{\Delta H°_f}(T)^{\ddagger} - \Sigma a_i \overline{\Delta H°_f}(A_i) \qquad \text{I-4.1-2}$$

$$\Delta S^{\ddagger} = \bar{S}°(T)^{\ddagger} - \Sigma a_i \bar{S}°(A_i) \qquad \text{I-4.1-3}$$

Note that the entropy of the transition state $(\bar{S}°(T)^{\ddagger})$ does not include the entropy contribution of the reaction coordinate. Finally,

$$\Delta G^{\ddagger} = \Delta H^{\ddagger} - T\Delta S^{\ddagger} = -RT \ln K^{\ddagger}. \qquad \text{I-4.1-4}$$

Again, the equilibrium constant $(K^{(\ddagger)})$ between the transition state and the reactant excludes the contribution of the reaction coordinate to the transition state.

4.2. Transition State Theory and the Rate Constant

a. The transition state form of a rate constant is given by the equation

$$k = \kappa \nu K'^{\ddagger}. \qquad \text{I-4.2-1}$$

Here κ is the transmission coefficient, ν is the frequency with which the activated complex crosses the transition state to products, and $K'^{\ddagger}$ is the complete equilibrium constant between the reactants and the transition state. When the reaction coordinate is factored out of the equilibrium constant, either as a very loose vibration or as a translation, I-4.2-1 becomes (see, for example K. J. Laidler, *Chemical Kinetics*, McGraw-Hill Book Co., New York, 2d ed., p. 72)

$$k = \frac{kT}{h} K^{\ddagger}. \qquad \text{I-4.2-2}$$

In the above, the transmission coefficient has been set equal to unity and $K^{\ddagger}$ has been previously defined (I-4.1-4). In this form, transition state theory reduces kinetics to thermodynamics. As such, the thermodynamics of reactants, products, and transition states have been a primary concern of this monograph. In fact, the principal criterion used to evaluate the reported reaction rate data has been the estimated thermochemistry of transition states.

b. Classical form.

Writing $K^{\ddagger}$ in terms of entropy and enthalpy one

2

obtains,

$$k = \frac{kT}{h} e^{\Delta S_T^{\ddagger}/R} \times e^{-\Delta H_T^{\ddagger}/RT} \qquad \text{I–4.2–3}$$

c. Statistical form.

From statistical thermodynamics we have the following relations:

$$Z = \left(\frac{QeV}{N}\right)^N; \qquad \text{I–4.2–4}$$

$$S^\circ = \frac{(H_T^\circ - H_0^\circ)}{T} + k \ln(Z) \qquad \text{I–4.2–5}$$

Substitution of the above into I–4.2–3 for the general activation reaction (I–4.1–1) gives,

$$k = \frac{kT}{h} \frac{\Phi^{\ddagger}}{\Pi_i \Phi_i^{a_i}} \left(\frac{e}{N}\right)^{\Delta n^{\ddagger}} e^{-\Delta H_0^{\ddagger}/RT} \qquad \text{I–4.2–6}$$

or

$$k = \frac{kT}{h} \frac{\bar{Q}^{\ddagger}}{\Pi_i Q^{a_i}} \left(\frac{V}{N}\right)^{\Delta n^{\ddagger}} e^{-\Delta E_0^{\ddagger}/RT} \qquad \text{I–4.2–7}$$

In the above, V has been factored from the translational partition functions (i.e., $\Phi = QV$) in order to more clearly indicate the choice of thermodynamic standard states and also the units of the rate constant.

4.3. Transition State Theory and the Relations Between the Experimental Activation Energy and the Enthalpy of Activation

a. By definition, the experimental activation energy is given by,

$$E = RT^2 \frac{d \ln k_{\exp}}{dT} = RT^2 \left[\frac{d}{dT} \ln \frac{kT}{h} + \frac{d}{dT} \ln \left(\frac{Q^{\ddagger}}{\Pi_i Q_i^{a_i}}\right) \right.$$

$$\left. + \Delta \dot{n}^{\ddagger} \frac{d}{dT} \ln \left(\frac{V}{N}\right) - \frac{d}{dT} \left(\frac{\Delta E_0^{\ddagger}}{RT}\right) \right] \qquad \text{I–4.3–1}$$

b. For a unimolecular reaction ($\Delta n^{\ddagger} = 0$), $\Delta H_T^{\ddagger} = \Delta E_T^{\ddagger}$. Then from I–4.3–1,

$$E_{\text{(uni)}} = RT + (\Delta E_T^{\ddagger} - \Delta E_0^{\ddagger}) + \Delta E_0^{\ddagger}, \text{ and}$$

$$E_{\text{(uni)}} = \Delta E_T^{\ddagger} + RT = \Delta H_T^{\ddagger} + RT \qquad \text{I–4.3–2}$$

c. For a bimolecular reaction ($\Delta n^{\ddagger} = -1$); $\Delta H_T^{\ddagger} = \Delta E_T^{\ddagger} - RT$.

(1) With the rate constant expressed in concentration units, k_c (e.g., k (l/mole-sec),

$$E_{c(\text{bi})} = RT + \Delta E_T^{\ddagger} = \Delta H_T^{\ddagger} + 2 RT \qquad \text{I–4.3–3}$$

(2) With k expressed in pressure units, k_p (e.g., k (atm^{-1} sec^{-1})).

(Note that $V = \dfrac{RT}{p}$ in 4.3–1.)

$$E_{p(\text{bi})} = RT + \Delta E_T^{\ddagger} - RT = \Delta E_T^{\ddagger}. \qquad \text{I–4.3–4}$$

Since

$$\Delta H_T^{\ddagger} = \Delta E_T^{\ddagger} - RT \qquad \text{I–4.3–5}$$

and

$$\Delta E_T^{\ddagger} = \Delta E_0^{\ddagger} + T\langle \Delta C_V^{\ddagger} \rangle, \qquad \text{I–4.3–6}$$

where

$$T\langle \Delta C_V^{\ddagger} \rangle \equiv \int_0^T \Delta C_V^{\ddagger} dT,$$

one may also write,

$$E_{p(\text{bi})} = \Delta H_T^{\ddagger} + RT$$

$$\text{I–4.3–7}$$

or,

$$E_{p(\text{bi})} = \Delta E_0^{\ddagger} + T\langle \Delta C_V^{\ddagger} \rangle. \qquad \text{I–4.3–8}$$

The latter relation (I–4.3–8) is discussed at some length with regard to radical-radical recombination reactions in the bond fission reaction section (V–3.0).

4.4. Transition State Theory and the Relations Between the Arrhenius A-Factor and the Entropy of Activation

a. Experimentally, the activation energies of reactions are usually obtained from Van't Hoff plots (i.e., $\log k$ versus $\frac{1}{T}$). Similarly, rate constants are usually reported in the Arrhenius form.

Thus,

$$k = A e^{-E_a/RT} \qquad \text{I–4.4–1}$$

The relations between the experimental activation energy and transition state theory have been presented in section I–4.3. From I–4.2–3 and the appropriate activation energy relations of I–4.3, the corresponding relations between the Arrhenius A-factors and the transition state entropies can be obtained.

1. Unimolecular reactions, units of k (sec^{-1}), (see I–4.3–2).

$$A = \frac{ekT}{h} e^{\Delta s^{\ddagger}/R} \text{ (sec}^{-1}). \qquad \text{I–4.4–2}$$

2. Bimolecular reactions, units of k (1/mole-sec), (see I–4.3–3).

$$A = \frac{e^2 kT}{h} e^{\Delta S^{\ddagger}/R} \text{ (1/mole-sec).} \qquad \text{I–4.4–3}$$

3. Bimolecular reactions, units of k (atm^{-1} sec^{-1}), (see I–4.3–7).

$$A = \frac{ekT}{h} e^{\Delta S^{\ddagger}/R} \text{ (atm}^{-1}\text{ sec}^{-1}\text{).} \qquad \text{I–4.4–4}$$

It should be emphasized that $\Delta S^{\ddagger}$ is always the entropy of activation for the *pressure* standard state and does not include the entropy contribution of the reaction coordinate in the transition state.

4.5. Thermodynamics and the Arrhenius Parameters of Bond Fission Reactions

a. For the reaction,

$$R - R' \underset{k_b}{\overset{k_f}{\rightleftharpoons}} R + R' \qquad \text{I–4.5–1}$$

the thermodynamics have been defined in section I–4.0 and the kinetic relations have been given in sections I–4.3 and I–4.4. Since $K = (k_f/k_b)$, we have

$$K = e^{\Delta S_T^{\circ}/R} \times e^{-\Delta H_T^{\circ}/RT} = \frac{A_f e^{-E_f/RT}}{A_{b(p)} e^{-E_b/RT}}. \qquad \text{I–4.5–2}$$

b. The activation energy for bond fission reactions.

1. For rate constants using the pressure standard state, the exponential terms are directly related to ΔH°. Thus,

$$E_{p(f)} = \Delta H_T^{\circ} + E_{p(b)}. \qquad \text{I–4.5–3}$$

Also, $\quad E_{p(f)} = \Delta H_T^{\circ} + \Delta E_0^{\ddagger} + (T)\langle \Delta C_V^{\ddagger} \rangle_{(b)}$

and since we have assumed $\Delta E_0^{\ddagger} = 0$, this becomes

$$E_{p(f)} = \Delta H_T^{\circ} + (T)\langle \Delta C_V^{\ddagger} \rangle_{(b)}. \qquad \text{I–4.5–4}$$

2. For rate constants using the concentration standard state,

$$E_c = E_p - \Delta n^{\ddagger} RT = E_p + RT = \Delta H_T^{\circ}$$

$$+ T\langle \Delta C_V^{\ddagger} \rangle + RT = \Delta E_T^{\circ} + 2RT. \qquad \text{I–4.5–5}$$

c. The A-factor for bond fission reactions.

1. When the rate constant for recombination is in pressure units, the A-factor ratio is directly

related to ΔS°. Thus,

$$A_{f(\text{sec}^{-1})} = A_b e^{\Delta S_T^{\circ}/R}$$

and $\quad A_f = k_{b(p)} e^{\langle \Delta C_V^{\ddagger} \rangle_b/R} \times e^{\Delta S_T^{\circ}/R}. \qquad \text{I–4.5–6}$

2. When the rate constant for recombination is in concentration units, conversion to pressure units and equation I–4.5–6 gives

$$A_{f(\text{sec}^{-1})} = \frac{k_{b(c)}}{RT} e^{\langle \Delta C_V^{\ddagger} \rangle_b/R} e^{\Delta S_T^{\circ}/R} \qquad \text{I–4.5–7}$$

5.0. Thermochemical Data Sources
See references [1–16], p. 61.

6.0. General Index

a. Filing order.

In general each reaction is listed on a separate sheet. Exceptions to this rule are those reactions which have been studied collectively under identical experimental conditions for correlation purposes (e.g., the study of inductive, resonance, and steric effects of group substitutions located some distance from the reaction center(s)).

b. Classification and subclassification.

Molecular reactions are classified in one of four reaction types: (1) Molecular eliminations (or complex fissions); (2) Isomerizations of noncyclic compounds; (3) Cyclic compound reactions; and (4) Simple bond fissions. (See index for complete details.) Free radical reactions are treated as a fifth and separate group. Within each of the four major categories, reactions are subgrouped according to mechanistic and structural similarities. This offers the reader the distinct advantage of being able to rapidly scan the results for many reactions of the same kind.

c. Reactions have been indexed alphabetically in terms of the reactant(s). The section index lists the categories and subgroups into which each reactant molecule has been filed.

7.0. Reaction Sheet Information

7.1. Reaction Thermodynamics

Tabulated below the reaction are the standard state (1 atm, ideal gas) molar entropies, heats of formation, and specific heats of reactants and products at 25 °C. In most cases the thermodynamic values listed are those calculated or estimated from group additivities (Appendix A). The probable errors in these values should rarely exceed

4

± 1.5 g/mole in $\bar{S}^\circ$ and $\bar{C}_p^\circ$ and ± 1.5 kcal/mole in $\Delta \bar{H}_f^\circ$. Estimates which have greater uncertainty have generally been placed in parenthesis. For convenience the estimated reaction entropy, enthalpy, and heat capacity are also given.

7.2. Rate Constants

The Arrhenius parameters of each study are given as $\log A(\text{sec}^{-1})$ and $E(\text{kcal/mole})$. A rate constant for each study calculated at a mean reaction temperature is also listed. This will facilitate comparisons of the experimental reaction rates of all the studies for any given reaction.

7.3. Experimental Information

Experimental details and other pertinent observations for each study are given as follows under several headings: Conditions, System, Surface, and Experimental.

a. *Conditions.*

1. The temperature range of study (degrees Kelvin).

2. The pressure range of study (mm Hg or torr).

3. The specific pressure at which rate constants for the Arrhenius plot have been obtained (always indicated by parentheses, in units of mm Hg).

b. *System.*

Possibilities are: static, flow, stirred flow, shock tube, or single-pulse shock tube.

c. *Surface.*

Effects are summarized as:

1. None. This indicates that rate constants obtained in a packed reaction flask were the same as those obtained in the unpacked vessel within experimental error.

2. $<X\%$. Maximum contributions of surface reaction were obtained by comparing the rate constant increase to the surface/volume ratio increases and estimated from the equation,

$$X\% = \left[\left(\frac{k_{s-k}}{k} \right) \Big/ \left(\frac{VS_s - SV_s}{SV_s} \right) \right] \times 100.$$

Here, k_s, V_s, and S_s equal the rate constant volume and surface area appropriate to the packed reaction vessel and k, S and V are the rate constant, surface, and volume of the unpacked flask.

3. ―――――. A bar or blank indicates that no mention of any experimental test for surface effects was made.

d. *Experimental.*

1. Methods of product and reactant analysis.

2. Methods of analysis or experimental measurement(s) employed for obtaining the data from which the rate constants were evaluated.

3. Pertinent experimental observations and findings (e.g., abnormal surface effects, pressure falloff behavior, unusual reaction side products, effects of added gases with regard to catalysis, inhibition, collisional activation (3d body effects), unusual mechanistic interpretations, significant theoretical calculations or observations).

7.4. References

References to each experimental study are numbered and listed on the same line as the Arrhenius parameters of that study.

7.5. Preferred Values or Evaluation

Preferred values will generally be those judged to be most consistent with the experimental reaction rate and transition state theory. In some instances, where experimental errors are believed to be large enough to accommodate changes in the reported Arrhenius parameters, preferred values are those estimated from transition state calculations.

7.6. Comments

Mechanistic interpretations by the authors are discussed here. In addition, results of transition state calculations are given for the purpose of comparison with the experimental values. Reactions reported to be unimolecular, but judged by the reviewers as questionable in this regard, have been cited as either *suspect* or *unreliable*. In all cases, under "Comments" the reasons for having made these evaluations are given and, where possible, other possibly more reasonable interpretations are suggested.

8.0. Glossary

8.1. Standard Thermodynamic and Kinetic Symbols

Symbol	Meaning	Value or Unit(s)
A	pre-experimental factor or A-factor (Arrhenius equation)	sec^{-1}
E	activation energy (Arrhenius equation)	kcal/mole
k	1) specific rate constant	
	2) Boltzmann constant	2) 1.3805×10^{-16} ergs/molec-deg
K_p	equilibrium constant in pressure units	$atm^{\Delta n}$
K_c	equilibrium constant in concentration units	$(moles\ liter)^{\Delta n}$
k_b	rate constant for a reverse (back) reaction	$(conc^{\Delta n}\ sec^{-1})$
k_{rec}	rate constant for a recombination reaction	$(conc^{\Delta n}\ sec^{-1})$
κ	transmission coefficient	
kcal	kilocalories	
g	entropy unit (gibbs)	
$S°$	molar standard state entropy (1 atm, ideal gas)	cal/deg-mole (gibbs/mole)
$\Delta H_f°$	molar standard state heat of formation (1 atm, ideal gas)	kcal/mole
$C_p°$	molar standard state specific heat (1 atm, ideal gas)	cal/deg-mole (gibbs/mole)
$\langle \Delta C_p° \rangle$	an average heat capacity change between two thermodynamic states over a temperature range	gibbs/mole
$\Delta G°$	molar gibbs free energy (1 atm, ideal gas)	kcal/mole
$(\ )_p$	sub p signifies the 1 atm standard state	
$(\ )_c$	sub c signifies the concentration (moles/liter) standard state	
$(\ )_T$	sub T signifies ' at the temperature T'	
$(\ )_0$	sub 0 signifies ' at 0 °K'	
N	Avogadro's number	
R	gas law constant	1.987 cal/mole, deg
		0.08203 l-atm/mole, deg
h	Planck constant	6.625×10^{-27} ergs-sec
α	collision efficiency of energy exchange	
T	temperature	degrees Kelvin
$\bar{T}$	mean temperature	degrees Kelvin
t	time	seconds
Δn	mole change in a chemical reaction	moles
e	Naperian natural log base	2.717
[ ]	1) concentration	1) moles/liter
	2) a quantity whose value has been estimated on the basis of the reported Arrhenius parameters	2) variable
( )	1) an estimated thermodynamic quantity which may entail errors in excess of 2 gibbs/mole or 2 kcal/mole	
	2) the pressure range of study employed for rate constant measurements used to determine the Arrhenius parameters	2) mm Hg (torr)
θ	energy equivalent of temperature $2.303(R)T$	kcal/mole
$(\ )^{\ddagger}$	transition state	
$\Delta S_T^{\ddagger}$	entropy of activation (excluding that of the reaction coordinate)	cal/deg-mole
$\Delta H_T^{\ddagger}$	enthalpy of activation (excluding that of the reaction coordinate)	kcal/mole
r.c.	reaction coordinate	
Φ	total molecular partition function	pure number
Q	total molecular partition function with V factored out (i.e. $QV = \Phi$)	V^{-1}
$Q^{\ddagger}$	total molecular partition function of the transition state (excluding the r.c.)	pure number

Z	1) total molar partition function	1) pure number
	2) kinetic theory collision frequency first-order rate constant	2) sec^{-1}
t_c	contact time in a flow system	
δ_P	partial pressure of a reactant	
P_T	total pressure	
RRK	Rice-Ramsperger-Kassel theory of unimolecular reactions	
RRKM	Rice-Ramsperger-Kassel-Marcus theory of unimolecular reactions	
$M_{1/2}$	pressure at which $k_{uni} = \frac{1}{2}k_\infty$ $\quad RRK - M_{1/2} = \dfrac{A_\infty}{Z}\left[\dfrac{sRT}{E_\infty + sRT}\right]^{s-1}$	
s	RRK number of effective oscillators exchanging energy with the reaction coordinate.	

8.2. Notations Used in Illustrations of Transition State Calculations

$(X \ominus Y)_z$	an internal rotation of group X against group Y around the $(X-Y)$ bond axis with a rotational barrier of Z kcal/mole (for values of various rotations see appendix)	
$(X \ominus \infty)_z$	an internal rotation of group X against an infinitely heavy group with rotational barrier of Z kcal/mole	
$(X_{4e})_t$	a torsional motion about a 4 electron (normal double bond) as in the olefin X (for definitions of X see appendix)	
$(X_{3e})_t$	a torsional motion about a 3 electron (3/2 order) bond as in the olefin X	
$(X-Y)_{(Z)}$	a single bond stretch between groups (or atoms) X and Y	Z is the vibration frequency in cm^{-1}
$(X \cdot Y)$	a 1-electron (or half) bond stretch between groups or atoms X and Y	
$(X \cdot \,^Y{\searrow}Z)$	a bond bend involving a single bond $(Y-Z)$ and a 1-electron bond $(X \cdot Y)$ about the XYZ angle	
$(x^{\nearrow Y}{\searrow}z)_r$	a bond bend about the XYZ angle	r is the frequency in cm^{-1}
$x{\cdot}{\overset{Y}{\frown}}z$	a resonance conditions with kekulé structures $(x{=}^Y{\searrow}z \rightleftharpoons x{\cdot}^{-Y}{=}z)$	
$DH^\circ(X-Y)$	the $(X-Y)$ bond dissociation energy	kcal/mole
$E_{(Res)}$	resonance energy	kcal/mole
E_{c_x}	the activation energy for an X atom ring closing reaction	kcal/mole
$E_{H\text{-mig.}}$	the activation energy for an H-atom migration reaction	kcal/mole

8.3. Symbols Designating Analytical Methods and Experimental Rate Measurement Methods

Symbol	Meaning	Symbol	Meaning
M.S.	Mass spectrometry	B.P.−P.V.	Boiling point separation− pressure volume product
CHEM.	Standard chemical techniques		
G.L.C.	Gas-liquid phase partition chromatography	St.	Static
		Fl	Flow
O.R.	Optical rotation	Sh	Shock tube
ρ	Density	S P Shock	Single-pulse shock tube
M.P.	Melting points	ΔP	Manometric measurements
U.V.	Ultraviolet spectroscopy	Pol.	Polarographic
V	Visible spectroscopy	n_r	Refractive Index
I.R.	Infrared spectroscopy		
N.M.R.	Nuclear magnetic resonance spectroscopy		

9.0. Experimental Errors

Detailed discussions of the experimental errors involved in kinetic measurements are referenced in most physical chemistry and kinetics texts. We do not intend to reiterate or extend such treatments here. Rather, our purpose is to indicate the general magnitude of the average errors which might reasonably be expected in unimolecular reaction rate studies so that the reliability of kinetic studies may be easily evaluated.

It is well known that the most serious errors in kinetic studies are systematic ones. Further, it is recognized that the most frequent systematic errors arise from secondary reactions, heterogeneous effects, or other chemical complications. One of the principal objectives of this monograph has been to recognize the studies containing errors of this nature and subsequently to classify them as either unreliable or suspect. However, the kinds of errors of interest here are those, both systematic and random, which might be encountered in studies having no chemical complications. By careful experimental techniques and precautions, random errors in analysis and temperature control can be kept to a minimum. Thus very high precision in experimental rate constants can be realized and rate constant parameters are often reported to four or five significant figures on the basis of least squares analysis of the resulting Arrhenius plots. However, the errors reported in such cases reflect only very good control over random experimental errors and can not be interpreted to mean that the real experimental errors are necessarily small. Systematic errors could easily be present, and their magnitudes are almost impossible to estimate without prior knowledge of the "correct" behavior of the systems being studied.

Possible sources of error in the measurement of a rate constant are: (1) time measurements, (2) concentration measurements, and (3) temperature measurements. The last is generally the major source of error. Temperature control and temperature homogeneity of the reactor (as in static experiments) or of the reaction zone (as in flow experiments) are both very difficult and very important experimental problems. This is particularly true for gas phase homogeneous and thermally induced unimolecular reactions because they are most often studied in the 300–700 °C temperature range. The use of well-stirred liquid thermostats above 250 °C is uncommon and temperature fluctuations of the order of ± 0.5 to ± 1 °C are the rule, rather than the exception, in air bath and solid core thermostats. At temperatures above 600 °K uncertainties in temperature control and measurement probably exceed these values in most cases.

Most gas-phase kinetic system product analysis in recent years has been made using gas-liquid partition chromatographic techniques. Unless extreme care is exercised in the integration of product peaks and in the determination of product detector sensitivities, analytical precisions of better than ± 2 percent are seldom achieved and errors of up to ± 5 percent are not unusual. Other analytical methods such as M.S., I.R., U.V., etc., have very comparable reliabilities. Since systematic errors in analysis are probably as large as random errors, on the average, one would not expect to obtain analytical measurements of accuracy much better than ± 4 to 5 percent.

Errors due to time measurements in static experiments are very small and may be ignored. In flow experiments, where residence times are not as well defined, time can be a more important source of error; however, it is generally less important than other uncertainties like temperature uniformity and control, or reaction zone volume.

In the completely general case of a dependent variable, $k = f(X_1, X_2 \cdots X_n)$, which is a known function of n independent variables $X_1 \cdots X_n$, the relative error in k due to errors in X_i is given by,[1]

$$\left(\frac{\Delta k}{k}\right)^2 = \sum_{i=1}^{n} \left(\frac{\partial \ln f}{\partial \ln X_i}\right)^2 \left(\frac{\Delta X_i}{X_i}\right)^2. \quad \text{(I–9.0–1)}$$

With $k = f(A_1, A_2, t_1, t_2, T)$; $E = g(k_1, k_2, T_1, T_2)$ and the relations,

$$k = \ln\left(\frac{N_1}{N_2}\right) \bigg/ (t_2 - t_1) \quad \text{(I–9.0.2)}$$

$$k = Ae^{-E/RT} \quad \text{–9.0–3)}$$

$$E = [RT_1T_2/(T_2 - T_1)] \ln (k_2/k_1) \quad \text{(I–9.0–4)}$$

one can evaluate the necessary partial differential coefficients, and obtain,

$$\frac{\Delta k}{k} = \left[\left(\frac{1}{\ln \frac{N_1}{N_2}}\right)^2 \left(\left(\frac{\Delta N_1}{N_1}\right)^2 + \left(\frac{\Delta N_2}{N_2}\right)^2\right) \right.$$

$$+ \left(\frac{t_2}{t_2 - t_1}\right)^2 \left(\frac{\Delta t_2}{t_2}\right)^2$$

$$\left. + \left(\frac{t_1}{t_2 - t_1}\right)^2 \left(\frac{\Delta t_1}{t_1}\right)^2 + \left(\frac{E}{RT}\right)^2 \left(\frac{\Delta T}{T}\right)^2 \right]^{1/2} \quad \text{(I–9.0–5)}$$

$$\frac{\Delta E}{E}=\left[\left(\frac{T_2}{T_2-T_1}\right)^2\left(\frac{\Delta T_1}{T_1}\right)+\left(\frac{T_1}{T_2-T_1}\right)^2\left(\frac{\Delta T_2}{T_2}\right)^2\right.$$
$$\left.+\left(\frac{1}{\ln\frac{k_2}{k_1}}\right)^2\left(\left(\frac{\Delta k_2}{k_2}\right)^2+\left(\frac{\Delta k_1}{k_1}\right)^2\right)\right]^{1/2}. \quad \text{(I–9.0–6)}$$

In the above, N_1, N_2, and t_1, t_2 are the initial and final concentrations and initial and final time measurements respectively used to determine the rate constant in any given run (I–9.0–2), and k_1, k_2, and T_1, T_2 are the rate constants and temperatures used to calculate the activation energy (I–9.0–4).

An examination of the coefficients (in I–9.0–5) indicates that in order to measure the rate constant to an accuracy of $X\%$ [1] $=\Delta k/k\times100$, it is necessary to

(1) measure the time with an accuracy of about

$$\frac{\Delta t}{t}\times100\simeq\left(\frac{t_2-t_1}{t_2}\right)\frac{X\%}{(2)^{\frac{1}{2}}}=\left(\frac{\text{time interval}}{\text{longest time}}\right)\frac{(X\%)}{(2)^{\frac{1}{2}}};$$
$$\text{(I–9.0–7)}$$

(2) measure temperature with an accuracy of about

$$\frac{\Delta T}{T}\times100=\frac{RT\,X\%}{E}; \quad \text{(I–9.0–8)}$$

(3) measure concentration with an accuracy of about

$$\frac{\Delta N}{N}\times100=\ln\left(\frac{N_1}{N_2}\right)\frac{X\%}{(2)^{1/2}}. \quad \text{(I–9.0–9)}$$

A very simple, straightforward, and reasonably reliable estimate of the error in the experimental activation energy can be made from (I–9.0–6). If one determines that errors in k, due to analysis and time variables, are some constant fraction[2] (y) of the error in k, due to temperature measurements and control, then (I–9.0–5) becomes,

$$\frac{\Delta k}{k}=(1+y)^{1/2}\left(\frac{E}{RT}\right)\left(\frac{\Delta T}{T}\right). \quad \text{(I–9.0–10)}$$

Substituting (I–9.0–10) and (I–9.0–4)^2 into (I–9.0–6) gives

$$\frac{\Delta E}{E}=(4+2y)^{1/2}\left(\frac{\overline{T}}{T_2-T_1}\right)\left(\frac{\Delta T}{T}\right). \quad \text{(I–9.0–11)}$$

For an "average" study with $\left(\frac{N_1}{N_2}\right)\simeq e$, $\frac{E}{RT}\simeq35$, $\Delta T\simeq\pm1$ °C, $T_2-T_1\simeq60$ °C, $\overline{T}\simeq600$ °K, $(\Delta N/N)\simeq0.04$, and $(\Delta t/t)\simeq0$, we find that analytical errors are approximately equal to errors arising from the temperature. Thus, $y\simeq1$ and $\frac{\Delta E}{E}=6^{1/2}\times\frac{1.0}{60}\simeq0.040.$ From the critical ratio of 35, this "average" reaction would have an activation energy of 42 kcal/mole, and hence, a probable error in E of $\Delta E\simeq1.7$ kcal/mole. A quick perusal of reported activation energies for identical systems from different laboratories tends to confirm this estimate. Thus, as a first approximation of the probable errors in the activation energy for a thermally induced gas phase homogeneous kinetic reaction, (I–9.0–11) is extremely useful and fairly reliable Finally, from (I–9.0–3), the uncertainty in the Arrhenius A-factor can be calculated from the uncertainty in the activation energy.

With $\quad \Delta E=E(4+2y)^{1/2}(\Delta T/T_2-T_1), \quad$ (I–9.0–12)

$$\Delta[\ln(A)]=\frac{\Delta E}{RT} \quad \text{(I–9.0–13)}$$

or

$$\Delta[\log A]=\frac{\Delta E}{2.3RT}\equiv\Delta E/\Theta. \quad \text{(I–9.0–14)}$$

---

[1] See reference 5, p. 61.

[3] We also set $T_1T_2=(\overline{T})^2$ and
$$\left(\frac{T_2}{T_2-T_1}\right)\simeq\left(\frac{T_1}{T_2-T_1}\right)\simeq\left(\frac{\overline{T}}{T_2-T_1}\right),$$
where $\overline{T}$ is the mean reaction temperature.

[2] $y=\left[\left(\frac{1}{\ln\frac{N_1}{N_2}}\right)^2\left[\left(\frac{\Delta N_1}{N_1}\right)^2+\left(\frac{\Delta N_2}{N_2}\right)^2\right]\right.$
$\left.+\left(\frac{t_2}{t_2-t_1}\right)^2\left(\frac{\Delta t_2}{t_2}\right)^2+\left(\frac{t_1}{t_2-t_1}\right)^2\left(\frac{\Delta t_1}{t_1}\right)^2\right]\Big/\left(\frac{E}{RT}\right)^2\left(\frac{\Delta T}{T}\right)^2$

II. Complex Fissions—Molecular Elimination Reactions

1.0. Four-Center Reactions

Most four-center reactions involve hydrogen halide eliminations from alkyl halides. Reaction heats are 10 to 20 kcal endothermic and reaction entropies range between 30 and 40 g/mole (positive). Surface catalysis is a characteristic of these reactions and "conditioning" of reaction cell walls (by repeated decompositions of the reactant or by other methods) is generally required in order to achieve reproducible rate behavior.

Free radical, chain processes often provide competitive reaction paths to products. The general rules which seem to apply are that competing free radical chain process *increase* in the series RCl, RBr, RI, and *decrease* with increasing alkyl substitution at the α-carbon position. Thus primary halides have more chain decomposition than do secondary halides, which in turn are less unimolecular than tertiary halides. These behaviors have been explained in terms of the relative rates of chain propagation versus chain termination [17, 18].

Rate constant parameters for the homogeneous unimolecular contributions to the eliminations have generally been obtained for systems under "maximum inhibition" of chains. Additions of inhibitors or free radical traps (e.g., propylene, toluene, cyclohexene, etc.) decrease the overall reaction rates by lowering the concentrations of radicals which can propagate chains. At maximum inhibition, rate constants are invariant (with further additions of inhibitor) and are minimum values. Residual reactions are therefore assumed to be molecular. Support for the assumption of the absence of chain processes at maximum inhibition and for the molecularity of the residual reactions comes from several sources. None individually constitute proof of the assumption, but taken collectively they do offer a strong argument for it. The evidence in the case of ethyl bromide, which in the uninhibited system is estimated to be 90 percent chain and 10 percent molecular, is as follows:

1. Maximum inhibition by different inhibitors always reduces decomposition rates to identical first order values [19].
2. Absence of dibenzyl, hydrogen, and ethane in the toluene carrier flow experiments on ethyl bromide [20] suggests that the rate of radical production (i.e., chain initiation) is very slow relative to hydrogen bromide elimination. This in turn implies that free radical chains are long in the uninhibited decomposition and are therefore readily susceptible to inhibition through trapping of the chain carriers. Support for long chains also comes from results on the photochemically initiated ethyl bromide decomposition [21].

3. The hydrogen/deuterium isotope effect in the ethyl bromide uninhibited and in maximum inhibited systems [22] is very different. This suggests that different mechanisms are operative.
4. The hydrogen/deuterium isotope effect for the uninhibited decomposition of ethyl chloride [22] is very similar to that observed in the inhibited ethyl bromide system. This suggests similar decomposition mechanisms, and the ethyl chloride reaction is believed to be an uncomplicated four-center molecular elimination.
5. The rate of decomposition for ethyl bromide in the induction period, which precedes the onset of the well-characterized chain decomposition, has the same Arrhenius parameters as those of the inhibited decomposition [23].
6. Addition of free radical sensitizers (e.g., Br_2 or allyl bromide) to maximally inhibited systems, or to those which apparently have no chain contribution (e.g., *t*-butyl bromide), temporarily accelerates rates, but as these catalysts are removed from the system by reaction, the rates return to those at maximum inhibition [24].
7. Theoretical calculations of the Arrhenius parameters for the reverse association reactions are consistent with the observed reaction rates at maximum inhibition.

In view of these observations and as a result of these reviewers' inability to propose any reasonable homogeneous chain mechanism in the presence of inhibitors which can account for the observed reaction rates, we feel that the residual reactions are essentially unimolecular processes.

1.1. Transition State Estimates of the *A*-factor of Four-Center Elimination Reactions [4]

Reasonable and fairly precise estimates of the Arrhenius *A*-factors for four-center elimination reactions have been made. The method, which involves rather straightforward thermodynamic considerations, is illustrated below for the ethyl chloride reaction. See reference [25] for a more complete discussion.

Ethyl Chloride

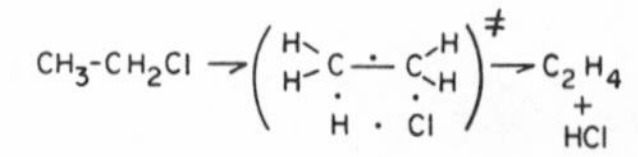

$$CH_3-CH_2Cl \rightarrow \left(\begin{array}{c} H \\ H-C \cdots C \\ | \quad \quad | \\ H \quad \cdot \quad Cl \end{array} \begin{array}{c} H \\ H \end{array} \right)^{\ddagger} \rightarrow \begin{array}{c} C_2H_4 \\ + \\ HCl \end{array}$$

The transition state has been represented in terms of one-, two-, and three-electron bonds. Frequency assignments for the fractional bond order stretches have been assigned using Badger's rule and Pauling's equations relating bond order and bound length [26]. In the absence of any other data, $\frac{1}{2}$-order bond bends have been assigned a frequency of ($\frac{1}{2}$) that for a unit order bend. In following the structural and vibrational frequency changes between the ground state and the transition state, it is clear that the largest entropy effect will arise from the restriction in the internal rotation as the partial Pi bond forms. Other frequency changes are less important. Estimates are shown in table II–1.

---

[1] Estimates of the *A*-factors reported on the data sheets have been made according to procedures outlined in ref. [25]. Methods illustrated here, however, entail some slight modifications of the earlier method which we feel constitutes an improvement. The modifications include some changes in bending frequencies (particularly for one electron bonds which are breaking in the reaction) and include changes in the choice of reaction coordinates. With regard to the latter modification, the reaction coordinate has been assigned to the lowest frequency motion in the transition state. For all but three and four center reactions, the reaction coordinate so designated may be identified with an internal rotation of the ground state rather than a bond stretch (as in ref. [25]). It should be noted however, that the results (*A*-factors) obtained from either method are almost identical for four- and six-center elimination reactions. Significant variations (and improvements) only arise in the cases of Cope and "ene" type isomerizations.

TABLE II–1. *Transition state estimates — ethyl chloride reaction*

Ground State			Activated Complex		
Vibrations	Frequencies (ωcm^{-1})	$S°$ (600 °K)	Vibrations	Frequencies (ωcm^{-1})	$S°$ (600 °K)
4(H–C–H)	1450	1.15	(H·C–C)	575	1.5
			(H·C–H)	725	1.2
			2(H–C–H)	1450	0.56
5(C—H)	3000	0	4(C—H)	3000	0
			(C · H)	2200	0.05
(C—C)	1000	0.65	C⋯C	1300	0.38
4(H–C–C)$_{w,t}$	1150	2.1	4(H–C–C)$_{w,t}$	1150	2.1
(H–C–Cl)	1100	0.6	(H–C·–Cl)	550	1.6
(CH$_3$–C—∞)$_{3.5}$ [a]		5.6	$(\overset{\cdot}{\diagdown}_x)_t$ [b]	400	2.1
(C—Cl)	650	1.3	(C · Cl)	490	1.8
(C–C–Cl)	400	2.1	r.c.		
Totals	$S_T^° = 13.5$			$S_T^{\ddagger} = 11.4$	

[a] The notation (CH$_3$–C—∞)$_{3.5}$ indicates an internal rotation of a methyl group against a relatively large mass rotor with a barrier to rotation of 3.5 kcal/mole.

[b] $(\overset{\cdot}{\diagdown}_x)_t$ indicates the propylene type torsion around a three-electron bond. Such torsion frequencies have been assigned values of $\frac{1}{2}$ the frequency of the corresponding torsion in the normal olefin (e.g., propylene in the above system).

The intrinsic entropy of activation is therefore estimated to be

$$\Delta S^{\ddagger}_{\text{int}} = 11.4 - 13.5 = -2.1 \text{ g/mole}.$$

The reaction coordinate degeneracy is 3 (i.e., there are three hydrogens on the methyl group which can react), and this gives a real entropy of activation of

$$\Delta S^{\ddagger} = -2.1 + R \ln 3 = +0.1 \text{ g/mole}.$$

Thus we estimate (600 °K),

$$A = \frac{ekT}{h} e^{\Delta S^{\ddagger}/R} = 10^{13.6} \text{ sec}^{-1} ; A_{\text{obs}} = 10^{13.6 \pm 0.5} \text{ sec}^{-1}.$$

The transition state calculations are for the most part relatively insensitive to the nature of the halogen. Note that the reaction coordinate has been assigned to that motion in the reactant which transforms into the lowest frequency motion in the transition state leading to reaction.

Estimated A-factors, in some reactions, seemed more reasonable than those reported. In these cases the preferred activation energy is the one calculated from the reported rate constant and the calculated A-factor.

2.0. Three-Center Eliminations

The A-factors of three-center elimination reactions have definite limits placed on them by thermodynamics and by transition state theory. Since no internal rotations are involved, entropies lost in activation cannot be very large. In the "tightest" possible activated complex, the entropy of activation may be equated to the negative of the sum of the entropies associated with the four bending and two stretching frequencies of the X and Y species in the reactant. It is unlikely that all six modes would contribute more than 5 to 7 g/mole at decomposition temperatures. This sets a lower limit on the frequency factor, $A \geq 10^{12} \text{ sec}^{-1}$. An absolute upper limit is set by the overall reaction entropy and Z (the collision frequency or maximum rate of the back reaction). Thus $A = A_b e^{\Delta S^{\circ}/R} \leq Z e^{\Delta S^{\circ}/R}$ Since usual values of Z and ΔS° are of the order of 10^9 atm^{-1} and 35 g/mole, respectively, a maximum value for the frequency factor of $A \leq 10^{16.6} \text{ sec}^{-1}$ is obtained. It is unlikely that either of these limits are actually approached and we believe that three-center elimination A-factors should be very close to normal (i.e., $A \simeq \left(\frac{ekT}{h}\right)$).

3.0. Five-Center Elimination Reactions

Decompositions of the nitroalkanes are the only known examples of reactions which probably proceed through five-center transition states. Reaction enthalpies and entropies are similar to the four- and six-center reactions and fall within the ranges of from 10 to 20 kcal endothermic and from 30 to 40 g/mole (positive), respectively. The reaction rates are surface sensitive; therefore conditioning of reaction chamber walls is required. Product complexity clearly indicates the occurrence of competitive free radical and heterogeneous processes.

3.1. Evaluation

By the transition state methods used to estimate A-factors for the four- and six-center reactions, the A-factor estimates of the five-center reactions are between one and two orders-of-magnitude higher than those reported. Either the data are complicated by an incomplete suppression of chain decomposition, or transition state methods for estimating A are inadequate. It should be noted that if the A-factors reported for the nitro compounds are correct, the reported entropies of activation correspond closely to the maximum possible entropy losses for activation.

4.0. Six-Center Elimination Reactions

Reaction thermodynamics are similar to those of other elimination reactions (i.e., $\Delta H^{\circ} = 10$–20 kcal; $\Delta S^{\circ} = 30$–40 g/mole). Wall conditioning is generally required in the static systems before reproducible rate behavior can be achieved. In other respects the reactions are well behaved, going smoothly to the expected products with no apparent complications arising from competing chain processes. The only exceptions to the above seem to be the chloroformate esters, which are extremely surface sensitive and give some products which are most reasonably explained in terms of chain processes.

4.1. Evaluation – Transition State Estimates of the A-Factors of Six-Center Elimination Reactions [4]

The six-center elimination reactions have relatively large negative entropies of activation. Since at least three internal rotations are restricted in the transition state, a maximum of about 24 g/mole (about 8 g/mole per internal rotation at 600 °K) could be lost in forming the ring. Observed entropies of activation are about half this amount; therefore the cyclic transition states must be reasonably loose. Our evaluation of the reported parameters has been based principally on transition state estimates of $\Delta S^\ddagger$ and the A-factors. As an example, the calculation of the frequency factor of the ethyl acetate reaction is illustrated below.

TABLE II–2.   *Transition state estimates—ethyl acetate reaction*

Ground State			Activated Complex		
Vibrations	Frequencies (ωcm^{-1})	$S°$ (600 °K) g/mole	Vibrations	Frequencies (ωcm^{-1})	$S°$ (600 °K) g/mole
			2(H–C–H)	1450	0.6
4(H–C–H)	1450	1.2	(H·C·C)	575	(1.5)
			(H·C·H)	725	(1.2)
$[2(CH_3)+2(CH_2)]_{w,t}$	1150	2.1	$4(CH_2)_{w,t}$	1150	2.1
(C=O)	1700	0.2	(C⋯O)	1325	0.3
(C—O)	1100	0.6	(C⋯O)	1400	0.3
(C—O)$_{ether}$	1200	0.5	(C · O)	700	1.2
(C—C)	1000	0.6	(C⋯C)	1300	0.4
5(C—H)	3000	0	4(C—H)	3000	0
			1(C · H)	2200	0.05
(CH$_2$)$_r$	700	1.2	(CH$_2$)$_r$	700	1.2
(O=C—O)	420	2.0	(O⋯C⋯O)	420	2.0
(C–O–C)	420	2.0	(C–O–C)	210	3.5
(C–C–O)	400	2.1	(C⋯C · O)	200	3.5
(CH$_3$⊂∞)$_{5.0}$		5.2	(⋯\\)$_t$	400	2.1
(iPr⊂nPr)$_{12}$		6.6	r.c.		
(Et⊂∞)$_{6.5}$		7.4	(⟩–\\)$_t$	125	4.4
Totals		$S_T° = 31.7$			$S_T^\ddagger = 24.3$

13

4.2. Ethyl Acetate

$$CH_3-C\overset{O}{\underset{O-CH_2-CH_3}{\big\langle}} \longrightarrow \left(CH_3-C\overset{O\cdots H}{\underset{O\,\cdot\,CH_2}{\big\langle}}\overset{\cdot}{CH_2}\right)^{\neq} \longrightarrow CH_3COOH + C_2H_4$$

Frequency assignments in the ground state and activated complex are detailed in table II–2 (excluding the 12 acid methyl frequencies).

The intrinsic entropy of activation is therefore estimated to be

$$\Delta S^{\ddagger}_{int} = 24.4 - 31.7 = -7.3 \text{ g/mole.}$$

The reaction path degeneracy is three, therefore the "real" entropy of activation is

$$\Delta S^{\ddagger} = -7.3 + R\ln 3 = -5.1 \text{ g/mole.}$$

We therefore estimate the ethyl acetate A-factor (700 K) as

$$A = \frac{ekT}{h}\, e^{\Delta S^{\ddagger}/R} = 10^{12.5}\text{sec}^{-1}; \; A_{obs} = 10^{12.6}\text{sec}^{-1}.$$

We believe that transition state estimates of the above kind are probably reliable on the average to better than a factor of 2.

III. Cyclic Compound Reactions

1.0. Characteristics

For convenience, cyclic compounds have been divided into several groups according to ring size (monocyclic reactants) and ring complexity (polycyclic reactants).

Experimental data for cyclic compound decompositions and isomerizations, especially cyclopropane and cyclobutane derivatives, are exceptionally good. The reactions are very well behaved kinetically, being for the most part free from surface effects and free from radical chain processes. Free radical chain inhibitors such as propylene, toluene, and nitric oxide are without effect on the observed reaction rates or reaction products. Also, rate constants determined using packed and unpacked reaction vessels are the same within experimental error. Many of the small ring (three- and four-membered rings) decompositions and isomerizations exhibit well behaved (i.e., consistent with theory) pressure falloff characteristics as predicted qualitatively by the old Lindemann theory (and quantitatively by the Rice-Ramsperger-Kassel-Marcus theory) of unimolecular reactions. There can be little doubt that these reactions are homogeneous, gas phase, unimolecular reactions.

2.0. The Biradical Mechanism

The mechanism of small ring compound decompositions has been the subject of controversy dating back to the first reaction of this type studied in any detail (cyclopropane). Two mechanisms were proposed, (1) a concerted process involving simultaneous C—C bond rupture and formation with an H-atom migration and (2) a consecutive step process proceeding through a biradical intermediate. In an elegant study of the *cis-trans* isomerization of 1,2-dideuterocyclopropane, Rabinovitch and Schlag showed that the rate of geometric isomerization was roughly 12 times faster than the structural isomerization to propylene and that the pressure falloff characteristics of the deuterated and undeuterated cyclopropanes were the same. The former result provided support for the biradical mechanism and the latter results indicated that the RRK (Rice-Ramsperger-Kassel) theory of unimolecular reactions was preferrable to the Slater theory. (See references [27], [28], and [29].) Differences of opinion, largely semantic, still exist with regard to the nature of the biradical intermediate. Whether the biradical is fully developed with little interaction between methylene ends or whether an appreciable interaction exists (an expanded ring) remains a subject of some debate.

The nature, and even the physical reality, of biradical intermediates in cyclic compound reactions has been argued extensively and will not be debated further here. However, there can be little question about the pragmatic value of the mechanism. From this review, our findings are that the kinetics of virtually all of the small ring compound reactions (with the exception of cyclobutenes) and the kinetics of the vast majority of the large ring and polycyclic compounds, are in excellent agreement with the biradical mechanism predictions, both qualitatively (with regard to reaction products) and quantitatively (with regard to transition state estimates of the Arrhenius parameters governing the formation of products).

Results of the transition state estimates made for these reactions are given on the data sheets with the preferred values. Thus, comparison ,with the experimental parameters can readily be made.

3.0. General Remarks Concerning Transition State Calculations

Estimates of activation entropies and enthalpies are based on the known or estimated thermodynamic properties of the reactants and biradical intermediates. For this purpose, the reader is referred to reference [3] (Thermochemical Data Sources). A partial list of the more useful molecular and free radical group additivity values is given in Appendix B. Methods employed in the estimation of the radical group additivities and their use are not reviewed here. The reader is referred to the references indicated above. However additivity values in the appendix should be sufficient to enable the reader to follow the transition state calculations illustrated below.

To facilitate activation entropy and enthalpy estimates, thermodynamic paths from reactants to transition states have been used. These paths are *not* to be confused with the kinetic (or mechanistic) reaction path. Circled numbers indicate the calculational steps in the thermodynamic estimates. Step ① is ring opening to the biradical at 298 °K; step ② is incorporation of resonance (if any) in the biradical at 298 °K; step ③ is the correction to $\Delta S°$ and $\Delta H°$ for the average heat capacity change for steps ① and ② over the temperature range of 298 °K to $\bar{T}$ experimental. Steps ④ and above are estimates of the activation entropies and enthalpies from the biradical to the various postulated transition states. These latter steps are detailed in terms of vibrational and rotational changes occurring. Enthalpy and entropy estimates, given below and above the arrows respectively, come from the additivity values. All entropy estimates are intrinsic entropies (i.e., symmetry numbers, optical isomer effects, and electron spin effects are not included). The activation entropy is calculated from the intrinsic entropy change by adding the entropy associated with the reaction path degeneracy, where reaction path degeneracy is related to the above by the equation

$$K_{(r.p.d.)} = \frac{\sigma n^{\ddagger}}{\sigma^{\ddagger} n}.$$

In the above, σ, n, and $\sigma^{\ddagger}$, $n^{\ddagger}$ are the overall symmetry numbers and number of optical isomers in the ground state and transition state respectively. With regard to spin, only ground state singlets are important. For this reason, electron spin in the biradical need not be (and has not been) included. A big contribution to step ④ insofar as $\Delta S^{\ddagger}$ is concerned, is the substitution of the contribution due to the reaction coordinate.

4.0. Transition State Estimates for Cyclopropanes

4.1. *Cis*-1 2-d_2-cyclopropane

a. Mechanism

$T = 770$ °K.

b. Transition state estimates

1. *Cis-trans* isomerization. $K_{r.p.d.} = 3$

$$\Delta S^{\ddagger}_{(c \to t)} = 10.0 + 1.9 - 2.5 + R \ln 3 = 11.6 \text{ g/mole}$$

$$A^{\ddagger}_{(c-t) \text{ est}} = \frac{1}{2} \frac{ekt}{h} e^{\Delta S^{\ddagger}/R} = 10^{15.9} \text{ sec}^{-1};$$

$$A_{obs} = \tfrac{1}{2} A_1 = 10^{15.7}, \ 10^{16.1} \text{ sec}^{-1}$$

$$E_{(c-t)} = 64.2 = 54.8 + Ec_3$$

$$Ec_3 = 9.3 \text{ kcal/mole}$$

2. Propene formation. $K_{r.p.d.} = 12$

$$\Delta S^{\ddagger}_{(prop)} = 10.0 + 1.9 - 9.9 + R \ln 12 = 7.0 \text{ g/mole}$$

$$A^{\ddagger}_{(prop) \text{ est}} = 10^{15.16} \text{ sec}^{-1};$$

$$A_{obs} = 10^{15.12} \text{ sec}^{-1}, \ 10^{15.20} \text{ sec}^{-1}$$

$$E_{prop} = 65.6 = 54.0 + 0.8 + E_{H-mig}$$

$$E_{H-mig} = 10.8 \text{ kcal/mole}.$$

c. Discussion

Geometric isomerization was experimentally observed to be about 12 times faster than structural isomerization; therefore $k_2 \gg k_3$. In addition, the rate constants for internal rotation can be shown to be much faster than either k_2 or k_3. This means that the rate-determining steps for *cis-trans* isomerization and for propylene formation are ring opening and H-migration, respectively. Thus the transition states indicated. Thermodynamics of the various steps in the calculation are:

$$\Delta X°_① = [X°(\dot{V}) - X°(\nabla)]_{298°K}$$

$$\langle \Delta C_P° \rangle_③ = 2.1 \text{ g/mole}$$

The entropy of the transition state for ring opening is assumed to differ from that of the biradical (excluding spin) by the entropy of the reaction coordinate vibration for ring closing.

$$\Delta S_{\circledS}^{\circ} = S^{\circ}[-2(.CH_2\!\!-\!\!\!\!\bigcirc\!\!\!\!-\!\!Et)_{2.3}$$

$$+ 2(P_{4e})_t - (H\overset{C}{\diagdown}C)_{1150\ r.c.}].$$

The entropy of the transition state for H-migration is fairly tight, and close to the entropy of the product olefin. Acitvation energies for C_3 ring closing and 1,2-H-migration from the biradical have been obtained from the preferred values of the experimental activation energies of geometric and structural isomerization, respectively. Cyclopropane is the "standard" reaction for all three-membered ring reactions, and these activation energies have therefore been used to estimate the activation energies of other three-membered ring reactions.

4.2. Vinylcyclopropane

a. Mechanism

b. Transition State Estimates (cis only)

$a=1$ cis effect (cyclopentene formation) (see table A–2).

$a=0$ (all diolefin products).

See table A–2 for group correction for a cis effect.

1. Cyclopentene: $K_{r.p.d.}=2$

$$\Delta S_{C.P.}^{\ddagger} = 10.5 - 5.6 + 1.5 - 6.7 + R \ln 2 = 1.1 \text{ g/mole}$$
$$A_{C.P.\ (est)} = 10^{13.8}\ sec^{-1}; \qquad A_{obs} = 10^{13.5},\ 10^{13.6}\ sec^{-1}$$
$$E_{C.P.} = 49.7 = 52.3 + 1.0 - 12.6 + 0.7 + Ec_5$$
$$Ec_5 = 8.3 \text{ kcal/mole}.$$

As in cyclopropane $k_2 > k_3$. This has been experimentally confirmed by Willcott and Cargle [30]. who showed that geometric equilibration

was at least five times faster than cyclopentene formation. Olefins are minor products; therefore $k_3 > (k_4 + k_5)$. Also, because of the development of allylic resonance in ring opening, only the cis biradical can close to cyclopentene. The activation energy deduced for C_5 ring closing (8.3 kcal/mole) could be attributed to several effects: ring strain (probable), loss of allylic resonance in ring closing (most probable) and/or the barrier to rotation of the ethyl group as it moves to the conformation required for ring closing. Calculations based on low frequencies observed in the Raman spectra of the rotational barriers in various methyl-substituted pentanes (see Appendix C, table 3) suggest barriers ranging from 5 to 12 kcal/mole, depending upon the degree of methyl substitution. Thus the latter effect could be important and could explain the higher than estimated activation energies observed for and for . Because of their substitutions, these reactants might be expected to have higher than "normal" rotational barriers in the biradical. Note that Ec_3 must be less than 10.0 kcal to account for the cis-trans results.

$$\Delta X_{\textcircled{1}}^{\circ} = [X^{\circ}\,(\text{\:}\diagup)_{cis} - X^{\circ}\,(\:\diagdown)]$$

$$\Delta S_{\textcircled{4}}^{\circ} = -S^{\circ}(Et\!\!-\!\!nPr)_{8.3(r.c.)}$$

$$\Delta S_{\textcircled{2}}^{\circ} = S^{\circ}[-(Et\!\!-\!\!nPr)_{2.6} + (CB_{3e})_t]\cdot$$

2. 1,4-pentadiene, $K_{r.p.d.} = 2$
$$\Delta S^{\ddagger}_{(1,\,4P)} = 11.1 - 5.0 + 1.5 - 6.0 + R \ln 2 = 3.0$$
$$A^{\ddagger}_{(1,\,4P)} = 10^{14.2} sec^{-1};\ A_{obs} = 10^{14.4}\ sec^{-1}$$
$$\dot{E}_{(1,\,4P)} = 52.3 + 0.7 + 10.8 = 63.8 \text{ kcal/mole};$$
$$E_{obs} = 57.3 \text{ kcal/mole}.$$

Because all carbons and the migrating hydrogen are confined to lie in a plane, movement of the electron at the central carbon atom must remove much of the allylic resonance of the biradical. The observed activation energy implies a loss of about half the allylic resonance. This means that the estimated A-factor (based on no resonance) in the transition state is too high and should be closer to about $10^{14.0}\ sec^{-1}$

3. Trans-1,3-pentadiene, $K_{r.p.d.} = 2$

$$X_{\textcircled{1}}^{\circ} = [X^{\circ}\,(\:\diagup) - X^{\circ}\,(\:\diagdown)]\ \text{for dienes}$$

$$S_{\circledS}^{\circ} = -\Delta S_{\textcircled{2}}^{\circ} + S^{\circ}[-(\cdot CH_2\!\!-\!\!\!\!\bigcirc\!\!\!\!-\!\infty)_{2.3} - (Et\!\!-\!\!nPr)_{2.6} +$$

$$-(P_{4e}) - (H\overset{C}{\diagdown}C)_{r.c.}$$

16

$$\Delta S^{\ddagger}_{(trans\,1,\,3P)} = 11.1 - 5.0 + 1.5 - 9.8 + R \ln 2 = -0.8$$
$$\text{g/mole}$$

$$A^{\ddagger}_{(trans\,1,\,3P)\,est} = 10^{13.3}\,\text{sec}^{-1}; \quad l_{obs} = 10^{13.0}\,\text{sec}^{-1}$$

$$E_{(trans\,1,\,3P)} = 42.3 - 12.6 + 0.7 + 10.8 = 51.2$$
$$\text{kcal/mole};$$

$$E_{obs} = 53.6\,\text{kcal/mole}$$

In the transition states for 1,3-pentadiene formation, the allylic resonance may be freely maintained, or at worst, reduced to the resonance values of the 1,3 diene product. The above estimates for full allylic resonance in the transition state are in reasonable agreement with the facts.

$$\Delta S^{\circ}_{6} = S^{\circ}[- (Et \smile nPr)_{2\cdot6} - (\cdot CH_2 \smile \infty)_{2\cdot3}$$
$$+ (tB_{4e})t + (P_{4e})_t - (H\overset{C}{\diagup\!\diagdown}C)_{r.c.}].$$

4.3. *Trans*-1-Methyl-2-Vinyl Cyclopropane

a. Mechanism for major path to *cis*-1,4-hexadiene:

Transition State Estimates ($T = 600\,°K$):

1. *Cis*-1,4-Hexadiene Formation (or *cis* → *trans* isomerization). $K_{r.p.d.} = 1$.

$$\Delta S^{\ddagger}(1,4H) = 12.5 - 5.0 + 1.5 - 2.3 = 6.7\,\text{g/mole}$$

$$A^{\ddagger}(1,4H)_{est} = 1/2\,\frac{ekT}{h}\,e^{\Delta S^{\ddagger}/R} = 10^{14.7}\,\text{sec}^{-1}$$

$$A_{obs} = 10^{14.8}\,\text{sec}^{-1}$$

$$E\,(1,4)_{est} = 50.9 - 12.6 + 0.7 + 9.3 = 48.3\,\text{kcal/mole}$$
$$E_{obs} = 48.6\,\text{kcal/mole}$$

The dominant reaction here (in sharp contrast to vinylcyclopropane) is the formation of the open chain compound. Comparison of the mechanisms in the two systems suggests that this occurs via isomerization to the *cis*-1-methyl-2-vinylcyclopropane, which then rapidly isomerizes to *cis*-1,4-hexadiene by the fast "Ene" reaction. It is reasonable to suppose that this *cis-trans* isomerization occurs from the more stable ground-state conformation in which the vinyl group is *trans* to the ring. The conformation with the vinyl group gauche to the ring is the form

required to produce cyclopentenes. There are two gauche forms possible, namely vinyl gauche to the α(C—C) bond, and vinyl gauche to the β(C—C) bond. The former can only rupture the opposite, or β(C—C) bond, while the converse is true of the latter. Both produce *cis* biradicals.

It is observed that *cis*-1-methyl-2-vinylcyclopropane isomerizes very rapidly to *cis*-1,4-hexadiene (step 3). This is a concerted 1,5-H-migration reaction. Therefore, the rate determining step for *cis*-1,4-hexadiene formation is ring opening (step 1), which leads to *cis*-1-methyl-2-vinyl-cyclopropane, which in turn reacts rapidly to form the diene. The factor of 1/2 in A arises from the fact that C_3 ring closing to the *cis* and *trans* forms of the reactant occurs with equal probabilities.

$$\Delta X^{\circ}_{1} = [x^{\circ}(\text{structure}) - x^{\circ}(\text{structure})]$$

$$\Delta S^{\circ} = -S^{\circ}(ET \smile nPr)_{2.6} + (tB_{3e})_t; \quad \Delta H^{\circ}_2 = -\text{allyl}$$
resonance

$$\Delta S^{\circ}_{4} = -S^{\circ}(C\overset{C}{\diagup\!\diagdown}C)\,350\,\text{cm}^{-1}\,(\text{as in cyclopropane})$$

b. 4-methyl-1-cyclopentene formation. $K_{r.p.d.} = 1$.

If ring opening occurs with the vinyl group gauche to the β(C—C) bond, a resonance-stabilized *cis* biradical will result, which can either C_3 ring close as above, or C_5 ring close to give a cyclopentene product. The latter process is slow compared to *cis-trans* isomerization; therefore, 4-methyl-1-cyclopentene is a minor product. In the original study, the minor product was mistakenly reported as 3-methyl-1-cyclopentene. This would require β(C—C) cleavage. Since in terms of the biradical mechanism β(C—C) cleavage is about 1.4 kcal/mole more endothermic than α(C—C) cleavage, this was an unexpected result. It appears, however, that the expected mechanism shown below is undoubtedly operative.

Mechanism for 4-methyl-1-cyclopentene formation. ($4MC_5$). $K_{r.p.d.} = 1$.

Transition State Estimates ($T = 600\,°K$)

$$\Delta X^{\circ}_{1} = [x^{\circ}(\text{structure}) - x^{\circ}(\text{structure})]$$

$\Delta S^\circ_{\textcircled{4}} = -S^\circ(nPr \in nPr)_{8.3} = -6.8$ g/mole

$\Delta S^\ddagger(4MC_5) = 11.9 - 5.6 + 1.0 - 6.8 = 0.5$ g/mole

$A^\ddagger(4MC_5)_{est} = 10^{13.7}$ sec^{-1}

$A_{obs} = 10^{13.7}$ sec^{-1}

$E(4MC_5)_{est} = 51.9 - 12.6 + 0.4 + 8.3 = 48.0$ kcal/mole

$E_{obs} = 48.6$ kcal/mole

5.0. Transition State Estimates for Cyclobutanes

5.1. Cyclobutane

a. Mechanism

$T = 714\ °K.$

$$\square \underset{2}{\overset{1}{\rightleftharpoons}} \sqcup^{\cdot} \overset{3}{\longrightarrow} 2\,C_2H_4$$

b. Transition State Estimates

$$\begin{array}{c}\Delta S^\circ: \\ \Delta H^\circ:\end{array} \quad \boxed{}\ \frac{12.2}{55.4}\ \sqcup^{\cdot}\ \frac{2.6}{1.2}\ \sqcup^{\cdot}\ \frac{-7.0}{E_{c_4}=6.6}\ (\ \vdots\ )^{\ddagger}$$

$$\textcircled{1}\qquad\textcircled{3}\qquad\textcircled{4}$$

1. Ethene formation. $K_{r.p.d.} = 4$

$\Delta S^\ddagger_{(ethene)} = 12.2 + 2.6 - 7.0 + R \ln 4 = 10.6$ g/mole

$A^\ddagger_{est} = \dfrac{1}{2}\dfrac{ekT}{h} e^{\Delta S^\ddagger/R} = 10^{15.6}$ sec^{-1}; $A_{obs} = 10^{15.6}$ sec^{-1}

$E_{ethene} = 55.4 + 1.2 + 6.6 = 63.2$ kcal/mole.

c. Discussion

The biradical mechanism, when applied to the kinetics of *cis-* and *trans-*1,2-dimethylcyclobutane indicate that in the cyclobutane reactions, all processes from the biradical occur at very comparable rates. That is, C_4 ring closing, decomposition and internal rotations of groups larger than (CH_3) and $(\cdot CH_2)$ are all comparable. Thus $k_3 \simeq k_2$, which accounts for the factor of $(\frac{1}{2})$ in the A-factor estimate. The activation energy for C_4 ring closing in the 1,2-dimethylcyclobutane systems was found to be 7.4 kcal/mole. This includes two gauche repulsions in the conformation preceding ring closing. There is only one gauche repulsion in the ring closing conformation of cyclobutane, hence $E_{c_4} \simeq 7.4 - 0.8 = 6.6$ kcal/mole.

$\Delta X^\circ_{\textcircled{1}} = \chi^\circ (\ \underset{\cdot}{\sqcup}^{\cdot}\ ) - \chi^\circ (\ \boxed{}\ )$

$\langle \Delta C^\circ_P \rangle_{\textcircled{3}} = 3.1$ g/mole

$\Delta S^\circ_{\textcircled{4}} = -S^\circ[(Et \in Et)_{6.6}\ r.c.]$

5.2. d_2-Methylene Cyclobutane

a. Mechanism

$$\boxed{}{}^{CD_2} \underset{2}{\overset{1}{\rightleftharpoons}} \ \cdot\ \sqcap^{\cdot}\ \overset{3}{\longrightarrow}\ \boxed{}_{(\cdot)d_2}$$

$$\Big\updownarrow 4$$

$$\cdot\ \sqcap^{\cdot}\ \overset{5}{\longrightarrow}\ \| + =c=$$

b. Transition State Estimates

$$\begin{array}{c}\Delta S^\circ: \\ \Delta H^\circ:\end{array}\quad \boxed{}^{CD_2}\ \frac{11.5}{53.2}\ \cdot\sqcap^{\cdot}\ \frac{-3.5}{-12.6}\ \cdot\sqcap^{\cdot}\ \frac{3.2}{1.4}\ \cdot\sqcap^{\cdot}\ \frac{-7.0}{6.6}\ (\ \vdots\ )^{\ddagger}$$

$$\textcircled{1}\qquad\textcircled{2}\qquad\textcircled{3}\qquad\textcircled{4}$$

$$\textcircled{3}\ \Big\downarrow\ \begin{array}{l}\Delta S^\circ = 2.9 \\ \Delta H^\circ = 1.4\end{array}$$

$$\begin{array}{c}\Delta S^\circ: \\ \Delta H^\circ:\end{array}\quad \cdot\sqcap^{\cdot}\ \frac{-7.0}{6.6}\ (\vdots\ \cdot\ )^{\ddagger}$$

$$\textcircled{5}$$

1. Isomerization. $K_{r.p.d.} = 2$ $(T \simeq 600\ °K)$

$$\Delta S^\ddagger_{isom} = 5.6\ \text{g/mole}$$

$A^\ddagger_{isom} = \dfrac{1}{2}\dfrac{ekT}{h} e^{\Delta S^\ddagger/R} = 10^{14.5}$ sec^{-1};

$A_{obs} = $ (not reported)

$E_{isom} = 48.6$ kcal/mole;

$E_{obs} = 49.5$ kcal/mole

c. Discussion

Full allylic resonance is achieved in the transition state. Steric inhibition of resonance in ring opening reactions does not seem to occur. The factor of 1/2 in $A^\ddagger$ comes from the fact that ring closing can occur one of two ways with equal probability; only one incorporates d_2 in the ring.

2. Decomposition,-allene formation. $K_{r.p.d.} = 2$ $(T \simeq 700\ °K)$

$$\Delta S^\ddagger_{(allene)} = 9.6\ \text{g/mole}$$

$A^\ddagger_{allene} = \dfrac{ekT}{h} e^{\Delta S^\ddagger/R} = 10^{15.7}$ sec^{-1};

$A_{obs} = 10^{15.1}, 10^{15.7}, 10^{15.8}$ sec^{-1}

$E_{allene} = 61.2$ kcal/mole;

$E_{obs} = 61.5, 63.3, 63.5$ kcal/mole.

Discussion

Decomposition cannot occur from the resonance stabilized biradical, since in order to develop the allene Pi bond, twisting of the conjugated resonance system is required. Hence the activation energy and A-factor for allene formation are similar to those for cyclobutane.

18

$$\Delta X_{①}^{\circ} = \chi^{\circ}(\ \text{⬡}\ ) - \chi^{\circ}(\ \text{⬜}\ )$$

$$\Delta S_{②}^{\circ} = S^{\circ}[-(.CH_2 \in \infty)_{0.6} + (iB_{3e})_t];$$

$$\Delta H_{②}^{\circ} = -E_{res}\text{(allyl)}$$

$$\langle \Delta C_p^0 \rangle_{③} = 4.6 \text{ g/mole};$$

$$\langle \Delta C_p^{\circ} \rangle_{③} = 3.4 \text{ g/mole}$$

$$\Delta S_{④}^{\circ} = \Delta S_{⑤}^{\circ} = -S^{\circ}(Et \in iPr)_{6.6}.$$

6.0. Polycyclic Compounds

Since the thermodynamic properties of almost all polycyclic compounds have not been experimentally determined, the thermodynamic estimates made in this monograph for the polycyclics are subject to greater uncertainties than are the estimates made for less elegant compounds. However, in view of the reasonably good agreements between the observed kinetic parameters and the calculated parameters (based on transition state estimates and the biradical mechanism) for most of the polycyclic reactions, it would be surprising if more than a few of the thermodynamic estimates were in error by more than ± 2 kcal/mole in ΔH_f°, and ± 2 g/mole in S°. Nevertheless, since errors of this magnitude are possible, transition state calculations have not been made as accurately as those for the small ring compounds. In particular, heat capacity effects have been ignored (although there is some indication that they may be small), entropy estimates have been made by analogy with the entropies of other cyclic compounds, and enthalpy estimates have been made relative to bond dissociation energies in alkanes. We believe that most transition state estimates given on the data sheets are good to about a factor of 3 in A and ± 3 kcal/mole in E.

6.1. Bicyclo[2.2.0]hexane→1,5-hexadiene

a. Mechanism

$$\text{⬡} \underset{2}{\overset{1}{\rightleftharpoons}} \text{⬡} \overset{3}{\rightarrow} \text{⬡}$$

b. Transition State Estimates

1 A-factor

If one assumes, by analogy with the cyclobutane reaction, that $k_3 \simeq k_2$, then the transition state for the reaction can be pictured as somewhere between the reactant and biradical, $(\text{⬡})^{\ddagger}$. Since the intrinsic entropy of the reactant and cyclohexane is very similar $(S_{int}^{\circ}(\text{⬡}) \simeq 74.0\ S_{int}^{\circ}(\text{⬡}) \simeq 72.7)$, it is possible to place the entropy of the transition state about $S_{int}^{\circ}(\text{⬡})^{\ddagger} \simeq 73.4$. Thus with $K_{r.p.d.} = 1$, $\Delta S^{\ddagger} \simeq -0.6$ and $A_{est}^{\ddagger} = \frac{1}{2}\frac{ekt}{h}e^{\Delta S^{\circ}/R} \simeq 10^{13.0}$ sec^{-1}; $A_{obs} = 10^{13.4}$ sec^{-1}.

2. Activation Energy

Since the ring strain in (⬡) is known to be close to the sum of the C_3 and C_4 ring strains, E strain (⬡) $\simeq 2(26.2) = 52.4$ kcal/mole. The transition state is close to the boat form of cyclohexane with a strain energy of something like 4 kcal/mole. Therefore, $\Delta H_{1,2}^{\circ} \simeq DH^{\circ}(C-C) - \Delta E$ strain $= 78.7 - 52.4 + 4.0 = 30.3$ kcal/mole. From this and other transition state estimates, it appears that to a good approximation all internal ring closing reactions have activation energies of about 8 kcal/mole (i.e., $E_3 \simeq 8$ kcal/mole). Thus, $E_{est} \simeq 38.3$ kcal/mole; $E_{obs} = 36.0$ kcal/mole.

6.2. 1,3-Dimethyl bicyclo [1,1,0] butane

a. Mechanism $\quad \text{⋈} \underset{2}{\overset{1}{\rightleftharpoons}} \cdot \text{⋏} \overset{3}{\underset{fast}{\longrightarrow}} \text{⋋}$

Process (3) must be faster than the decomposition of (⬜) to $2(=)$ since it is much more exothermic, and process (2) is a normal C_3 ring closing reaction. Therefore $k_3 \gg k_2$ and the rate determining step is ring opening, step 1.

1. A-factor Estimate

Since $S_{int}^{\circ}(\text{⋏}) = 85.5$, one estimates,

$$\Delta S_{1,2(int)}^{\circ} = S^{\circ}(\text{⋏}) - S^{\circ}(\text{⋈}) = 85.3 - 79.8 = 5.5 \text{ g/mole}.$$

$$\Delta S_{(2)}^{\ddagger} = -(\text{C} \overset{/}{\underset{\backslash}{\text{C}}}\text{C})\ 350\ \text{cm}^{-1} = -2.2 \text{ g/mole};$$

$$K_{r.p.d.} = 4$$

$\Delta S_{est}^{\ddagger} = 6.1$ g/mole; $A_{est} = 10^{14.7}$ sec^{-1}; $A_{obs} = 10^{14.45}$ sec^{-1}

2. Activation Energy Estimate

The ring strain in the reactant has been measured to be [31] $E_{strain} = 67.4$ kcal/mole, therefore,

$$\Delta H_{1,2}^{\circ} = DH^{\circ}(C-C) - \Delta E_{strain} = 77.3 - (67.4 - 27.6) = 37.5 \text{ kcal/mole}.$$

Thus, $E_{act} \simeq \Delta H_{1,2}^{\circ} + E_2 = 37.5 + 9.3 = 46.8$ kcal/mole. If there is a 4 kcal resonance stabilization in the cyclopropyl biradical (see bicyclopropyl), then the estimated activation energy is lower by this amount, i.e., $E_{act} \simeq 42.8$ kcal/mole; $E_{obs} = 43.3$ kcal/mole. The alternative mechanism is a concerted reaction breaking two opposing $C-C$ bonds at once. It is difficult to account for the A-factor on this basis.

19

IV. Isomerization Reactions (Other Than Cyclic Compound Reactions)

The isomerization reactions are of four basic types: (1) *cis-trans* olefin isomerizations, (2) structural allyl migration isomerizations, known commonly as "Claissen" or "Cope" rearrangements, (3) 1–5 H-migration isomerizations, known as "reverse ene" or simply "ene" reactions, and (4) cyanide isocyanide isomerizations, which are a distinct class by themselves.

1.0. Cope Rearrangements

Cope rearrangements are relatively well behaved reactions, not particularly surface sensitive nor subject to free radical chain reaction complications. Their activation energies are in the 30 to 35 kcal/mole range and entropies of activation are negative. In the Cope isomerization, a 1,5-diene rearranges by forming a new sigma bond between the vinyl carbon atoms 1 and 6 with concurrent π bond migration and scission of the 3-4 C-C bond. The transition state is six-centered and A factor estimates of reasonable reliability (i.e. within about ± 2 g/mole) can be made by methods similar to those employed for the ester elimination reactions. An A-factor calculation is illustrated below.

1,1,6,6-d_4-1,5-hexadiene:

Frequency assignments of the ground state and transition state are shown in table IV–1. (Only those which change in the activation process have been listed.)

TABLE IV–1. *Transition state estimates — 1,1,6,6-d₄-1,5-hexadiene isomerization*

Ground state (600 °K)			Activated complex (600 °K)		
Vibrations	Frequencies ω cm^{-1}	Entropies $S°$ (g/mole)	Vibrations	Frequencies ω cm^{-1}	Entropies $S°$ (g/mole)
2$(Et\!-\!\infty)_{2.5}$		17.0	2$(CB2_{3e})t$	200	7.
$(nPr\!-\!nPr)_{5.3}$		7.7	r.c.		
$(P_{4e})t$	800	1.0	$(P_{3e})t$	400	2.
2(C—C with C)	400	4.2	2(C—C with C)	200	7.
3(C—C)	1000	2.1	4(C—C)	1300	1.
2(C=C)	1650	0.4	(C . C)	675	1.
Totals		$S° = 32.4$			$S^{\ddagger} = 19.$

The intrinsic entropy of activation (equal to the real activation entropy, since the reaction path degeneracy is unity) is given as,

$$\Delta S^{\ddagger} = 19.2 - 32.4 = -13.2 \text{ g/mole}$$
$$A_{(est)} = 10^{10.6} \text{ sec}^{-1}; \quad A_{(obs)} = 10^{11.1} \text{ sec}^{-1}$$

The kinetics of a number of other Cope rearrangements in solution (results below) have been measured by Foster, Cope, and Daniels [32]. 1-ethyl-propenyl allylmalonitrile $\rightarrow$ 1-ethyl-2-methyl-4-pentenylidene-malonitrile (log $k = 10.94 - 25.78/\theta$ between 392–413 °K); 1-cyclohexenyl allyl malonitrile $\rightarrow$ 2 allyl cyclohexylidene malonitrile (log $k = 10.8 - 26.16/\theta$, 392–413 °K); ethyl (1,3-dimethyl-1-butenyl)-allylcyanoacetate $\rightarrow$ ethyl(1-methyl-2-isopropyl-4-pentenylidene)-cyanoacetate (log $k = 10.36 - 28.62/\theta$, 453–473 °K).

2.0. "Ene" Isomerizations

In an "ene" reaction, a 1,5 hydrogen migration is accompanied either by migration of two π bonds (giving an isomerization), or by one π bond migration and a bond scission (giving a molecular elimination). Ester elimination reactions are examples of the latter reaction path. The former path ("ene" isomerizations) are similar in their behavior to the Cope rearrangements. They are well behaved experimentally, often proceed toward an equilibrium state in which reactants are still appreciable, and have activation energies in the 30 to 35 kcal/mole range with sizable (of the order of 10 to 15 g/mole) negative activation entropies. Transition state estimates seem consistently to predict A-factors of up to an order of magnitude higher than those observed experimentally. It is possible that the six-center "ene"

20

isomerization transition states are less polar, and therefore tighter, than other "ene" reactions. Substituent effect studies, such as the sigma-rho relations observed for the acetate and benzoate esters by Smith, et al., would be interesting studies for these reactions.

2.1. Transition State Estimate of the A-Factor for an "Ene" Isomerization

cis-2-methyl penta-1,3-diene

$\longrightarrow$ 4-methyl penta-1,3-diene

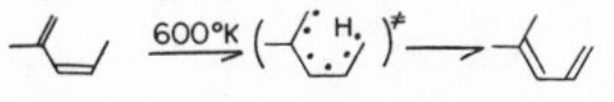

Frequencies of the ground and transition states are detailed in table IV-2.

The reaction path degeneracy is 3; therefore the estimated activation entropy is,

$$\Delta S^{\ddagger} = 14.6 - 25.3 + R \ln 3 = -8.5 \text{ g/mole}$$
$$A_{est}(500\ ^{\circ}\text{K}) = 10^{11.6} \text{ sec}^{-1};$$
$$A_{obs} = 10^{11.2} \text{ sec}^{-1}.$$

3.0. *Cis-Trans* Isomerizations

The *cis-trans* isomerization reactions are particularly difficult reactions to study because they are so sensitive to wall and free radical catalysis. The low Arrhenius parameters of early studies were attributed to nonadiabatic (singlet $\rightarrow$ triplet $\rightarrow$ singlet) reaction paths. However, in every case subsequent studies have shown that the low parameters were a result of heterogeneity or free radical processes.

TABLE IV-2. *Transition state estimates — cis-2-methyl penta-1,3-diene isomerization*

Ground state (600 °K)			Activated complex (600 °K)		
Vibrations	Frequencies ω cm^{-1}	Entropy S° (g/mole)	Vibrations	Frequencies ω cm^{-1}	Entropy S° (g/mole)
$(iPr \in nPr)_5$...........................		7.9	$(2MB_{3e})_t$...........................	r.c.	
$(CB_{4e})_t$...........................	400	2.1	$(CB_{3e})_t$...........................	200	3.5
$(Me \in \infty)_{2.5}$...........................		6.3	$(P_{3e})_t$...........................	400	2.1
$2(C=C)$...........................	1650	0.5	$4(C \doteq C)$...........................	1300	1.8
$2(C-C)$...........................	1000	1.4			
$(C-H)$...........................	3000	0	$(C \cdot H)$...........................	2200	0
$2(H \overset{C}{\frown} H)$...........................	1450	0.6	$2(H \overset{C}{\frown} H)$...........................	1000	1.2
$(Me \in \infty)_{1.0}$...........................		6.5	$(Me \in \infty)_{3.0}$...........................		6.0
Totals...........................		$S^{\circ} = 25.3$			$S^{\ddagger} = 14.6$

Transition state estimates of the rate constant parameters of the *cis-trans* isomerizations are in reasonable agreement with most of the data. Estimates of both the activation energy and the Arrhenius A-factors have been made. The method is illustrated below for *cis*-but-2-ene and for isostilbene.

3.1. *Cis*-but-2-ene

a. *A*-factor Estimate

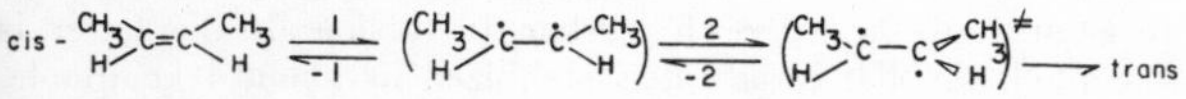

The reaction coordinate is taken as the torsion about the double bond. For calculation purposes, the mechanism is represented in terms of the intermediate formation of a flat biradical, followed by rotation about the remaining sp^2-sp^2 single bond with the latter rate determining. The more important frequency changes between the ground and transition states are given in table IV-3.

$\Delta S^{\ddagger}_{600} = +0.4 - 0.2 = +0.2$ g/mole
$A^{\ddagger} = 10^{13.6+0.1} = 10^{13.7}$ sec^{-1}; $A_{obs} = 10^{13.8}$ sec^{-1}

b. Activation Energy Estimate

The activation energy is taken as the enthalpy of the reaction to the biradical, plus the energy required to rotate about the single bond to the perpendicular conformation. Thus,

$$E_a = D(C=C)^5 + E_2 \text{ (rotation)}^6 = 56.4 + 6 = 62.4$$
$$\text{kcal/mole}$$
$$E_{obs} = 62.8 \text{ kcal/mole.}$$

3.2. Isostilbene

a. *A*-Factor Estimate

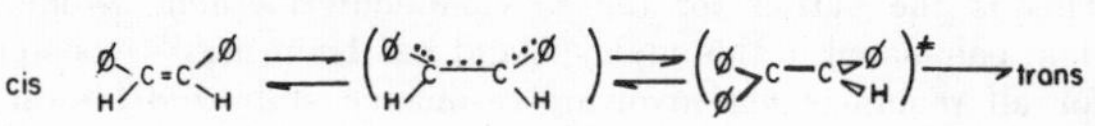

TABLE IV-3. *Transition state estimates — cis-but-2-ene isomerization*

Ground state	Transition state	ΔC_p	ΔS (600 °K)
symmetry (two paths)			+1.4
stretch (C=C), 1650 cm⁻¹	(C—C) 1000 cm⁻¹	+0.5	+0.5
bends 2(C⟍C) 420 cm⁻¹	2(C⟍C) 400 cm⁻¹	0	+0.2
torsion *cis*-but-2-ene 400 cm⁻¹	r.c.	−0.9	−2.1
2(CH₃ ∞)₁.₀	2(CH₃ ∞)₂.₀	−0.8	+0.4
Totals		−1.2	+0.4

Vibrational frequencies and corresponding entropies for the ground and transition states are detailed in table IV-4.

TABLE IV-4. *Transition state estimates — Isostilbene isomerization*

Ground state	Transition state	$\Delta S^{\ddagger}$
symmetry (two paths)		1.4
(C=C) 1650 cm⁻¹	(C—C) 1000 cm⁻¹	0.5
2(C⟍C) 420 cm⁻¹	2(C⟍C) 400 cm⁻¹	0.2
2(φ ∞)₄	2(φ ∞)₁₄	−3.4
cis-torsion (400 cm⁻¹)	r.c.	−2.1
Total		$\Delta S^{\ddagger} = -3.4$ g/mole

$$\Delta S^{\ddagger} = -3.4 \text{ g/mole}$$
$$A_{est} = 10^{12.8} \text{ sec}^{-1}; \quad A_{obs} = 10^{12.7} \text{ sec}^{-1}$$

[5]

$$\curvearrowright \longrightarrow \curvearrowright \cdot + 2H\cdot$$

ΔH_f°: (−30.1) (R:) (104.2)

$\Delta H_r^{\circ} = 2DH^{\circ}(\text{C—H}_{sec}) = 189$ kcal
ΔH_f° (R:) $= 189 - 104.2 - 30.1 = 54.7$ kcal/mole
$D(\text{C=C})_{\pi} = \Delta H_f^{\circ}$ (R:) $- \Delta H_f^{\circ}(\diagup\!\!=\!\!\diagdown) = 54.7 - (-1.7) = 56.4$ kcal.

Since heat capacity effects are small, all reaction heats have been equated to those calculated at $T = 298°$K.

[6] E_2 (i.e., the barrier to rotation), is taken as about 6 kcal/mole. This is the barrier for the *cis*-1,2-dideuterioethene isomerization, calculated in this manner, and has been used consistently for all reactions *not* involving resonance stabilized biradicals.

b. Activation Energy Estimate

$$\emptyset\diagdown\text{CH}_2\!\!-\!\!\text{CH}_2\diagup\emptyset \longrightarrow \emptyset\diagdown\dot{\text{C}}\text{H}\!\!-\!\!\dot{\text{C}}\text{H}\diagup\emptyset + 2\text{H}$$

ΔH_f°: (34.3) (R:) 2(52.1)

$2DH^{\circ}$ (C—H)[7] $= \Delta H_R^{\circ} = 163$ kcal/mole
ΔH_f° (R:) $= 163 - 104.2 + 34.3 = 93$ kcal/mole
$E_a = \Delta H_f^{\circ}$ (R:) $- \Delta H_f^{\circ}$ (isostilbene)
$\qquad + E$ (barrier to rotation)
$E_a = 93 - 58 + 6 = 41$ kcal/mole
$E_{obs} = 42.8$ kcal/mole

In actual practice, since the rotational barrier around the $sp^2 - sp^2$ bond cannot be known, instead of estimating the activation energies in these reactions, the observed activation energy (when $A_{calc} = A_{obs}$), or the corrected activation energy (using A_{calc} to obtain E_{corr}) have been used to calculate rotational barriers. The rotational barriers and resonance energies for the various groups which have been used and have been found to give reasonable agreement with the observed kinetics are listed for each reaction. Further experiments

It is possible to rationalize the origin of this 6 kcal/mole barrier to rotation, as follows: The isomerization barrier of *trans*-1,3-buta-diene to the *cis* form is about 4 kcal/mole. This may be thought of in terms of the butadiene resonance, or simply as a resistance of the $sp^2 - sp^2$ carbon to torsion. If the latter is accepted, the flat biradical is stabilized by about 4 kcal/mole. An additional steric barrier to rotation of the order of 2-4 kcal may also exist. The iodine atom and NO catalyzed *cis-trans* isomerization reactions whose rates are rotationally limited, all involve activation energies of this order [33]. Thus, a 6 kcal barrier to rotation for nonresonant biradical species seems quite reasonable.

[7] DH° (C—H) $= DH^{\circ}$ (C—H), as in *n*-butane − Resonance (benzyl)
$\qquad = 94.5 - 13.0 = 81.5$ kcal/mole

are needed to verify or discredit these estimates. It should be noted, however, that the resonance energies proposed are also quite consistent with the resonance energies calculated from transition state "fits" to the bond fission reactions involving corresponding groups (i.e., see also bond fissions),

and with the resonance energies obtained from the kinetics of some small ring compound reactions (see cyclobutane derivatives).

For a review of *cis,trans* isomerization reactions, including solution results, see references [15, 33, and 34].

V. Simple Bond Fission Reactions

1.0. Characteristics

Although seemingly appropriate to this monograph, early studies of the decomposition kinetics of hydrocarbons, ethers, aldehydes, and ketones have been omitted. The reason for their omission is that these reactions are extremely complex and the experimental methods employed in their study, prior to about the 1950s (e.g., pressure-time determinations of reaction order, classical wet chemistry product analysis, etc.), did not permit estimation of the individual parameters for the elementary reactions in the mechanism. A reasonably complete review of this literature prior to 1953 has been made by Steacie [35]. With the advent of gas-liquid phase partition chromatography, it soon became possible to perform mass balances as a function of time, detect trace quantities of products, and to begin to study the individual steps of the decomposition mechanism. Most of the studies reported here have been made since 1950.

Bond fission reactions (i.e., the initiation reactions in decompositions) have always been of prime interest to kineticists and thermodynamicists. The kinetic literature in this area is extensive although, as will become apparent, not particularly reliable. Interest in bond fission reactions stems principally from the relations presumed valid between the Arrhenius parameters for dissociation and the thermodynamic properties of the free radical products. The most common assumption has been that the activation energy for radical-radical recombination reactions (concentration units) is zero. Often the difference between activation energies of recombination for rate constants measured in concentration units as opposed to the value obtained for rate constants expressed in pressure units (i.e., $E_c - E_p = RT$) has been ignored. In addition, heat capacity effects on the reaction enthalpy as well as on the activation energy for radical recombination have generally not been properly considered. The usual procedure has been to equate the experimental activation energy at the temperature T to the reaction enthalpy at $T = 298$ °K, and then to calculate the heat of formation of the product free

radicals (i.e., $E_{(T)} \simeq \Delta H^\circ_{298}$). There are clearly some very grave oversimplifications involved in this procedure which could lead to erroneous results even when quite reliable kinetic data are available. Fortunately, it does appear on closer analysis that the assumption $E_{(T)} \simeq \Delta H^\circ_{298}$ should not be in error by much more than 1 or 2 RT. However, for reactions carried out at temperatures in the neighborhood of 1000 °K, an error of 1–2 RT will introduce uncertainties of the order of 2 to 4 kcal in the pertinent free radical heats of formation.

In section I-4.5, the thermodynamics of bond fission reactions and their relationship to the Arrhenius parameters of bond fission have been presented. The results are based on two assumptions: (1) that transition state theory is valid; (2) that the activation energy of radical recombination is zero *at 0 °K* ($\Delta E^\ddagger_o$ (rec) = 0). Thus we have for the decomposition Arrhenius parameters:

$$E = \Delta H^\circ_T + T \langle \Delta C^\ddagger_{V(\text{rec})} \rangle \qquad (V\text{–}1.0\text{–}1)$$

$$A \ (\text{sec}^{-1}) = \frac{k_{\text{rec}} \ (1/\text{mole-sec})}{(RT)} \times \exp\left(\frac{\langle \Delta C^\ddagger_{V(\text{rec})} \rangle}{R}\right)$$
$$\times \exp\left(\frac{\Delta S^\circ_T}{R}\right). \qquad (V\text{–}1.0\text{–}2)$$

The few radical-radical recombination rate constants which have been measured have generally been reported in concentration units. This is the reason for the above form of the A-factor equation. It is clear, from eq (V–1.0–1), that the activation energy of dissociation cannot be properly equated to the reaction enthalpy at 298 °K, but rather depends critically on the average heat capacity change for the recombination reaction $\langle \Delta C^\ddagger_V \rangle$. Only if both are zero is the usual assumption valid. In principle the reaction heat capacity change can be determined readily by direct experimental measurements or by statistical thermodynamic calculations. It therefore may be considered known or accessible. However, $\langle \Delta C^\ddagger_{V(\text{rec})} \rangle$ can be obtained only by inference from the kinetics. If nature behaves in a particularly perverse and erratic manner, then each system could be unique and it would be quite impossible to generalize in any accurate way about the kinetic-thermodynamic relations of bond fission reactions.

If one assumes that nature is not so perverse, then one is forced to conclude that much, if not most, of bond fission rate data is not very reliable. This is, in fact, our present assessment of the data. This is not unreasonable since the experimental complexities in these systems render many of the results highly suspect. In addition, in those systems (hydrocarbons) for which apparently fairly reliable kinetic data on the reactions in both directions exist (i.e., dissociation and recombination), there are very serious discrepancies between the thermodynamics and kinetics which can only be resolved by making some rather questionable assumptions about the nature of the free radical products.

In the following sections we discuss these problems in some detail. Our purpose is to indicate the current discrepancies between the data and theory. Further studies will be needed before the problems can be satisfactorily resolved.

2.0. Reliability of the Experimental Data

A perusal of reported Arrhenius parameters for the same reaction from different laboratories quickly reveals the serious discrepancies which exist in the results. Large differences in the parameters (i.e., up to three or four orders of magnitude in A and up to or in excess of 10 kcal/mole in E) are the rule rather than the exception. As examples, the extreme range of reported A and E values for the decompositions of ethane and azomethane are respectively, $10^{14.7-17.45}$ sec^{-1}, 79.3–91.7 kcal/mole; $10^{14.2-17.3}$, 46–55.4 kcal/mole. The trend in results with time (presumably later studies are more reliable) is toward the higher parameters. The poor precision and lack of consistency between studies clearly indicate that the reactions are complex and that their study poses many experimental and interpretative problems.

There are basically two classes of simple bond fission reactions: those which occur with no or with negligible chain-stimulated decomposition; those which have long chain decomposition pathways. In the former class, which is small and includes some of the azo and peroxide reactions, the rate-determining step for the reaction is bond rupture. This is the reaction of interest. Results on these reactions are generally fairly reliable. The most serious complicating feature encountered is surface catalysis, which can be estimated or eliminated experimentally. The vast majority of bond fission reactions involve free radical chain processes. These have been studied by one of two techniques. Both attempt to isolate the initiation (bond rupture) reaction from all subsequent chain processes.

The most common technique employed has been to carry out the decomposition in the presence of various free radical scavengers. Toluene, propylene, aniline, and cyclopentene are a few of the substances employed for this purpose. It is assumed that the free radical products of the bond fission reactions react exclusively and metathetically with these additives (via H-atom abstraction) to produce resonance-stabilized inert free radicals. It is further assumed that the stabilized radicals formed are unable to stimulate chain decomposition of the reactant and that their principal fate is radical-radical termination. In this case (i.e., complete chain suppression) the observed kinetic parameters will correspond to those of the bond fission reaction of interest. The same assumptions concerning the effectiveness of radical traps in suppressing chain reactions have been made in studying molecular elimination reactions. For molecular eliminations (which have lower activation energies and proceed at lower temperatures than bond fission reactions) it was concluded that the assumptions were probably valid. However, there is considerable evidence to show that the assumption of complete chain suppression in the presence of inhibitors is not valid in many bond fission systems. For example, McNesby and Gordon [36] showed that allyl radicals abstract hydrogen efficiently at temperatures above 500 °K, and that they are capable of continuing chain processes. Bryce and Hardiman [37] confirmed this result, showing that allyl radicals sensitized the chain decomposition of n-pentane at $T \geqslant 400$ °C. The dual role of NO as a radical trap and as a radical chain sensitizer has also been demonstrated and discussed at length [38]. Finally, the importance of benzyl radical H-abstraction reactions in the free radical chain decomposition of reactants in toluene carrier experiments has been demonstrated [39].

It seems clear, therefore, that the Arrhenius parameters obtained for reactions capable of chain decomposition must be viewed with caution when studied by the inhibitor technique. This is particularly true when the reaction of interest takes place at temperatures above 400 °C and forms the same products in the presence or absence of the inhibitor. The results of the toluene carrier technique are examples in point. Arrhenius parameters resulting from these studies are usually too low and the existence of some chain decomposition seems evident. Unfortunately, activation energies from these studies have historically provided erroneously low estimates for many important free radicals.[8]

A second technique more recently used to give a direct measure of the kinetics of bond fission reactions uses the single pulse shock tube. In such studies the reactant and a comparative rate standard (i.e., a molecule whose unimolecular decomposition rate constant parameters are well known) at very low concentration in an inert gas medium are shocked to reaction temperatures. The reaction mixture is then quenched in a period short relative to the lifetime of the free radical chain processes of decomposition and also short relative to radical diffusion times to the walls. The observed kinetic parameters should therefore correspond to those of the homogeneous gas phase initiation (bond fission) reaction. Activation energies determined by the single pulse shock tube technique have all been in very reasonable agreement with estimated reaction enthalpies. However, the A-factors obtained in hydrocarbon systems predict anomalous values for the entropies of the free radical products and therefore must also be accepted with some caution. (See V–6.0.) Application of the S.P.Sh. technique to bond fission reactions has thus far been limited to a very few systems. However, the method does appear to have great promise.

3.0. Kinetic and Thermodynamic Complications in Radical-Radical Recombination Reactions

In section I–4.3–8, it was shown that if the activation energy for radical-radical recombination at 0 °K was set equal to zero, the experimental activation energy for recombination when the rate constant is expressed in pressure units is given by $E_{p\ (rec)} = T \langle \Delta C_V^{\ddagger} \rangle_{(rec)}$.[9]

The usual assumption of a zero activation energy for recombination is equivalent to setting $\langle \Delta C_V^{\ddagger} \rangle_{rec} = 0$. By applying simple equipartition of energy principles to the recombination reaction, it is possible to get some idea of the limiting values which $\langle \Delta C_{V(rec)}^{\ddagger} \rangle$ can assume.

---

[a] Most of the heats of formation of free radicals used in this monograph have been determined either by competitive bromination techniques or by iodination experiments (see refs. [7] and [40]). The mechanism of these processes is now well understood, the errors are small, and the internal agreement between the two experimental systems is excellent. There can be little doubt that the values so obtained are the best ones presently available.

[9] $\langle \Delta C_V^{\ddagger} \rangle$ represents the average heat capacity of activation over the temperature range of 0 to T °K. More exactly,

$$T \langle \Delta C_V^{\ddagger} \rangle = \int_0^T \Delta C_V^{\ddagger} dT.$$

Case I—Simple fission into an atom + radical:

$$R - X \rightleftharpoons (R - - - X)^{\ddagger} \rightleftharpoons R + X.$$

The three additional translational degrees of freedom of the products originate from the reaction coordinate $(R - X)$ stretch, and the two bending modes of X relative to the R skeleton. The two extreme values for $\langle \Delta C_I^{\ddagger} \rangle$ then are:

a. X – bends very loose in the transition state $(hv \ll kT)$, $\langle \Delta C_{V\ rec}^{\ddagger} \rangle = 2R - \frac{3}{2}R = -\frac{1}{2}R$

b. X – bends very tight in the transition state $(hv \gg kT)$ $\langle \Delta C_{V\ rec}^{\ddagger} \rangle = \frac{3}{2}R$

Of course one must also consider other vibrational and internal rotational changes which may occur between the free radicals and the transition state. The most serious of these would be changes in internal rotational barriers. However, following Hammond's thermic postulate [41], (which places the geometry of a very low activation energy, highly exothermic reaction close to the geometry of the reactants) it would seem reasonable to assume that such changes are small and may be ignored. Since one would expect that stretching of the reaction coordinate bond would result in some considerable loosening of the atom bending modes, condition (a) would seem more reasonable (i.e., $\langle \Delta C_{V(rec)}^{\ddagger} \rangle = -\frac{1}{2}R$).

Case II—Dissociation into two complex radical fragments:

$$R - R^1 \rightleftharpoons (R - - R^1)^{\ddagger} \rightleftharpoons R + R^1.$$

The six additional external degrees of freedom in the product radicals (i.e., three translations and three rotations) convert mainly to the $(R - R^1)$ stretch, the $(R \leftharpoons R^1)$ internal rotation, and the four rocking modes of R and R^1 relative to each other in the transition state. The extreme values of $\Delta C_{V(rec)}^{\ddagger}$ then are:

a. When the four rocks become low-frequency vibrations in the transition state,

$$\Delta C_{V(rec)}^{\ddagger} = \frac{9R}{2} - 3R = \frac{3R}{2}.$$

b. When the four rocks have negligible restraining force and transform to rotations in the transition state, $\Delta C_{V(rec)}^{\ddagger} = 5R/2 - 3R = -R/2$.

Again, by Hammond's thermic postulate, the latter condition is probably the more probable case. Also, by the same argument, barriers to group rotations in the radicals and transition state should probably be equivalent. Thus, $\Delta C_{V(rec)}^{\ddagger} = -R/2$.

Although heat capacities of activation within $R/2$ of zero are favored here, it is clear that values differing from zero by up to $3/2\ R$ are possible.

Also, the exact relation between the bond fission reaction activation energy and the reaction enthalpy is not currently known and need not be the same for all reactions.

It is interesting to note that an extension of the Benson-Fueno [42] theory of atom recombination to a loosely coupled transition state in which free rotation still exists for recombining radicals yields,

$$E_{rec} = -\tfrac{1}{2}RT \text{ and } \Delta C_{V(rec)}^{\ddagger} - \tfrac{1}{2}R,$$

in agreement with case (b) above (standard states, 1 mole/liter).

4.0. Method of Analysis

Since the uncertainties associated with $\Delta C_{V(rec)}^{\ddagger}$ are not apt to be resolved soon,[10] it seemed best at this time to follow convention and assign $\Delta C_{V(rec)}^{\ddagger} = 0$ for all reactions. As previously indicated, this assumption is probably good to about $\pm \tfrac{1}{2}R$. It follows from (I–4.5–4) and (I–4.5–7) that for decomposition,

$$E = \Delta H_T^{\circ}$$

and

$$A_f = (k_c/RT)e^{\frac{\Delta S_T^{\circ}}{R}}$$

Agreement between the observed activation energy and the estimated reaction enthalpy at the mean reaction temperature was the single most important criterion used in evaluating the Arrhenius parameters reported for a reaction. This procedure was followed for all reactions whose product free radical heats of formation were reasonably well known. Since estimated reaction heat capacities both at 298 °K and the mean reaction temperature are probably reliable to about ± 1.0 g/mole and the usual errors in the free radical heats of formation are of the order of 0.5–1 kcal/mole, the errors associated with the estimated activation energies (or reaction enthalpies at T) are probably not greater than ± 2 or 3 kcal/mole.

Often the estimated activation energy of a reaction indicated that the reported Arrhenius parameters were much too low to be reasonable. If the reported rate constants for these reactions were thought to be reliable, preferred "corrected" Arrhenius parameters were calculated by scaling the "low" parameters to the "corrected" activation energy.

In all reactions, rate constants for radical-radical recombinations have been calculated from the estimated reaction entropies [3–VI] and the preferred A-factors. This was judged to be a particularly interesting thing to do, since a wealth of data on radical-radical recombination rate constants could determine what, if any, correlations exist between these rates and the geometry, resonance, and size of the recombining radicals.[11] If the estimates of the error limits for the activation energies are valid, the recombination rate constants estimated in this way should be good to about a factor of five (or 0.7 $\log_{10}$ units). The calculated recombination rate constants (see section V–9.0) do suggest some correlation between radical structure and the magnitude of the recombination rate constants. These are shown in table V–1.

TABLE V–1. *Radical-radical recombination rates*

Type of recombination	Range of values [a]
atom – radical	$k_{rec} = 10^{10.8 \pm 0.5}$ 1/mole-sec
diatomic radical – radical	$k_{rec} = 10^{10.0 \pm 0.5}$ 1/mole-sec
(alkyl) radical – radical	$k_{rec} = 10^{9.8 \pm 0.5}$ 1/mole-sec
(oxy) radical – radical	$k_{rec} = 10^{9.1 \pm 0.5}$ 1/mole-sec
(resonance stabilized) radical – radical	$k_{rec} = 10^{8.4 \pm 0.5}$ 1/mole-sec

[a] The error limits do not include uncertainties in rotational barriers in radicals or in activation energies of recombination. The latter two effects could add an additional uncertainty of perhaps another power of 10 in k_{rec}. (See sections V–6.0 and V–6.1.)

Small radicals tend to have values on the high ends of the ranges and the more complex radicals tend to have lower values. Thus, although not exceptionally important, steric effects do seem to play a minor role in the recombination process. It appears that resonance stabilization in the radicals tends to reduce the rate constants for recombination by about a factor of five.

The calculated recombination rate constants of radicals produced in the amine and hydrazine decompositions are about two orders of magnitude lower than the above (table V–9). This could be a real effect peculiar to (RN·) radicals or it could mean that the Arrhenius parameters reported for

---

[10] The rotating sector technique used for determining the absolute rates of radical-radical recombination is not presently accurate enough to measure very small activation energies (i.e., 0–2 kcal/mole).

[11] Such generalizations are very common in the literature. The most unusual assumption is that all radicals recombine with rate constants of about

$$k_c \simeq 10^{10} \text{ l/mole-sec.}$$

hese bond fission reactions are low. In the past the atter alternative has generally turned out to be correct. If the Arrhenius parameters are low, then the heats of formation currently accepted for the amine and anilino radicals are also too low (i.e., by about 4–5 kcal/mole) (see section V–8.0).

4.1. Illustrations of Analysis Methods

The general method of analysis used for the bond fission reactions is illustrated below for three decomposition reactions: ethane, benzyl bromide, and azomethane.

a. Ethane Decomposition

$$C_2H_6 \rightarrow 2CH_3. \qquad \bar{T} = 855 \; °K.$$

Reaction thermodynamics are given in table V–2.

TABLE V–2. *Ethane decomposition thermodynamics*

	C_2H_6	CH_3	$X^°_{298}$	$X^°_T = 855 \; °K$
$S^°$(g/mole)	54.9	46.4	37.9	40.0
$\Delta H^°_f$(kcal/mole)	−20.2	34.0	88.2	89.5
$C^°_p$(g/mole)	12.6	8.3	4.0	
$C^°_{p(1000)}$(g/mole)	29.6	14.4	−0.8	$\langle 2.0 \rangle_{298-855}$

The heats of formation for all pertinent species are well known. Entropies and heat capacities have been obtained from group additivities and from molecular thermodynamic calculations [3, 43]. Experimental parameters are (see data sheet for references):

$\log A$:	14.7	15.45	16.0	16.37	17.47
E:	79.3	87	86	88.0	91.74
$\log k$:	5.58	6.80	6.00	6.14	5.99

From thermochemistry we estimate at 855 °K an activation energy of 89.5 kcal/mole, which is within RT of the latter two sets of parameters. Scaling the A-factor to the estimated activation energy gives

Preferred: $\log k = 16.85 - 89.5/\theta = -6.04.$

From equation I–4.5–7, the reaction entropy at 855 °K, and the adjusted A-factor for decomposition, one can calculate a rate constant for methyl-methyl recombination of,

$$k_{rec}(1/\text{mole-sec}) = RT(A)e^{-\Delta S^°/R} = 10^{9.9} \, 1/\text{mole-sec}.$$

The experimental rate constant for recombination determined at about 400 °K has been measured at values between $10^{10.3}$ and $10^{10.6}$ l/mole-sec [44, 45,

46]. The difference between the experimental and calculated recombination rate constants is about a factor of three, which is within experimental error and is regarded here as a reasonably good agreement.

b. Benzyl-bromide

$$ØCH_2Br \rightarrow ØCH_2· + Br·$$

Heats of formation of all species are again known with reasonable certainty. Entropies and heat capacities are also believed to be fairly accurate. The thermodynamics of the reaction are shown in table V–3.

The thermodynamics predict an activation energy of 56.7 kcal/mole. The reported Arrhenius parameters are $\log k = 13.0 - 50.5/\theta$, which are certainly too low. Since the rate constants are probably representative of the decomposition, preferred parameters have been obtained by scaling to the thermodynamic activation energy.

TABLE V–3. *Benzyl bromide decomposition thermodynamics*

	$ØCH_2Br$	$ØCH_2·$	Br·	$\Delta X^°_{298}$	$\Delta X^°_{820}$
$S^°_{(298)}$	88.4	75.3	41.8	28.7	30.6
$\Delta H^°_{f(298)}$	16.0	45.0	26.7	55.7	56.7
$C^°_{p(298)}$	28.2	25.6	5.0	2.4	
$C^°_{p(1000)}$	64.5	60.6	5.0	1.1	$\langle 1.9 \rangle_{298-820°K}$

Preferred: $\log k = 14.65 - 56.7/\theta$

From eq I–4.5–7, the reaction entropy at 820 °K, and the adjusted A-factor for decomposition, one can calculate the rate constant for the benzyl-radical-bromine atom recombination.

$$k_{rec} = (RT)(A)e^{-\Delta S^°/R} = 10^{9.62} \, 1/\text{mole-sec}.$$

The kinetic theory collision frequency for bromine atoms and benzyl radicals, using $\sigma_{1,2} \simeq 4.7 \; A°$, gives a second order rate constant of $Z = 10^{11.35}$ 1/mole-sec. An estimation of the A-factor for recombination from this value can be made from the following considerations. Statistically, only one in four collisions leads to the (attractive) singlet ground state (i.e., three out of four collisions form a repulsive triplet state and therefore do not lead to recombination). Empirically our results seem to show that resonance in the product radicals infers a "tighter" transition state and A-factors of recombination seem to be lower than "normal" for resonance stabilized radicals by about a factor of five. This might be considered to be a resonance induced steric factor. Thus one can predict, $A_{rec} \simeq 1/20 \times 10^{11.35} \simeq 10^{10.0}$ 1/mole-sec. It has been shown (I–4.3–3) that for a recombination reaction in concentration units, the experimental activation energy should be, $[E_c = \Delta E_T^{\ddagger} + RT]$. When $\Delta E_o^{\ddagger} = 0$ and $<\Delta C_{V(rec)}^{\ddagger} = 0$, this gives $E_c = RT$. Thus our estimated recombination rate constant from collision theory is $k_{rec} = 10^{10.0} \times e^{-1} = 10^{9.57}$ 1/mole-sec. Although certainly fortuitous, the excellent agreement between the two calculated recombination rate constants is probably significant. First it tends to support the preferred Arrhenius parameters obtained by adjusting the reported values to the thermodynamic estimates of the activation energy, and second, it tends to support the usual assumption of high efficiency for radical-radical recombination reactions (i.e., that recombination rates may be estimated from kinetic theory collision frequencies).

c. Azomethane $CH_3N=NCH_3 \rightarrow CH_3N=N \cdot$

The heat of formation of the ($CH_3N=N \cdot$) radical has not been measured by other methods, therefore the azomethane reaction is representative of reactions evaluated in terms of estimated A-factors of dissociation. The estimated reaction thermodynamics are shown in table V–4.

TABLE V–4. *Azomethane decomposition thermodynamics*

	$(CH_3N)_2$	(CH_3)	$(N=NCH_3)$	ΔX_{298}°	$\Delta X_{550\ ^{\circ}K}^{\circ}$
$S_{(298)}^{\circ}$	71.0	46.4	64.2	39.6	40.0
$\Delta H_{f(298)}^{\circ}$	43.8	34.0	62.3	52.7	52.7
$C_{(298)}^{\circ}$	20.1	8.3	4.0	1.9	
					$\langle 0.6 \rangle_{298-550}$
$C_{p(800)}^{\circ}$	35.9	12.7	22.0	1.6	

Experimental parameters are:
        (see data sheet for references)

$\log A$:	14.2	15.7	16.5	17.3	14.5	15.9	16.5
E:	46	51.2	53.3	55.4	49.4	50.2	52.5

A recombination rate constant of the order of the methyl-methyl recombination should be good to about a factor of 2 or 3. Thus we assume $k_{rec} = 10^{10.0\pm0.5}$ 1/mole-sec. From eq I–4.5–7 and the reaction entropy at 550 °K, one calculates

$$A_f = \frac{k(c)}{RT} e^{\Delta S^{\circ}/R} = 10^{17.1\pm0.5} \text{sec}^{-1}.$$

From the thermochemistry one obtains

$$E_{act(est)} = 52.7 \text{ kcal}.$$

These estimates are in good agreement with most of the data. Heats of formation of azomethane and the product radical are those obtained from the azo and amine data analysis (see V–7.0, 8.0).

5.0. High and Low A-Factors in Bond Fission Reactions

Most of the early kinetic studies of bond fission reactions reported A-factors in the range of 10^{13} sec^{-1}. These values were consistent with the Rice-Ramsperger-Kassel theory of unimolecular reactions (which stated that all A-factors for such reactions should be in the range of molecular vibration frequencies) and were therefore termed "normal". Such confidence was placed in the constancy of "normal" frequency factors, that some experimentors were content to measure unimolecular reaction rate constants at one temperature, assume $A = 10^{13}$ sec^{-1}, and then calculate the reaction activation energy.

As more data were accumulated, an increasing number of "abnormal" high-frequency factor reactions were found. Originally it appeared that the activation energies for many of these reactions were higher (e.g., mercury alkyls) or were lower (e.g., azoalkanes) than any single bond dissociation energy in the molecule. (This conclusion was usually based on erroneous values of the pertinent free radical heats of formation.) Simultaneous bond rupture of two or more bonds was therefore considered likely. A number of "multiple critical oscillator theories," which essentially formulated theoretical A-factor expressions for simultaneous multiple bond rupture, were proposed to explain the high A-factors [47, 48, 49]. As more reliable heat of formation data became available, it soon became apparent that the activation energies of most of these anomalous reactions were not really anomalous, but instead, were quite close to the bond dissociation energies of the weakest bonds. In addition, estimates of radical entropies and dissociation reaction entropies, in conjunction with reasonable assumptions about the rate constants of recombination, soon indicated that high A-factors (i.e., 10^{15-17} sec^{-1}) should be the rule rather than the exception [27, 50]. This certainly is supported by the findings of this monograph. The more recent experimental results in all systems invariably and consistently support higher Arrhenius

TABLE V–5. *Hexamethylethane decomposition thermodynamics*

hexamethylethane $((CH_3)_3C—C(CH_3)_3) \xrightarrow{T=1050 \,°K} 2 \ t\text{-butyl} \ ((CH_3)_3C \cdot)$

	HME	(t–Bu) $V=0$	$V=4$	$V=8$	$V=0$ ΔX°_{298}	ΔX°_T	$V=4$ ΔX°_{298}	ΔX°_T	$V=8$ ΔX°_{298}	ΔX°_T
S°_{298}	93.2	75.4	70.3	67.6	57.6	47.4	47.4	44.7	42.0	40.1
$\Delta H^\circ_{f(298)}$	−54.7	6.8	6.8	6.8	68.3	62.2	68.3	66.7	68.3	67.2
$C^\circ_{p(298)}$	45.9	18.7	22.6	21.7	−8.5	⟨−8.2⟩	−0.7	⟨−2.2⟩	−2.5	⟨−1.5⟩
$C^\circ_{p(1000)}$	106.2	49.2	51.3	52.8	−7.8		−3.6		−0.6	
$\log k_{(1050)}$					5.02		3.50		2.39	

parameters. We have found no reaction whose A-factor needed to be rationalized by a multiple reaction path process. The contrary seems true. High A-factors are more consistent with transition state estimates of the entropies of activation for single-bond rupture than are low A-factors. Also, recombination rate constants calculated for such reactions have values close to those one might predict from kinetic theory considerations, and are therefore intuitively reasonable. Thus, we feel that single bond rupture is the only important reaction path *in gas phase* bond dissociation reactions and that the "normal" low A-factors reported for many bond fission reactions will eventually be shown to be incorrect.

6.0. Rotational Barriers in Radicals and Single Shock Tube Kinetic Results

Single-pulse shock tube techniques have provided what appear to be fairly reliable measures of the rate constant parameters of bond dissociation in a number of hydrocarbons. In addition, absolute rate constant determinations for methyl, ethyl, isopropyl, and t-butyl radical recombinations have also been made. It is possible, therefore, to check the kinetics of the hydrocarbon decompositions with the estimated reaction thermodynamics. A quick perusal of the results indicates that the reported activation energies (ignoring heat capacity corrections for the moment) are in fairly good agreement with the estimated reaction enthalpies at the mean reaction temperatures. However, the A-factor entropy relations are somewhat surprising. Proper estimation of radical entropies could be the major problem. For example, the symmetries of the radicals are not known, although recent evidence seems to support sp^2 hybridization (or flat radicals). In addition, the barriers to internal rotations are also not known, although E.S.R. results tend to indicate

that they are generally low. It has usually been assumed that on geometric grounds, the methyl rotational barriers in the ethyl and t-butyl radicals are zero. However, the reaction kinetics suggest considerably higher barriers, as the calculations in table V–5 illustrate.

The heat capacities and entropies of the t-butyl radical have been calculated by straightforward molecular considerations for three possible rotational barriers, $V=0$, $V=4$, $V=8$ kcal/mole [12] and $\sigma = 6(3)^3$. It is quite apparent that the entropy of the t-butyl radical is very sensitive to the magnitude of the internal barriers to methyl rotation. This is also the case for the reaction enthalpy and entropy. From the kinetics. $k_{rec} = 10^{9.5}$ l/mole-sec and $\log k_{diss} = 16.3 - 68.5/\theta$

$$k_{diss\,(1050\,°K)} = 2.09.$$
$$E = \Delta H^\circ_T = 68.5 \text{ kcal.}$$
$$\Delta S^\circ = 2.303R \ \log\left(\frac{RTA_f}{k_{rec}}\right) = 40.0 \text{ g/mole.}$$

The log of the rate constant for dissociation calculated from the experimental recombination rate constants and the estimated thermodynamics are given in the last row of the above table. It is apparent that the best agreement between experimental and calculated rate constants, enthalpies, and entropies of reaction is obtained for rotational barriers of 8 kcal/mole. The same conclusion is reached by similar analysis of the other hydrocarbon dissociation reactions.

As a second example, the dissociation reaction thermodynamics of 2,3-dimethylbutane to two isopropyl radicals are shown in table V–6.

---

[12] For details of the methods used in making these estimates from molecular and thermodynamic considerations, see ref. [3–VI] and appendices A and C.

TABLE V-6. 2,3-Dimethylbutane decomposition thermodynamics

$$\text{2,3-dimethylbutane } (\!\!\succ\!\!\prec) \xrightarrow{T=1100\ ^\circ\text{K}} \text{2 isopropyl } (\succ\!\!\cdot)$$

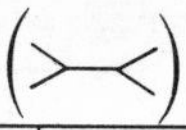

	2,3DMB	$V=0$	$V=4$	$V=8$	$V=0$ ΔX°_{298}	ΔX°_T	$V=4$ ΔX°_{298}	ΔX°_T	$V=8$ ΔX°_{298}	ΔX°_T
S°_{298}	87.4	69.0	65.4	63.8	50.6	46.3	43.4	43.4	40.2	41.8
$\Delta H^\circ_{f(298)}$	−42.5	17.6			77.7	75.1	77.7	77.7	77.7	78.7
$C^\circ_{p(298)}$	33.6	15.1	17.7	17.1	−3.4	(−3.3)	1.8	(0)	0.6	(1.2
$C^\circ_{p(1000)}$	79.1	37.9	39.1	40.3	−3.3		−0.9		1.5	
$\log k_{(1100)}$					3.27		2.15		1.5	

From the kinetics, $k_{rec} = 10^{10.0}$ 1/mole-sec [13] and $\log k_{diss} = 16.1 - 76.0/\theta = 1.02$

$$E = \Delta H^\circ_T = 76.0 \text{ kcal}$$

$$\Delta S^\circ = 4.575 \log \left(RT \times \frac{10^{16.1}}{10^{10.0}} \right) = 39.2 \text{ g/mole}.$$

Again the entropy of reaction and overall rate constant for dissociation estimated for the $V = 8.0$ kcal barrier to rotation give the best agreement with the observed kinetics.

The discrepancy between the reaction entropies and the A-factors of dissociation and recombination means one of three things. The rate constants of dissociation are too low, the rate constants for recombination are too high, the entropies of the product radicals are lower than expected (i.e., rotational barriers are of the order of 8 kcal/mole).

It is difficult to see how rotational barriers in radicals (e.g., t-butyl radical) can be significantly greater than zero. It is also difficult to believe that radical-radical recombination rates can be in error by the several orders of magnitude needed to reconcile the kinetic results with the thermodynamic estimates.

From the two representative reactions illustrated above, we see that (with the exception of the $V = 0$ kcal/mole rotational barrier model in hexamethylethane), the reaction enthalpies are all within ± 2 kcal/mole of the observed activation energies.

This experimental equivalence of E_a and ΔH°_T (within experimental error) strongly supports the validity of the single-pulse shock tube data (see V-3.0, 4.0). Thus the dilemma is posed and further study along these lines is needed.

6.1. Rotational Barrier Entropy Corrections

In table V-7 are listed the entropy changes per rotor in going from the alkane (RH) to the free radical (R.) as a function of barrier change and temperature. Values listed have been calculated from the data source for table C-5. A "normal" average barrier of $V = 4.0$ kcal/mole has been assumed for the rotations in the alkane. Other entropy changes such as electron spin and vibrational frequency differences are not included.

TABLE V-7. Free radical rotational barrier entropy corrections

T °K	ΔS°/rotor $V(4.0 \to 0)$	ΔS°/rotor $V(4.0 \to 2)$	ΔS°/rotor $V(4.0 \to 8)$
300	+1.8	+0.9	−0.7
500	+1.3	+0.7	−0.7
800	+0.8	+0.5	−0.8
1000	+0.4	+0.1	−0.7

All values are in units of g/mole.

If not otherwise indicated, the entropies of radicals given on the data sheets are for normal rotational barriers (i.e., no correction for barrier change in the radical relative to the alkane). This seemed the most reasonable procedure to follow since the true barriers are not known. However, one can readily convert the calculated reaction entropy at the reaction temperatures to the reaction entropy corresponding to 0, 2, and 8 kcal/mole rotational barriers with fairly good accuracy by applying the above corrections. For example, in the hexamethylethane decomposition (see table V-5), the reaction entropy at 1050 °K for normal (i.e., 4 kcal/mole) rotational barriers in the product t-butyl radicals is $\Delta S^\circ(V=4)_{1050} = 44.7$ g/mole. To obtain the reaction entropy when rotational barriers are 8 kcal/mole one applies the corrections of table V-7. Thus

---

[13] The value of $k_{rec} = 10^{10.8}$ l/mole-sec reported in the literature [51] is higher than either methyl or ethyl radical recombinations and therefore seems too high.

$\Delta S°(V-8)_{1050} = \Delta S°(V=4)_{1050} + 6(-0.7) = 40.5$ g/mole. This may be compared to the value of 40.1 g/mole which is obtained from the relation, $\Delta S°(V=8)_{1050} = \Delta S°(V=8)_{298} + \langle \Delta C_p° \rangle_{298-1050}^{V=8} \times \ln(1050/298)$.

When not otherwise indicated, the recombination rate constants given on the data sheets refer to values calculated for 4.0 kcal/mole barriers in the radicals. If recombination rate constants estimated for other barrier values are desired, they may readily be obtained from the corrected reaction entropies as indicated above. In general, "higher" than normal rotational barriers will raise the recombination rate constants while lower barriers will produce the opposite effect. For the hydrocarbon decompositions the calculated recombination rate constants have been listed with error limits. For example, $k_{rec}(tBu.+tBu) = 10^{8.2\pm0.8}$ l/mole-sec. The high and low limits refer to estimated values based on rotational barriers in the radicals of 8 and 0 kcal/mole, respectively. It should be remembered that similar uncertainties exist in the calculated recombination rate constants for all radicals with internal rotation barrier uncertainties.

7.0. Problems in the Kinetics of Azo Compound Decompositions

The kinetic data on azo compound reactions are extensive; however they are not easily analyzed by thermochemical considerations, since neither heats of formation of the product radicals nor heats of formation of the azo compounds themselves have been independently determined. The single exception to the above is the heat of formation of azoisopropane where combustion techniques give, $\Delta H_f°(iPrN{=}NiPr)_{gas} = 19.5 \pm 1.0$ kcal/mole.

It is possible to generate all of the unknown heats of formation (i.e., of both radicals and compounds) from the experimental activation energies for decomposition and from the azoisopropane heat of formation *if* we make the following assumptions: (1) Kinetics of the alkyl azo compound decompositions pertain to single bond rupture. (2) Group additivities are valid in the radicals as well as in the parent azo compounds. (3) The azo radical group value $[N_A{-}(N_A \cdot)(C)]$ is not affected by the nature of the alkyl group bonded to the nitrogen opposite the radical center. We will discuss the first of these assumptions later. The latter two are quite reasonable since one can envisage no real reason why any unusual next to nearest neighbor interracions should be important in the azo compounds or in the azo radicals.[14] In the following, the method of deriving

the pertinent enthalpy group additivities is given, and the "reasonableness" of the resulting groups is examined by comparison to well established group values of a similar kind.

Consider the single bond rupture of a linear chain, symmetrical, azo compound.

I. $RN{=}NR \longrightarrow R\cdot + \cdot N{=}NR$

$$\Delta H° = DH°(RNN{-}R).$$

The reaction enthalpy written in terms of the various groups whose natures are changing is given by

$$E_a = \Delta H_1 = [N_A{-}(N_A \cdot)(C)] + [C{-}(H)_X(C)_{3-x}]$$
$$- [2(N_A{-}C)] + [C{-}(N_A)(H)_X(C)_{3-x}] - n_A G.$$

Here the group notations have their usual significance and n_A is the number of gauche (G) interractions around the $(C{-}N_A)$ bond which is breaking. We assume from the kinetics that the reaction enthalpies for dissociation of azomethane, azoethane, azoisopropane, and azobutane are 52.5, 50.0, 47.5, and 43.5 kcal/mole, respectively (see data sheets). The heat of formation of azoisopropane gives a fifth relation. There are a total of six group unknowns ($[N_A{-}(N_A \cdot)(C)]$, $[C{-}N_A]$, and four $[C{-}(N_A)(H)_X(C)_{3-x}]$). By making the usual assumption, that a methyl group in all environments is the same as the methyl in alkanes, the equations can be solved and the group values (column 2, table V-8) are obtained. A comparison with the other group values in the table shows that the alkyl azo groups are very similar to the hydrocarbon groups and significantly less stabilizing than are the alkyl amine and alkyl oxygen groups. Such a variation is qualitatively expected since the ($-N{=}N-$) group should not be as effective in polarizing adjacent alkyl groups as should O and N atoms. The derived group additivities of table V-8 are therefore not unreasonable.

Using the groups, it is now possible to predict the activation energies of other azo compound reactions. Predictions and observed values are shown in table V-9. Since the estimates should be good to about ±2 kcal/mole, it is clear that there is very good agreement between observed and estimated activation energies. Note also that the transition state (biradical mechanism) estimated A-factors of the pyrazoline decompositions and azirine decompositions are in excellent agreement with those observed.

It can be argued, and legitimately so, that the assumption of single bond rupture in alkyl azo compounds coupled with the fitting of the thermodynamics to the kinetics is begging the real question

---

[14] The radical center is fairly localized on the end azo nitrogen and an interaction between that radical center and groups more than two atoms away does not seem reasonable.

TABLE V-8. *Enthalpy (kcal/mole) group additivities*

Group	ΔH_f°	Group	ΔH_f°	Group	ΔH_f°
$[N_A\!-\!(N_A\cdot)(C)]$	72.4	$[C\!-\!(C_d)(H)_2(C)]$	−4.8	$[C\!-\!(N)(H)_2]$	−6.6
$[N_A\!-\!C]$	32.0	$[C\!-\!(C_d)(H)(C_2]$	−1.5	$[C\!-\!(N)(H)(C)]$	−5.2
$[C\!-\!(N_A)(H)_3]$	−10.1	$[C\!-\!(C_d)(C)_3]$	+1.7	$[C\!-\!(N)(C)_2]$	−3.2
$[C\!-\!(N_A)(H)_2(C)]$	−5.8	$[C\!-\!(C)_2(H)_2]$	−5.0	$[C\!-\!(O)(H)_2(C)]$	−8.5
$[C\!-\!(N_A)(H)(C)_2]$	−2.1	$[C\!-\!(C)_3(H)]$	−1.9	$[C\!-\!(O)(H)(C)_2]$	−7.0
$[C\!-\!(N_A)(C)_3]$	+0.3	$[C\!-\!(C)_4]$	+0.5	$[C\!-\!(O)(C)_3]$	−6.6

and necessarily "forcing" the good agreement between prediction and observation displayed in table V-9. It is well known that the enthalpy of the second $(C\!-\!N_A)$ bond rupture is very exothermic. Thus in azomethane,

II. $CH_3N\!=\!NCH_3 \xrightarrow{\,1\,} CH_3N\!=\!N\cdot + CH_3\cdot$
$DH^\circ(CH_3N\!=\!N\!-\!CH_3) = DH_1^\circ \geqslant 52.5$ kcal/mole.

III. $CH_3N\!=\!N\cdot \xrightarrow{\,2\,} CH_3\cdot + N_2$
$DH^\circ(CH_3N\!=\!N\cdot) = DH_2^\circ \leqslant -28.3$ kcal/mole.

Since,

$$DH_1^\circ - DH_2^\circ = 2\Delta H_f^\circ(CH_3) - \Delta H_f^\circ(CH_3N\!=\!NCH_3)$$
$$= 68.0 - 43.8 = 24.2 \text{ kcal/mole.}$$

Simultaneous stretching of the second $(C\!-\!N_A)$ bond in the process of the first bond rupture, as a result of the DH_2° exothermicity (which increases with the stabilization of the radical leaving group), could lead to a lower energy configuration of the transition state and therefore result in an activation energy significantly lower than the weakest bond dissociation energy in the molecule. Such a decomposition mode has been favored by many and has been termed simultaneous or concerted two-bond rupture (see section V-5.0). There is very good evidence to support two-bond rupture in some special systems studied *in solution*. Thus comparing the activation energies observed for the decomposition of the following compounds,

$\emptyset CH(CH_3)N\!=\!NCH_3$ [52] $(E = 38.6)$,
$\emptyset CH(CH_3)N\!=\!NCH(CH_3)_2$ [53] $(E = 36.5)$,

and

$\emptyset CH(CH_3)N\!=\!NCH(CH_3)\emptyset$ [53] $(E = 32.6)$

all in kcal/mole, we see a successive decrease in activation energies and increase in reaction rates

as the stability of the second R group is increased by CH_3 and $\emptyset$ substitutions.[15]

On the other hand, the isotope studies of Seltzer [53] indicate that there is very little second $(C\!-\!N_A)$ bond stretch in the transition state when the second R leaving group is methyl. Thus for the compounds,

$\emptyset CH(CH_3)N\!=\!NCH_3$

$\emptyset CD(CH_3)N\!=\!NCH_3$

and $\emptyset CH(CH_3)N\!=\!NCD_3$

decomposition rates at 161 °C in solution were 1.16, 1.04, and 1.19×10^{-4} sec^{-1}, respectively. The single deuterium substitution at the α-carbon center involved in the first bond rupture, produced an appreciable secondary isotope effect; however, complete deuteration of the methyl (second R) leaving group had almost no effect on the reaction rate.

All these facts suggest that some two-bond rupture may occur in cases where substitution α to the N_A can lead to appreciable stabilization of the second R leaving group (i.e., the R of the azo radical), but that one-bond rupture is the principal decomposition mode for simpler azo compounds.

One bond rupture is, therefore, the favored reaction mode for all the gas phase azo compound decompositions in this monograph. The rather good agreement between the predicted and observed activation energies for the azotoluene reaction (where a benzyl resonance stabilization of the second R leaving group is possible), lends further support to the above assertion.

Thermodynamics of Single-Bond Rupture

If one-bond rupture in the alkyl azo compounds is correct, the activation energies observed are necessarily direct measures of the $(C\!-\!N_A)$ bond

[15] Also, while azobenzene does not decompose to radicals thermally, $\emptyset N\!=\!NC(\emptyset)_3$ [54] decomposes at an appreciable rate at 50 °C while $(\emptyset)_3CN\!=\!NC(\emptyset)_3$ [55] is so unstable it cannot be isolated even at −40 °C.

TABLE V–9. *Summary of predicted and observed activation energies in azo compound decompositions.*

Reactant	$E_{(calc)}$	$E_{(obs)}$	log A_{calc}	log A_{obs}
$CH_3N{=}NCH_3$	[a] 52.5	52.5		
$C_2H_5N{=}NC_2H_5$	[a] 50.0	51.2, 48.5		16.0, 15.7
$n\text{-}C_4H_9N{=}NC_4H_9\text{-}n$	50.0	47.5, 53.2		15.45, 17.71
$(CH_3)_2CHCH_2N{=}NCH_2CH(CH_3)_2$	50.0	49.0		16.2
$iPrN{=}NiPr$	[a] 47.5	40.7		13.75
$C_2H_5(CH_3)CHN{=}NCH(CH_3)C_2H_5$	47.5	48.4		17.28
$CH_3N{=}NCH(CH_3)_2$	47.5	47.8		15.45
$tBuN{=}NtBu$	[a] 43.5	42.8, 43.0		16.34, 17.15
(cyclopentene ring, N=N)	44.0	42.4	16.0	15.9
(methyl-substituted ring, N=N)	44.0	41.0	16.0	15.83
(methyl-substituted ring, N=N)	41.5	41.0		15.67
(dimethyl ring, N=N)	37.5	40.0		15.83
(dimethyl chain, N=N cis)	41.5	40.3		15.5
(dimethyl chain, N=N)	37.5	38.9		15.42
(tetramethyl chain, N=N)	37.5	37.7	14.6	14.48
(N=N bicyclic structure)	30.7	33.17		13.89
(N=N bicyclic structure)	30.7	31.9	13.9	13.73
(cyclopentane spiro, N=N)	30.7	30.5		13.4
(cyclohexane spiro, N=N)	30.7	30.87		13.34
$ØCH_2N{=}NCH_2Ø$	37.4	35.0		14.1

[a] Values assumed in order to obtain the radical and reactant thermochemical group values.
[b] Activation energies of the azo compounds have been obtained from the biradical mechanism,

example:

$$E_1 = \Delta E^\circ_{1,2} + E_2 = DH^\circ(tBuN{=}NtBu) - E_{strain} - RT + E_2$$

Assume

$$E_2 \simeq V_0 \text{ (internal rotation of } R{\rightleftharpoons}N{=}N{\cdot}) \simeq 1 \text{ kcal/mole}$$

Then

$$E_1 = DH^\circ(tBuN{=}NtBu) - E_{strain}; \quad E_{strain} \simeq 6 \text{ kcal/mole}.$$

dissociation energies. The thermochemistry of azomethane, reactions II and III, gives the relations, $DH_1^\circ + DH_2^\circ = 24.2$ kcal/mole. Also, the difference between the first and second dissociation energies should roughly equal the second pi bond energy in nitrogen. $DH_1^\circ - DH_2^\circ = \pi_{2(N=N)}$. From the reaction enthalpies one then obtains $\pi_{2(N=N)} = 80.8$ kcal/mole. Similarly, two-bond rupture requires that $\pi_{2(N=N)} > 80.8$ kcal/mole. By way of comparison we note that the pi bond energy in carbonyl compounds ($\pi_{(C=O)}$) is 75 kcal/mole, and the pi bond energies in alkenes and alkynes are ($\pi_{2(c=c)}$) = 73 kcal/mole and ($\pi_{1(c=c)}$) = 60.0 kcal/mole, respectively. A second pi bond energy in nitrogen much in excess of 81 kcal/mole does not therefore seem very likely.

8.0. Some Problems in the Amine and Hydrazine Decompositions

The Arrhenius A-factors of the hydrazine and amine decompositions are all less than the normal ekT/h value; some are significantly lower. Such a situation implies negative entropies of activation, which, in the case of simple bond fission reactions, is just not reasonable. We have chosen to discuss the thermal decompositions of the amines and hydrazines because their studies are typical ones in which the toluene carrier and aniline carrier techniques have been employed, and because the heats of formation of the product radicals have not as yet been determined by other methods.

There is and will be a natural tendency to use the activation energies in these studies to determine the heats of formation of the product amine radicals. Since the reported kinetic parameters are certainly too low, such procedures could lead to confusing the literature for a time with heats of formation of the amine radicals which are very probably too low by as much as 4 to 6 kcal/mole. Such a history has already transpired in the cases of the alkyl, benzyl, and allyl radicals. A quick perusal of the dissociation reaction enthalpies of the hydrocarbons based on the more recent and reliable heats of formation of the above radicals quickly reveals that the original Arrhenius parameters reported in the hydrocarbon decompositions (via the toluene carrier technique) were too low. The present situation for the amines and hydrazines is almost certainly the same. Recombination rate constants of the product radicals have been estimated from the reported A-factors and the reaction entropies. These are compared with the structurally similar hydrocarbon radical recombination reactions in table V–10.

It is seen that considerably lower recombination rates for amine radicals (with values lower by about 1.4 powers of 10 per nitrogen at the bond fission center) are calculated. If these recombination rate constants were correct, they would represent the lowest rates of their kind known. One would then have to conclude that there is something very peculiar about free radicals with the odd electron on nitrogen. It should be noted that the calculated

TABLE V–10. *Recombination rate constants (k_{rec} l/mole-sec).*

Recombination rate constants for nitrogen compounds			Hydrocarbon analog	
Reaction	^{a} log k_{rec} (experimental)	log k_{rec} (analog exp)	Reaction	
$N_2O_4 \rightleftharpoons 2NO_2$	8.2	9.8	$CH_3 + CH_3$	
$N_2O_5 \rightleftharpoons NO_2 + NO_3$	8.6	9.8	$CH_3 + CH_3$	
$N_2H_4 \rightleftharpoons 2NH_2$	6.2	9.8	$CH_3 + CH_3$	
$CH_3NH-NH_2 \rightleftharpoons CH_3NH + NH_2$	5.9	9.6	$CH_3 + C_2H_5$	
$(CH_3)_2N-NH_2 \rightleftharpoons (CH_3)_2N + NH_2$	6.1	9.6	$(CH_3)_2CH + CH_3$	
$ØNH-NH_2 \rightleftharpoons ØNH + NH_2$	5.8	9.0	$ØCH_2 + CH_3$	
$ØNHCH_3 \rightleftharpoons ØNH + CH_3$	7.5	9.0	$ØCH_2 + CH_3$	
$ØCH_2-NH_2 \rightleftharpoons ØCH_2 + NH_2$	6.6	9.0	$ØCH_2 + CH_3$	
$ØCH_2-NHCH_3 \rightleftharpoons ØCH_2 + NHCH_3$	5.9	8.7	$ØCH_2 + C_2H_5$	
$CH_3N=NCH_3 \rightleftharpoons CH_3 + NNCH_3$	9.2			
$(CH_3)_2CHN=NCH(CH_3)_2 \rightleftharpoons iPr + NNiPr$	9.4			
$tBuN=NtBu \rightleftharpoons tBu + NNtBu$	9.9			

^{a} Calculated from the observed A-factors for decomposition and the estimated decomposition reaction entropies.

TABLE V-11. *Amine radical thermochemistry via adjusted decomposition Arrhenius parameters*

Reaction	$\log A$ (scaled)	E (scaled)	ΔH°_{298}	$\Delta H^\circ_f(R\cdot)$
$N_2H_4 \rightarrow 2\,NH_2$	16.6	71.2	71.2	47.0 ($NH_2\cdot$)
$CH_3NHNH_2 \rightarrow CH_3NH + NH_2$	16.7	64.8	63.8	40.0 [a] (CH_3NH)
$(CH_3)_2NNH_2 \rightarrow (CH_3)_2N + NH_2$	16.9	62.7	63.0	37.4 [a] [$(CH_3)_2N$]
$\emptyset NHNH_2 \rightarrow \emptyset NH + \cdot NH_2$	15.5	51.1	51.1	55.4 [a] ($\emptyset NH$)
$\emptyset NHCH_3 \rightarrow \emptyset NH + CH_3\cdot$	15.3	67.7	67.7	54.4 ($\emptyset NH$)
$\emptyset CH_2NH_2 \rightarrow \emptyset CH_2 + NH_2$	15.3	69.8	68.5	44.5 (NH_2)
$\emptyset CH_2NHCH_3 \rightarrow \emptyset CH_2 + HNCH_3$	15.7	69.0	68.0	44.5 (CH_3NH)
$\emptyset N(CH_3)_2 \rightarrow \emptyset NCH_3 + CH_3$	15.0	65.2	64.8	53.5 [b] ($\emptyset NCH_3$)

[a] Obtained using the "best" value for $\Delta H^\circ_f(NH_2) = 45.0$ kcal/mole.

[b] There is good reason to suspect the group additivity values in this system. Methyl substitution at a nitrogen center in the alkyl amines produces a slight stabilization (1.8 kcal/mole). One might expect a similar behavior for aryl amines. However the group values predict a slight decrease in stability in the aryl amines. If the group values are wrong for the latter, then $\Delta H^\circ_f(\emptyset NCH_3) = 49.6$ kcal/mole.

recombination rate constants for azo and alkyl radicals are very similar to the hydrocarbon analogs, although some question concerning the proper interpretation of the azo compound kinetics does exist (see V-7.0).

By far the more reasonable alternative is that the recombination rate constants should be close to normal (i.e., like their hydrocarbon counterpart). Thus the preferred A-factors for the amine and hydrazine reactions should be higher than observed by about the differences indicated in table V-10.

If the higher A-factors are assumed and the experimental rate constants are accepted, then "more reasonable" activation energies and heats of formation of the pertinent radicals can be estimated. The results of such estimates are summarized in table V-11.

Our "best" values for the various amine radical heats of formation are:

$$\Delta H^\circ_f(NH_2) = 45.0 \text{ kcal/mole}$$

$$\Delta H^\circ_f(CH_3NH) = 41.7 \text{ kcal/mole}$$

$$\Delta H^\circ_f(N(CH_3)_2) = 37.4 \text{ kcal/mole}$$

$$\Delta H^\circ_f(\emptyset NH) = 55.0 \text{ kcal/mole}$$

$$\Delta H^\circ_f(\emptyset NCH_3) = 49.6 \text{ kcal/mole}$$

The $DH^\circ(N-H)$ bond dissociation energies (kcal/mole) in several compounds compared to

analogous $DH^\circ(C-H)$ and $DH^\circ(HO-H)$ values are shown below.

$$DH^\circ(CH_3-H) = 104$$

$$DH^\circ(CH_3CH_2-H) = 98$$

$$DH^\circ(NH_2-H) = 109.1$$

$$DH^\circ(CH_3NH-H) = 98.4$$

$$DH^\circ(HO-H) = 118.9$$

$$DH^\circ(CH_3O-H) = 104.1$$

$$DH^\circ(F-H) = 134$$

The sequence of increasing bond strengths seems inherently reasonable. This sequence would not exist if the kinetics were accepted as reported (i.e., with $\Delta H^\circ_f(NH_2) = 41$ kcal/mole).

9.0 Summary of the Calculated A-Factors for Radical-Radical Recombination Reactions.[a]

Reaction	$\log k_{rec}$
atoms + radical	
$\emptyset CH_2\cdot + H\cdot$	10.5
$CH_2=CH-CH_2\cdot + H\cdot$	10.4–11.7 (10.7)

See footnote at end of table.

Reaction	log k_{rec}	Reaction	log k_{rec} ± barrier uncertainties
atoms + radical		*radical-radical*	
		$2CH_3O\cdot$	9.9
		$2C_2H_5O\cdot$	8.9
$\cdot CH_2(CH_3)C=CH_2 + H\cdot$	10.5–11.7 (10.7)	$2n\text{-}2C_3H_7O\cdot$	8.9
$CH_3\cdot + H\cdot$	11.4	$2tBuO\cdot$	8.3
$\emptyset\cdot + Br\cdot$	10.4		
$CH_2=CH-CH_2\cdot + Br\cdot$	unreliable	$CH_3\cdot + CH_3O\cdot$	9.9
$\emptyset CH_2\cdot + Br\cdot$	9.9	$C_2H_5\cdot + C_2H_5O\cdot$	[9.7 assumed]
$\emptyset CO + Br\cdot$	9.5	$CH_3\cdot + CH_3\cdot$	9.9
$\emptyset CH_2\cdot + Cl\cdot$	9.6		
$\emptyset CO\cdot + Cl\cdot$	10.9 (too high)	$2C_2H_5\cdot$	$10.0 \begin{smallmatrix}+0.2\\-0.3\end{smallmatrix}$
$C_2H_5\cdot + I\cdot$	9.8		
$NO_2\cdot + Cl\cdot$	9.5	$CH_3 + tBu\cdot$	$9.3 \begin{smallmatrix}+0.5\\-0.3\end{smallmatrix}$
diatomic radicals + radical		$CH_3 + CH_3\dot{C}HCH(CH_3)_2$	9.0 ± 0.5
$\emptyset CH_2\cdot + HS\cdot$	9.7	$2iPr\cdot$	9.2 ± 0.3
$CH_3\cdot + HS\cdot$	9.4 (in falloff)	$2tBu\cdot$	$8.3 \begin{smallmatrix}+0.9\\-0.6\end{smallmatrix}$
$C_2H_5\cdot + HS\cdot$	10.2		
$t\text{-}BuO\cdot + \cdot OH$	9.9	$iPr\cdot + tBu\cdot$	$8.7 \begin{smallmatrix}+0.8\\-0.4\end{smallmatrix}$
$iPrO\cdot + \cdot OH$	9.9		
$C_2H_5O\cdot + \cdot OH$	9.7	$CH_3\cdot + NO_2$	10.0
$CH_3O\cdot + \cdot OH$	9.6	$C_2H_5\cdot + NO_2$	9.9
$CH_3O\cdot + NO$	9.4	$CH_3\cdot + CH_3NN\cdot$	9.4
$C_2H_5O\cdot + NO$	9.8	$C_2H_5\cdot + C_2H_5NN\cdot$	9.0
$n\text{-}C_3H_7O\cdot + NO$	10.1	$n\text{-}C_4H_9\cdot + n\text{-}C_4H_9NN\cdot$	9.0
$i\text{-}PrO\cdot + NO$	9.9	$i\text{-}Bu\cdot + (CH_3)_2CHN{=}N\cdot$	9.0
$n\text{-}C_4H_9O\cdot + NO$	10.1	$sec\text{-}Bu\cdot + CH_3CH_2CH(CH_3)N{=}N\cdot$	8.4 ± 0.3
		$i\text{-}Pr\cdot + (CH_3)_2CHN{=}N\cdot$	8.5 ± 0.3
		$t\text{-}Bu\cdot + (CH_3)_3CN{=}N\cdot$	$8.9 \begin{smallmatrix}+0.5\\-0.9\end{smallmatrix}$
		$CF_3\cdot + CF_3N{=}N\cdot$	8.6
		radical-radical (resonance stabilized)	
		$\emptyset CH_2\cdot + CH_3\cdot$	9.0
		$\emptyset CH_2\cdot + C_2H_5\cdot$	$8.7 \begin{smallmatrix}+0.2\\-0.1\end{smallmatrix}$
		$\emptyset CH_2\cdot + n\text{-}C_3H_7$	$8.7 \begin{smallmatrix}+0.2\\-0.1\end{smallmatrix}$
		$\emptyset\dot{C}HCH_3 + CH_3\cdot$	8.6 ± 0.2
		$CH_3\emptyset CH\dot{C}H_2 + CH_3\cdot$	9.1 ± 0.2
		$\emptyset\dot{C}(CH_3)_2 + CH_3\cdot$	$\langle 7.8 \rangle \pm 0.3$
		$\emptyset CH_2\cdot + \cdot SCH_3$	8.2 from kinetics
		$\emptyset S\cdot + CH_3\cdot$	8.7
		$\emptyset CH_2\cdot + \cdot COOH$	$\langle 8.3 \rangle$ assumed (kinetics = $10^{7.8}$ l/mole-sec)
		$\emptyset_2CH + \cdot COOH$	$\langle 8.1 \rangle$ assumed

[a] The *A*-factors have been calculated from the reaction entropy (ΔS_r^0) and the preferred *A*-factors for decomposition using eq I–4.5–7 ($\Delta C_r^\ddagger = 0$).

We have also assumed that the activation energies of all recombination reactions at 0 °K are zero, and that rotational barriers about bonds to radical centers are about the same in the radical as in the parent molecule formed by replacing the radical center by a (C—H) bond. The kinds of variations one might expect if rotational barriers were reduced to zero *or* increased as high as 8 kcal/mole are indicated for a few instances by lower and upper limits (respectively). These are *barrier uncertainties only*. Actual error limits could be much larger.

Reaction	$\log k_{rec} \pm$ barrier uncertainties	Reaction	$\log k_{rec} \pm$ barrier uncertainties
$\emptyset CH_2CO + \emptyset CH_2\cdot$	8.7	$\emptyset CO_2\cdot + \emptyset CH_2\cdot$	8.9
$CH_3\dot{C}O + \emptyset CH_2\cdot$	8.7	$CH_3\cdot +$ allyl.	9.8
$CF_3\cdot + \emptyset CO$	8.4	$2\ CH_3\dot{C}O$	8.5
$\emptyset\cdot + \emptyset\dot{C}O$	8.8	$CH_3 + CH_3\dot{C}O$	9.1
$CH_3\cdot + \emptyset\dot{C}O$	8.9	$CH_3\cdot + CH_3SO_2\cdot$	7.8
$2\ \emptyset\dot{C}O$	8.8	allyl$\cdot + CH_3SO_2\cdot$	7.6
$2\ nPrCO_2\cdot$	8.7	benzyl$\cdot + CH_3SO_2\cdot$	8.0
$2\ C_2H_5CO_2\cdot$	8.8	$CH_3\cdot + (CH_3)_2\dot{C}C\equiv N$	7.4
$2\ CH_3CO_2\cdot$	8.7	$CH_3\cdot + \emptyset C(\dot{C}H_3)C\equiv N$	7.4
$CH_3CO_2\cdot + \emptyset CH_2\cdot$	8.4	$CH_3\cdot + \cdot CH_2C\equiv N$	7.9

VI. Free Radical Reactions

1.0. Characteristics and Reliability of the Experimental Data

Direct experimental kinetic data on free radical unimolecular reactions (isomerizations and decompositions) are quite limited. Fewer than 50 such reactions are reported here. Some reactions appropriate to this monograph may have been overlooked;[16] however, we believe their number to be few.

With the very substantial increase in reliable thermodynamic data on free radicals (i.e., experimentally determined heats of formation and third law entropy estimates) and with some fairly reliable measurements of the kinetics of the back reactions, it has been possible to calculate with reasonable confidence the kinetic parameters of the free radical reactions compiled here. Such calculations, as may be seen on the data sheets, are not often in agreement with the experimental results. We take this to mean that much of the unimolecular rate data on free radical reactions is not very reliable. This is really not surprising in view of the experimental difficulties and mechanistic complications which must be resolved before reliable kinetic results can be realized. It is perhaps instructive to briefly examine some of these problems.

To study the kinetics of a radical reaction, the following are necessary: (1) to generate unambiguously the radical of interest; (2) to identify and analyze specifically the products of the reaction; and (3) to place the kinetics on an absolute basis.

Requirement No. 1. A number of techniques for generating radicals have been employed. These include $Hg(^3P_1)$ photosensitization of alkanes, photochemical decomposition of aldehydes and ketones, radical sensitized decompositions of aldehydes, and atom and radical additions to olefins (i.e., chemical activation). The Hg photosensitization studies are nonselective with regard to radical geometry. Thus with propane both isopropyl and n-propyl radicals are formed.

Requirement No. 2. In chemical activation processes addition can occur on either side of the double bond. This often leads to different radical species. Also, the radicals formed are "hot." This can lead to pressure dependent kinetics.

Photochemical and radical sensitized decompositions of aldehyde systems were designed to overcome the first requirement since it was believed, with some supporting evidence, that the only important reactions in these systems were:

Photochemical $\quad RCHO + h\nu \xrightarrow{a} R + CHO$

followed by $\quad CHO + M \xrightarrow{fast} CO + H + M$

Sensitized $\quad R' + RCHO \xrightarrow{b} R'H + RCO$

$\quad RCO \xrightarrow{fast} R + CO.$

---

[16] Pertinent kinetic results are often buried in the reaction scheme details of studies directed toward other objectives and have not been properly abstracted.

However, H-abstractions at other positions lead to complications, particularly with regard to Requirement No. 2. For example, in the photochemical decomposition of isobutyraldehyde, the reactions of interest are:

$$(CH_3)_2CHCHO + R \cdot \xrightarrow{1} (CH_3)_2CH\dot{C}O \ (R\dot{C}O) + RH$$

$$R'\dot{C}O \xrightarrow{2} (CH_3)_2\dot{C}H \ (iPr\cdot) + CO$$

$$[iPr\cdot \xrightarrow{3} H + C_3H_6$$

$$[iPr\cdot \xrightarrow{4} CH_3 + C_2H_4]$$

$$2iPr\cdot \xrightarrow{5} (iPr)_2$$

Decompositions 3 and 4 * may be monitored by the rates of H_2 or C_3H_6 production and of CH_4 or C_2H_4 production, respectively. Complications are as follows: Down chain (type I) primary process fission (6) will lead to increased yields of methane

$$(CH_3)_2CHCHO \xrightarrow{6} CH_3\dot{C}HCHO + CH_3$$

and, at higher temperatures, hydrogen (7). Calvert [56] has examined the data

$$CH_3\dot{C}HCHO \xrightarrow{7} H + CH_3CH=C=O$$

for this type of process and found it to be important.

Reactions (8) and (9) lead to increased propylene and H_2 yields:

$$R + A \xrightarrow{8} \cdot CH_2 - CH(CH_3)CHO(R''CO) + RH$$

$$R''\dot{C}O \xrightarrow{9} C_3H_6 + \dot{C}HO.$$

Corrections for these reactions have usually been made by determining the kinetics of reaction 8 at lower temperatures where reactions 3 and 4 are not important and subtracting the calculated propylene yields due to reaction 8 at higher temperature from the total propylene yields. The difference is then attributed to reaction 3. A possible complication with this procedure, however, is that the nature of the radical R (in reaction 8) undoubtedly changes with temperature. Thus at low temperatures, R is principally $iPr\cdot$ while at high temperatures R is principally H and CH_3. This almost certainly will result in an increased importance to reactions 8 and 9, since the H-abstraction selectivity favoring the aldehydic hydrogen will no longer be very great. In fact, with H-atoms, abstraction from the methyl groups of the aldehyde may even be favored. It is evident that identification of product yields with specific radical decomposition processes is not straightforward.

Requirement No. 3. Assuming that the radicals of interest are properly generated and their decomposition products can be unambiguously determined, the reaction rates must still be placed on an absolute basis. Generally decomposition and isomerization rates are measured relative to a monitoring or reference reaction whose kinetics are known. Radical-radical recombinations are the obvious choices. However, at the higher temperatures where the radicals are decomposing at an appreciable rate, the recombination reactions have ceased to be important and their products are not easily measured accurately. The usual procedure is to determine the relative rates of H-abstraction to recombination at low temperatures (reactions 11 and 10 respectively).

$$R\cdot + R\cdot \xrightarrow{10} R_2$$

$$R\cdot + A \xrightarrow{11} RH + A_{-H}\cdot$$

Corrections for the formation of RH by disproportionation (12) are also made.

$$R\cdot + R\cdot \xrightarrow{12} RH + R_{-H}$$

The radical decomposition is then measured relative to the formation of RH via H-abstraction from the parent compound.

Two difficulties are evident in this procedure. First, the H-abstraction parameters may well change with temperature since abstraction at other positions on A may become increasingly more important. Second, radical-radical recombination rates are not known very accurately. As a result, the values for reaction 10 are guessed, and generally range from 10^{10} l/mole-sec to 10^{11} l/mole-sec. This leads to an uncertainty of at least a factor of 3 in the absolute reaction rates.

It appears that all systems have complications and that a full understanding of all the secondary radical reactions taking place in any system is essential to a proper interpretation of kinetic data on any particular radical reaction. A good summary of the experimental approaches employed in the

---

*Reaction 4 probably doesn't occur.

study of the alkyl radical reactions has been given by Kerr and Trotman-Dickenson [57].

In a relatively large fraction of the studies reviewed, no A-factors were reported. This is unfortunate, although understandable in view of the historic interest principally in activation energies. When such omissions occurred, given sufficient data in the paper, we have attempted to calculate the A-factors. These values are indicated by parenthesis on the data sheets. Assumptions required in these A-factor estimates are noted on the data sheets under "comments." We would like to suggest that considerably more work in the direct study of free radical unimolecular reactions is needed and should be pursued. Among the objectives of such work should be the determining of both Arrhenius parameters A and E, and their correlation with the reaction thermodynamics.

2.0. Transition State Estimates of the A-factor for Radical Decompositions

If one assumes that the transition states for the free radical reactions are relatively "tight" and that the vibrational frequencies of the various bonds are those suggested in Appendices B and C, then fairly reasonable estimates of the A-factors for these reactions can be made. Below are illustrated transition state calculations for decompositions of the n-propyl radical.

A. H-atom elimination: ($T \sim 600$ °K)

$$CH_3CH_2\dot{C}H_2 \rightarrow (CH_3\overset{|}{\dot{C}}H \dot{-} \dot{C}H_2)^{\ddagger} \rightarrow CH_3CH=CH_2+H$$

$\sigma = 6,\ n = 2 \qquad \sigma^{\ddagger} = 3,\ n^{\ddagger} = 2$

$$\Delta S_A^{\ddagger} = S^{\circ}\left[(P_{3e})_t + (H \overset{C}{\diagdown} C)_{575} + (H \overset{\cdot C}{\diagdown} H)_{725} \right.$$
$$\left. + (C \dot{-} C)_{1300} + (C \cdot H)_{|r.c.\ 2200}\right] -$$
$$S^{\circ}\left[(\cdot CH_2 \overset{\ni}{\in} Et)_{v=4} + (H \overset{C}{\diagdown} C)_{1150} + (H \overset{C}{\diagdown} H)_{1450}\right.$$
$$+ (C-H)_{3000} +$$
$$\left.(C-C)_{1000}\right] + R \ln\left(\frac{\sigma n^{\ddagger}}{\sigma^{\ddagger} n}\right) = [2.1 + 1.5 + 1.1 + 0.4$$

$+\text{r.c.}] - [5.6 - 0.9 + 0.5 + 0.3 + 0.7] + R \ln 4 = +1.7$

$A_{\text{H-atom}}$

$$= \frac{ek\bar{T}}{h}\left\{\frac{\Delta S_A^{\ddagger}}{R}\right\} = 10^{13.9}\ \text{sec}^{-1}$$

B. CH_3 Elimination: ($T \sim 600$°K)[17]

$$CH_3CH_2CH_2 \cdot \longrightarrow (CH_3 \cdot\ CH_2 \dot{-} \dot{C}H_2)^{\ddagger} \rightarrow CH_3 + CH_2=CH_2$$

$\sigma = 6,\ n = 1 \qquad \sigma^{\ddagger} = 3,\ n^{\ddagger} = 1$

$$\Delta S_B^{\ddagger} = S^{\circ}\left[(C \cdot C)_{r.c.} + (C \dot{-} C) + (P_{3e})_t + (C \overset{C}{\diagup} C)\right.$$
$$\left. + 2(CH_3)_{3e\ \text{rocks} \atop 400}\right]$$
$$- S^{\circ}\left[2(C-C) + (\cdot CH_2 \overset{\ni}{\in} Et)_4 + (C \overset{C}{\diagup} C)\right.$$
$$\left. + 2(CH_3)_{4e\ \text{rocks} \atop 1150}\right] + R \ln\left(\frac{6}{3}\right)$$
$$= [0.4 + 2.1 + 3.8 + 2(2.1)] - [2(0.7) + 4.7$$
$$+ 2.4 + 2(0.5)] + 1.4$$

$\Delta S_B^{\ddagger} = +2.4$

$$A_{\text{CH}_3\ \text{elim}} \simeq \frac{ek\bar{T}}{h} e\Delta S_B^{\ddagger}/R \simeq 10^{14.0}\ \text{sec}^{-1}$$

---

[17] We have lowered the methyl rocks in the transition state by about a factor of three. See S. W. Benson, *Thermochemical Kinetics*, John Wiley & Sons, New York (1968), p. 69.

Appendix A—Thermodynamic Group Additivities[11]

TABLE A-1. *Hydrocarbons. Group values for ΔH_f°, S°, and C_p° (1 atm std state).*

Group	$\Delta H_{f(298)}^\circ$	S_{298}°	C_p°						
			300	400	500	600	800	1000	1500
C—(H)₃(C)	−10.08	30.41	6.19	7.84	9.40	10.79	13.02	14.77	17.58
C—(H)₂(C)₂	−4.95	9.42	5.50	6.95	8.25	9.35	11.07	12.34	14.25
C—(H)(C)₃	−1.90	−12.07	4.54	6.00	7.17	8.05	9.31	10.05	11.17
C—(C)₄	0.50	−35.10	4.37	6.13	7.36	8.12	8.77	8.76	8.12
Cₐ—(H)₂	6.26	27.61	5.10	6.36	7.51	8.50	10.07	11.27	13.19
Cₐ—(H)(C)	8.59	7.97	4.16	5.03	5.81	6.50	7.65	8.45	9.62
Cₐ—(C)₂	10.34	−12.70	4.10	4.61	4.99	5.26	5.80	6.08	6.36
Cₐ—(Cₐ)(H)	6.78	6.38	4.46	5.79	6.75	7.42	8.35	8.99	9.98
Cₐ—(Cₐ)(C)	8.88	−14.6	(4.40)	(5.37)	(5.93)	(6.18)	(6.50)	(6.62)	(6.72)
Cₐ—(C_B)(H)	6.78	6.38	4.46	5.79	6.75	7.42	8.35	8.99	9.98
Cₐ—(C_B)(C)	8.64	(−14.6)	(4.40)	(5.37)	(5.93)	(6.18)	(6.50)	(6.62)	(6.72)
Cₐ—(C_t)(H)	6.78	6.38	4.46	5.79	6.75	7.42	8.35	8.99	9.98
C—(Cₐ)(C)(H)₂	−4.76	9.80	5.12	6.86	8.32	9.49	11.22	12.48	14.36
C—(Cₐ)₂(H)₂	−4.29	(10.2)	(4.7)	(6.8)	(8.4)	(9.6)	(11.3)	(12.6)	(14.4)
C—(Cₐ)(C_B)(H)₂	−4.29	(10.2)	(4.7)	(6.8)	(8.4)	(9.6)	(11.3)	(12.6)	(14.4)
C—(C_t)(C)(H)₂	−4.73	10.30	4.95	6.56	7.93	9.08	10.86	12.19	14.20
C—(C_B)(C)(H)₂	−4.86	9.34	5.84	7.61	8.98	10.01	11.49	12.54	13.76
C—(Cₐ)(C)₂(H)	−1.48	(−11.69)	(4.16)	(5.91)	(7.34)	(8.19)	(9.46)	(10.19)	(11.28)
C—(C_t)(C)₂(H)	−1.72	(−11.19)	(3.99)	(5.61)	(6.85)	(7.78)	(9.10)	(9.90)	(11.12)
C—(C_B)(C)₂(H)	−0.98	(−12.15)	(4.88)	(6.66)	(7.90)	(8.75)	(9.73)	(10.25)	(10.68)
C—(Cₐ)(C)₃	1.68	(−34.72)	(3.99)	(6.04)	(7.43)	(8.26)	(8.92)	(8.96)	(8.23)
C—(C_B)(C)₃	2.81	(−35.18)	(4.37)	(6.79)	(8.09)	(8.78)	(9.19)	(8.96)	(7.63)
C_t—(H) }	26.93	24.7	5.27	5.99	6.49	6.87	7.47	7.96	8.85
C_t—(C)	27.55	6.35	3.13	3.48	3.81	4.09	4.60	4.92	6.35
C_t—(Cₐ)	29.20	(6.43)	(2.57)	(3.54)	(3.50)	(4.92)	(5.34)	(5.50)	(5.80)
C_t—(C_B)	(29.20)	6.43	2.57	3.54	3.50	4.92	5.34	5.50	5.80
C_B—(H)	3.30	11.53	3.24	4.44	5.46	6.30	7.54	8.41	9.73
C_B—(C)	5.51	−7.69	2.67	3.14	3.68	4.15	4.96	5.44	5.98
C_B—(Cₐ)	5.68	−7.80	3.59	3.97	4.38	4.72	5.28	5.61	5.75
C_B—(C_t)	5.68	−7.80	3.59	3.97	4.38	4.72	5.28	5.61	5.75
C_B—(C_B)	5.26	−8.64	3.33	4.22	4.89	5.27	5.76	5.95	(6.05)
Cₐ	34.20	6.0	3.9	4.4	4.7	5.0	5.3	5.5	5.7

[11] These group values have been taken from ref. 3—Section I-5.0.

TABLE A-1. *Next-nearest neighbor corrections*

Group	$\Delta H_{f(298)}^\circ$	S_{298}°	C_p°						
			300	400	500	600	800	1000	1500
alkane gauche correction	0.80								
alkene gauche correction	0.50								
cis correction	[a] 1.00	([b])	−1.34	−1.09	−0.81	−0.61	−0.39	−0.26	0
ortho correction	0.57	−1.61	1.12	1.35	1.30	1.17	0.88	0.66	−0.05

[a] When one of the groups is *t*-Butyl, *cis* correction = 4.00, when both are *t*-Butyl, *cis* correction = ~10.00, and when there are two *cis* corrections around one double bond, the total correction is 3.00.

[b] +1.2 for but-2-ene, 0 for all other 2-enes, and −0.6 for 3-enes.

TABLE A-1. *Corrections to be applied to ring compound estimates*

Ring (σ)	$\Delta H^\circ_{f(298)}$	S°_{298}	C°_p						
			300	400	500	600	800	1000	1500
cyclopropane (6)	27.6	32.1	−3.05	−2.53	−2.10	−1.90	−1.77	−1.62	(−1.52)
cyclopropene (2)	53.7	33.6							
cyclobutane (8)	26.2	29.8	−4.61	−3.89	−3.14	−2.64	−1.88	−1.38	−0.67
cyclobutene (2)	29.8	29.0	−2.53	−2.19	−1.89	−1.63	−1.48	−1.33	−1.22
cyclopentane (10)	6.3	27.3	−6.5	−5.5	−4.5	−3.8	−2:8	−1.93	−0.37
cyclopentene (2)	5.9	25.8	−5.98	−5.35	−4.89	−4.14	−2.93	−2.26	−1.08
cyclopentadiene	6.0								
cyclohexane (6)	0	18.8	−5.8	−4.10	−2.9	−1.3	1.1	2.2	3.3
cyclohexene (2)	1.4	21.5	−4.28	−3.04	−1.98	−1.43	−0.29	0.08	0.81
cyclohexadiene 1,3	4.8								
cyclohexadiene 1,4	0.5								
cycloheptane (1)	6.4	15.9							
cycloheptene	5.4								
cycloheptadiene 1,3	6.6								
cycloheptatriene 1,3,5 (1)	4.7	23.7							
cycloöctane (8)	9.9	16.5							
cis-cycloöctene	6.0								
trans-cycloöctene	15.3								
cycloöctatriene 1,3,5	8.9								
cycloöctatetraene	17.1								
cyclononane	12.8								
cis-cyclononene	9.9								
trans-cyclononene	12.8								
spiropentane (4)	63.5	67.6							
bicyclo(1,1,0)-butane (2)	68.4	69.2							
bicyclo(2,1,0)-pentane	55.3								
bicyclo(3,1,0)-hexane	32.7								
bicyclo(4,1,0)-heptane	28.9								
bicyclo(5,1,0)-octane	29.6								
bicycloheptadiene	29.7								

TABLE A-2. *Oxygen containing compounds. Group Contributions to* ΔH°_f, S°, *and* C°_p

Group	$\Delta H^\circ_{f(298)}$	S°_{298}	C°_p						
			300	400	500	600	800	1000	1500
CO—(CO)(C$_B$)	(−30.5)	(12.0)	(5.5)						
CO—(CO)(C)	−29.2								
CO—(CO)(O)	(−32.6)								
CO—(O)(C$_d$)	−33.5								
CO—(O)(C$_B$)	−42.4								
CO—(O)(C)	−33.4	14.78	5.97	6.70	7.4	8.02	8.87	9.36	
CO—(O)(H) [a]	−29.5	34.93	7.03	7.87	8.82	9.68	11.16	12.20	
CO—(C$_d$)(H)	−31.7	(32.9)	(6.0)						
CO—(C$_B$)$_2$	−39.1	(12.0)							
CO—(C$_B$)(C)	−37.6	(13.7)	(6.1)						
CO—(C$_B$)(H) [b]	−31.7	(32.9)	(6.5)						
CO—(C)$_2$	−31.5	15.01	5.59	6.32	7.09	7.76	8.89	9.61	
CO—(C)(H)	−29.6	34.93	7.03	7.87	8.82	9.68	11.16	12.20	
CO—(H)$_2$	−27.7	53.67	8.47	9.38	10.46	11.52	13.37	14.81	

41

TABLE A-2. *Oxygen containing compounds. Group Contributions to ΔH_f°, S°, and C_p° — Continued*

Group	$\Delta H_{f(298)}^\circ$	S_{298}°	C_p°						
			300	400	500	600	800	1000	1500
O—(CO)₂	−50.9	(8.5)	(3.4)						
O—(CO)(O)	−19.0	(8.4)	(3.5)						
O—(CO)(Cd) ᶜ	−41.3								
O—(CO)(C)	−41.3	8.39	(3.5)						
O—(CO)(H)	−60.3	24.52	3.81	4.98	5.80	6.34	7.19	7.75	
O—(O)(C)	−4.5	(9.0)							
O—(O)(H)	−16.27	28.52	5.17	5.79	6.28	6.66	7.15	7.51	8.17
O—(Cd)₂	−32.8	8.1	(4.2)						
O—(Cd)(C)	−31.3	(8.5)	(3.5)						
O—(CB)₂	−19.3	(8.1)	(4.2)						
O—(CB)(C)	−22.6	(8.3)	(3.8)						
O—(CB)(H) ᵈ	−37.9	29.1	4.3	4.5	4.8	5.2	6.0	6.6	
O—(C)₂	−23.7	8.68	3.4	3.7	3.7	3.8	4.4	4.6	
O—(C)(H)	−37.88	29.07	4.33	4.45	4.82	5.23	6.02	6.61	
Cd—(CO)(O)	6.3								
Cd—(CO)(C)	9.4								
Cd—(CO)(H) ᵉ	7.68								
Cd—(O)(Cd) ᶠ	8.9								
Cd—(O)(C) ᵍ									
Cd—(O)(H) ʰ	10.3								
	8.6	8.0	4.16	5.03	5.81	6.50	7.65	8.45	9.62
CB—(CO)	9.7	−9.6	(3.9)						
CB—(O)	−1.8	−10.2	3.9	5.3	6.2	6.6	6.9	6.9	
C—(CO)₂(H)₂	−7.2								
C—(CO)(C)₂(H) ⁱ	−1.8	(−12.0)	(5.0)						
C—(CO)(C)(H)₂	−5.0	9.6	6.2	7.7	8.7	9.5	11.1	12.2	
C—(CO)(H)₃ ʲ	−10.08	30.41	6.19	7.84	9.40	10.79	13.02	14.77	17.58
C—(O)₂(C)₂	−18.1								
C—(O)₂(C)(H)	−17.2								
C—(O)₂(H)₂	−17.7								
C—(O)(CB)(H)₂	−6.6	9.7							
C—(O)(Cd)(H)₂	−6.9								
C—(O)(C)₃	−6.60	−33.56	4.33	6.19	7.25	7.70	8.20	8.24	
C—(O)(C)₂(H)	−7.00	−11.35	4.80	6.64	8.10	8.73	9.81	10.40	
C—(O)(C)(H)₂	−8.5	10.3	4.99	6.85	8.30	9.43	11.11	12.33	
C—(O)(H)₃ ᵏ	−10.08	30.41	6.19	7.84	9.40	10.79	13.02	14.77	17.58

Corrections to be Applied to Ring Compound Estimates

Group	$\Delta H_{f(298)}^\circ$	S_{298}°	300	400	500	600	800	1000	1500
Strain ether oxygen gauche	0.3								
Di-tertiary ethers	8.4								
	26.9	31.4	−2.0	−2.8	−3.0	−2.6	−2.3	−2.3	
	25.7	27.7	−4.6	−5.0	−4.2	−3.5	−2.6	+0.2	
	6.0								
	1.5								
	4.2								
	4.0								
	1.3								

TABLE A-2. *Oxygen containing compounds. Group Contributions to ΔH_f°, S°, and C_p°—Continued*

Group	$\Delta H_{f(298)}^\circ$	S_{298}°	C_p° 300	400	500	600	800	1000	1500
	−6.2								
	2.5								
	6.0								
	3.4								
	1.1								
	1.4								
	4.6								

[a] $CO—(O)(H) \equiv CO—(C)(H)$, assigned.
[b] $CO—(C_B)(H) \equiv CO—(C_d)(H)$, assigned.
[c] $O—(CO)(C_d) \equiv O—(CO)(C)$, assigned.
[d] $O—(C_B)(H) \equiv O—(C)(H)$, assigned.
[e] $C_d—(CO)(H) \equiv$ mean of $C_d—(C_d)(H)$ and $C_d—(C)(H)$, assigned.
[f] $C_d—(O)(C_d) \equiv C_d—(C_d)(C)$.
[g] $C_d—(O)(C) \equiv C_d—C_2$.
[h] $C_d—(O)(H) \equiv C_d—(C)(H)$, assigned.
[i] $C—(CO)(C)_2(H)$, estimated.
[j] $C—(CO)(H)_3 \equiv C—(C)(H)_3$, assigned.
[k] $C—(O)(H)_3 \equiv C—(C)(H)_3$, assigned.

TABLE A–3. *Group contributions to C_p°, S°, and $\Delta H_f^{\circ\ b,\ c}$ (1 atm std state) for nitrogen-containing compounds.*

Group	ΔH° (kcal/mole)	S° (e. u.)	C_p° (e. u.) 300	400	500	600	800	1000	1500
C–(N)(H)₃	−10.08	30.41	6.19	7.84	9.40	10.79	13.02	14.77	17.58
C–(N)(C)(H)₂	−6.6	d 9.8	d 5.25	d 6.90	d 8.28	d 9.39	d 11.09	d 12.34	
C–(N)(C)₂(H)	−5.2	d −11.7	d 4.67	d 6.32	d 7.64	d 8.39	d 9.56	d 10.23	
C–(N)(C)₃	−3.2	d −34.1	d 4.35	d 6.16	d 7.31	d 7.91	d 8.49	d 8.50	
N–(C)(H)₂	4.8	29.71	5.72	6.51	7.32	8.07	9.41	10.47	12.28
N–(C)₂(H)	15.4	8.94	4.20	5.21	6.13	6.83	7.90	8.65	9.55
N–(C)₃	24.4	−13.46	3.48	4.56	5.43	5.97	6.56	6.67	6.50
N–(N)(H)₂	11.4	29.13	6.10	7.38	8.43	9.27	10.54	11.52	13.19
N–(N)(C)(H)	20.9	9.61	4.82	5.8	6.5	7.0	7.8	8.3	9.0
N–(N)(C)₂	29.2	−13.80							
N–(N)(C_B)(H)	22.1								
N_I–(H) ᵃ									
N_I–(C)	21.3								
N_I–(C_B) ᵉ	16.7								
N_A–(H) ᵃ	25.1	26.8	4.38	4.89	5.44	5.94	6.77	7.42	8.44
N_A–(C)	32.0	8.0	4.0	4.4	4.7	4.8	5.1	5.3	5.2
N–(C_B)(H)₂	4.8	29.71	5.72	6.51	7.32	8.07	9.41	10.47	12.28
N–(C_B)(C)(H)	14.9								
N–(C_B)(C)₂	26.2								
N–(C_B)₂(H)	16.3								
C_B–(N)	−0.5	−9.69	3.95	5.21	5.94	6.32	6.53	6.56	
N_A–(N)	23.0								
CO–(N)(H)	−29.6	34.93	7.03	7.87	8.82	9.68	11.16	12.20	
CO–(N)(C)	−32.8	16.2	5.37	6.17	7.07	7.66	9.62	11.19	
N–(CO)(H)₂	−14.9	24.69	4.07	5.74	7.13	8.29	9.96	11.22	
N–(CO)(C)(H)	−4.4	d 3.9							
N–(CO)(C)₂									
N–(CO)(C_B)(H)	+0.4								
N–(CO)₂(H)	−18.5								
N–(CO)₂(C)	−5.9								
N–(CO)₂(C_B)	−0.5								

ᵃ N_I = double bonded nitrogen in Imines; N_I—(C_B) = pyridine N.
N_A = double bonded nitrogen in Azo compounds.
ᵇ No *cis* corrections applied to Imines or Azo compounds.
ᶜ Gauche corrections of +0.8 kcal/mole to ΔH_f° applied just as for hydrocarbons.
ᵈ Estimates by authors.
ᵉ For ortho or para substitution in pyridine add −1.5 kcal/mole per group.

TABLE A–3. *Group contributions to C_p°, S°, and $\Delta H_f^{\circ\,b,\,c}$ (1 atm std state) for nitrogen-containing compounds.* — Continued

Group	ΔH° (kcal/mole)	S° (e. u.)	C_p° (e. u.)						
			300	400	500	600	800	1000	1500
Corrections to be applied to Ring Compound Estimates									
ethyleneimine	27.7	d 31.6							
azetidine	d 26.2	d 29.3							
pyrrolidine	6.8	26.7	−6.17	−5.58	−4.80	−4.00	−2.87	−2.17	
piperidine	1.0								
(ring)	3.4								
(ring)	8.5								
C—(CN)(C)(H)$_2$	+22.5	40.20	11.10	13.40	15.50	17.20	19.7	21.30	
C—(CN)(C)$_2$(H)	+25.8	19.80	11.00	12.70	14.10	15.40	17.30	18.60	
C—(CN)(C)$_3$		−2.80							
C—(CN)$_2$(C)$_2$		28.40							
C$_d$—(CN)(H)	37.4	36.58	9.80	11.70	13.30	14.50	16.30	17.30	
C$_d$—(CN)$_2$	84.1								
C$_d$—(NO$_2$)(H)		44.4	12.3	15.1	17.4	19.2	21.6	23.2	25.3
C$_B$—(CN)	35.8	20.50	9.8	11.2	12.3	13.1	14.2	14.9	
C$_T$—(CN)	63.8	35.40	10.30	11.30	12.10	12.70	13.60	14.30	15.30
C—(NO$_2$)(C)(H)$_2$	−15.1	d 48.4							
C—(NO$_2$)(C)$_2$(H)	−15.8	d 26.9							
C—(NO$_2$)(C)$_3$		d 3.9							
C—(NO$_2$)$_2$(C)(H)	−14.9								
O—(NO)(C)	−5.9	41.9	9.10	10.30	11.2	12.0	13.3	13.9	14.5
O—(NO$_2$)(C)	−19.4	48.50							

[a] N_I = double bonded nitrogen in Imines: N_I—(C_B) = pyridine N.
N_A double bonded nitrogen in Azo compounds.
[b] No *cis* corrections applied to Imines or Azo compounds.
[c] Gauche corrections of +0.8 kcal/mole to ΔH_f° applied just as for hydrocarbons.
[d] Estimates by authors.
[e] For ortho or para substitution in pyridine add −1.5 kcal/mole per group.

45

TABLE A–4. *Halo-alkanes group contribution to* $\Delta H^\circ_{f(298)}$, S°_{298} *and* C°_p, *ideal gas at 1 atm std. state*

Group	$\Delta H^\circ_{f(298)}$	S°_{298}	C°_p					
			300	400	500	600	800	1000
C—(F)₃(C)	−158.4	42.5	12.7	15.0	16.4	17.9	19.3	20.0
C—(F)₂(H)(C)	(−109.3)	39.1	9.9	12.0		15.1		
C—(F)(H)₂(C)	−51.8	35.4	8.1	10.0	12.0	13.0	15.2	16.6
C—(F)₂(C)₂	−97.0	17.8	9.9	11.8	13.5			
C—(F)(H)(C)₂	−48.4							
C—(F)(C)₃	−43.9							
C—(F)₂(Cl)(C)	−106.3	40.5	13.7	16.1	17.5			
C—(Cl)₃(C)	−20.7	50.4	16.3	18.0	19.1	19.8	20.6	21.0
C—(Cl)₂(H)(C)	(−18.9)	43.7	12.1	14.0	15.4	16.5	17.9	18.7
C—(Cl)(H)₂(C)	−15.6	37.8	8.9	10.7	12.3	13.4	15.3	16.7
C—(Cl)₂(C)₂	(−19.5)							
C—(Cl)(H)(C)₂	−12.8	17.6	9.0	9.9	10.5	11.2		
C—(Cl)(C)₃	−12.8	−5.4	9.3	10.5	11.0	11.3		
C—(Br)₃(C)		55.7	16.7	18.0	18.8	19.4	19.9	20.3
C—(Br)(H)₂(C)	−5.4	40.8	9.1	11.0	12.6	13.7	15.5	16.8
C—(Br)(H)(C)₂	−3.4							
C—(I)(H)₂(C)	7.95	42.5	9.2	11.0	12.9	13.9	15.8	17.2
C—(I)(H)(C)₂	10.7	22.2	(8.7)					
C—(I)(C)₃	13.0	(0.0)	(9.7)					
C—(Cl)(Br)(H)(C)		45.7	12.4	14.0	15.6	16.3	17.9	19.0
N—(F)₂(C)	−7.8							
N—(F)(C₂)	(7).							
N—(F₂)(C)	(−99)							

TABLE A-4. *Halo-alkenes, alkynes and arenes group contributions to* $\Delta H^\circ_{f(298)}$, S°_{298} *and* C°_p *ideal gas at 1 atm std. state*

Group	$\Delta H^\circ_{f(298)}$	S°_{298}	C°_p					
			300	400	500	600	800	1000
C_d—$(F)_2$	−77.5	37.3	9.7	11.0	12.0	12.7	13.8	14.5
C_d—$(Cl)_2$	−1.8	42.1	11.4	12.5	13.3	13.9	14.6	15.0
C_d—$(Br)_2$		47.6	12.3	13.2	13.9	14.3	14.9	15.2
C_d—$(F)(Cl)$		39.8	10.3	11.7	12.6	13.3	14.2	14.7
C_d—$(F)(Br)$		42.5	10.8	12.0	12.8	13.5	14.3	14.7
C_d—$(Cl)(Br)$		45.1	12.1	12.7	13.5	14.1	14.7	
C_d—$(F)(H)$	−37.6	32.8	6.8	8.4	9.5	10.5	11.8	12.7
C_d—$(Cl)(H)$	2.1	35.4	7.9	9.2	10.3	11.2	12.3	13.1
C_d—$(Br)(H)$	12.7	38.3	8.1	9.5	10.6	11.4	12.4	13.2
C_d—$(I)(H)$		40.5	8.8	10.0	10.9	11.6	12.6	13.3
C_T—(Cl)		33.4	7.9	8.4	8.7	9.0	9.4	9.6
C_T—(Br)		36.1	8.3	8.7	9.0	9.2	9.5	9.7
C_T—(I)		37.9	8.4	8.8	9.1	9.3	9.6	9.8
Arenes								
C_B—(F)	−42.8	16.1	6.3	7.6	8.5	9.1	9.8	10.2
C_B—(Cl)	−3.8	18.9	7.4	8.4	9.2	9.7	10.2	10.4
C_B—(Br)	10.7	21.6	7.8	8.7	9.4	9.9	10.3	10.5
C_B—(I)	24.0	23.7	8.0	8.9	9.6	9.9	10.3	10.5
C—$(C_B)(F)_3$	−162.7	42.8	12.5	15.3	17.2	18.5	20.1	21.0
C—$(C_B)(Br)(H)_2$	−6.9							
C—$(C_B)(I)(H)_2$	8.4							
Corrections for Next Nearest Neighbors								
ORTHO (F)(F)	5.0	0	0	0	0	0	0	0
ORTHO (Cl)(Cl)	2.2							
ORTHO (Alk)(Halogen)	0.6							
Cis (Halogen)(Halogen)	(0)							
Cis (Halogen)(Alk)	(0)							

TABLE A–5. *Group contributions for estimation of thermochemical properties of free radicals* [a] (*1 atm std state*).

Radical	$\Delta H^\circ_{f(298)}$ [b]	$S^\circ_{(298)}$	C_p°						
			300	400	500	600	800	1000	1500
[·C−(C)(H)₂]	35.82	31.20	5.99	7.24	8.29	9.13	10.44	11.47	13.14
[·C−(C)₂(H)]	37.45	10.74	5.16	6.11	6.82	7.37	8.26	8.84	9.71
[·C−(C)₃]	37.00	−10.77	4.06	4.92	5.42	5.75	6.27	6.35	6.53
[C−(C·)(H)₃]	−10.08	30.41	6.19	7.84	9.40	10.79	13.02	14.77	17.58
[C−(C·)(C)(H)₂]	−4.95	9.42	5.50	6.95	8.25	9.35	11.07	12.34	14.25
[C−(C·)(C)₂(H)]	−1.90	−12.07	4.54	6.00	7.17	8.05	9.31	10.05	11.17
[C−(C·)(C)₃]	1.50	−35.10	4.37	6.13	7.36	8.12	8.77	8.76	8.12
[C−(O·)(C)(H)₂]	6.1	36.4	7.9	9.8	10.8	12.8	15.0	16.4	
[C−(O·)(C)₂(H)]	7.8	14.7	7.7	9.5	10.6	12.1	13.7	14.5	
[C−(O·)(C)₃]	8.6	−7.5	7.2	9.1	9.8	11.1	12.1	12.3	
[C−(S·)(C)(H)₂]	32.4	39.0	9.0	10.6	12.4	13.6	15.8	17.4	
[C−(S·)(C)₂(H)]	35.5	17.8	8.5	10.0	11.6	12.3	13.8	14.6	
[C−(S·)(C)₃]	37.5	−5.3	8.2	9.8	11.3	11.8	12.2	12.3	
[·C−(H₂)(C_d)]	23.2	27.65	5.39	7.14	8.49	9.43	11.04	12.17	14.04
[·C−(H)(C)(C_d)]	25.5	7.02	4.58	6.12	7.19	8.00	9.11	9.78	10.72
[·C−(C)₂(C_d)]	24.8	−15.00	4.00	4.73	5.64	6.09	6.82	7.04	7.54
[C_d−(C·)(H)]	8.59	7.97	4.16	5.03	5.81	6.50	7.65	8.45	9.62
[C_d−(C·)(C)]	10.34	−12.30	4.10	4.71	5.09	5.36	5.90	6.18	6.40
[·C−(C_B)(H)₂]	23.0	26.85	6.49	7.84	0.10	9.98	11.34	12.42	14.14
[·C−(C_B)(C)(H)]	24.7	6.36	5.30	6.87	7.85	8.52	9.38	9.84	10.12
[·C−(C_B)(C)₂]	24.5	−15.46	4.72	5.48	6.20	6.65	7.09	7.10	6.94
[C_B−C·]	5.51	−7.69	2.67	3.14	3.68	4.15	4.96	5.44	5.98
[C−(·CO)(H)₃]	−5.4	66.6	12.74	14.63	16.47	18.17	21.14	23.27	
[C−(·CO)(C)(H)₂]	−0.3	45.8	12.7	14.5	15.8	16.8	19.2	20.7	
[C−(·CO)(C)₂(H)]	2.6	(23.7)	(11.5)	(12.8)	(14.3)	(15.5)	(17.4)	(18.5)	
[·N−(H)(C)]	c (51.8)	30.23	5.38	5.67	5.89	6.09	6.60	6.97	7.74
[·N−(C)₂]	c (57.6)	10.24	3.72	4.13	4.38	4.53	4.86	4.95	4.91
[C−(·N)(C)(H)₂]	−6.6	9.8	5.25	6.90	8.28	9.39	11.09	12.34	
[C−(·N)(C)₂(H)]	−5.2	−11.7	4.67	6.32	7.64	8.39	9.56	10.23	
[C−(·N)(C)₃]	c (−3.2)	34.1	4.35	6.16	7.31	7.91	8.49	8.50	
[·C−(H)₂(CN)]	d (54.2)	58.5	10.66	12.82	14.48	15.89	18.08	19.80	
[·C−(H)(C)(CN)]	d (52.8)	40.0	9.1	11.4	13.1	14.4	16.3	17.4	
[·C−(C)₂(CN)]	d (52.1)	19.6	8.8	10.4	11.3	12.3	13.7	14.5	
[·N−(H)(C_B)]		27.3	4.6	5.4	6.0	6.4	7.2	7.7	8.6
[·N−(C)(C_B)]		(6.5)	(3.9)	(4.2)	(4.7)	(5.0)	(5.6)	(5.8)	(5.9)
[C_B−N·]	−0.5	−9.69	3.95	5.21	5.94	6.32	6.53	6.56	
[C−(CO₂·)(H)]	−49.7	71.4	14.4	17.8	20.4	23.1	27.1	29.6	

See footnotes at end of table.

TABLE A—5. *Group contributions for estimates of thermochemical properties of free radicals*[a] *(1 atm std state).*—Con.

Radical	$\Delta H^\circ_{f(298)}$ [b]	$S^\circ_{(298)}$	C_p°						
			300	400	500	600	800	1000	1500
$C—(CO_2\cdot)(H)_2(C)$]	−43.9	49.8	15.5	18.5	20.3	22.3	27.5	27.2	
$C—(CO_2\cdot)(H)(C)_2$]	−41.0								
$C—(N_A)(H)_3$]	−10.08	30.41	6.19	7.84	9.40	10.79	13.02	14.77	17.58
$C—(N_A)(C)(H)_2$]	−5.8	9.42	5.50	6.95	8.25	9.35	11.07	12.34	14.25
$C—(N_A)(C)_2(H)$]	−2.3	−12.07	4.54	6.00	7.17	8.05	9.31	10.05	11.17
$C—(N_A)(C)_3$]	+0.5	−35.10	4.37	6.13	7.36	8.12	8.77	8.76	8.12
$N_A—C$]	32.0	8.0	4.0	4.4	4.7	4.8	5.1	5.3	5.2
$N_A—(N_A\cdot)(C)$]	72.4	36.1	7.8	8.2	8.4	8.6	8.9	9.0	9.0

Internal Rotation Barrier Corrections (However see also V−6.0 and Appendix C)

	S°	300	400	500	600	800	1000	1500
1. $V_0(RH) \to 2/3\ V_0(R\cdot)$								
$(CH_3\text{-}C\text{-}R)\,\sigma = 3$	+0.5	0	−0.1	−0.2	−0.3	−0.3	−0.3	−0.2
$(\infty\text{-}C\text{-}R)\ _\sigma = 3$	+0.5	0.1	0.1	0	−0.2	−0.3	−0.4	−0.4
2. $V_0(CH_3\text{-}C\text{-}RH) \to V_0'(CH_3\text{-}C\text{-}R\cdot)$								
$V_0 = 3.5,\ V_0' = 0$	1.5	−1.1	−1.1	−1.1	−1.0	−0.8	−0.6	−0.4

3. Mass corrections in conjugated systems

(i) If the masses on each side of a resonance stabilized bond in a radical have the same number of C atoms (i.e., are roughly equal), subtract 0.7 g/mole from the entropy, e.g. $\left(CH_2 = C \dot{-} C \begin{smallmatrix} CH_3 \\ \\ H \end{smallmatrix} \right)$ $m_1 = CH_2,\ m_2 = (CH_3 + H)$.

(ii) If the masses (as above) differ by one C atom, subtract 0.3 g/mole from S°, e.g. $(CH_2 = C \dot{-} CH_2)$ $m_1 = CH_2,\ m_2 = H_2$.

[a] Units are ΔH°_f (kcal/mole), S° (g/mole), C_p° (g/mole). Entropies include electron degeneracy and conjugation effects. Corrections for changes in rotational barriers of groups bonded to the radical center relative to the saturated hydrocarbons are required.

[b] Heats of formation group values, with the exception of the alkoxy radicals, are those derived by assuming equivalent bond dissociation energies for all (X—H) bonds of the same type (i.e., primary, secondary, or tertiary (X—H) bonds).

[c] These heats of formation are based on the amine decomposition kinetics and are probably too low by up to 4 kcal/mole (see V−7.0 and 8.0).

[d] These heats of formation have been calculated assuming resonance stabilizations of 10.8 kcal/mole in ($\cdot CH_2CN$), and 12.6 kcal/mole in ($CH_3\dot{C}HCN$ and $(CH_3)_2\dot{C}CN$).

To illustrate the use of the group table for radicals, the following examples are given:

I. Estimate ΔH_f°, S°, and C_p° of the neopentyl radical $((CH_3)_3C-CH_2\cdot)$ $\sigma = 6$, assume ($\cdot CH_2$—tBu has $V = 0$ or $V = 2$.

Groups [a]	Contributions				
	ΔH_f°	S° (V = 0)	S° (V = 2)	C_p° (V = 0)	C_p° (V = 2)
$3[C-(H)_3(C\cdot)]$	3(−10.08)	3(30.41)	91.23	3(6.19)	18.57
$[\cdot C-(H_2)(C)]$	35.82	31.20	31.20	5.99	5.99
$[C-(C\cdot)(C)_3]$	0.50	−35.10	−35.10	4.37	4.37
(symmetry) $\sigma = 6(27)$		−10.10	−10.10		
$\Delta(V_0)$ correction [b]		1.60	+1.00	−1.1	−0.6
Totals	5.63	[78.83]	78.23	[27.83]	28.33

[a] Units are kcal/mole (ΔH_f°); kcal/mole-deg (S° and C_p°).
Brackets denote preferred values.
[b] See Appendix C and V−6.0.

II. Estimate ΔH_f°, S°, C_p° of the t-butoxy radical $(CH_3)_3CO$.

Groups	Contributions		
	ΔH_f°	S°	C_p° (300)
$3[C-(C)(H)_3]$	−30.24	91.2	18.57
$[C-(O\cdot)(C)_3]$	8.6	−7.5	7.20
symmetry $(\sigma = (3)^4)$		−8.7	
Totals	−22.64	75.0	25.77

III. Estimate ΔH_f°, S°, and C_p° of the secondary butyl radical. $(CH_3CHCH_2CH_3)$ $\sigma = 9$, $\sigma_{int\ rot} = 1$, $V = 2/3\ V_0(RH)$.

Groups	Contributions		
	ΔH_f°	S° (2/3 V_0)	C_p° (300)
$[C-(H)_3(C\cdot)]$	−10.08	30.41	6.19
$[C-(H)_3(C)]$	−10.08	30.41	6.19
$[C-(H)_2(C)(C\cdot)]$	−4.95	9.42	5.50
$[\cdot C-(H)(C)_2]$	37.45	10.74	5.16
symmetry		−4.40	
$\Delta V_0(CH_3\ominus\cdot R)$		+0.50	0.0
$\Delta V_0(\infty\ominus\cdot R)$		+0.50	0.1
Totals	2.34	77.58	23.14

Appendix B – Frequencies Used in Transition State Calculations

TABLE B–1. *Bond stretching frequencies*

Stretches	ω (cm⁻¹) frequencies	Stretches	ω (cm⁻¹) frequencies
C=O	1700	C$\dot{-}$O	1400
C—O ethers	1100	(C·O) ethers	710
C—O acids, esters	1200	(C·O) acids, esters	770
C=C	1650	C$\dot{-}$C	1300
C—C	1000	C·C	675
C—H	3000	C·H	2200
C—F	1100	C·F	820
C—Cl	650	C·Cl	490
C—I	500	C·I	375
C—Br	560	C·Br	420

TABLE B–2. *Bond angle bending frequencies*

Bends [a b]	ω (cm⁻¹) frequencies	Bends	ω (cm⁻¹) frequencies
H–C–H	1450	H·C–H	725
$(H–C–C)_{t,w}$ or $(CH_2)_{w,t}$	1150	(H·C–C)	575
(H–O–C)	1200	(H·O–C)	600
(H–C=C)	1150	(H–C·C)	800
(C–C=C)	420	(C·C=C)	210
(C–C=O)	420	(C–C·C)	400
(C=C=C)	850	(C=C·C)	635
$(H–C–C)_r$ or (CH_2) rocks	700	(H–C·C)	700
$(H–C=C)_r$	700	(H·C=C)	350
(C–C–Cl)	400	(C–C·Cl)	200
(C–C–Br)	360	(C–C·Br)	180
(C–C–I)	320	(C–C·I)	160
(C–C–C)	350	(C–C·C)	175
(C–O–C)	400	(C–O·C)	200
(C–C–O)	400	(C–C·O)	200
(O–C–O)	400	(O–C·O)	200

Notes to Table B–2:

[a] Note that the normal single bond bending frequencies are consistent with the relation, $\omega_1/\omega_2=(\mu_2/\mu_1)^{1/2}$. Deviations from this relation seldom exceed 50 cm⁻¹.

$$\mu=\left(\frac{M_A M_B}{M_A+M_B}\right) \text{ for the bond } (A\overset{R}{\leftrightarrow}B)$$

[b] Methyl and methylene wags and twists, whose frequencies range from 1000–1300 cm⁻¹ have been equated with $(H–C–C)_{t,w}$ bends and assigned a mean frequency of 1150 cm⁻¹. Methylene rocks have lower frequencies (i.e., ~ 700 cm⁻¹) which correspond closely to the out of plane (H–C–C) bends in olefins.

TABLE B–3. *Bond Torsion Frequencies*

Torsions	ω (cm⁻¹) Frequencies	Torsions	ω (cm⁻¹) Frequencies
ethylene $(Et_{4e})_t$	1000	$(Et_{3e})_t$	500
propylene $(P_{4e})_t$	800	$(P_{3e})_t$	400
isobutene $(iB_{4e})_t$	700	$(iB_{3e})_t$	350
cis-2-butene $(CB_{4e})_t$	400	$(CB_{3e})_t$	200
trans-2-butene $(tB_{4e})_t$	300	$(tB_{3e})_t$	150
2-methylbut-2-ene $(2MB_{4e})_t$	250	$(2MB_{3e})_t$	125
tetramethylethylene $(TME_{4e})_t$	210	$(TME_{3e})_t$	105

TABLE B-4. *Approximate entropies and heat capacities of bond vibrations.*

Stretches	Frequency (cm^{-1})	$S°$ (300)	$C_p°$ (300)	$C_p°$ (500)	$C_p°$ (800)	$C_p°$ (1000)
C—H	3000	0.0	0.0	0.0	0.3	0.5
C—O	1100	0.1	0.3	0.8	1.4	1.6
C—F	1100	0.1	0.3	0.8	0.3	0.5
C—Cl	650	0.4	0.9	1.5	1.8	1.9
C—Br	560	0.6	1.1	1.6	1.9	1.9
O—H	3100	0.0	0.0	0.0	0.2	0.5

Torsions	Frequency (cm^{-1})	$S°$ (300)	$C_p°$ (300)	$C_p°$ (400)	$C_p°$ (500)	$C_p°$ (600)	$C_p°$ (800)	$C_p°$ (1000)	$C_p°$ (1500)
$(P_{4e})_t$	800	0.2	0.7	1.0	1.3	1.5	1.7	1.8	1.9
$(iB_{4e})_t$	700	0.3	0.8	1.1	1.4	1.6	1.8	1.8	1.9
$(P_{3e})_t$	400	1.0	1.5	1.7	1.8	1.8	1.9	1.9	2.0
$(CB_{4e})_t$	400	1.0	1.5	1.7	1.8	1.8	1.9	1.9	2.0
$(iB_{3e})_t$	350	1.2	1.6	1.7	1.8	1.9	1.9	1.9	2.0
$(tB_{4e})_t$	300	1.4	1.7	1.8	1.9	1.9	1.9	2.0	2.0
$(2MB_{4e})_t$	250	1.8	1.8	1.9	1.9	2.0	2.0	2.0	2.0
$(CB_{3e})_t$	200	2.2	1.8	1.9	1.9	2.0	2.0	2.0	2.0
$(tB_{3e})_t$	150	2.7	1.9	2.0	2.0	2.0	2.0	2.0	2.0
$(2MB_{3e})_t$	125	3.1	1.9	2.0	2.0	2.0	2.0	2.0	2.0

Bends

Bends	Frequency (cm^{-1})	$S°$ (300)	$C_p°$ (300)	$C_p°$ (400)	$C_p°$ (500)	$C_p°$ (600)	$C_p°$ (800)	$C_p°$ (1000)	$C_p°$ (1500)
$\left.\begin{array}{c} \text{C} \\ / \;\backslash \\ \text{(H H);} \\ \text{N} \\ / \;\backslash \\ \text{(H N)} \\ \text{C} \\ / \;\backslash \\ \text{(H C);} \end{array}\right\}$	1450	0.03	0.10	0.30	0.54	0.78	1.17	1.40	1.70
$\begin{array}{c} \text{O} \\ / \;\backslash \\ \text{(H C)} \end{array}$	1150	0.05	0.24	0.54	0.86	1.10	1.40	1.60	1.80
(C=C=C)	850	0.17	0.57	1.0	1.2	1.4	1.6	1.8	1.9
$\left.\begin{array}{c} \text{C} \\ / \;\backslash \\ \text{(C O);} \\ \text{C} \\ / \;\backslash \\ \text{(C F);} \\ \text{C} \\ / \;\backslash \\ \text{(C C)} \end{array}\right\}$	420	0.9	1.4	1.6	1.7	1.8	1.9	2.0	2.0
$\begin{array}{c} \text{C} \\ / \;\backslash \\ \text{(C Cl)} \end{array}$	400	1.0	1.5	1.7	1.7	1.8	1.9	2.0	2.0
$\begin{array}{c} \text{C} \\ / \;\backslash \\ \text{(C Br)} \end{array}$	360	1.2	1.6	1.7	1.8	1.9	1.9	2.0	2.0

Appendix C—Internal Rotations

TABLE C-1. *Entropies* [b,c] *of free internal rotors as a function of temperature*

Free rotors	Hybrid-ization	$Q_{f(300\,°K)}$ [a]	$T(°K)$				
			300	500	600	700	800
(∞)C⁻ methyl	Sp³	11.6/3 = 3.7	5.9	6.4	6.55	6.7	6.85
(∞)C⁻ methylene	Sp²	8.4/2 = 4.2	5.2	5.75	5.9	6.1	6.25
(∞)C⁻ Ethyl	Sp³	37.0	8.2	8.7	8.9	9.0	9.15
(∞)C⁻ i-propyl	Sp³	52.5	8.9	9.4	9.6	9.7	9.75
(∞)C⁻ t-butyl	Sp³	64.5	9.3	9.8	9.95	10.1	10.25
(∞)C⁻ (¹Et)	Sp²	35.0	8.05	8.55	8.75	8.85	9.0
(∞)C⁻ (·iPr)	Sp²	49.7	8.75	9.25	9.45	9.55	9.6

[a] The partition functions of free rotation were calculated from the relation,

$$Q_f = \left(\frac{8\Pi^3 I k T}{h^2}\right)^{1/2}.$$

[b] With equal masses, change entropy by −0.7 g/mole. For an opposing rotor heavier by 1 carbon group, change the free rotor entropy by −0.3 g/mole.

[c] Entropies were estimated from tables prepared by Pitzer, et al., [10], pp. 441–446.

TABLE C-2. *Some characteristic torsion barriers,* V (*kcal/mole*) *to rotation about single bonds for methyl groups*

Bond	V	Bond	V
CH₃—CH₃	2.9	CH₃—OH	1.1
CH₃—C₂H₅	2.8	CH₃—OCH₃	2.7
CH₃—isopropyl	3.6	CH₃—NH₂	1.9
CH₃-t-butyl	4.7	CH₃—NHCH₃	3.3
CH₃—CH═CHCH₃ cis	[a] 0.75	CH₃—N(CH₃)₂	4.4
CH₃—CH═CHCH₃ trans	1.95	CH₃—SiH₃	1.7
CH₃-vinyl	2.0	CH₃—SiH₂(CH₃)	1.7
CH₃—CH₂F	3.3	CH₃—PH₂	2.0
CH₃—CF₃	3.5	CH₃—SH	1.3
CF₃—CF₃	4.4	CH₃—SCH₃	2.1
CH₂Cl—CF₃	5.8	CH₃—CHO	1.2
CCl₃—CCl₃	10.8	CH₃—COCH₃	0.8
CH₃—CH₂Br	3.6	CH₃—allene	1.6
CH₃—CH₂I	3.2	CH₃—(isobutene)	2.2
CH₃—phenyl	0	CH₃—CO(OH)	0.5
CH₃—CCCH₃	0	CH₃—(epoxide ring)	2.6
CH₃—NO₂	0	(CH₃)₂N—COCH₃	20.0
CH₃O—NO	9.0	CH₃—OCHO	1.2
CH₃O—NO₂	9.0	CH₃—ONO₂	2.3
CH₃O—CO(CH₃)	13	CH₃—O vinyl	3.4

For a more complete compilation, see J. Dale, Tetrahedron **22**, 3373 (1966).

[a] Note: There seems to be a quite general "*cis* effect" such that F, Cl, CH₃, and CN, *cis* to a CH₃ lowers the CH₃ barrier by ∼ 1.4 kcal.

TABLE C–3. *Some characteristic barriers, V (kcal/mole) to rotation about single bonds for groups larger than methyl* [a]

Group	V
C_2H_5 — C_3H_7 ( )	4.2, 5.3
tBu — nPr ( )	10.9
	6.5
	7.0
	8.9
	4.2, 4.4
	9.3, 11.0
	10.8
	7.8

[a] U. A. Zirnet and M. M. Sushinskii, Optics and Spectroscopy **16,** 489 (1964).

TABLE C–4. *Decrease in entropy of free rotors as functions of barrier height (V), temperature (T, °K) and partition function, Q_f*

(V/RT)	$1/Q_f$		
	0.0	0.2	0.4
0.0	0.0	0.0	0.0
1.0	0.1	0.1	0.1
2.0	0.4	0.4	0.4
3.0	0.8	0.8	0.7
4.0	1.1	1.1	1.0
5.0	1.4	1.4	1.2
6.0	1.7	1.6	1.4
8.0	2.0	2.0	1.7
10.0	2.3	2.2	1.9
15.0	2.7	2.6	2.2
20.0	3.1	2.9	2.4

Note: Values listed are $\Delta S = S_f^\circ - S_h^\circ$ in g/mole. Taken from same source as table C–5.

TABLE C–5. *Molar heat capacity, C_p° (g/mole) of hindered rotor as a function of barrier (V), temperature and partition function, (Q_f)*

V/RT	$(1/Q_f)$				
	0.0	0.2	0.4	0.6	0.8
0.0	1.0	1.0	1.0	1.0	1.0
0.5	1.1	1.1	1.1	1.0	1.0
1.0	1.2	1.2	1.2	1.1	1.1
1.5	1.5	1.4	1.3	1.2	1.1
2.0	1.7	1.7	1.5	1.4	1.2
2.5	1.9	1.9	1.7	1.5	1.3
3.0	2.1	2.0	1.8	1.6	1.3
4.0	2.3	2.2	2.0	1.7	1.4
6.0	2.3	2.2	1.9	1.5	1.2
8.0	2.2	2.1	1.7	1.3	0.9
10.0	2.1	2.0	1.5	1.0	0.7
15.0	2.1	1.8	1.2	0.7	0.4
20.0	2.0	1.7	1.0	0.5	0.2

Tables from Thermodynamics, G. N. Lewis and M. Randall, revised by K. S. Pitzer and L. Brewer, McGraw-Hill Publishing Co., New York, N.Y. (1961).

$$Q_f = \frac{3.6}{\sigma} \left\{ \frac{I_r T}{100} \right\}^{1/2}$$ with I_r in AMU—ang^2 and T in °K.

σ = symmetry of barrier (e.g., 3 for —CH_3, 2 for —CH_2, etc.)

Appendix D. Thermodynamic Properties of Free Radicals

TABLE D-1. *Preferred Values of Free Radical Heats of Formation and Their Source*

Uncertainty limits on ΔH_f° of radicals are very hard to give. Even these ΔH_f° values believed to be the best known are probably uncertain to ± 1 kcal/mole. The uncertainties given below, therefore, are best guesses.

Ketones

$\Delta H_f^\circ(\emptyset\dot{C}O)$
(21.0 ± 2)

From the observed activation energies for the decompositions of acetophenone, benzophenone, benzoyl bromide, and benzil decompositions one obtains 21.0, 21.0, 18.3 and 22.4 kcal/mole respectively.

$\Delta H_f^\circ(CF_3\cdot)$
(−112.5 ± 2)

Bromination studies of Whittle (see C_2F_6 decomposition).

$\Delta H_f^\circ(\emptyset CH_2\cdot)$
(45.0 ± 1)

Iodination studies by Benson, et al. (see toluene decomposition).

$\Delta H_f^\circ(\emptyset CH_2\dot{C}O)$
(20.6 ± 2)

Estimated by additivity relations from ΔH_f°(acetyl), see R. Walsh and S. W. Benson, J. Phys. Chem. **70**, 3751 (1966).

$\Delta H_f^\circ(CH_3)$
(34.0 ± 1)

Iodination studies on methane, see D. M. Golden, R. Walsh and S. W. Benson, J. Am. Chem. Soc. **87**, 4053 (1965).

$\Delta H_f^\circ(CH_3\dot{C}O)$
(−5.4 ± 1)

See $\Delta H_f^\circ(\emptyset CH_2\dot{C}O)$.

Esters

$\Delta H_f^\circ(CH_3CO_2\cdot)$
(−49.7 ± 2)

From the decomposition kinetics of benzylacetate and diacetyl peroxide.

$\Delta H_f^\circ(\emptyset CO_2\cdot)$
(−21.7 ± 2)

From the decomposition kinetics of benzylbenzoate and supported by additivity calculations based on $(CH_3CO_2\cdot)$ heat of formation.

Peroxides

$\Delta H_f^\circ(CH_3O\cdot)$
(3.9 ± 1)

From the decomposition kinetics of dimethyl peroxide.

$\Delta H_f^\circ(C_2H_5O\cdot)$
(4.9 ± 1)

Additivity calculation from dimethyl peroxide value. Kinetics of the $(C_2H_5O)_2$ decomposition give $\Delta H_f^\circ(C_2H_5O\cdot) = -4.9$ kcal/mole.

$\Delta H_f^\circ(n-C_3H_7O\cdot)$
(−9.7 ± 1)

Kinetics of decomposition of $(C_3H_7O)_2$ additivity relations based on $(CH_3O\cdot)$ give $\Delta H_f^\circ(C_3H_7O\cdot) = -10.0$ kcal/mole.

$\Delta H_f^\circ(tBuO\cdot)$
(−21.5 ± 1)

From the decomposition kinetics of $(tBuO)_2$ which depend critically on the corrected heat of formation of the parent peroxide. The most recent value of $\Delta H_f^\circ(tBuO)_2 = -80.5$ kcal/mole, G. Baker, J. H. Littlefield, R. Shaw, and J. C. J. Thynne, J. Chem. Soc. 6970 (1965) has been used here. Additivity calculations based on $(CH_3O\cdot)$ give $\Delta H_f^\circ(tBuO\cdot) = -21.3$ kcal/mole.

$\Delta H_f^\circ(C_2H_5CO_2\cdot)$
(−55.0 ± 2)

Good agreement between the value from additivity based on $\Delta H_f^\circ(CH_3CO_2\cdot)$ and the decomposition kinetics of $(C_2H_5CO_2)_2$.

$\Delta H_f^\circ(C_3H_7CO_2\cdot)$
(−60.0 ± 2)

See comments for $\Delta H_f^\circ(C_2H_5CO_2\cdot)$.

$\Delta H_f^\circ(\cdot COOH)$
(−53.3 ± 3)

Determined from the decomposition kinetics of phenylacetic acid (ref. 2). This is considered the most reasonable result because the recombination rate constant calculated is close to that observed for the recombination of propyl + benzl radicals. Also, D(H—COOH) = 87.3 kcal/mole, which is close to the corresponding bond dissociation energy in acetaldehyde (D(CH₃CO—H)).

$\Delta H_f^\circ(\emptyset_2\text{CH}\cdot)$
(59.3 ± 6)

Based on an assumed recombination rate constant of $k_{rec}\simeq10^{8.1}$ 1/mole-sec. The heat of formation gives a total resonance energy which is lower by 4 kcal/mole than the sum of two benzyl resonances (i.e., Res=22.8 kcal/mole compared to 2(13.5)=27 kcal/mole). If the results of Back and Sehon on phenylacetic acid and diphenylacetic acid are accepted one obtains $\Delta H_f^\circ(\text{C}\emptyset_2\text{CH}\cdot)\simeq65.3$ kcal/mole and a resonance energy of 16.7 kcal/mole. This heat of formation is not presently established.

$\Delta H_f^\circ(i\text{PrO}\cdot)$
(-12.4 ± 1)

Based on $\Delta H_f^\circ(\text{CH}_3\text{O}\cdot)$ and additivity relations. The kinetics of the isopropylnitrite decomposition give $\Delta H_f^\circ(-16.7$ kcal/mole). The additivity estimate is believed to be the more reliable.

$\Delta H_f^\circ(\text{CH}_2{=}\text{CHCH}_2\cdot)$
(39.6 ± 1.5)

Measured by iodination studies on propylene as $\Delta H_f^\circ(\text{allyl.})=40.6$ kcal/mole. A. S. Rogers, D. M. Golden and S. W. Benson, J. Am. Chem. Soc. **88**, 3196 (1966) and from a study of the iodine catalyzed isomerization of 1-butene as 38.0, E. K. Egger, D. M. Golden and S. W. Benson, J. Am. Chem. Soc. **86**, 5420 (1964). The kinetics of the allylmethyl sulphone decomposition support the lower value.

$\Delta H_f^\circ(\cdot\text{CH}_2(\text{CH}_3)\text{C}{=}\text{CH}_2)$
(29.6 ± 2)

Calculated with additivity relations from $\Delta H_f^\circ(\text{allyl})$.

$\Delta H_f^\circ(\text{C}_2\text{H}_5\cdot)$
(25.7 ± 1)

Iodination studies. D. B. Hartley and S. W. Benson, J. Chem. Phys. **39**, 132 (1963).

$\Delta H_f^\circ(n\text{-C}_3\text{H}_7\cdot)$
(20.7 ± 1)

Additivity relations based on $\Delta H_f^\circ(\text{C}_2\text{H}_5\cdot)$.

$\Delta H_f^\circ(i\text{Pr}\cdot)$
(17.6 ± 1)

Iodination studies. P. S. Nangia and S. W. Benson, J. Am. Chem. Soc. **86**, 2773 (1964).

$\Delta H_f^\circ(t\text{Bu}\cdot)$
(6.8 ± 1)

Iodination studies. H. Teranishi and S. W. Benson, J. Am. Chem. Soc. **85**, 2887 (1963).

$\Delta H_f^\circ(\emptyset\cdot)$
(80.0 ± 1)

Iodination studies. A. S. Rogers, D. M. Golden, and S. W. Benson, J. Am. Chem. Soc. **89**, 4578 (1967). This gives $\overline{\text{DH}}^\circ(\emptyset{-}\text{H})=112.3\pm1$ kcal/mole.

$\Delta H_f^\circ(\emptyset\dot{\text{C}}(\text{H})\text{CH}_3)$
(36.6 ± 3)

Based on the assumption of D(C—H) secondary bond dissociation energy in $\emptyset{-}\text{CH}_2{-}\text{CH}_3$ =95−13.5 (benzl resonance)=81.5 kcal/mole. The $\Delta H_f^\circ(\emptyset\dot{\text{C}}\text{HCH}_3)$ from the kinetics is 31.6 kcal/mole.

$\Delta H_f^\circ(\emptyset\dot{\text{C}}(\text{CH}_3)_2)$
(26.3)

Based on the assumption of D(C—H) tertiary bond dissociation energy in $\emptyset\text{CH}{-}(\text{CH}_3)_2$ is 91−13.5=87.5 kcal/mole.

$\Delta H_f^\circ(\text{HS}\cdot)$
(35.5 ± 3)

Based on recent mass spectrometric studies on sulfides. J. A. Kerr, Chem. Revs. **66**, 465 (1966).

$\Delta H_f^\circ(\emptyset\text{S}\cdot)$
(49.5)

Based on the kinetics of the phenyl methyl sulfide decomposition.

$\Delta H_f^\circ(\text{CH}_3\text{S}\cdot)$
(28.0 ± 3)

Based on the decomposition kinetics of $\emptyset\text{CH}_2\text{SCH}_3$ and on an assumed rate constant for recombination, $k_{rec}\simeq10^{8.8}$ 1/mole-sec (a mean between the rate constants of recombination for $\text{CH}_3\cdot+\emptyset\text{CH}_2\cdot$ and $\text{C}_2\text{H}_5\cdot+\emptyset\text{CH}_2\cdot$). Appearance potential work places $\Delta H_f^\circ(\text{CH}_3\text{S})<31.8$ kcal/mole, T. F. Palmer and F. P. Lossing, J. Am. Chem. Soc. **84**, 4661 (1962).

$\Delta H_f^\circ(\text{CH}_3\text{SO}_2\cdot)$
(-60.5 ± 3)

Based on the decomposition kinetics of dimethylsulfone, however see comments for this reaction.

56

$\Delta H_f^\circ(\cdot CH_2—C\equiv N)$
(51.1±3)

Based on the decomposition kinetics of ethyl cyanide. Resonance energy equal $\simeq$ 12.5 kcal/mole. Analysis of the activation energy for the *cis-trans* isomerization of β-cyanostyrene gives 10 kcal/mole for the resonance energy.

$\Delta H_f^\circ(CH_3)_2\dot{C}—C\equiv N$
(33.8±3)

Based on the kinetics of the *t*-butylcyanide decomposition. Resonance energy obtained is 10.6 kcal/mole.

$\Delta H_f^\circ(\emptyset\dot{C}(CH_3)CN)$
(54.4±3)

Based on the decomposition kinetics of cumyl cyanide. Resonance energy = 22.1 kcal/mole which is close to the sum of the benzyl and cyano resonance energies (i.e., $\sim$ 13.5 + 10.6 = 24.1 kcal/mole, respectively).

$\Delta H_f^\circ(CF_2:)$
(−39.7±2)

Based on the equilibrium for the elimination reaction, $HCF_2Cl \rightleftarrows HCl + CF_2:$, and the equilibrium for the tetrafluoroethylene decomposition, $C_2F_4 \rightleftarrows 2CF_2:$.

$\Delta H_f^\circ(CF_3\dot{C}{=}CF_2)$
(−177.6)

Based on the kinetics of the dissociation of perfluoroisobutene (not very reliable).

$\Delta H_f^\circ(\cdot CCl_3)$
(18.5±2)

Based on the analysis of the bromination of chlororform, S. W. Benson, J. Chem. Phys. **43**, 2044 (1965).

$\Delta H_f^\circ(CH_3N_2\cdot)$
(66.0)

The decomposition kinetics of azomethane give $\Delta H_f^\circ = 70.3$ kcal/mole.

$\Delta H_f^\circ(R—N{=}N\cdot)$
$(R = n$ alkyl)

See section V-8.0. Values in brackets below come directly from the kinetics.

$\Delta H_f^\circ(C_2H_5CH(CH_3)N{=}N\cdot)$
(47.0)

[46.4]

$\Delta H_f^\circ(tBuN{=}N\cdot)$
(43.5)

[41.4]

$\Delta H_f^\circ(NH_2\cdot)$
(43.3±3)

Best compromise from the kinetics of all amine and hydrazine decompositions (see section V-8.1). [41.0]

$\Delta H_f^\circ(CH_3\dot{N}H)$
(41.7)

[34.9]

$\Delta H_f^\circ[(CH_3)_2N\cdot]$
(37.4)

[31.9]

$\Delta H_f^\circ(\emptyset\dot{N}H)$
(52.8)

[47.3]

$\Delta H_f^\circ(\emptyset\dot{N}CH_3)$
(49.6) or (53.5)

[48.6]

TABLE D–2. *Calculated Thermodynamic Properties* [a,b,c,d] *of Free Radicals:* entropies and heat capacities

Radical	σ	$S°$	300	400	500	600	800	1000	1500	V_0^d
CH₃·	6	46.4	8.3	9.1	10.1	10.9	12.6	14.0	16.3	
C₂H₅·[a,b]	6	[59.5	11.1	14.1	16.8	19.1	22.9	25.8	30.5	0]
		58.9	11.6	14.6	17.1	19.3	23.0	25.9	30.5	2
		58.3	11.4	14.6	17.3	19.6	23.3	26.1	30.6	4
		57.9	10.7	14.0	16.9	19.4	23.4	26.3	30.9	8
C₃H₇·	6	68.9	16.6	20.9	24.9	28.4	33.8	38.1	44.7	0
n-propyl		[68.1	17.7	21.8	25.5	28.9	34.1	38.3	44.9	2]
		67.3	17.7	22.0	26.1	29.4	34.6	38.7	45.1	4
		66.6	17.3	21.8	25.9	29.5	35.0	39.3	45.7	8
i—C₃H₇·	18	68.8	15.3	19.6	23.6	27.1	32.9	37.4	44.3	0
isopropyl		[67.0	17.5	21.4	24.8	28.2	33.5	37.8	44.7	2]
		65.6	17.5	21.8	26.0	29.2	34.5	38.6	45.1	4
		64.2	16.7	21.4	25.6	29.4	35.3	39.8	46.3	8
CH₃ĊHCH₂CH₃	9									
sec-butyl		[77.6	23.1	28.4	33.3	37.8	44.9	50.3	58.9]	2/3 V_0^e
(CH₃)₃C·	6(27)	[74.6	19.3	25.1	29.9	35.1	42.9	48.9	58.4	0]
V₀(isoC₄H₁₀)=4.0		72.5	21.7	26.9	31.4	36.0	43.5	49.2	58.7	2
		70.4	21.1	27.5	32.3	37.5	44.7	50.4	59.0	4
		68.6	19.3	26.0	31.4	36.9	45.3	51.3	60.2	8
Ø·	2	69.1	18.96	25.56	31.01	35.50	42.20	46.76	53.74	
ØCH₂·	2	75.4	25.36	33.18	40.08	45.63	54.00	59.91	68.77	
ØĊHCH₃	3	[85.1	30.4	40.0	47.8	54.7	64.8	71.8	82.2]	2/3 V_0^e
ØO·	2	73.7	22.5	29.8	35.8	40.6	47.5	52.3	....	
ØS·	2	76.5	23.6	30.6	36.5	41.2	47.9	52.5	....	
ØĊ(CH₃)₂	18	[90.6	36.0	46.1	55.4	63.3	75.2	83.7	96.5]	2/3 V_0^e,
CH₃S·		57.6	9.9		13.4		17.0	18.8		
CH₃CH₂S·		67.2	15.2	18.4	21.8	24.4	28.8	32.2		
(CH₃)₂CHS·		74.2	20.9	25.7	30.4	33.9	39.8	44.1		
(CH₃)₃CS·		77.2	26.8	33.3	39.4	44.2	51.3	56.6		
CH₃O·	3	54.3	9.1		12.6		16.8	18.9		
CH₃CH₂O·	3	64.6	14.1	17.6	20.2	23.6	28.0	31.2		
(CH₃)₂CHO·	9	71.1	20.1	25.2	29.4	33.7	39.7	44.0		
(CH₃)₃CO·	81	75.0	25.8	32.6	37.9	43.5	51.2	56.6		
CH₂=CHCH₂·	2	62.1	14.6	18.5	21.8	24.4	28.8	31.9	36.8	13.0
CH₂=C(CH₃)CH₂·	6	68.8	20.8	26.1	30.5	34.1	40.0	44.4	51.2	15.0
CH₂=CHĊHCH₃	3	70.8	20.0	25.4	29.9	33.8	39.9	44.3	51.1	15.0
										3.0

TABLE D-2. *Calculated Thermodynamic Properties*[a,b,c,d] *of Free Radicals:* entropies and heat capacities—*Continued*

Radical	σ	$S°$	300	400	500	600	800	1000	1500	V_0
$CH_3CO_2\cdot$	6	66.6	12.7	14.6	16.5	18.2	21.1	23.3		
$CH_3CH_2CO_2\cdot$	6	76.2	18.9	22.3	25.2	27.7	32.2	35.5		
$NH_2\cdot$	2	48.4	8.1		9.1		10.3	11.6		
$\cdot CH_2C\equiv N$	2	58.5	10.7	12.8	14.5	15.9	18.1	19.8		
$CH_3\dot{C}HC\equiv N$	3	[68.8	15.3	19.1	22.2	24.9	29.0	31.9		]2/3V_0^e
$(CH_3)_2\dot{C}-C\equiv N$	18	[75.8	21.2	25.8	29.1	33.2	39.0	43.5		]2/3V_0^e
$CH_3\dot{N}H$	3	[59.0	11.3	13.3	15.1	16.8	19.5	21.7	25.3]	2/3V_0^e
$(CH_3)_2\dot{N}$	18	[66.2	15.7	19.2	22.7	25.7	30.5	34.3	39.9]	2/3V_0^e
$Ø\dot{N}H$	1	75.3	24.8	32.8	39.2	44.2	51.4	56.3		13
$Ø\dot{N}CH_3$	3	[83.3	30.2	39.3	47.0	53.3	62.6	69.0		]2/3$V_0^{e,\ 13}$
$\cdot COOH$	1	60.7	10.2	11.8	12.9	13.7	15.4	16.3		13
$(CH_3)_3CCH_2\cdot$	$(3)^36$	[78.8	27.8	35.8	42.6	48.6	59.5	63.9	73.7	0]
		78.2	28.3	36.3	42.9	48.8	59.6	64.0	73.7	2
		77.6	28.1	36.3	43.1	49.1	59.9	64.2	73.8	4
		77.2	27.4	35.7	42.7	48.9	60.0	64.4	74.1	8
$CH_3\dot{C}HCH(CH_3)_2$	27	86.4	25.9	33.3	40.0	45.9	55.1	62.1	73.1	0
		[84.7	28.1	35.0	41.3	46.9	55.7	62.5	73.3	2]
		83.0	28.5	35.7	42.5	48.0	56.8	63.4	73.7	4
		81.5	27.7	35.2	42.2	48.3	57.6	64.6	75.0	8

[a] There is a small correction (+0.3 g/mole) to the ethyl radical entropy obtained from the grou ɔs, due to the differences in reduced moments of inertia for roughly equivalent opposed mass rotors.

[b] Brackets indicate the values favored by the authors.

[c] Note that the values of this table represent our best estimates and have been generated over the period of preparation of this monograph (roughly 2 years). Values on some data sheets may be somewhat different but such differences should not exceed ±1−2 g/mole in either the entropy or heat capacity.

[d] V_0 denotes the barriers to rotation for the alkyl or aryl groups bonded to the radical centers.

[e] V_0 for nonconjugated groups bonded to the radical center are assumed to be 2/3 their value in the corresponding saturated compound.

REFERENCES TO SECTIONS I-VI AND APPENDICES

[1] JANAF (United States Joint Army Navy Air Force) Interim Thermochemical Tables, Vols. 1 and 2 (Thermal Laboratory, The Dow Chemical Co., Midland, Mich., 1965).

[2] American Petroleum Institute Research Project 44 (API tables), Carnegie Institute of Technology (Chemical Thermodynamic Properties Center, Texas A&M Univ., College Station, Tex., 1966).

[3] Additivity Rules for the Estimation of Thermochemical Properties:
    I. Hydrocarbons, Benson, S. W., et al., Chem. Revs. **69** (1969).
    II. Oxygen compounds, Benson, S. W., et al., Chem. Revs. **69** (1969).
    III. Nitrogen containing compounds, Benson, S. W., et al., Chem. Revs. **69** (1969).
    IV. Halogen substituted compounds, Benson, S. W., et al., Chem. Revs. **69** (1969).
    V. Organometallic and organo-nonmetallic compounds, Benson, S. W., et al., Chem. Revs. **69** (1969).
    VI. Free radicals and polycyclic compounds, O'Neal, H. E., and Benson, S. W., Int. J. Chem. Kinetics (1969).

[4] Janz, J. G., Estimation of the Thermodynamic Properties of Organic Molecules (Academic Press, New York, N.Y., 1958).

[5] Benson, S. W., The Foundations of Chemical Kinetics (McGraw-Hill Book Co., Inc., New York, N.Y., 1960).

[6] Benson, S. W., J. Chem. Ed. **42**, 502 (1965).

[7] Kerr, J. A., Chem. Revs. **66**, 465 (1966).

[8] Purnell, J. H., and Quinn, C. P., J. Chem. Soc., 4049 (1964).

[9] Mortimer, C. T., Reaction Heats and Bond Strengths (Pergamon Press, New York, N.Y., 1962).

[10] Lewis, G. N., and Randall, M., revised by Pitzer, K. S., and Brewer, L., Thermodynamics, 2d ed. (McGraw-Hill Book Co., Inc., New York, N.Y., 1961).

[11] Keller, R., Basic Tables in Chemistry (McGraw-Hill Book Co., Inc., New York, N.Y., 1967).

[12] The Handbook of Chemistry and Physics, 47th ed. (The Chemical Rubber Co., Cleveland, Ohio, 1966–67).

[13] NBS Tech. Note 270–3 (Jan. 1968).

[14] Bernstein, H. J., J. Phys. Chem. **69**, 1550 (1965).

[15] Benson, S. W., Thermochemical Kinetics (John Wiley & Sons, New York, N.Y., 1968).

[16] O'Neal, H. E., and Ring, M. A., Inorg. Chem. 5, 435 (1966).

[17] Maccoll, A., and Thomas, P. J., J. Chem. Soc. 979 (1955).

[18] Barton, D. H. R., et al., Trans. Faraday Soc. **45**, 725 (1949).

[19] Thomas, P. J., J. Chem. Soc. 1192 (1959).

[20] Blades, A. T., and Murphy, G. W., J. Am. Chem. Soc. **74**, 6219 (1952).

[21] Barker, R., and Maccoll, A., J. Chem. Soc. 2839 (1963).

[22] Blades, A. T., Gilderson, P. W., and Wallbridge, M. G. H., Can. J. Chem. **40**, 1526, 1533 (1962).

[23] Goldberg, A. E., and Daniels, F., J. Am. Chem. Soc. **79**, 1314 (1957).

[24] Harden, G. D., and Maccoll, A., J. Chem. Soc. 2454 (1955).

[25] O'Neal, H. E., and Benson, S. W., J. Phys. Chem. **71**, 2903 (1967).

[26] Pauling, L., The Nature of the Chemical Bond, 3d ed. (Cornell Univ. Press, Ithaca, N.Y., 1960), pp. 221–264.

[27] Trotman-Dickenson, A. F., Gas Kinetics (Butterworths Sci. Publ., London, 1955).

[28] Schlag, E., and Rabinovitch, B. S., J. Am. Chem. Soc. **82**, 5996 (1960).

[29] Benson, S. W., J. Chem. Phys. **34**, 521 (1961).

[30] Willicott, M. R., and Cargle, V. H., J. Am. Chem. Soc. **89**, 723 (1967).

[31] Turner, R. B., Tet. Letters **15**, 997 (1965).

[32] Foster, E. G., Cope, A. C., and Daniels, F., J. Am. Chem. Soc. **69**, 1893 (1947).

[33] Benson, S. W., Egger, K. W., and Golden, D. M., J. Am. Chem. Soc. **87**, 468 (1965).

[34] Cundall, R. B., Progress in Reaction Kinetics, Vol. 2 (The Macmillan Book Co., New York, N.Y., 1964), p. 167.

[35] Steacie, E. W. R., Atomic and Free Radical Reactions, Vol. 1 (Reinhold Publ. Corp., New York, N.Y., 1954).

[36] McNesby, J. R., and Gordon, A. S., J. Am. Chem. Soc. **79**, 4593 (1957).

[37] Bryce, W. A., and Hardiman, M. S., Can. J. Chem. **40**, 1031 (1962).

[38] Voevodski, V. V., Trans. Faraday Soc. **55**, 65 (1959); Kinetika i Kataliz **5**, 603 (1964). Wojcieckowski, B. W., and Laidler, K. J., Can. J. Chem. **38**, 1027 (1960). Wojcieckowski, B. W., and Laidler, K. J., Trans. Faraday Soc. **59**, 369 (1963). Norrish, R. G. W., and Pratt, G. L., Nature **197**, 143 (1963). Ree, T., Yakn, K., and Eyring, H., Trans. Faraday Soc. **58**, 2375 (1962). Gowenlock, B. G., Progress in Reaction Kinetics, Vol. 3 (Pergamon Press, New York, N.Y., 1965), p. 171.

[39] Blades, A. T., and Steacie, E. W. R., Can. J. Chem. **32**, 1142 (1954).

[40] Fettis, G. C., and Knox, J. H., Progress in Reaction Kinetics, Vol. 2 (The Macmillan Book Co., New York, N.Y., 1964), p. 1.

[41] Hammond, G. S., J. Am. Chem. Soc. **77**, 334 (1955).

[42] Fueno, T., and Benson, S. W., J. Chem. Phys. **36**, 1597 (1962).

[43] Purnell, J. H., and Quinn, C. P. J. Chem. Soc. 4049 (1964).

[44] Mosley, F., and Robb, J. C., Proc. Roy. Soc. (London). **A243**, 130 (1957).

[45] Shepp, A., J. Chem. Phys. **24**, 939 (1956).

[46] Kistiakowsky, G. B., and Roberts, E. K., J. Chem. Phys. **21**, 1637 (1953).

[47] Pritchard, H. O., J. Chem. Phys. **25**, 267 (1956).

[48] Steel, C., J. Chem. Phys. **31**, 899 (1959).

[49] Schlag, E. W. R., J. Chem. Phys. **35**, 2117 (1961).

[50] Steel, C., and Laidler, K. J., J. Chem. Phys. **34**, 1827 (1961).

[51] Metcalfe, E. L., and Trotman-Dickenson, A. F., J. Chem. Soc., 4260 (1962).

[52] Overberger, C. G., and DiGuilio, A. V., J. Am. Chem. Soc. **81**, 2154 (1959).

[53] Seltzer, S., and Dunne, F. T., J. Am. Chem. Soc. **87**, 2628 (1965).

[54] Walling, C., Free Radicals in Solution (John Wiley & Sons, Inc., New York, N.Y., 1957), p. 576.

[55] Welland, H., Hove, H., and Borner, K., Ann. Chem. **446,** 31 (1926).

[56] Calvert, J., Chem. Revs. **59,** 569 (1959).

[57] Kerr, J. A., and Trotman-Dickenson, A. F., Progress in Reaction Kinetics, Vol. 1 (Pergamon Press, New York, N.Y., 1961), p. 107.

[58] Dale, J., Tetrahedron **22,** 3373 (1966).

[59] Zirnett, U. A., and Sushinskii, M. M., Optics and Spectroscopy **16,** 489 (1964).

[60] Walsh, R., and Benson, S. W., J. Phys. Chem. **70,** 3751 (1966).

[61] Golden, D. M., Walsh, R., and Benson, S. W., J. Am. Chem. Soc. **87,** 4053 (1965).

[62] Baker, G., Littlefield, J. H., Shaw, R., and Thynne, J. C. J., J. Chem. Soc., 6970 (1965).

[63] Rogers, A. S., Golden, D. M., and Benson, S. W., J. Am. Chem. Soc. **88,** 3196 (1966).

[64] Egger, E. K., Golden, D. M., and Benson, S. W., J. Am. Chem. Soc. **86,** 5420 (1964).

[65] Hartley, D. B., and Benson, S. W., J. Chem. Phys. **39,** 132 (1963).

[66] Nangia, P. S., and Benson, S. W., J. Am. Chem. Soc. **86,** 2773 (1964).

[67] Teranishi, H., and Benson, S. W., J. Am. Chem. Soc. **85,** 2887 (1963).

[68] Rogers, A. S., Golden, D. M., and Benson, S. W., J. Am. Chem. Soc. **89,** 4578 (1967).

[69] Palmer, T. F., and Lossing, F. P., J. Am. Chem. Soc. **84,** 4661 (1962).

[70] Benson, S. W., J. Chem. Phys. **43,** 2044 (1965).

1. Complex Fissions —

Molecular Elimination Reactions

Reaction: Chloroethane (ethyl chloride)

$$C_2H_5Cl \ (I) \rightarrow C_2H_4 \ (II) + HCl \ (III)$$

	I	II	III
$\Delta H^\circ_{f(298)}$	-26.3	12.5	-22.1
$S^\circ_{(298)}$	66.0	52.5	44.6
$C^\circ_{p(298)}$	15.1	10.4	7.0

$\Delta S^\circ = 31.1$ g/mole
$\Delta H^\circ = 16.7$ kcal/mole
$\Delta C_p^\circ = 2.3$ g/mole

log A	E	log k_T (700)	Conditions	System	Surface	References
13.16	56.46	-4.46	740–940 °K 1% in Ar	S.P. shock	————	[1] W. Tsang, J. Chem. Phys. **41**, 2487 (1964).
14.2	59.5	-4.37	671–766 °K 20–200 torr	static	none	[2] D. H. R. Barton and K. E. Howlett, J. Chem. Soc., 165 (1949).
14.6	60.8	-4.38	685–729 °K 20–200 torr	static	————	[3] K. E. Howlett, J. Chem. Soc. 3695 (1952).
13.51	56.61	-4.16	684–744 °K 136–210 torr	static	none	[4] H. Hartman, H. G. Bosche, and H. Heydtmann, Zeit. für Physik. Chemie, N.F. **42**, 329 (1964).
14.0	58.4	-4.25	675–794 °K 0.2–134 torr	static	————	[5] K. A. Holbrook and A. R. W. Marsh, Trans. Faraday Soc. **63**, 643 (1967).

Preferred:
  log $k = 13.2 - 56.5/\theta$.
  log $A_{est} = 13.3$ (see section II–1.0).

Experimental

[1] Analysis is G.L.C. on ethylene. Comparative internal rate standard was 2-chloropropane.

[2] Rates by ΔP. Stoichiometry confirmed by HCl titration.

[3] Rates by ΔP. Pressure dependence observed below 8 torr. Addition of HCl and ethylene did not affect the rate at pressures greater than 8 torr.

[4] Rates by HCl titration. 1,1,2,2d_4 isotope effect studied by A. T. Blades, P. W. Gilderson, and M. G. H. Wallbridge, Can. J. Chem. **40**, 5126 (1962).

Reaction: 1-Chloropropane (*n*-propyl chloride)

$$CH_3CH_2CH_2Cl \ (I) \rightarrow CH_3CH=CH_2 \ (II) + HCl \ (III)$$

	I	II	III
$\Delta H^\circ_{f(298)}$	-31.3	4.8	-22.1
$S^\circ_{(298)}$	75.4	63.6	44.6
$C^\circ_{p(298)}$	20.6	15.3	7.0

$\Delta S^\circ = 32.8$ g/mole
$\Delta H^\circ = 14.0$ kcal/mole
$\Delta C^\circ_p = 1.7$ g/mole

log A	E	log k_T (700)	Conditions	System	Surface	References
13.45	55.0	-3.72	693–751 °K 50–155 torr	static	none	[1] D. H. R. Barton, A. J. Head, and R. J. Williams, J. Chem. Soc. 2039 (1951).
13.50	55.08	-3.69	672–733 °K 243–301 torr	static	none	[2] H. Hartman, H. G. Bosche, and H. Heydtmann, Zeit für Physik. Chemie, N.F. **42**, 329 (1964).

Preferred:

log $k = 13.45 - 55.0/\theta$
log $A_{est} = 13.2$ (see section II–1.0).

Experimental

[1] Rates by ΔP. Not inhibited by added propylene.
[2] Rates by HCl titration.

Reaction: 1-Chlorobutane (*n*-butyl chloride)

$$CH_3(CH_2)_2CH_2Cl \ (I) \rightarrow CH_3CH_2CH{=}CH_2 \ (II) + HCl \ (III)$$

	I	II	III
$\Delta H^\circ_{f(298)}$	-36.2	0	-22.1
$S^\circ_{(298)}$	84.8	73.6	44.6
$C^\circ_{p(298)}$	26.1	20.5	7.0

$\Delta S^\circ = 33.4$ g/mole
$\Delta H^\circ = 14.1$ kcal/mole
$\Delta C^\circ_p = 1.4$ g/mole

log A	E	log k_T (700)	Conditions	System	Surface	References
14.0	57.0	-3.79	700–744 °K 10–135 torr	static	none	[1] D. H. R. Barton, A. J. Head, and J. R. Williams, J. Chem. Soc. 2039 (1951).
13.63	55.15	-3.58	663–723 °K 116–308 torr	static	none	[2] H. Hartman, H. G. Bosche, and H. Heydtmann, Zeit für Physik Chemie, N.F. **42,** 329 (1964).
14.5	57.9	-3.57	664–731 °K 80–200 torr	static	————	[3] H. Hartman, H. Heydtmann, and G. Rinck, Zeit für Physik Chemie, N.F. **28,** 85 (1961).

Preferred:
   log $A = 13.63 - 55.15/\theta$
   log $A_{est} = 13.2$ (see section II–1.0 and 1-chloropentane).

Experimental

[1] Rates by ΔP; unaffected by added propylene.
[2] Rates by HCl titration.
[3] Arrhenius parameters of this study revised in|[2]. Rates by HCl titration. Confirmed stoichiometry ($\Delta P = \Delta(HCl)$).

Reaction: 1-Chloropentane (n-pentyl chloride)

$$CH_3(CH_2)_3CH_2Cl \ (I) \rightarrow CH_3(CH_2)_2CH{=}CH_2 \ (II) + HCl \ (III)$$

	I	II	III
$\Delta H^\circ_{f(298)}$	-41.2	-4.9	-22.1
$S^\circ_{(298)}$	94.2	82.8	44.6
$C^\circ_{p(298)}$	31.6	26.2	7.0

$\Delta S^\circ = 33.2$ g/mole
$\Delta H^\circ = 14.2$ kcal/mole
$\Delta C^\circ_p = 1.6$ g/mole

log A	E	log k_T (700)	Conditions	System	Surface	References
14.61	58.3	-3.59	669–729 °K 50–450 torr	static	~ 5%	[1] R. C. S. Grant and E. S. Swinbourne, J. Chem. Soc. 4423 (1965).
13.81	55.33	-3.46	662–723 °K 103–211 torr	static	negligible	[2] H. Hartman, H. G. Bosch, and H. Heydtmann, Zeit für Physik Chemie, N.F. **42**, 329 (1964).

Preferred:
$\log A = 13.81 - 55.33/\theta$;
$\log A_{est} = 13.2$ (see section II-1.0).

Comments: The A-factors appear to increase with the increasing size of the alkyl group in the n-alkylchloride series. Such an effect, if real, is difficult to rationalize. It seems more reasonable to consider this trend an apparent one only, especially in view of the rather sizable discrepancies in the rate constants reported for the same reactions by different investigators.

Experimental

[1] Rate by ΔP. Checked stoichiometry by HCl titration and G.L.C. analysis.
Olefin composition: 96% 1-pentene
1% 2-pentene
3% propene + butane + ethane.
[2] Rate by HCl titration.

Reaction: 1-Chloro-2-methylpropane (isobutyl chloride)

$$(CH_3)_2CHCH_2Cl \ (I) \longrightarrow CH_2{=}C(CH_3)_2 \ (II) + HCl \ (III)$$

	I	II	III
$\Delta H^\circ_{f(298)}$	-37.5	-4.0	-22.1
$S^\circ_{(298)}$	82.1	70.2	44.6
$C^\circ_{p(298)}$	25.8	21.3	7.0

$\Delta S^\circ = 32.7$ g/mole
$\Delta H^\circ = 11.4$ kcal/mole
$\Delta C^\circ_p = 2.5$ g/mole

log A	E	log k_T (700)	Conditions	System	Surface	References
14.02	56.85	-3.72	690–717 °K	static	none	[1] K. E. Howlett, J. Chem. Soc., 4487 (1952).

Preferred:

log $k_{est} = 12.9 - 53.2/\theta$ (see section II–1.0).

Comments: Rate constant is reliable but the Arrhenius parameters are probably high.

Since in the formation of the four-center transition state in this reaction a rather sizable internal rotation is lost, an A-factor greater than normal (ekT/h) is not reasonable (particularly in this reaction where there is no reaction degeneracy). The transition state estimate of the A-factor is therefore preferred and the activation energy has been adjusted accordingly.

Experimental

[1] Rates by ΔP and HCl titration. Pressure dependence observed below 6 torr total pressure.

Reaction: 2-Chloropropane (isopropyl chloride)

$$(CH_3)_2CHCl \; (I) \longrightarrow CH_2\!\!=\!\!CHCH_3 \; (II) + HCl \; (III)$$

	I	II	III
$\Delta H^\circ_{f(298)}$	-33.0	4.8	-22.1
$S^\circ_{(298)}$	74.0	63.6	44.6
$C^\circ_{p(298)}$	21.4	15.3	7.0

$\Delta S^\circ = 34.2$ g/mole
$\Delta H^\circ = 15.7$ kcal/mole
$\Delta C^\circ_p = 0.9$ g/mole

$\log A$	E	$\log k_T$ (650)	Conditions	System	Surface	References
13.64	51.1	-3.53	740–940 °K	S. P. shock		[1] W. Tsang, J. Chem. Phys. **41**, 2487 (1964).
13.4	50.5	-3.58	680 °K 60–135 torr	static		[2] K. E. Howlett, J. Chem. Soc., 3695 (1952).
13.4	50.5	-3.58	640–679 °K	static	$\sim 12\%$	[3] D. H. R. Barton and A. J. Head, Trans. Faraday Soc. **46**, 114 (1950).

Preferred:
$\log k = 13.6 - 51.1/\theta$
$\log A_{est} = 13.7$ (see section II–1.0).

Experimental

[1] Rates by G.L.C. analysis on propylene. Comparative rate standard was *t*-butyl chloride and ethyl bromide.
[2] Rates by ΔP. Pressure dependence in rate constants observed at $P = 4$ torr.
[3] Rates by ΔP; unaffected by added propylene.

Reaction: 2-Chloro-2-methylpropane (*t*-butyl chloride)

$$(CH_3)_3CCl \ (I) \longrightarrow CH_2{=}C(CH_3)_2 \ (II) + HCl \ (III)$$

	I	II	III
ΔH_f°	-43.1	-4.0	-22.1
$S_{(298)}^\circ$	77.4	70.2	44.6
$C_{p(298)}^\circ$	27.9	21.3	7.0

$\Delta S^\circ = 37.4$ g/mole
$\Delta H^\circ = 17.0$ kcal/mole
$\Delta C_p^\circ = 0.4$ g/mole

log A	E	log k_T (*600*)	Conditions	System	Surface	References
13.9	46.2	-2.93	750–950 °K 1% in Ar	S. P. shock	————	[1] W. Tsang, J. Chem. Phys. **40**, 1498 (1964).
13.74	44.69	-2.53	700–850 °K 1% in Ar	S. P. shock	————	[2] W. Tsang, J. Chem. Phys. **40**, 1171 (1964).
13.77	45.0	-2.62				[3] S. Wong, Ph. D. Thesis, Univ. of London. (1958).
12.4	41.4	-2.68	563–614 °K 40–240 torr	static	small	[4] D. H. Barton and P. F. Onyon, Trans. Faraday Soc. **45**, 725 (1949).
14.2	46.0	-2.55	547–645 °K 27–213 torr	static	small	[5] B. Brearley, G. B. Kistiakowsky, and C. H. Stauffer, J. Am. Chem. Soc. **58**, 43 (1936).
13.7	44.9	-2.65	557–582 °K 38–61 torr			[6] R. L. Failes and V. R. Stimson, Aust. J. Chem. **15**, 437 (1962).

Preferred:
  log $k = 13.8 = 45.0/\theta$
  log $A_\text{est} = 13.8$ (see section II-1.0).

Experimental

[1] Rates from G.L.C. analysis on *i*-butene. Uncertainties in temperatures of the shock and therefore not as reliable as [2].

[2] Rates by G.L.C. Isopropyl bromide used as an internal comparative rate standard.

[4] Rates by ΔP; stoichiometry confirmed by HCl titration. Initial fast reactions found to be heterogeneous. Rates unaffected by added propylene.

[5] Rates by ΔP. Catalysis by surfaces decreased with surface "conditioning."

[6] Rates by ΔP; unaffected by large pressures of SF_6.

Reaction: 2-Chlorobutane (*sec*-butyl chloride)

$$\xrightarrow{\ a\ } cis\ CH_3CH{=}CHCH_3\ (II)\ +\ HCl\ (V)$$

$$CH_3CHCH_2CH_3\ (I) \xrightarrow{\ b\ } trans\ CH_3CH{=}CHCH_3\ (III) + HCl$$

$$\underset{Cl}{|} \xrightarrow{\ c\ } CH_2{=}CHCH_2CH_3\ (IV) + HCl$$

	I	II	III	IV	V
$\Delta H^\circ_{f(298)}$	-37.2	-1.7	-2.7	0	-22.1
$S^\circ_{(298)}$	83.4	72.1	70.9	73.6	44.6
$C^\circ_{p(298)}$	26.9	18.9	21.0	20.5	7.0

	a	b	c
$\Delta S^\circ =$	33.3	32.1	34.8 g/mole
$\Delta H^\circ =$	13.4	12.4	15.1 kcal/mole
$\Delta C^\circ_p =$	-1.0	1.1	0.6 g/mole

Path	log A	E	log k_T (630)	Conditions	System	Surface	References
total	13.62	49.6	-3.58	603–663 °K 149–290 torr	static	< 5%	[1] A. Maccoll and R. H. Stone, J. Chem. Soc., 2756 (1961).
total	14.0	50.6	-3.55	589–666 °K	static	none	[2] H. Heydtmann and G. Rinck, Zeit. für Physik. Chemie, N.F. **30**, 250 (1961).
a	13.29	52.66					
b	13.57	51.83					
c	13.64	51.65					
total	14.07	50.75	-3.53	571–696 °K 74–225 torr	static		[3] H. Heydtmann and G. Rinck, Zeit. für Physik. Chemie **36**, 75 (1963).

Preferred: log $k = 14.0 - 50.6/\theta$;
log $k_{est} = 14.0 - 50.6/\theta$ (see section II–1.0).

cis + trans but-2-ene: log $A_{est} = 13.1$ $E_{est} = 49.2$
but-1-ene: log $A_{est} = 13.4$ $E_{est} = 51.2$

Experimental

[1] Rates by ΔP. Product analysis by G.L.C. *Cis/trans*-but-2-ene ratios found to represent near equilibrium proportions. *Cis/trans* isomerization catalysed by HCl and carbonaceous surface. Olefin product distribution roughly given by 40 percent 1-butene; 60 percent 2-butene.

[2] Rates by ΔP. Stoichiometry confirmed by HCl titration and G.L.C. analysis of olefin products. Product distributions roughly 50 percent 1-butene, 25 percent *cis* and 25 percent *trans*-2-butene.

[3] Study similar to that of [2]. G.L.C. analysis gave 43 percent *trans* and 20 percent *cis*-2-butene. This product distribution is in good agreement with that reported by Maccoll and Stone [1].

Reaction: 2-Chloro-2-methylbutane (*t*-amyl chloride)

$$(CH_3)_2(C_2H_5)CCl \text{ (I)} \xrightarrow{a} CH_2{=}C(CH_3)CH_2CH_3 \text{ (II)} + HCl \text{ (IV)}$$
$$\xrightarrow{b} (CH_3)_2C{=}CHCH_3 \text{ (III)} + HCl$$

	I	II	III	IV
$\Delta H^\circ_{f(298)}$	-46.5	-8.6	-10.2	-22.1
$S^\circ_{(298)}$	89.0	81.9	81.1	44.6
$C^\circ_{p(298)}$	33.4	26.7	25.1	7.0

	a	*b*
$\Delta S^\circ =$	37.5	36.7 g/mole
$\Delta H^\circ =$	15.8	14.2 kcal/mole
$\Delta C^\circ_p =$	0.3	-1.3 g/mole

log A	E	log k_T (570)	Conditions	System	Surface	References
14.65	46.0	-2.98	543–600 °K	static	none	[1] D. Brearley, G. B. Kistiakowsky, and C. H. Stauffer, J. Am. Chem. Soc. **58,** 43 (1956).

Preferred: log $k = 13.7 - 44.0/\theta$. (see section II–1.0).

	E_{est}
log $A_{(a)} = 13.8$	45.2
log $A_{(b)} = 13.1$	43.2

Comments: The rate constant is reasonable, but the Arrhenius parameters seem high. Since the *t*-butyl and *t*-amyl bromide eliminations have almost identical *A*-factors, it is reasonable to expect similar behavior in the chloride system; log A (*t*-butyl) = 13.7; log $A_{est} = 13.8$. The estimated *A*-factor for *t*-amyl chloride is therefore preferred to the experimental value.

Experimental

[1] Rates by ΔP. Formation of both olefins assumed, although no product analyses were made.

Reaction: Chlorocyclopentane (cyclopentyl chloride)

	I	II	III
$\Delta H^\circ_{f(298)}$	-26.3	7.9	-22.1
$S^\circ_{(298)}$	82.5	69.2	44.6
$C^\circ_{p(298)}$	23.5	18.1	7.0

$\Delta S^\circ = 31.3$ g/mole
$\Delta H^\circ = 12.1$ kcal/mole
$\Delta C^\circ_p = 1.6$ g/mole

log A	E	log k_T (600)	Conditions	System	Surface	References
13.47	48.3	-4.11	582–649 °K 40–400 torr	static	———————	[1] E. S. Swinbourne, J. Chem. Soc. 4668 (1960).

Preferred:
   log $k = 13.1-47.4/\theta$ (see section II–1.0).

Comments: The A-factors of the cyclopentyl chloride and cyclopentyl bromide decompositions should be very similar. The loss of pseudo rotation of the cyclopentane ring in the activated complex (evident in the cyclopentyl bromide results) is not evident here. However, we feel it should be, and therefore have lowered the A-factor.

Experimental

   [1] Rates by ΔP and by HCl titration. Cyclopentene identified by I.R. Added Br_2 produced only slight rate accelerations.

Reaction: Chlorocylclohexane (cyclohexyl chloride)

	I	II	III
$\Delta H^\circ_{f(298)}$	-37.3	-1.7	-22.1
$S^\circ_{(298)}$	83.1	74.3	44.6
$C^\circ_{p(298)}$	29.1	25.3	7.0

$\Delta S^\circ = 35.8$ g/mole
$\Delta H^\circ = 13.5$ kcal/mole
$\Delta C^\circ_p = 3.2$ g/mole

log A	E	log k_T (600)	Conditions	System	Surface	References
13.77	50.0	-4.44	591–658 °K 40–400 torr	static	none	[1] E. S. Swinbourne, Aus. J. Chem. **11**, 314 (1958).
13.88	50.2	-4.40	623–749 °K	stirred flow		[2] W. C. Herndon, M. B. Henley, and J. M. Sullivan, J. Phys. Chem. **67**, 2842 (1963).

Preferred:
 log $k = 13.8 - 50.0/\theta$
 log $A_{est} = 13.5$ (see section II–1.0).

Experimental

[1] Rates by ΔP and by HCl titration not affected by added propylene or cyclohexene. Possible pressure dependence below 5–10 torr pressure.
[2] Anaylsis by G.L.C.

Reaction: 1-Chloro-1-phenylethane (α-phenylethyl chloride)

$$\text{ØCH}-\text{CH}_3 \text{ (I)} \longrightarrow \text{ØCH}=\text{CH}_2 \text{ (II)} + \text{HCl (III)}$$
$$\mid$$
$$\text{Cl}$$

	I	II	III
$\Delta H^\circ_{f(298)}$	-0.6	35.2	-22.1
$S^\circ_{(298)}$	94.4	82.5	44.6
$C^\circ_{p(298)}$	34.4	29.2	7.0

$\Delta S^\circ = 32.7$ g/mole
$\Delta H^\circ = 13.7$ kcal/mole
$\Delta C^\circ_p = 1.8$ g/mole

log A	E	log k_T (610)	Conditions	System	Surface	References
10.78	39.3	-3.30	583–638 °K			[1] B. Stevenson, Ph. D. Thesis, Univ. of London (1957).
12.6	44.9	-3.49				[2] M. R. Bridge, Ph. D. Thesis, Univ. of London (1964). (Under A. Maccoll.)

Preferred:
    $\log k = 12.9 - 45.4/\theta$.

Comments: The *A*-factor of this reaction is much too low even if benzyl resonance (loss of the phenyl internal rotation) were developed. A maximum entropy loss can be estimated as $\Delta S^\ddagger_{max} = -S^\circ$ (CH_3 rotation + Ø rotation) $+ R \ln \dfrac{\sigma}{\sigma^\ddagger} \simeq -(5.9 + 8.4) + 2.2 = 12.1$ g/mole and $A^\ddagger_{min} = 10^{10.9}$ sec^{-1}.

However, most four- and six-center transition states are quite loose and a more reasonable estimate gives $\log A_{est} = 12.9$ (with benzyl stiffening). It should be noted that the Arrhenius parameters of the corresponding bromide (α-phenylethyl bromide) are in reasonable agreement with the higher values predicted by the transition state calculation.

Experimental

[2] Private communication. No conditions given. Added to monograph after above comments. Note the excellent agreement between calculated and observed parameters.

Reaction: (−)Menthyl chloride

	I	II	III	IV
$\Delta H^\circ_{f(298)}$	−60.9	−30.3	−29.8	−22.1
$S^\circ_{(298)}$	112.8	104.3	102.5	44.6
$C^\circ_{p(298)}$	50.2	47.0	47.3	7.0

	a	b
$\Delta S^\circ =$	36.1	34.8 g/mole
$\Delta H^\circ =$	8.5	9.0 kcal/mole
$\Delta C^\circ_p =$	3.8	4.1 g/mole

Path	log A	E	log k_T (600)	Conditions	System	Surface	References
a	12.0	42.6	−3.51	592–624 °K 5.9–31.5 torr	static	none	[1] D. H. R. Barton, A. J. Head, and R. J. Williams, J. Chem. Soc., 453 (1952).
b	12.6	45.0	−3.76	672–716 °K ~ 10 torr	flow	see below	[2] As above.
a+b	11.9	42.4	−3.52	573–623 °K			[3] T. Bamkole, Ph.D. Thesis, Univ. of London (1964).

Preferred:
   log $k_a = 13.5 − 48.5/\theta$;
   log $k_b = 13.5 − 50.0/\theta$ (see section II–1.0).

Comments: The predicted isomer ratios are $(a:b) \simeq \left(\dfrac{3.5}{1}\right)$.

The rate constants are almost an order of magnitude larger (600 °K) than those for cyclohexyl chloride. A factor of 3 would be expected for path a (*i.e.*, the substituent effect on E_a at the β-carbon). The factor of 3 remaining suggests some surface decomposition, which is in line with the low Arrhenius parameters. Transition state estimates of the gas phase reaction are preferred.

Experimental

[1] Rates by HCl titration. Product menthenes determined by optical rotation assuming no racemization and gave ~ 30 percent p-menth-2-ene independent of temperature (3:1 of a:b).

[2] Rates constant parameters determined using results of both dynamic and static methods. Surface effects were very large unless the walls were "conditioned."

Reaction: Neomenthyl chloride

	I	II	III	IV
$\Delta H^{\circ}_{f(298)}$	−59.3	−29.8	−30.3	−22.1
$S^{\circ}_{(298)}$	112.8	102.5	104.3	44.6
$C^{\circ}_{p(298)}$	50.2	47.3	47.0	7.0

	a	b
$\Delta S^{\circ} =$	34.3	36.1 g/mole
$\Delta H^{\circ} =$	7.4	6.9 kcal/mole
$\Delta C^{\circ}_p =$	4.1	3.8 g/mole

Path	log A	E	log k_T (600)	Conditions	System	Surface	References
$a+b$	11.04	40.9	−3.89	573–623 °K			[1] T. Bamkole, Ph.D. Thesis, Univ. of London (1964).

Preferred:

Suspect. For reaction a, however, we prefer log $k_a = 13.5 - 50.0/\theta$.

Comments: The Arrhenius parameters are far too low to be reasonable. One would expect rate constants and rate constant parameters to be similar to those of cyclohexyl chloride. Path b should not occur at all unimolecularly in the gas phase, since the four-center HX eliminations occur only from *cis* comformations. Surface reactions and catalysis seem probable. This is supported by the fact that the observed decomposition rate for neomenthyl chloride is faster (factor of 3) than that for cyclohexyl chloride.

Experimental

[1] The ratio of product isomers was $\left(\dfrac{p\text{-menth-3-ene}}{p\text{-menth-2-ene}}\right) \simeq \dfrac{1}{5.7}$.

Reaction: Endo-2-chlorobornane (bornyl chloride)

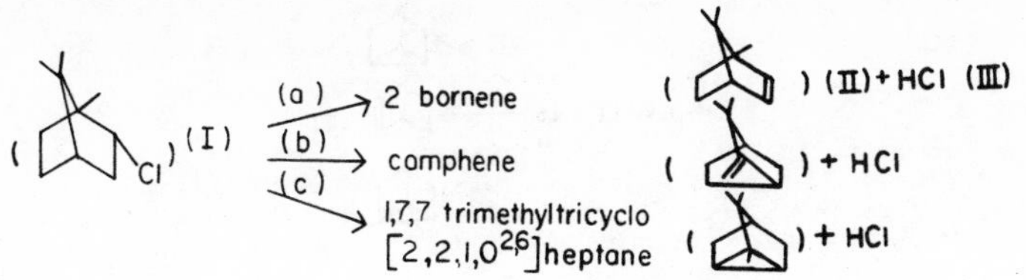

	I	II	III
$\Delta H^\circ_{f(298)}$	-39.7	$+0.2$	-22.1
$S^\circ_{(298)}$	103	92	44.6
$C^\circ_{(298)}$	————	————	7.0

a

$\Delta S^\circ = 33.6$ g/mole

$\Delta H^\circ = 17.8$ kcal/mole

$\Delta C^\circ_p =$

Path	log A	E	log k_T (600)	Conditions	System	Surface	References
Total	13.99	50.55	-4.46	none given	————	————	[1] R. C. Bicknell and Allan Maccoll, Chem. and Ind., 1912 (1961).
Total	13.78	50.6	-4.59	593–663 °K			[2] R. C. Bicknell, Ph. D Thesis, Univ. of London (1962).

Preferred:

Suspect, although the rate parameters are reasonable. log $A_{(a)} = 13.5 - 50/\theta$.

Comments: Paths b and c are not here considered reasonable for a gas phase reaction. Further confirmation of "carbonium ion" intermediates would seem necessary. Formation of camphene and tricyclene at the walls seems more likely. The reaction rates and parameters do, however, seem quite reasonable since they compare favorably to those of cyclohexyl chloride.

Experimental

[1] Rates by G.L.C. analysis. Product distribution: tricyclene (55 percent), camphene (25 percent), bornylene (20 percent). Extensive rearrangements of the reactant structure, as in paths b and c, were taken as evidence for the heterolytic nature of the HX elimination reactions.

Reaction: Exo-2-chlorobornane (isobornyl chloride)

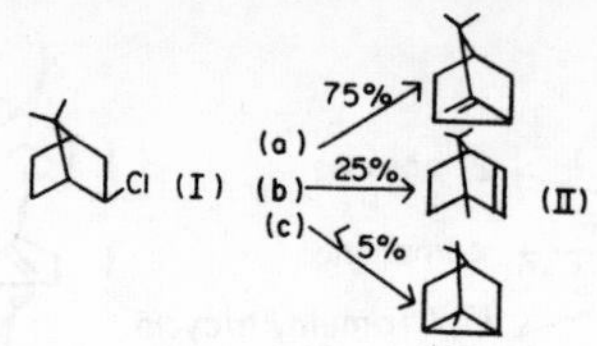

	I	II	III
$\Delta H^\circ_{f(298)}$	-38.1	0.2	-22.1
$S^\circ_{(298)}$	103	92	44.6
$C^\circ_{p(298)}$	————	————	7.0

$\Delta S^\circ = 33.6$ g/mole
$\Delta H^\circ = 16.2$ kcal/mole
$\Delta C^\circ_p =$

log A	E	log k_T (605)	Conditions	System	Surface	References
14.78	49.7		583–623 °K			[1] R. C. Bicknell, Ph. D. Thesis, Univ. of London (1962).

Preferred:

Suspect.

Comments: The A-factor appears to be much too high, particularly for path a, which would involve extensive structural rearrangement and a loss of one methyl rotation. The reaction rates also appear to be too high if cyclohexyl chloride is used as a comparative standard. A study of the individual reaction paths would be useful in establishing the unimolecularity of this reaction and its isomer, bornyl chloride.

Experimental

[1] Rates by G.L.C. analysis. Product distribution was 75 percent camphene, 25 percent bornylene, and less than 5 percent tricyclene. (See comments on bornyl chloride.)

Reaction: 1,1-Dichloroethane (ethylidene dichloride)

$$C_2H_4Cl_2(I) \longrightarrow ClHC = CH_2 (II) + HCl (III)$$

	I	II	III
$\Delta H^\circ_{f(298)}$	−28.2	8.9	−22.1
$S^\circ_{(298)}$	71.9	62.9	44.6
$C^\circ_{p(298)}$	18.3	13.1	7.0

$\Delta S^\circ = 35.6$ g/mole
$\Delta H^\circ = 15.0$ kcal/mole
$\Delta C^\circ_p = 1.8$ g/mole

log A	E	log k_T (700)	Conditions	System	Surface	References
12.08	49.5	−3.37	671–766 °K 20–200 torr	static	none	[1] D. H. R. Barton and K. E. Howlett, J. Chem. Soc., 165 (1949).
11.65	48.3	−3.43	685–722 °K 20–200 torr	static	————	[2] K. E. Howlett, J. Chem. Soc., 3695 (1952).
13.45	53.5	−3.25	641–723 °K 150–410 torr	static	none	[3] H. Hartman, H. Heydtmann, and G. Rinck, Zeit. für Physik. Chemie **28**, 71 (1961).

Preferred:

log $k = 13.45 − 53.5/\theta$.
log $A_{est} = 13.6$ (see section II–1.0).

Comments: The rate constants are in good agreement, although only the most recent study reports reasonable Arrhenius parameters.

Experimental

[1] Rates by ΔP and HCl titration. No acetylene produced. Not inhibited by propylene. $P_f/P_i \simeq 2$.
[2] Rates fell off below 17 torr. High-pressure rate restored with added HCl.
[3] Rates by ΔP and HCl titration. No total pressure effect observed between 150 and 410 torr.

Reaction: 2,2-Dichloropropane

$$CH_3CCl_2CH_3 \text{ (I)} \longrightarrow CH_2=CClCH_3 \text{ (II)} + HCl \text{ (III)}$$

	I	II	III
$\Delta H^\circ_{f(298)}$	-32.3	0.9	-22.1
$S^\circ_{(298)}$	78.2	71.0	44.6
$C^\circ_{p(298)}$	23.9	18.4	7.0

$\Delta S^\circ = 37.4$ g/mole
$\Delta H^\circ = 11.1$ kcal/mole
$\Delta C^\circ_p = 1.5$ g/mole

log A	E	log k_T (640)	Conditions	System	Surface	References
11.9	43.9	-3.09	603–683 °K 7–40 torr	static	none	[1] K. E. Howlett, J. Chem. Soc., 945 (1953).

Preferred:
   $\log k = 14.0 - 50/\theta$.

Comments: The rate constant is reasonable, although the Arrhenius parameters seem low. By analogy with the rate constant parameters of ethyl chloride ($10^{13.2-56.5/\theta}$) and 1,1-diethyl chloride ($10^{13.5-53/\theta}$), one would expect 2,2-dichloropropane to have parameters similar to those of isopropyl chloride (i.e., a somewhat higher A-factor and a lower activation energy by about 3 kcal/mole. The transition state estimate of A with adjusted E is therefore preferred.

Experimental

[1] Rates by ΔP and by HCl titration were unaffected by added propylene. $P_f/P_i \simeq 2$.

action: 1,1-Dichloropropane

$$CHCl_2CH_2CH_3 \quad (I) \longrightarrow CHCl{=}CHCH_3 \ (II) + HCl \ (III)$$

	I	II	III
$\Delta H^\circ_{f(298)}$	−32.3	0.7	−22.1
$S^\circ_{(298)}$	81.3	71.5	44.6
$C^\circ_{p(298)}$	23.8	18.3	7.0

$S^\circ = 34.8$ g/mole
$H^\circ = 10.9$ kcal/mole
$C^\circ_p = 1.5$ g/mole

log *A*	*E*	log k_T (*700*)	Conditions	System	Surface	References
12.76	51.2	−3.22	653–713 °K 6–61 torr	static		[1] K. E. Howlett, J. Chem. Soc., 945 (1953).

eferred:
log $k = 13.5–53.5/\theta$.

mments: The reported Arrhenius parameters of this reaction seem low (see comments on 2,2-dichloro-opane). Parameters similar to those of 1,1-dichloroethane would be expected. A transition state estimate *A* is therefore preferred (see section II–1.0).

Experimental

[1] Rated by ΔP and by HCl titration determined under conditions of maximum inhibitions with isobutene. Rate nstants appeared to be pressure dependent below 30 torr pressure. $P_f/P_i \simeq 2$.

Reaction: 1,2-Dichloropropane

$$CH_2ClCHClCH_3(I) \quad \xrightarrow{a} \quad CH_2\!\!=\!\!CHCH_2Cl(II) + HCl(V)$$

$$\xrightarrow{b} \quad ClCH\!=\!CHCH_3(III) + HCl$$

$$\xrightarrow{c} \quad CH_2\!=\!CHClCH_3(IV) + HCl$$

	I	II	III	IV	V
$\Delta H^\circ_{f(298)}$	-38.3	-1.3	0.7	0.9	-22.1
$S^\circ_{(298)}$	83.6	73.3	71.5	71.0	44.6
$C^\circ_{(298)}$	24.1	18.2	18.3	18.4	7.0

b

$\Delta S^\circ = 32.5$ g/mole
$\Delta H^\circ = 16.9$ kcal/mole
$\Delta C_p^\circ = 1.2$ g/mole

Path	log A	E	log k_T (700)	Conditions	System	Surface	References
Total	13.8	54.9	-3.34	689-725 °K	static	$< 5\%$	[1] D. H. Barton and A. J. Head, Tran Faraday Soc. **46** 114 (1950).

Preferred:
  log $k = 13.8-54.9/\theta$
Estimated:
  log $A_{(a)} = 13.1$ $E_a \simeq 54.2$ kcal/mole
  log $A_{(b)} = 13.3$ $E_b \simeq 53.2$ kcal/mole
  log $A_{(c)} = 12.8$ $E_c \simeq 53.2$ kcal/mole

Comments: (see section II-1.0).

Experimental

[1] Rates by ΔP. No induction periods and no effects by Cl_2 or O_2 in small amounts or or by added propylene. T the reaction is self-inhibiting. In the time period of the study $P_f/P_i \simeq 2.0$. Over prolonged periods $P_f/P_i \simeq 2.5$, indica a slow elimination of HCl from one of the olefin products. Analysis was not performed, but in a prior study (D. H. R. ton, J. Chem. Soc., 148 (1949)), a mixture of olefins was observed.

Reaction: 1,1,1-Trichloroethane

$$CCl_3CH_3 \text{ (I)} \longrightarrow Cl_2C{=}CH_2 \text{ (II)} + HCl \text{ (III)}$$

	I	II	III
$\Delta H^\circ_{f(298)}$	−30.1	4.3	−22.1
$S^\circ_{(298)}$	75.0	68.3	44.6
$C^\circ_{p(298)}$	22.5	16.5	7.0

$S^\circ = 37.9$ g/mole
$H^\circ = 12.3$ kcal/mole
$C^\circ_p = 1.0$ g/mole

log A	E	log k_T (700)	Conditions	System	Surface	References
14.07	54.2	−2.85	683–713 °K 70–80 torr	static	~12%	[1] P. F. Onyon and D. H. R. Barton, J. Am. Chem. Soc. **72**, 988 (1950).
14.0	54.0	−2.85		flow	————	[2] N. Spokes and S. W. Benson, to be published.

Preferred:
    log $k = 14.1 - 54.2/\theta$.
    log $A_{est} = 13.9$ (see section II–1.0).

Experimental

[1] Rates by ΔP and HCl titration determined under maximum inhibition conditions using propylene. Under maximum inhibition, rates were independent of P_o with no induction periods. ($P_f/P_i \sim 2.0$). Free radical chain decomposition dominated in the pure trichloroethane decomposition.
[2] Analysis by M.S.

Reaction: 1-Chloro-1-methoxyethane (α-chloroethyl methyl ether)

$$CH_3CHClOCH_3 \ (I) \longrightarrow CH_2{=}CHOCH_3 \ (II) + HCl \ (III)$$

	I	II	III
$\Delta H^\circ_{f(298)}$	−63.7	−25.1	−22.1
$S^\circ_{(298)}$	86.0	72.5	44.6
$C^\circ_{p(298)}$	24.4	18.5	7.0

$\Delta S^\circ = 31.1$ g/mole
$\Delta H^\circ = 16.5$ kcal/mole
$\Delta C^\circ_p = 1.1$ g/mole

log A	E	log k_T (480)	Conditions	System	Surface	References
11.46	33.3	−3.70	453–523 °K 33–420 torr	static	~20%	[1] P. J. Thomas, J. Chem. Soc., 136 (1961).

Preferred: Suspect.
  $\log k = 13.1 - 36.9/\theta$ (see section II−1.0).

Comments: The estimated equilibrium constant for the above reaction is about 20 atm at 480 °K so that back reaction is appreciable at more than 50 percent decomposition. There must be unknown experimental complications, perhaps some polymerization of the vinyl ether or wall reactions or both. Although the reported rate constants may be fairly representative of the reaction indicated, the reported A-factor is certainly too low. The maximum loss in activation entropy for this reaction can be estimated in terms of the total loss of a methyl rotation, plus the symmetry change between transition and initial states:

$$(\Delta S^\ddagger_{\min} \simeq -6.4 + R\ln 3) = -4.2 \text{ g/mole.}$$

Thus
$$A^\ddagger_{\min} = \frac{ekT}{h} \times 10 \left(\frac{\Delta S^\ddagger}{4.575}\right) \sim 10^{12.5} \text{ sec}^{-1}.$$

The transition state calculation of A and adjusted E_{act} are preferred, although E still seems too low.

Experimental

[1]. Rates by ΔP; unaffected by added cyclohexene. $P_f/P_i \simeq 1.75$ was believed to be a result of the reverse process and the attainment of an equilibrium state (see discussion). HCl was titrated *in situ* with NH_3. See also 1-chloro-ethoxyethane.

Reaction: 1-Chloro-1-ethoxyethane (α-chloroethyl ethyl ether)

$$CH_3CHClOCH_2CH_3 \text{ (I)} \longrightarrow CH_2{=}CHOCH_2CH_3 \text{ (II)} + HCl \text{ (III)}$$

	I	II	III
$\Delta H^\circ_{f(298)}$	-71.9	-33.3	-22.1
$S^\circ_{(298)}$	96.3	82.8	44.6
$C^\circ_{p(298)}$	29.8	23.9	7.0

$\Delta S^\circ = 31.1$ g/mole
$\Delta H^\circ = 16.5$ kcal/mole
$\Delta C^\circ_p = 1.1$ g/mole

log A	E	log k_T (450)	Conditions	System	Surface	References
10.52	30.3	-4.20	164–221 °C 20–280 torr	static	~ 15%(?)	[1] R. I. Failes and V. R. Stimson, Austr. J. Chem. **20**, 1553 (1967)

Preferred: Suspect.
  log $k = 13.2 - 36.0/\theta$.

Comments: Independent measurements of the back reaction showed that it was predominantly heterogeneous, particularly at the lowest temperature (144 °C). This, of course, is not consistent with a homogeneous forward reaction. Reported Arrhenius parameters are much too low.

Experimental

[1]. Vessel required coating with allyl bromide pyrolysis products before reproducible results could be obtained. Only one set of runs was made at 194 °C with S/V increased eight-fold to check homogeneity. Back reaction rate under similar conditions increased two-fold in rate for eight-fold S/V increase.

Reaction: Trichloromethyl chloromethanoate (trichloromethyl chloroformate)

$$\underset{\substack{\| \\ O}}{Cl-C-OCCl_3} \ (I) \longrightarrow 2[Cl_2C=O] \ (II)$$

	I	II
$\Delta H^\circ_{f(298)}$	-111	-52.5
$S^\circ_{(298)}$	100	67.5
$C^\circ_{p(298)}$	29.7	14.3

$\Delta S^\circ = 35.0$ g/mole
$\Delta H^\circ = 6.0$ kcal/mole
$\Delta C^\circ_p = -1.1$ g/mole

log A	E	log k_T (560)	Conditions	System	Surface	References
13.15	41.5	-3.04	533–583 °K 4.5–16.4 torr	static	none	[1] H. C. Ramsperger and G. Waddington, J. Am. Chem. Soc. **55**, 214 (1933).

Preferred:
   log $k = 13.14 - 41.5/\theta$.

Comments: A four-center transition state estimate gives log $A_{est} = 13.0$ (see section II–1.0).

Experimental

[1] Rate by ΔP. $(P_f/P_o) = 2.0 \pm .02$. "Clean" surfaces accelerated the reaction; wall conditioning was essential for reproducibility.

Reaction: Bromoethane (ethyl bromide)

$$C_2H_5Br \; (I) \longrightarrow C_2H_4 \; (II) + HBr \; (III)$$

	I	II	III
$\Delta H^\circ_{f(298)}$	-16.1	12.5	-8.7
$S^\circ_{(298)}$	69.0	52.5	47.4
$C^\circ_{p(298)}$	15.3	10.4	7.0

$\Delta S^\circ = 30.9$ g/mole
$\Delta H^0 = 19.9$ kcal/mole
$\Delta C^0_p = 2.1$ g/mole

log A	E	log k_T (700)	Conditions	System	Surface	References
12.86	52.3	3.47	790–890 °K	flow	————	[1] A. T. Blades and G. W. Murphy, J. Am. Chem. Soc. **74**, 6219 (1952).
13.45	53.9	3.37	655–703 °K 25–567 torr	static	< 10%	[2] P. J. Thomas, J. Chem. Soc., 1192 (1959).
12.95	52.2	3.34	796–906 °K 6–44 torr	flow	————	[3] A. T. Blades, Can. J. Chem. **36**, 1043 (1958).
12.85	52.0	3.38	583–749 °K 50–300 torr	static	————	[4] A. E. Goldberg and F. Daniels, J. Am. Chem. Soc. **79**, 1314 (1957).
13.19	53.7	3.57	740–940 °K 1% in Ar	S.P. shock	————	[5] W. Tsang, J. Chem. Phys. **41**, 2487 (1964).

Preferred:
   log $k = 13.45 - 53.9/\theta$
   log $A_{est} = 10^{13.3}$ sec^{-1} (see section II–1.0).

Experimental

[1] Analysis and rates from HBr titration. Toluene carrier technique. The absence of C_2H_6, H_2 and $(\emptyset CH_2)_2$ in the products was cited as evidence against a (C-Br) split as the initiation step of the concurrent free radical chain process.*

[2] Rates by ΔP under conditions of maximum inhibition. The chain component of the decomposition was estimated at 90 percent.

[3] Toluene carrier technique. Rates from HBr titration. The ethyl d_5 isotope effect was studied.

[4] Rate constants were obtained from the initial reaction rates and from the rates in the presence of n-hexane.

[5] Single pulse shock. Rates by HBr titration. Isopropyl bromide was used as the comparative rate standard. 1,1,2,2-d_4 isotope effect studied by A. T. Blades, P. W. Gilderson, and M. G. H. Wallbridge, Can. J. Chem. **40**, 5126 (1962).

---

*This is not a valid conclusion if the chain length for ethyl bromide is long, which is indeed suggested by the photochemical data. See Barker and Maccoll, J. Chem. Soc., 2839 (1963).

Reaction: 1-Bromopropane (n-propyl bromide)

$$C_3H_7Br \text{ (I)} \longrightarrow C_3H_6 \text{ (II)} + HBr \text{ (III)}$$

	I	II	III
$\Delta H^{\circ}_{f(298)}$	-21.1	4.8	-8.7
$S^{\circ}_{(298)}$	78.4	63.6	47.4
$C^{\circ}_{p(298)}$	20.8	15.3	7.0

$\Delta S^{\circ} = 32.6$ g/mole
$\Delta H^{\circ} = 17.2$ kcal/mole
$\Delta C^{\circ}_p = \ \ 1.5$ g/mole

log A	E	log k_T (700)	Conditions	System	Surface	References
13.0	50.7	-2.83	790–890 °K	flow	————	[1] A. T. Blades and G. W. Murphy, J. Am. Chem. Soc. **74**, 6219 (1952).
12.9	50.7	-2.93	623–663 °K 60–500 torr	static	none	[2] A. Maccoll and P. J. Thomas, J. Chem. Soc., 5033 (1957).

Preferred:
   log $k = 13.0 - 50.7/\theta$
   log $A_{\text{est}} = 13.2$ (see section II–1.0).

Experimental

[1] Rates by HBr titration. Toluene carrier technique employed.
[2] Rates and analysis by HBr titration. Stoichiometry confirmed ($\Delta P = \Delta(HBr)$). Rates were accelerated by added O_2. Relative inhibition efficiencies of propylene, cyclohexene, and 2,4-dimethyl-pent-2-ene were obtained.

Reaction: 1-Bromobutane (*n*-butyl bromide)

$$CH_3CH_2CH_2CH_2Br \text{ (I)} \longrightarrow CH_2{=}CHCH_2CH_3 \text{ (II)} + HBr \text{ (III)}$$

	I	II	III
$\Delta H^\circ_{f(298)}$	-26.0	0	-8.7
$S^\circ_{(298)}$	87.8	73.6	47.4
$C^\circ_{p(298)}$	26.3	20.5	7.0

$\Delta S^\circ = 33.2$ g/mole
$\Delta H^\circ = 17.3$ kcal/mole
$\Delta C^\circ_p = 1.2$ g/mole

log A	E	log k_T (670)	Conditions	System	Surface	References
13.18	50.9	-3.42	644–692 °K 34–470 torr	static	< 10%	[1] A. Maccoll and P. J. Thomas, J. Chem. Soc., 5033 (1957).
12.92	50.5			static		[2] M. R. Bridge and J. L. Holmes, J. Chem. Soc. B, 713 (1966).

Preferred:
log $k = 13.2 - 51.0/\theta$
log $A_{est} = 13.2$ (see section II–1.0).

Experimental

[1] Rates determined by HBr titration (Δ(HBr)$=\Delta$P). Cyclohexene reduced the rate by less than 10 percent.

[2] Unpaired electron content and reactivity of carbons produced by pyrolysis of allylbromide, *cis*-but-2-ene iso-butene + EtBr examined by E.S.R. showed that spin content of carbons does not catalyze elimination from *n*BuBr or *i*PrBr as suggested as a possibility by Laidler and Wojciechowski (Trans. Faraday Soc. **59**, 369 (1963)).

Reaction: 1-Bromopentane (*n*-pentyl bromide)

$$CH_3(CH_2)_3CH_2Br \; (I) \longrightarrow CH_2{=}CH(CH_2)_2CH_3 \; (II) + HBr \; (III)$$

	I	II	III
$\Delta H^\circ_{f(298)}$	−31.0	−4.9	−8.7
$S^\circ_{(298)}$	97.2	82.8	47.4
$C^\circ_{p(298)}$	31.8	26.2	7.0

$\Delta S^\circ = 33.0$ g/mole
$\Delta H^\circ = 17.4$ kcal/mole
$\Delta C^\circ_p = 1.4$ g/mole

log A	E	log k_T (670)	Conditions	System	Surface	References
13.09	50.5	−3.38	653–703 °K 22–338 torr	static	< 10%	[1] J. H. S. Green, A. Maccoll, and P. J. Thomas, J. Chem. Soc., 184 (1960).

Preferred:
   $\log k = 13.09 - 50.5/\theta$.
   $\log A_{est} = 13.2$ (see section II–1.0).

Experimental

[1] Rates determined by HBr titration under maximum inhibition of chains with cyclohexene in seasoned reaction vessel. Chain component estimated at 46 percent.*

------

*With such a sizable chain component, the homogeneous unimolecular rate constants are subject to rather poor precision.

92

Reaction: 1-Bromohexane (n-hexyl bromide)

$$C_6H_{13}Br \text{ (I)} \longrightarrow C_6H_{12} \text{ (II)} + HBr \text{ (III)}$$

	I	II	III
$\Delta H^\circ_{f(298)}$	-35.9	-9.9	-8.7
$S^\circ_{(298)}$	106.6	92.2	47.4
$C^\circ_{p(298)}$	37.3	31.6	7.0

$\Delta S^\circ = 33.0$ g/mole
$\Delta H^\circ = 17.3$ kcal/mole
$\Delta C^\circ_p = 1.3$ g/mole

log A	E	log k_T (670)	Conditions	System	Surface	References
13.14	50.5	-3.33	653–703 °K 33–267 torr	static	< 10%	[1] J. H. S. Green, A. Maccoll, and P. J. Thomas, J. Chem. Soc., 184 (1960).

Preferred:
log $k = 13.14 - 50.5/\theta$.
log $A_{\text{est}} \simeq 13.2$ (see section II–1.0).

Experimental

[1] Rates determined by HBr titration under maximum inhibition with cyclohexene. Chain contribution about 37 percent, indicating rather poor precision for the unimolecular rate constant measurements.

Reaction: 1-Bromo-2-methylpropane (isobutyl bromide)

$$(CH_3)_2CHCH_2Br \text{ (I)} \longrightarrow CH_2\!=\!C(CH_3)_2 \text{ (II)} + HBr \text{ (III)}$$

	I	II	III
$\Delta H^\circ_{f(298)}$	-26.7	-4.0	-8.7
$S^\circ_{(298)}$	85.1	70.2	47.4
$C^\circ_{p(298)}$	26.0	21.3	7.0

$\Delta S^\circ = 32.5$ g/mole
$\Delta H^\circ = 14.0$ kcal/mole
$\Delta C^\circ_p = 2.3$ g/mole

log A	E	log k_T (660)	Conditions	System	Surface	References
13.05	50.4	-3.7	509–565 °K 48–100 torr	static	$< 10\%$	[1] G. D. Harden and A. Maccoll, J. Chem. Soc., 1197 (1959).

Preferred:
   log $k = 13.05 - 50.4/\theta$

Comments: Reliable as reported; log $A_{est} \simeq 12.9$ (see section II–1.0).

Experimental

[1] Rates obtained from pressure measurements under maximum inhibition with cyclohexene. Chain contributio to the uninhibited decomposition estimated at 90 percent. Relative inhibition efficiencies of cyclohexene, cyclopent diene, and 2,4-dimethylpent-2-ene were obtained.*

---

*Because of the large chain component, rather poor precision in the measured unimolecular rate constants is expected.

94

Reaction: 2-Bromopropane (isopropyl bromide)

$$\begin{array}{c} CH_3 \\ \searrow \\ CH_3 \end{array} CH\!-\!Br\ (I) \longrightarrow C_3H_6\ (II) + HBr\,(III)$$

	I	II	III
$\Delta H^\circ_{f(298)}$	-23.7	4.8	-8.7
$S^\circ_{(298)}$	77.4	63.6	47.4
$C^\circ_{p(298)}$	21.1	15.3	7.0

$\Delta S^\circ = 33.6$ g/mole
$\Delta H^\circ = 19.8$ kcal/mole
$\Delta C^\circ = 1.2$ g/mole

log A	E	log k_T (600)	Conditions	System	Surface	References
13.6	47.7	-3.77	686–760 °K	flow	————	[1] A. T. Blades and G. W. Murphy, J. Am. Chem. Soc. **74**, 6219 (1952).
13.62	47.8	-3.79	583–623 °K 26–120 torr	static	$< 10\%$	[2] A. Maccoll and P. J. Thomas, J. Chem. Soc., 969 (1955); A. Maccoll, J. Chem. Phys. **19**, 977 (1951).
12.74	47.0	-4.38	347–497 °K 10–150 torr			[3] N. Semenov, D.A.N. SSSR, 301 (1955); G. B. Sergeev, Dok. Akad. Nauk. SSSR **106**, 299 (1956).

Preferred:
    log $k = 13.6 - 47.8/\theta$
    log $A_{\text{est}} = 13.7$ (see section II–1.0).

Experimental

[1] Rates determined by HBr titration. Toluene carrier technique.
[2] Rates determined by HBr titration ($\Delta P = \Delta(HBr)$). Maximum inhibition with cyclohexene. Chain contribution less than 10 percent.

Reaction: 2-Bromobutane (*sec*-butyl bromide)

$$CH_3CHCH_2CH_3 \ (I) \xrightarrow{\ a\ } CH_2{=}CHCH_2CH_3 \ (II) + HBr \ (IV)$$
$$\overset{|}{Br} \qquad\qquad \xrightarrow{\ b\ } cis \text{ and } trans \ CH_3CH{=}CHCH_3 \ (III) + HBr$$

	I	II	III	III	IV
$\Delta H_f^\circ{}_{(298)}$	−27.9	0	−1.7	−2.7	−8.7
$S^\circ{}_{(298)}$	86.8	73.6	72.1	70.9	47.4
$C_{p(298)}^\circ$	26.6	20.5	18.9	21.0	7.0

a
$\Delta S^\circ = 34.2$ g/mole
$\Delta H^\circ = 19.2$ kcal/mole
$\Delta C_p^\circ = \ 0.9$ g/mole

Path	log A	E	log k_T (600)	Conditions	System	Surface	References
$a+b$	12.63	43.8	−3.32	573–623 °K 25–343 torr	static	< 10%	[1] A. Maccoll and P. J. Thomas, J. Chem. Soc., 2445 (1955).
$a+b$	13.53	46.47	−3.39	572–627 °K 2–300 torr	static		[2] M. N. Kale, A. Maccoll, and P. J. Thomas, J. Chem. Soc., 3016 (1958).
$a+b$	13.0	45.5	−3.55	603–673 °K 10–200 torr	static		[3] G. B. Sergeev, Dok. Akad. Nauk. SSSR **106**, 299 (1956).

Preferred: log k $= 13.5–46.5/\theta$
  Estimated:
  log A_a $= 13.3$ $E_a = 47.8$
  log A_b $= 13.1$ $E_b = 45.8$
  log $A_{a+b} = 13.7–47.0/\theta$ (see section II–1.0).

Experimental

[1] Rates determined under maximum inhibitions with cyclohexene. Chain contribution less than 5 percent. Analysis by HBr titration, $\Delta(HBr) = \Delta P$.

[2] Revised Arrhenius parameters of [1] from repeated study under similar conditions. Since HBr catalyzes the isomerization of butenes, analysis of the isomeric butenes was not made.

Reaction: 4-Bromo-1-pentene

$$CH_2\!=\!CHCH_2CHCH_3 \text{ (I)} \quad \xrightarrow{\ a\ } CH_2\!=\!CHCH_2CH\!=\!CH_2 \text{ (II)} + HBr \text{ (V)}$$
$$\xrightarrow{\ b\ } cis\ CH_2\!=\!CHCH\!=\!CH_2CH_3 \text{ (III)} + HBr$$
$$\overset{|}{Br} \qquad \xrightarrow{\ c\ } trans\ CH_2\!=\!CHCH\!=\!CH_2CH_3 \text{ (IV)} + HBr$$

	I	II	III	IV	V
$\Delta H^\circ_{f(298)}$	−2.6	25.2	18.7	18.6	−8.7
$S^\circ_{(298)}$	94.4	79.7	77.5	76.4	47.4
$C^\circ_{p(298)}$	29.4	25.1	22.6	24.7	7.0

a

$\Delta S^\circ = 32.7$ g/mole
$\Delta H^\circ = 19.1$ kcal/mole
$\Delta C^\circ_p = 2.7$ g/mole

Path	log A	E	log k_T (600)	Conditions	System	Surface	References
Total	12.94	44.7	−3.34	573–623 °K 112–206 torr	static	< 10%	[1] P. J. Thomas, J. Chem. Soc., 1192 (1959).

Preferred: Rate constant reliable.
  Estimated: (see section II–1.0).
    log A_a = 13.3 E_a = 47.8
    log A_{b+c} = 13.1 E_{b+c} = 45.8
    log A_{a+b+c} = 13.7 E_{a+b+c} + 47.θ.

Comments: The overall reaction rate is comparable to that observed for *sec*-butyl bromide. This suggests that the allylic resonance possible for paths *b* and *c* does not appreciably develop in the transition state. The Arrhenius parameters, by comparison with *sec*-butyl bromide, look slightly low. The transition state estimate is preferred.

Experimental

[1] Rates were determined by ΔP under conditions of maximum inhibition with cyclohexene. The normal decomposition was kinetically complex. Analysis by HBr titration. $\Delta P = \Delta(HBr)$. No analysis of the olefin products was made.

Reaction: Bromocyclopentane (cylcopentyl bromide)

Br
⬠ (I) → cyclopentene ⬡ (II) + HBr (III)

	I	II	III
$\Delta H^\circ_{f(298)}$	-17.0	7.9	-8.7
$S^\circ_{(298)}$	85.9	69.2	47.4
$C^\circ_{p(298)}$	23.7	18.1	7.0

$\Delta S^\circ = 30.7$ g/mole
$\Delta H^\circ = 16.2$ kcal/mole
$\Delta C^\circ_p = 1.4$ g/mole

log A	E	log k_T (600)	Conditions	System	Surface	References
11.9	41.4	-3.18	573–633 °K 38–106 torr	static	<10%	[1] S. J. W. Price, R. Shaw, and A. F. Trotman-Dickinson, J. Chem. Soc., 3855 (1956).
12.84	43.7	-3.07	573–633 °K 12–92 torr	static	<10%	[2] M. N. Kale and A. Maccoll J. Chem. Soc., 5020 (1957).

Preferred:
log $k = 12.8 - 43.7/\theta$
log $A_{est} = 12.8$ (see section II–1.0).

Comments: The lower Arrhenius parameters of [1] could have resulted from a small chain component. Loss of the pseudo rotation of the cyclopentane ring in the transition state is consistent with the relatively low A-factor of [2].

Experimental

[1] Rates by ΔP. Stoichiometry confirmed, Δ(HBr) $= \Delta$P. Observed short induction periods. Inhibition with cyclohexene reduced rates by less than 10 percent.
[2] Rates by ΔP. No induction periods observed and no effect on the rate by added cyclohexene.

Reaction: Bromocyclohexane (cyclohexyl bromide)

$$\underset{(I)}{\overset{Br}{\bigcirc}} \longrightarrow \text{cyclohexene} \; (\bigcirc, \text{II} \;) + \text{HBr (III)}$$

	I	II	III
$\Delta H^\circ_{f(298)}$	-28.0	-1.7	-8.7
$S^\circ_{(298)}$	86.5	74.3	47.4
$C^\circ_{p(298)}$	28.8	25.3	7.0

$\Delta S^\circ = 35.2$ g/mole
$\Delta H^\circ = 17.6$ kcal/mole
$\Delta C^\circ_p = 3.5$ g/mole

log A	E	log k_T (600)	Conditions	System	Surface	References
13.52	46.1	-3.27	573–623 °K 40–400 torr	static	none	[1] J. H. S. Green and A. Maccoll, J. Chem. Soc., 2499 (1955).

Preferred:
   log $k = 13.52 - 46.1/\theta$;
   log $A_{\text{est}} = 13.5$ (see section II–1.0).

Experimental

[1] Rates obtained from pressure measurements. Stoichiometry confirmed by HBr titration. ($\Delta P = \Delta(\text{HBr})$). Rates unaffected by additions of cyclohexene or small amounts of allyl bromide or bromine, implying that the reaction is self-inhibiting and free from chain-induced decomposition.

Reaction: 1-Bromo-1-phenylethane (α-phenylethyl bromide)

$$\text{ØCHCH}_3 \text{ (I)} \longrightarrow \text{ØCH}{=}\text{CH}_2 \text{ (II)} + \text{HBr (III)}$$
$$\underset{\text{Br}}{|}$$

	I	II	III
$\Delta H^{\circ}_{f(298)}$	8.7	35.2	−8.7
$S^{\circ}_{(298)}$	97.4	82.5	47.4
$C^{\circ}_{p(298)}$	34.1	29.2	7.0

$\Delta S^{\circ} = 32.5$ g/mole
$\Delta H^{\circ} = 17.8$ kcal/mole
$\Delta C^{\circ}_p = 2.1$ g/mole

log A	E	log k_T (545)	Conditions	System	Surface	References
12.18	38.8	−2.7	528–558 °K			[1] B. Stevenson, Ph.D. Thesis, Univ. of London (1957).

Preferred:
   log $k = 12.8 - 38.8/\theta$.

Comments: Transition state estimate of A, assuming benzyl stiffening in the transition state, gives log $A_{\text{est}} = 12.9$.

Reaction: 2-Bromo-2-methylpropane (*t*-butyl bromide)

$$(CH_3)_3CBr \; (I) \longrightarrow C_4H_9Br \; (II) + HBr \; (III)$$

	I	II	III
$\Delta H^\circ_{f(298)}$	-30.5	-4.0	-8.7
$S^\circ_{(298)}$	80.4	70.2	47.4
$C^\circ_{p(298)}$	27.9	21.3	7.0

$\Delta S^\circ = 37.2$ g/mole
$\Delta H^\circ = 17.8$ kcal/mole
$\Delta C^\circ_p = 0.4$ g/mole

log A	E	log k_T (525)	Conditions	System	Surface	References
13.3	40.5	-3.56	509–565 °K 48–100 torr	static	< 10%	[1] G. B. Kistiakowsky and C. H. Stauffer, J. Am. Chem. Soc. **59**, 165 (1937).
14.0	42.0	-3.48	503–553 °K 40–400 torr	static		[2] G. D. Harden and A. Maccoll, J. Chem. Soc., 2455 (1955).
13.5	41.5	-3.77	700–900 °K 1% in Ar	S.P. shock		[3] W. Tsang, J. Chem. Phys. **40**, 1498 (1964).
13.24	41.0	-3.84	538–598 °K 10–150 torr			[4] G. B. Sergeev, Dok. Akad. Nauk. SSSR **106**, 299 (1956).
13.87	41.49	-3.40	700–900 °K 1% in Ar	S.P. shock		[5] W. Tsang, J. Chem. Phys. **40**, 1171 (1964).

Preferred:
log $k = 13.8 - 41.8/\theta$
log $A_{est} = 13.8$ (see section II–1.0).

Experimental

[1] Reaction proceeds to an equilibrium state (i.e., $P_f/P_i < 2$). Rates by pressure measurements.

[2] No inhibition observed with added cyclohexene or with cyclopentadiene. No appreciable rate acceleration observed with added bromine or allylbromide. The reaction is therefore self-inhibiting and free from radical-induced decomposition. Rates by pressure increase.

[3] Rates by G.L.C. analysis of isobutene.

Reaction: 2-Bromo-2-methylbutane (*t*-amyl bromide)

$$C_2H_5(CH_3)_2CBr \text{ (I)} \xrightarrow{\;a\;} (CH_3)_2C=CHCH_3 \text{ (II)} + HBr \text{ (IV)}$$
$$\xrightarrow{\;b\;} CH_2=C(CH_3)CH_2CH_3 \text{ (III)} + HBr$$

	I	II	III	IV
$\Delta H^\circ_{f(298)}$	-33.9	-10.2	-8.6	-8.7
$S^\circ_{(298)}$	92.0	81.1	81.9	47.4
$C^\circ_{p(298)}$	33.4	25.1	26.7	7.0

$\Delta S^{\circ \, a} = 36.5$ g/mole
$\Delta H^\circ = 15.0$ kcal/mole
$\Delta C^\circ_p = -1.3$ g/mole

Path	log A	E	log k_T (525)	Conditions	System	Surface	References
$a+b$	13.6	40.5	-3.26	493–543 °K 80–363 torr	static	<10%	[1] G. D. Hardin, J. Chem. Soc., 5024 (1957).

Preferred:
  Reliable as reported: $\log k = 13.6 - 40.5/\theta$.

Comments:
  Estimated: $\log A_a = 13.1$ $E_a \simeq 39.8$ kcal/mole
  $\log A_b = 13.8$ $E_b \simeq 41.8$ kcal/mole
  $\log A_{a+b} = 13.7$ $E_{a+b} \simeq 40.2$ kcal/mole (see section II-1.0).

Experimental

  [1] Rates by pressure increase. Reaction proceeds to an equilibrium state ($P_f/P_i < 2$). Rates unaffected by addition of cyclohexene. Large pressures of added bromine produced only a slight acceleration. I.R. analysis indicated the major olefin formed to be 2-methylbut-2-ene.

Reaction: 2,3-Dimethyl-2-bromobutane.

$$\xrightarrow{\ a\ } CH_2 = C(CH_3)CH(CH_3)_2 \text{ (II)} + HBr \text{ (IV)}$$

$$(CH_3)_2BrCCH(CH_3)_2 \text{ (I)}$$

$$\xrightarrow{\ b\ } (CH_3)_2C = C(CH_3)_2 \text{ (III)} + HBr$$

	I	II	III	IV
$\Delta H^\circ_{f(298)}$	-39.5	-14.8	-15.9	-8.7
$S^\circ_{(298)}$	98.9	87.4	86.7	47.4
$C^\circ_{p(298)}$	38.6	32.5	30.5	7.0

	a	b
$\Delta S^\circ =$	35.9	35.2 g/mole
$\Delta H^\circ =$	16.0	14.9 kcal/mole
$\Delta C^\circ_p =$	0.9	-1.1 g/mole

Path	log A	E	log k_T (510)	Conditions	System	Surface	References
$a+b$	13.54	39.0	-3.17	483–533 °K 50–400 torr	static	<10%	[1] G. D. Harden and A. Maccoll, J. Chem. Soc., 5028 (1957).

Preferred:

$\log k = 13.54 - 39.0/\theta$;

Estimated: $\log k_a = 13.6 - 41.4/\theta$

$\log k_b = 12.8 - 38.4/\theta$

$\log k_{a+b} = 13.6 - 39.2/\theta$ (see section II-1.0).

Comments: The calculated equilibrium constant for path b gives $K_{eq} = 10^{3.82}$ torr, which corresponds to an equilibrium state at about 90 percent decomposition (in agreement with observation).

Experimental

[1] Rates by ΔP. Reaction stated to proceed to an equilibrium state. Cyclohexene reduced the rate by 6 percent. Olefin products were not analyzed but the major product was believed to be 2,3-dimethyl-2-butene.

Reaction: 1,1-Dibromoethane (ethylidene dibromide)

$$HBr_2CCH_3 \ (I) \longrightarrow CHBr{=}CH_2 \ (II) + HBr \ (III)$$

	I	II	III
$\Delta H^\circ_{f(298)}$	-10.1	18.7	-8.7
$S^\circ_{(298)}$	78.7	65.7	47.4
$C^\circ_{p(298)}$	18.7	13.2	7.0

$\Delta S^\circ = 34.4$ g/mole
$\Delta H^\circ = 20.1$ kcal/mole
$\Delta C^\circ_p = 1.5$ g/mole

log A	E	log k_T (660)	Conditions	System	Surface	References
12.9	49.5	-3.5	623–703 °K			[1] P. T. Good, Ph.D. Thesis. Univ. of London (1956).

Preferred:
   log $k_{est} = 13.5 - 51.3/\theta$ (see section II–1.0).

Comments: Parameters seem slightly low, but not unreasonable. Prefer transition state estimate.

Reaction: Iodoethane (ethyl iodide)

$$C_2H_5I \ (I) \longrightarrow C_2H_4 \ (II) + HI \ (III)$$

	I	II	III
$\Delta H^\circ_{f(298)}$	-2.2	12.5	6.2
$S^\circ_{(298)}$	70.7	52.5	49.3
$C^\circ_{p(298)}$	15.4	10.4	7.0

$\Delta S^\circ = 31.1$ g/mole
$\Delta H^\circ = 20.9$ kcal/mole
$\Delta C_p^\circ = 2.0$ g/mole

log A	E	log k_T (740)	Conditions	System	Surface	References
14.1	52.8	-1.49	704–774 °K 0.6–4 × 10^{-2} torr $P_T \simeq$ 2–18 torr	flow	———————	[1] Joe-Hyun Yang and D. C. Conway, J. Chem. Phys. **43**, 1296 (1965).
13.36	50.0	-1.40	603–665 °K 27–273 torr	static	< 2%	[2] A. N. Bose and S. W. Benson, J. Chem. Phys. **37**, 2935 (1962).

Preferred:
   log $k = 13.36 - 50.0/\theta$
   log $A_{est} = 13.3$ (see section II–1.0).

Experimental

[1] Toluene carrier technique. Determined rates from scintillation counter measurements of the C^{14} content of the ethylene formed. The ethyl iodide was C^{14} labeled. The (C—I) bond rupture reaction (C$_2$H$_5$I $\longrightarrow$ C$_2$H$_5$ + I) was competitive (see fission reactions).

[2] Rates were followed by pressure change. The back reaction was also studied in the temperature range 562–604 °K, log $k_b = 8.52 - 28.9/\theta$ (with k_b in units of l/mole-sec). Both rate constants are in good agreement with the thermodynamics.

Reaction: 2-Iodopropane (isopropyl iodide)

$$(CH_3)_2CHI \longrightarrow CH_2=CHCH_3 \ (II) + HI \ (III)$$

	I	II	III
$\Delta H^\circ_{f(298)}$	−9.5	4.8	6.2
$S^\circ_{(298)}$	79.0	63.6	49.3
$C^\circ_{p(298)}$	21.0	15.3	7.0

$\Delta S^\circ = 33.9$ g/mole
$\Delta H^\circ = 20.5$ kcal/mole
$\Delta C^\circ_p = 1.3$ g/mole

log A	E	log k_T (600)	Conditions	System	Surface	References
14.46	48.2	−3.09	558–630 °K 8–150 torr	static		[1] J. L. Holmes and A. Maccoll Proc. Chem. Soc., (London), 175 (1957).
14.49	47.96	−2.98	563–630 °K 8–87 torr	static	none	[2] J. L. Holmes and A. Maccoll, J. Chem. Soc., 5919 (1963).
12.96	43.5	−2.88	543–573 °K 17.4–50 torr	static		[3] H. Teranishi and S. W. Benson, J. Chem. Phys. **40,** 2946 (1964).
12.90	42.9	−2.72	565–609 °K	static	——————	[4] J. L. Jones and R. A. Ogg J. Am. Chem. Soc. **59,** 1939 (1937).
13.67	45.07	−2.74	680–850 °K < 1% in Ar	S. P. shock		[5] W. Tsang, J. Chem. Phys. **41,** 2487 (1964).

[overall reaction stoichiometry: $2RI \longrightarrow I_2 + C_3H_6 + C_3H_8$ since $RI + HI \longrightarrow RH + I_2$ (fast)]

Preferred:
log $k_a = 13.53 - 45.0/\theta$
log $A_{est} = 13.3$ (see section II–1.0).

Comments: Kinetics of the back reaction (addition) have been measured by A. N. Bose and S. W. Benson J. Chem. Phys. **37,** 1081 (1962). They obtained $k_b = 10^{7.89-23.4/\theta}$ 1/mole-sec. With the reaction thermodynamics, this gives the preferred values for the elimination reaction.

Experimental

[1] Analysis by G.L.C. Autocatalytic below 558 °K. Arrhenius parameters revised in [2].
[2] Analysis by G.L.C. and spectrophotometry. Overall reaction $2iPrI \longrightarrow C_3H_6 + C_3H_8 + I_2$. Rates were unaffected by I_2, NO, and HI. Rates by ΔP and by I_2 titration. Rate constants reported were for $iPrI$ disappearance (k and $k_a = \frac{1}{2}k$.
[3] Rates followed spectrophotometrically. Some pressure fall-off below 30 torr pressure.
[4] Rates by ΔP measurements. Iodine was titrated, giving $\Delta I_2 = \Delta P$; 3 percent HI was detected as an end product.
[5] Comparative internal rate standards were t-BuCl and t-BuBr.

Reaction: 2-Iodobutane (*sec*-butyl iodide)

$$CH_3CHICH_2CH_3 \text{ (I)}
\begin{cases}
\xrightarrow{\;a\;} CH_2{=}CHCH_2CH_3 \text{ (II)} + HI \text{ (V)} \\
\xrightarrow{\;b\;} \textit{cis}\ CH_3CH{=}CHCH_3 \text{ (III)} + HI \\
\xrightarrow{\;c\;} \textit{trans}\ CH_3CH{=}CHCH_3 \text{ (IV)} + HI
\end{cases}$$

	I	II	III	IV	V
$\Delta H^\circ_{f(298)}$	-14.4	0	-1.7	-2.7	6.2
$S^\circ_{(298)}$	89.8	73.6	72.1	70.9	49.3
$C^\circ_{p(298)}$	26.2	20.5	18.9	21.0	7.0

a

$\Delta S^\circ = 33.1$ g/mole
$\Delta H^\circ = 20.6$ kcal/mole
$\Delta C^\circ_p = 1.3$ g/mole

Path	log A	E	log k_T (560)	Conditions	System	Surface	References
$a+b+c$	14.9	47.9	-3.18	523–603 °K 8–120 °K	static	none	[1] J. L. Holmes and A. Maccoll, J. Chem. Soc., 5919 (1963).

(overall reaction stoichiometry: $2RI \longrightarrow I_2 + C_4H_{10} + C_4H_8$)
initial elimination followed by: $RI + HI \xrightarrow{\text{fast}} RH + I_2$　　*

Preferred: $\log k_{a+b+c} = 13.65 - 44.7/\theta$.

Comments: The reported Arrhenius parameters seem high. Transition state estimates (see section II–1.0) give:

$\log k_a = 13.3 - 45.0/\theta$
$\log k_{b+c} = 13.1 - 43.0/\theta$

The calculated values are similar to those of isopropyl iodide, as expected by comparison to the results of the analogous chloride and bromide reactions.

Experimental

[1] Rates by ΔP in initial stages and corresponded to $\Delta(I_2)$ titration. Olefin and alkene (C_4H_8) production determined by G.L.C.

---

*Estimates of the decomposition reactions ($b + c$) and (a) have been obtained from a study of the back reactions (addition) in a static system between 565 and 606 °K by P. S. Nangia and S. W. Benson, J. Chem. Phys. **41**, 530 (1964). Results given were:

$$k_{b+c} = 10^{10.65} \times 10^{-37.5/\theta} \text{ sec}^{-1};$$
$$k_a = 10^{12.61} \times 10^{142.7/\theta} \text{ sec}^{-1}.$$

Both of the above A-factors are probably too low.

Reaction: 2-Iodo-2-methylpropane (*t*-butyl iodide)

$$(CH_3)_3CI \text{ (I)} \longrightarrow CH_2{=}C(CH_3)_2 \text{ (II)} + HI \text{ (III)}$$

	I	II	III
$\Delta H^\circ_{f(298)}$	−17.3	−3.7	6.2
$S^\circ_{(298)}$	82.4	70.4	49.3
$C^\circ_{p(298)}$	28.3	21.3	7.0

$\Delta S^\circ = 37.3$ g/mole
$\Delta H^\circ = 19.8$ kcal/mole
$\Delta C^\circ_p = -0.0$ g/mole

log A	E	log k_T (700)	Conditions	System	Surface	References
13.73	38.08	1.83	650–760 °K < 1% in Ar	S. P. Sh.	————	[1] W. Tsang, J. Chem. Phys. **41**, 2487 (1964).
						[2] See below.

Preferred:

log $k = 13.73 - 38.08/\theta$

log $A_{est} = 13.8$ (see section II–1.0).

Experimental

[1] Comparative internal rate standard was isopropyl iodide.

[2] Reverse addition reaction measured in static system between 474–518 °K by A. N. Bose and S. W. Benson, J. Chem. Phys. **38**, 878 (1963). Calculated rate constant for decomposition was $k = 10^{12.52} \times 10^{-36.4/\theta}$ sec^{-1}. These parameters seem too low.

Reaction: 2-Methyl-2-propanol (*t*-butyl alcohol)

$$(CH_3)_3COH \ (I) \longrightarrow (CH_3)_2C{=}CH_2 \ (II) + H_2O \ (III)$$

	I	II	III
$\Delta H^\circ_{f(298)}$	-74.7	-4.0	-57.8
$S^\circ_{(298)}$	77.9	70.2	45.1
$C^\circ_{p(298)}$	27.3	21.3	8.0

$\Delta S^\circ = 37.4$ g/mole
$\Delta H^\circ = 12.9$ kcal/mole
$\Delta C^\circ_p = 2.0$ g/mole

log *A*	E	log k_T (800)	Conditions	System	Surface	References
14.68	65.5 ± 7	-3.21	778–824 °K 3–325 torr	static	none	[1] R. F. Schultz and G. B. Kistiakowsky, J. Am. Chem. Soc. **56**, 395 (1934).
11.51	54.5	-3.38	760–893 °K 20–400 torr	static	none	[2] J. A. Barnard, Trans. Faraday Soc. **55**, 947 (1959).
13.4	61.6	-3.43	1050–1300 °K <1% in Ar	S. P. shock	————	[3] W. Tsang, J. Chem. Phys. **40**, 1498 (1964).

Preferred:
  $\log k = 13.4 - 61.6/\theta$
  $\log A_{\text{est}} = 13.6$ (see section II–1.0).

Experimental

[1] Rates determined by ΔP. Stoichiometry confirmed by analysis of remaining alcohol by refractive index.
[2] Rates by ΔP. Analysis by G.L.C. confirmed stoichiometry. Added NO had no effect on rates.
[3] Analysis by G.L.C.

Reaction: 2-Methyl-2-butanol (*t*-amyl alcohol)

$$(CH_3)_2C_2H_5COH \xrightarrow{\;a\;} \text{2-methyl-1-butene (II)} + H_2O \text{ (IV)}$$
$$\xrightarrow{\;b\;} \text{2-methyl-2-butene (III)} + H_2O$$

	I	II	III	IV
$\Delta H^\circ_{f(298)}$	-78.1	-8.6	-10.2	-57.8
$S^\circ_{(298)}$	89.5	81.9	81.1	45.1
$C^\circ_{p(298)}$	32.8	26.7	25.1	8.0

	a	b	
$\Delta S^\circ =$	37.5	36.7	g/mole
$\Delta H^\circ =$	11.7	10.1	kcal/mole
$\Delta C^\circ_p =$	1.9	0.3	g/mole

Path	$\log A$	E	$\log k_T$ (770)	Conditions	System	Surface	References
$a+b$	13.52	60	-3.51	757–799 °K 19.4–324 torr	static	none	[1] R. F. Schultz and G. B. Kistiakowsky, J. Am. Chem. Soc. **56**, 395 (1934).

Preferred: $\log k = 13.5 - 60.0/\theta$
  Estimated: (see section II–1.0).
    $\log A_a = 13.5$ $E_a - E_b \simeq 2$ kcal
    $\log A_b = 12.6$ $\log k_{a+b} \simeq 13.0 - 58.3/\theta$

Experimental

[1] Rates by ΔP. Refractive index measurements on the remaining alcohol confirmed stoichiometry.

Reaction: Methanoic acid (formic acid) (a)

$$HCOOH\ (I)\xrightarrow{\ a\ }H_2\ (II)+CO_2\ (III)$$

Methanoic acid dimer (formic acid dimer) (b)

$$(HCOOH)_2\xrightarrow{\ b\ }2H_2O\ (IV)+2CO\ (V)$$

	I	II	III	IV	IV
$\Delta H^\circ_{f(298)}$	−88.5	0	−94.1	−26.4	−57.8
$S^\circ_{(298)}$	59.4	31.2	51.1	47.3	45.1
$C^\circ_{p(298)}$	10.8	7	8.9	7.0	8.0

a

$\Delta S^\circ = 22.9$ g/mole
$\Delta H^\circ = -5.6$ kcal/mole
$\Delta C^\circ_p = 5.1$ g/mole

Path	log A	E	log k_T (760)	Conditions	System	Surface	References
a	4.8	30.6	−4.00	709–805 °K 3–650 torr	static	none	[1] Sir Cyril Hinshel-wood, Proc. Roy. Soc. **A255**, 444 (1960).
b	13.6	42.6	1.35	(as above)			(as above)

Preferred:
   Not reliable.

Comments: The absence of any appreciable inhibition by isobutene and propylene might be expected, since formic acid would also be an efficient free radical scavenger. The pressure dependence leading to postulation of path b would seem more reasonably explained in terms of a free radical chain. It is very difficult to visualize a geometry of the dimer leading readily to H_2O and CO. As for path a, the Arrhenius parameters are prohibitive for either a unimolecular or a chain process. The most reasonable explanation of the products is that they arise from reactions at the walls or from H-atom chains or both.

Experimental

[1] Rates of both reactions obtained from ΔP. M.S. analysis of products. Rates were unaffected by added propylene and isobutene but slightly accelerated with NO. Surface effects in Pyrex vessels were large and gave 1/2 order kinetics. Rates reported were for carbon-coated reaction vessels. A linear dependence of the CO formation on the initial pressure was interpreted in terms of a unimolecular decomposition of the dimer. Based on the monomer pressure, $k(CO) = 10^{7.46-28.5/\theta}$ l/mole-sec.

Reaction: Ethanoic acid (acetic acid)

$$CH_3COOH \ (I) \begin{array}{c} \xrightarrow{a} CH_2=CO \ (II) + H_2O \ (III) \\ \xrightarrow{b} CH_4 \ (IV) + CO_2 \ (V) \end{array}$$

	I	II	III	IV	V
$\Delta H^\circ_{f(298)}$	−103.7	−14.6	−57.8	−17.9	−94.1
$S^\circ_{(298)}$	70.1	57.1	45.1	44.5	51.1
$C^\circ_{p(298)}$	16.0	11.4	8.0	8.5	8.9

	a	b
$\Delta S^\circ =$	32.1	25.5 g/mole
$\Delta H^\circ =$	31.3	−8.3 kcal/mole
$\Delta C^\circ_p =$	3.4	1.4 g/mole

Path	log A	E	log k_T (870)	Conditions	System	Surface	References
a	12.95	67.5	−4.00	773–973 °K 12.9–166 torr	flow	small (C)	[1] C. H. Bamford and M. J. S. Dewar, J. Chem. Soc., 2877 (1949)
b	11.90	62.0	−3.67	(as above)			(as above)

Evaluation:

　　a. Possibly reliable although suspect.

　　b. Not reliable, probably a free radical chain decomposition or surface reaction.

Comments:

　　a. The parameters for path *a* are not unreasonable for a unimolecular four-center reaction; however any chain process propagated by H-abstraction from the methyl group would lead to ketene + H_2O formation

　　b. This reaction (*b*) would involve pentavalent carbon in the transition state and therefore appear highly improbable. Abstraction of the acidic-H would yield the observed products. A chain process therefore seems likely for both reaction paths. A study of this reaction in a mixture of normal and deuterated aceti acid would be useful for distinguishing the molecular and free radical paths of decomposition.

Experimental

[1] Rates determined by conventional gas analysis techniques on the products. Ketene was determined by adsorp tion in weakly acidic glycerol. (C) Carbon-coated walls were required for reproducibility. Reaction very surface-sensitiv in clean reaction cells.

Reaction: 1,2-Ethanedioic acid (oxalic acid)

$$HOOC\text{—}COOH \text{ (I)} \longrightarrow HCOOH \text{ (II)} + CO_2 \text{ (III)}$$

	I	II	III
$\Delta H^\circ_{f(298)}$	-181.6	-88.5	-94.1
$S^\circ_{(298)}$	76.2	59.4	51.1
$\Delta C^\circ_{p(298)}$	20.0	10.8	8.9

$\Delta S^\circ = 34.3$ g/mole
$\Delta H^\circ = -1.0$ kcal/mole
$\Delta C^\circ_p = -0.3$ g/mole

log A	E	log k_T (405)	Conditions	System	Surface	References
11.9	30.0	-4.29	390–420 °K 0.9 torr	static		[1] Gabriel Lapidus, Donald Barton, and Peter E. Yankwich, J. Phys. Chem. **68**, 1863 (1964).

Preferred:

   $\log k = 10^{11.9} - 30.0/\theta$.

Comments: The transition state estimate of A for the four-center elimination of CO_2 gives $\log A_{est} = 12.4$ (see section II–1.0).

Experimental

[1] Rates determined by ΔP. Chemical analysis of products checked stoichiometry to ± 1.4 percent. (Based on four-center transition state split out of CO_2.)

Reaction: Propanonitrile (ethyl cyanide)

$$\xrightarrow{\ a\ } H_2 \text{ (II)} + CH_2\!\!=\!\!CHCN \text{ (III)}$$
$$C_2H_5CN \text{ (I)} \xrightarrow{\ b\ } HCN \text{ (IV)} + C_2H_4 \text{ (V)}$$
$$\xrightarrow{\ c\ } CH_3 + CH_2CN$$

	I	II	III	IV	V
$\Delta H^\circ_{f(298)}$	12.7	0	43.6	32.3	12.5
$S^\circ_{(298)}$	68.4	31.2	64.2	48.2	52.5
$C^\circ_{p(298)}$	17.3	7	15.3	8.6	10.4

	a	b
$\Delta S^\circ =$	27	32.3 g/mole
$\Delta H^\circ =$	30.9	32.1 kcal/mole
$\Delta C^\circ =$	5.0	1.7 g/mole

Path	log A	E	log k_T (1000)	Conditions	System	Surface	References
a	12.4	64.6	−1.72	958–1038 °K 6.5–15.8 torr	flow	none	[1] Margaret Hunt, J. A. Kerr, and A. F. Trotman-Dickenson, J. Chem. Soc. 5074 (1965).
b	15.0	77.3	−1.90	as above			
c	14.1	72.7	−1.79	as above (see bond fission reactions)			

Preferred:
   Suspect.

Comments: Hydrogen has been observed as a product in all the aniline carrier studies, and its origin ha
not been satisfactorily explained. Yields of hydrogen were not significantly greater in this study as oppose
to others. Path a cannot, therefore, be taken too seriously. Path b is a possible reaction path; however
the A-factor is too high for an elimination reaction. It is more reasonable that both path a and b product
arise from free-radical-induced decompositions of ethyl cyanide:

$$R\cdot + C_2H_5CN \longrightarrow RH + \cdot CH_2CH_2CN \longrightarrow RH + C_2H_4 + CN.$$
$$R\cdot + C_2H_5CN \longrightarrow RH + CH_3CHCN \longrightarrow RH + CH_2\!=\!CHCN + H.$$

Experimental

[1] Aniline carrier technique. Rates were based on C_2H_4 formation (path b), and H_2 production (path a). Analyse
were performed by standard gasometric techniques and checked by G.L.C. (See bond fissions for a discussion of path c.

2-Methyl-2-aminopropane (*t*-butyl amine)

$$(CH_3)_3C—NH_2 \text{ (I)} \longrightarrow (CH_3)_2C=CH_2 \text{ (II)} + NH_3 \text{ (III)}$$

	I	II	III
$\Delta H_{f(298)}^{\circ}$	−28.6	−4.0	−11.0
$S_{(298)}^{\circ}$	78.1	70.2	46.0
$C_{p(298)}^{\circ}$	28.3	21.3	8.5

$\Delta S^{\circ} = 38.1$ g/mole
$\Delta H^{\circ} = 13.6$ kcal/mole
$\Delta C_p^{\circ} = 1.5$ g/mole

log A	E	log k_T (790)	Conditions	System	Surface	References
14.23	67.0	(−4.27)	771–814 °K 50–180 torr	static	none	[1] H. O. Pritchard, R. G. Sowden, and A. F. Trotman-Dickenson, J. Chem. Soc. 546 (1954).

Preferred:
    Suspect (see also *t*-BuNH$_2 \longrightarrow$ (CH$_3$)$_2$C=NH + CH$_4$).

Comments: Since a chain process seems likely for the parallel decomposition mode of *t*-butyl amine, a chain process propagated by NH$_2$ radicals seems highly probable for this reaction also. The "molecular split" proposed requires confirmation. The chain processes would be:

Chain initiation: t-BuNH$_2 \longrightarrow t$-Bu· + NH$_2$·

Chain (1) R + t-BuNH$_2 \xrightarrow{(1)}$ RH + ·CH$_2$—C(CH$_3$)$_2$NH$_2$

        ·CH$_2$C(CH$_3$)$_2$NH$_2 \longrightarrow$ CH$_2$=C(CH$_3$)$_2$ + NH$_2$·

Chain (2) R· + t-BuNH$_2 \xrightarrow{(2)}$ RH + t-BuṄH

        t-BuṄH $\longrightarrow$ (CH$_3$)$_2$C=NH + CH$_3$·

Experimental

[1] Rates followed by ΔP and by chemical analysis of the products. A parallel reaction path to form CH$_4$ and C$_3$H$_7$N also occurred. The ratio of ammonia/methane $\simeq 1/2.5 \pm 0.1$ over the entire temperature range. Added toluene had no effect.

Reaction: 2-Methyl-2-aminopropane (*t*-butyl amine)

$$(CH_3)_3CNH_2 \text{ (I)} \longrightarrow (CH_3)_2C{=}NH \text{ (II)} + CH_4 \text{ (III)}$$

	I	II	III
$\Delta H^\circ_{f(298)}$	-28.6	2.5	-17.9
$S^\circ_{(298)}$	78.1	71.3	44.5
$C^\circ_{p(298)}$	28.3	20.1	8.5

$\Delta S^\circ = 37.7$ g/mole
$\Delta H^\circ = 13.2$ kcal/mole
$\Delta C^\circ_p = 0.3$ g/mole

log A	E	log k_T (790)	Conditions	System	Surface	References
14.64	67.0	-3.86	771–814 °K 50–180 torr	static	none	[1] H. O. Pritchard, R. G. Sowden, and A. F. Trotman-Dickenson, J. Chem. Soc. 546 (1954).

Preferred:
  Suspect.

Comments: This elimination (if unimolecular) would involve pentavalent carbon in the transition state which seems unreasonable. A free radical chain propagated by CH_3 radicals would yield the expected products. (See *t*-butyl amine $\longrightarrow NH_3 +$ isobutene.) The absence of an appreciable effect on the rate by toluene does not exclude a chain process, since the olefin products would also be good radical traps. Chain processes in the absence of toluene would therefore be the same as those with added toluene. One should note the similarity of this reaction to the decomposition of neopentane, which is known to be a chain process. $k = 10^{11.7-51.5/\theta}$ (1/moles)$^{1/2}$ sec^{-1}, which gives a pseudo first-order rate constant: $k = 10^{10.4-51.5/\theta}$ sec^{-1}, and log $k(790) = -3.8$.

Experimental

[1] Exact nature of the product C_3H_7N was not determined. Acetone diphenylhydrazone was obtained from a solution of C_3H_7N in dilute sulfuric acid. Rates determined by ΔP and chemical analysis were unaffected by added toluene.

Reaction: Methanoloxime (formaldoxime)

$$CH_2NOH \; (I) \longrightarrow HCN \; (II) + H_2O \; (III)$$

	I	II	III
$\Delta H^\circ_{f(298)}$	0	31.2	-57.8
$S^\circ_{(298)}$	64	48.2	45.1
$C^\circ_{p(298)}$	13.6	8.6	8.0

$\Delta S^\circ = 29.3$ g/mole
$\Delta H^\circ = -26.6$ kcal/mole
$\Delta C^\circ_p = 3.0$ g/mole

log A	E	log k_T (650)	Conditions	System	Surface	References
9.5	39.0	-3.61	623–688 °K 69–104 torr	static	appreciable on clean surfaces	[1] H. A. Taylor and H. Bender, J. Chem. Phys. **9**, 761 (1941).

Preferred:
Not reliable as a unimolecular process.

Comments: The Arrhenius parameters are prohibitively low for a unimolecular elimination reaction. Observations of strong catalysis by O_2 and of surface effects suggest both heterogeneous and radical contributions to the rate of decomposition. Acetaldoxime decomposition has been shown to be a free radical reaction. G. L. Pratt and J. H. Purnell, Trans. Faraday Soc. **58**, 692 (1962).)

Experimental

[1] Rates by ΔP with assumed stoichiometry of $1 \rightarrow 2$. Observed $(P_f/P_o) \rightleftharpoons 1.8 \rightarrow 1.9$. Marked catalysis by NO and by O_2. Initial rates were used to obtain the rate constants since the products reacted further to give CO, NH_3, and small amounts of N_2, H_2, and C_2H_6. The reaction was heterogeneous on cleaned surfaces.

Reaction: Ethanamide (acetamide)

$$CH_3-\overset{\overset{\displaystyle O}{\|}}{C}-NH_2 \text{ (I)} \begin{cases} a \nearrow (CH_2CO) \text{ (II)} + NH_3 \text{ (III)} \\ b \searrow CH_3CO \text{ (IV)} + \cdot NH_2 \text{ (V)} \end{cases}$$

	I	II	III	IV	V
$\Delta H^\circ_{f(298)}$	-57.8	-14.6	-11.0	-5.6	(41)
$S^\circ_{(298)}$	69	57.8	46.0	64.2	46.4
$C^\circ_{p(298)}$	15.7	12.4	8.5	12.3	8.1

	a	b	
$\Delta S^\circ =$	34.8	41.6	g/mole
$\Delta H^\circ =$	32.2	93.2	kcal/mole
$\Delta C^\circ_p =$	5.2	4.7	g/mole

Path	log A	E	log k_T (1250)	Conditions	System	Surface	References
$a+b$	14.7	73.4	1.87	1209–1293 °K 9.5–12.0 torr	flow		[1] Margaret Hunt, J. A. Kerr, and A. F. Trotman-Dickenson, J. Chem. Soc. 5074 (1965).

Preferred:
   Suspect.

Comments: At the very high reaction temperatures employed, a free radical chain decomposition of ethana mide propogated by the anilino radical (ØNH) should occur. Preferential H-abstraction from the methy group (expected on bond energy considerations) would lead to the major reaction products, ketene and am monia. This seems a more likely reaction path than the unimolecular four-center process proposed. The thermodynamics of reaction b indicate that the (CO—N) split proposed is rather improbable. An initiation reaction involving a (CO—C) split seems more likely. A four-center elimination with an A-factor of about $10^{13.0}$ sec^{-1} is probable. In this case $E \sim 68$ kcal/mole.

Experimental

[1] Aniline carrier technique. Rates were based on the NH_3 production. Small amounts of H_2, CH_4, and CO were also formed. Methane and CO were found in near equal amounts, indicating path b as a minor process. Data were no accurate enough to treat path b quantitatively.

Reaction: 1,2-Ethanediamide (oxamide)

$$NH_2-\overset{\overset{O}{\|}}{C}-\underset{\underset{O}{\|}}{C}-NH_2(I)\longrightarrow 2H_2O\ (II) + C_2N_2\ (III)$$

	I	II	III
$\Delta H^{\circ}_{f(298)}$	-95	-57.8	73.6
$S^{\circ}_{(298)}$	80.0	45.1	57.9
$C^{\circ}_{p(298)}$	19.2	8.0	13.6

$\Delta S^{\circ} = 68.1$ g/mole
$\Delta H^{\circ} = 53.0$ kcal/mole
$\Delta C^{\circ}_p = 10.4$ g/mole

log A	E	log k_T (680)	Conditions	System	Surface	References
10.25	41.4	-3.05	593–763 °K 140–300 torr	static	none	[1] F. M. Taylor and L. L. Bircumshaw, J. Chem. Soc. 3405 (1956).

Preferred:

Not reliable.

Comments: Arrhenius parameters are much too low for a homogenous unimolecular reaction. The heat of the reaction exceeds the observed activation energy. The reaction cannot be unimolecular if the thermodynamics are even close to correct. A free radical chain decomposition or heterogeneous decomposition are the only reasonable prospects.

Experimental

[1] Rates determined by ΔP. $(P_{\infty}/P_0) = 3.0 \pm 0.06$. Addition of products did not affect the rate. Added nitrogen gave unusual effects: small amounts decreased the rate and larger amounts increased it to a constant value. Cyanogen was estimated by conductometric titrations of the cyanate-cyanide with silver nitrate. (Z. Anal. Chem. **99**, 415 (1934).)

Reaction: Ethanethiol (ethyl mercaptan)

$$C_2H_5SH \ (I) \xrightarrow{\ a\ } C_2H_4 \ (II) + H_2S \ (III)$$
$$\xrightarrow{\ b\ } C_2H_5\cdot \ (IV) + HS\cdot \ (V)$$

	I	II	III	IV	V
$\Delta H^\circ_{f(298)}$	-11.0	12.5	-4.8	25.7	(35.5)
$S^\circ_{(298)}$	71.8	52.5	49.2	57.8	46.7
$C^\circ_{p(298)}$	17.2	10.4	8.1	12.1	7.1

	a	b
$\Delta S^\circ =$	29.9	32.7 g/mole
$\Delta H^\circ =$	18.7	72.2 kcal/mole
$\Delta C^\circ_p =$	1.3	2.0 g/mole

Path	log A	E	log k_T	Conditions	System	Surface	References
a	13.0	51.2	-0.09	785–938 °K $\delta P \simeq 0.7$ mm Hg $P_T \sim 12$ mm Hg	flow	(see below)	[1] A. H. Sehon and B. deB. Darwent, J. Am. Chem. Soc. **76,** 4806 (1954).
b	13.48	63 ± 1	-2.53	(as above)			

Comments: Path *a:* $\log k_a = 13.0 - 51.5/\theta$; $\log A_{est} = 13.1$ (see section II–1.0).

Path *b:* Reported parameters are low. We prefer, $\log k = 15.5 - 72.2/\theta$.

Experimental

[1] The elimination reaction was predominant at the lower temperatures. At the higher temperatures, appreciab dibenzl was produced, indicating radical production (path *b*). Some surface dependence was observed in path *a* at th extreme low temperatures. The *A*-factors reported were assumed. (See bond fissions for evaluation of path *b* parameters

Reaction: 2-Methyl-2-propanethiol (*t*-butyl mercaptan)

$$(CH_3)_3CSH \text{ (I)} \longrightarrow (CH_3)_2{=}CH_2 \text{ (II)} + H_2S \text{ (III)}$$

	I	II	III
$\Delta H^\circ_{f(298)}$	-26.4	-4.0	-4.8
$S^\circ_{(298)}$	79.2	70.2	49.2
$C^\circ_{p(298)}$	28.9	21.3	8.1

$\Delta S^\circ = 40.2$ g/mole
$\Delta H^\circ = 17.6$ kcal/mole
$\Delta C^\circ_p = 0.5$ g/mole

log A	E	log k_T (*1090*)	Conditions	System	Surface	References
13.3	55.0	2.27	950–1230 °K < 1% in Ar	S. P. shock		[1] W. Tsang, J. Chem. Phys. **40**, 1498 (1964).

Preferred:
log $k = 13.4 - 55.3/\theta$.
log $A_{est} = 13.6$ (see section II–1.0).

Experimental

[1] Rates by G.L.C. analysis.

Reaction: 2,2-Difluoroethyltrifluorosilane

$$CHF_2CH_2SiF_3 \text{ (I)} \longrightarrow CHF{=}CH_2 \text{ (II)} + SiF_4 \text{ (III)}$$

	I	II	III
$\Delta H^\circ_{f(298)}$	-406	-31.5	-384
$S^\circ_{(298)}$	95.0	60.4	67.4
$C^\circ_{p(298)}$	31.6	11.9	17.6

$\Delta S^\circ = 32.8$ g/mole
$\Delta H^\circ = -9.5$ kcal/mole
$\Delta C^\circ_p = -2.1$ g/mole

log A	E	log k_T (460)	Conditions	System	Surface	References
12.27	32.72	-3.27	424–494 °K 10–180 torr	static	$< 5\%$	[1] R. N. Haszeldine, P. J. Robinson, and R. F. Simmons, J. Chem. Soc 1890 (1964).

Preferred:
   log $k = 12.27 - 32.72/\theta$.

Comments: Transition state calculation gives log $A_{est} = 12.3$ (see section II–1.0).
   This cannot be a chain reaction: the A-factor is too high and the activation energy too low; therefor the four-center molecular interpretation above seems correct.

Experimental

   [1] Rates determined by ΔP. Chemical and I.R. analysis of products confirmed the stoichiometry. Rates unaffecte by additions of NO and cyclohexene.

Reaction: 2-Chloroethyltrichlorosilane

$$ClCH_2CH_2SiCl_3 \text{ (I)} \longrightarrow C_2H_4 \text{ (II)} + SiCl_4 \text{ (III)}$$

	I	II	III
$\Delta H^\circ_{f(298)}$	-141	12.5	-152
$S^\circ_{(298)}$	102.6	52.5	79.1
$C^\circ_{p(298)}$	33.2	10.4	21.6

$\Delta S^\circ = 29$ g/mole
$\Delta H^\circ = 1.5$ kcal/mole
$\Delta C^\circ_p = -1.2$ g/mole

log A	E	log k_T (650)	Conditions	System	Surface	References
11.26	45.5	(−4.04]	629–690 °K 37–50 torr	static	none	[1] I. M. T. Davidson, C. Eaborn, and M. N. Lilly, J. Chem. Soc. 2624 (1964).

Preferred:

   log $k = 12.3 - 48.5/\theta$ (from transition-state calculation of the *A*-factor; see section II–1.0).

Comments: The rate of formation of the minor product, vinyltrichlorosilane, via a four-center molecular elimination of HCl can be estimated (by analogy with the *n*-PrCl reaction rate) to be an order of magnitude slower than the observed rate. This is consistent with the experimental findings and tends to support the molecular mechanism proposed for the overall reaction.

   One cannot exclude the possibility that this reaction is a free-radical process, however.

$$\text{Chain: } SiCl_3\cdot + ClCH_2CH_2SiCl_3 \longrightarrow SiCl_4 + \cdot CH_2CH_2SiCl_3$$

$$\cdot CH_2CH_2SiCl_3 \longrightarrow C_2H_4 + SiCl_3\cdot$$

Such a chain is consistent with the fact that the (Si—Cl) and (C—H) bonds are stronger than the (C—Cl) and (Si—H) bonds, respectively. Olefins could therefore be very poor traps for silyl radicals, while halogen abstraction could be very fast and specific.

Experimental

   [1] Rates followed by ΔP. Analysis of products by G. L. C. No effect of NO or cyclohexene. Two parallel first-order reactions detected by product analysis occurred, producing HCl + vinyltrichlorosilane and trichlorosilane + vinyl-chloride. Arrhenius parameters could not be obtained for these reactions, although one would expect the former to have parameters similar to *n*-propylchloride.

Reaction: 2-Chloroethylethyldichlorosilane

$$\text{ClCH}_2\text{CH}_2-\text{SiCl}_2(\text{C}_2\text{H}_5) \text{ (I)} \longrightarrow \text{C}_2\text{H}_4 \text{ (II)} + \text{Cl}_3\text{SiC}_2\text{H}_5 \text{ (III)}$$

	I	II	III
$\Delta H^\circ_{p(298)}$	-128	12.5	-135
$S^\circ_{(298)}$	115	52.5	93.0
$C^\circ_{p(298)}$	41.6	10.4	29.8

$\Delta S^\circ = 30.5$ g/mole
$\Delta H^\circ = 5.5$ kcal/mole
$\Delta C^\circ_p = -1.4$ g/mole

log A	E	log k_T (650)	Conditions	System	Surface	References
12.26	46.5	-3.37	629–670 °K 6–25 torr	static	none	[1] I. M. Davidson and C. J. L. Metcalfe, J. Chem. Soc. 2630 (1964).

Preferred:

$\log k = 12.26 - 46.5/\theta$

$\log A_{\text{est}} = 12.3$ (see section II-1.0; however, also see comments on 2-chloroethyltrichlorosilane.

Experimental

[1] Rates by ΔP and G.L.C. analysis of products were unaffected by added propylene. A parallel reaction producing HCl and $\text{CH}_2{=}\text{CHSiCl}_2(\text{C}_2\text{H}_5)$ accounted for 10 percent of products. Arrhenius parameters for this elimination were not obtained.

Reaction: 2-Chloroethyldiethylchlorosilane

$$ClCH_2CH_2-Si(C_2H_5)_2Cl \ (I) \longrightarrow C_2H_4 \ (II) + (C_2H_5)_2SiCl_2 \ (III)$$

	I	II	III
$\Delta H^\circ_{f(298)}$	-111.6	12.5	-118.3
$S^\circ_{(298)}$	127	52.5	105
$C^\circ_{p(298)}$	50.0	10.4	38.2

$\Delta S^\circ = 30.5$ g/mole
$\Delta H^\circ = 5.8$ kcal/mole
$\Delta C^\circ_p = -1.4$ g/mole

log A	E	log k_T (600)	Conditions	System	Surface	References
11.88	41.1	-3.09	571–625 °K	static	none	[1] I. M. T. Davidson and M. R. Jones, J. Chem. Soc. 5481 (1965).

Preferred:

log $k = 12.40 - 42.7/\theta$. However, see comments on 2-chloroethyltrichlorosilane.

Experimental

[1] Rates determined by ΔP and G.L.C. analysis and were unaffected by added NO or propylene in a greaseless system. Stopcock grease was observed to promote a heterogeneous reaction.

Reaction: Ethene

$$C_2H_4 \text{ (I)} \longrightarrow C_2H_2 \text{ (II)} + H_2 \text{ (III)}$$

	I	II	III
$\Delta H^\circ_{f(298)}$	12.5	53.9	0
$S^\circ_{(298)}$	52.5	48.0	31.2
$C^\circ_{p(298)}$	10.4	10.5	7

$\Delta S^\circ = 26.7$ g/mole
$\Delta H^\circ = 41.4$ kcal/mole
$\Delta C^\circ_p = 7.1$ g/mole

log A	E	log k_T	Conditions	System	Surface	References
		(1550)				
8.87	46.5	2.31	1300–1800 °K	S.P. shock		[1] G. B. Skinner and E. M. Sokolski, J. Phys. Chem. **64**, 1028 (1960).
		(1300)				
11.95	65.0	1.03	1170–1425 °K	S.P. shock		(as above)

Preferred:
The reaction must be a chain process.

Comments: Haugen and Benson (J. Phys. Chem. **71**, 1735 (1967)) have recently proposed a free radical mechanism which accounts for all the experimental data. Such a large change in Arrhenius parameters for any molecular reaction is unreasonable.

Experimental

[1] Arrhenius parameters changed with the temperature range studied. Analysis by G.L.C. Since the authors were unable to propose a free radical mechanism with Arrhenius parameters of the order observed, and since they believed a free radical mechanism could not account for the constant product ratios observed over the wide range of decompositions studied (i.e., 2 to 95 percent ethylene decomposition), they proposed a molecular split.

Reaction: Formyl fluoride

$$\text{HCOF (I)} \longrightarrow \text{HF (II)} + \text{CO (III)}$$

	I	II	III
$\Delta H^\circ_{f(298)}$		-64.2	-26.4
$S^\circ_{(298)}$		41.5	47.3
$C^\circ_{p(298)}$		7.0	7.0

$\Delta S^\circ =$
$\Delta H^\circ =$
$\Delta C_p^\circ =$

log A	E	log k_T (430)	Conditions	System	Surface	References
2.3	10.0	2.78	378–473 °K 2–400 torr	static	none, in coated reaction cells.	[1] G. Fischer and A. S. Buchanan, Trans. Faraday Soc. **60**, 378 (1964).

Preferred:
Not reliable; probably heterogeneous.

Comments: The Arrhenius parameters of this reaction are much too low to be reasonable. Reinvestigations of reactions for molecules of moderate complexity in which electronic state crossover paths have been proposed have invariably found that the reaction was heterogeneous. (e.g., *cis* $\longrightarrow$ *trans* isomerisation but-2-ene).

Experimental

[1] Rates based on the production of CO. Added CO, O_2, and HF did not affect the reaction rates although SiF_4 reduced the rates somewhat. A nonadiabatic reaction (singlet $\longrightarrow$ triplet $\longrightarrow$ singlet) of low energy and probability was proposed.

Reaction: *Trichloromethane (chloroform)

$$HCCl_3 \text{ (I)} \longrightarrow :CCl_2 \text{ (II)} + HCl \text{ (III)}$$

	I	II	III
$\Delta H^\circ_{f(298)}$	-25.0	$\left(40 \pm 5 \right)$	-22.1
$S^\circ_{(298)}$	69.8		44.6
$C^\circ_{p(298)}$	15.7		7.0

$\Delta S^\circ =$
$\Delta H^\circ = 43 \pm 5$ kcal/mole
$\Delta C^\circ_p =$

log A	E	log k_T (820)	Conditions	System	Surface	References
11.42	47.0	-1.10	783–857 °K $1.18 \longrightarrow 35.9$ torr $P_t > 15$ torr	flow	$< 10\%$	[1] A. E. Shilov and R. D. Sabirova, Russ. J. Phys. Chem. **34**, 408 (1960).

Preferred:
Suspect. Free radical chain processes are indicated.

Comments: The Arrhenius parameters of this reaction are too low for a three-center molecular elimination. At least a partial free radical contribution to the rate seems reasonable, not only on the basis of the kinetic parameters, but also on the basis of the products. Decomposition of DCCl₃ in toluene gave only ≈35 percent DCl although the ratio was unaffected by wide changes in temperature, contact time, and DCCl₃/toluene ratios. One should have 100 percent DCl if the decomposition is entirely molecular. Semeluk and Bernstein, J. Am. Chem. Soc **79**, 46 (1957); J. Am. Chem. Soc. **76**, 3793 (1954) have interpreted their results on this reaction in terms of a free radical mechanism, although some of their mechanistic details are known to be wrong. A transition state A-factor estimate gives log $A_{est} = 13.7$.

Experimental

[1] Rates determined by formation of HCl. Added toluene had no effect. Almost no dibenzyl was detected. First order above 15 torr pressure. Decomposition of DCCl₃ also studied with and without toluene.

---

*Reaction products: HCl, C_2Cl_4, C_2Cl_6, and smaller amounts of other chlorinated ethanes.

Reaction: Chlorodifluoromethane

$$CF_2HCl \ (I) \longrightarrow CF_2: \ (II) + HCl \ (III)$$

	I	II	III
$\Delta H^\circ_{f(298)}$	-112.3	(-39.7)	-22.1
$S^\circ_{(298)}$	66.4	59.6	44.6
$C^\circ_{p(298)}$	13.1	9.1	7.0

$\Delta S^\circ = 37.8$ g/mole
$\Delta H^\circ = 50.5$ kcal/mole
$\Delta C^\circ_p = 3.0$ g/mole

log A	E	log k_T (890)	Conditions	System	Surface	References
13.84	55.8	(0.14)	803–973 °K	static		[1] J. W. Edwards and P. A. Small, Nature **202**, 1329 (1964).
———	51.4 ±2.5		(943–1023 °K)			[2] F. Gozzo and C. R. Patrick, Nature **202**, 80 (1964).

Preferred:
  log $k = 13.84 - 55.8/\theta$.

Comments: Transition state estimation of A suggests approximate minimum and maximum values of: log $A_{min} = 10^{13.1}$; log $A_{max} = 10^{14.2}$ (see section II–2.0).

  Assuming the reaction is correct as reported, and that the back reaction (CF$_2$: + HCl→) has $E = X$ kcal/mole, it is possible to obtain a limit for the heat of formation of the CF$_2$: biradical. $\Delta H^\circ_f(CF_2:) = (-34.4 - X)$. The tetrafluoroethylene decomposition results place $\Delta H^\circ_f(CF_2:) = -39.7$, which makes $E_b = X = 5.3$ kcal/mole. This is a reasonable value for CF$_2$: addition to HCl.

Experimental

[1] and [2] No experimental details given. The CF$_2$: radicals dimerize, producing C$_2$F$_4$.

Reaction: *Nitroethane

$$CH_3CH_2NO_2 \text{ (I)} \longrightarrow C_2H_4 \text{ (II)} + HONO \text{ (III)}$$

	I	II	III
$\Delta H^\circ_{f(298)}$	−24.4	12.5	−18.5
$S^\circ_{(298)}$	75.6	52.5	58
$C^\circ_{p(298)}$	21.6	10.4	9.6

$\Delta S^\circ = 34.9$ g/mole
$\Delta H^\circ = 18.4$ kcal/mole
$\Delta C^\circ_p = -1.6$ g/mole

log A	E	log k_T (650)	Conditions	System	Surface	References
11.35	41.4	−2.57	687–715 °K 5–10% reactant	flow	————	[1] K. A. Wilde, Ind. Eng. Chem. **48**, 769 (1956).
11.53	41.5	−2.42	583–713 °K 4–40 torr	static	< 10%	[2] deM. Claude Frejacques, Compt. Rend. **231**, 1061 (1950).
10.83	39.7	−2.52	593–714 °K	static & flow		[3] K. A. Wilde, J. Phys. Chem. **61**, 385 (1957).
13.0	47.0	−2.80	628–678 °K 50–300 torr	static	∼ 10%	[4] T. L. Cottrell, T. E. Graham, and T. J. Reid, Trans. Faraday Soc. **47**, 1089 (1951).
12.4	45	−2.62	(by reevaluation of data)			[5] G. N. Spokes and S. W. Benson, J. Am. Chem. Soc. **89**, 6030 (1967).

Preferred:
   $\log k = 12.4 - 45/\theta$.

Comments: The complexities of this reaction (partial chain contribution to the rate) are such that appreciable uncertainty in the parameters is possible. Nitrous acid can decompose ($2HONO \rightleftharpoons H_2O + NO + NO_2$), thus providing a ready source of radicals for a radical-induced decomposition of nitroethane; NO_2 is a powerful chain initiator. The experimental A-factors require an extremely tight activated complex (i.e., almost total loss of both internal rotations.) By analogy with six-center transition state reactions, one would expect an A-factor in excess of 10^{13} sec^{-1} (see also 2-nitropropane).

Experimental

[1] Polarographic analysis of nitroalkane for rate determinations. I.R. used for qualitative product identification. Increased rate at $T > 715$ °K attributed to concurrent (C–N) bond split. Additions of NO_2 and H_2O did not affect the decomposition rates.

[2] Rates determined from ΔP. Stoichiometry of the reaction independent of initial pressure and almost independent

---

*Final products: C_2H_4, NO, H_2O (major); HCN, NO_2, CO_2, RCHO (minor).

(*Continued*)

f the temperature.
    [3] Rate by I.R. analysis on nitroethane. Kinetics of the high-temperature reaction believed to be initiated by the
C—N) bond fission (see bond fissions) were also studied.
    [4] Rates were obtained from the initial slopes of the pressure-time curves.

Reaction: *1-Nitropropane

$$CH_3CH_2CH_2NO_2 \text{ (I)} \longrightarrow CH_3CH{=}CH_2 \text{ (II)} + HONO \text{ (III)}$$

	I	II	III
$\Delta H^\circ_{f(298)}$	-29.4	4.8	-18.5
$S^\circ_{(298)}$	85.0	63.6	58
$C^\circ_{p(298)}$	27.1	15.3	9.6

$\Delta S^\circ = 36.6$ g/mole
$\Delta H^\circ = 15.7$ kcal/mole
$\Delta C^\circ_p = -2.2$ g/mole

log A	E	log k_T (650)	Conditions	System	Surface	References
11.74	41.5	-2.21	583–713 °K 4–40 torr	static	< 10%	[1] deM. Claude Frejacques, Compt. Compt. Rend. **321**, 1061 (1950).
13.4	47.7	-2.63	687–733 °K	flow		[2] K. A. Wilde, Ind. Eng. Chem. **48**, 769 (1956).
11.5	42	-2.63	700–1100 °K	VLPP (very low pressure pyrolysis)		[3] G. N. Spokes and S. W. Benson, J. Am. Chem. Soc. **89**, 6030 (1967).

Preferred:
    log $k = 13.4 - 47.7/\theta$.

Comments: Transition state calculation of A gives log $A_{est} = 13.2$ (See comments on nitroethane).

Experimental

    [1] Rates by ΔP.
    [2] Rates by polarographic analysis on nitropropane.
    [3] Reaction products were complex: propylene, NO, H_2O (principal products); HCN, NO_2, CO_2, and aldehydes (minor products).

---

*Final products are complex (see [3] above).

Reaction: *2-Nitropropane

$$CH_3CHNO_2CH_3 \text{ (I)} \longrightarrow CH_3CH{=}CH_2 \text{ (II)} + HONO \text{ (III)}$$

	I	II	III
$\Delta H^\circ_{f(298)}$	-34.0	4.8	-18.5
$S^\circ_{(298)}$	83.4	63.6	58
$C^\circ_{p(298)}$	26.8	15.3	9.6

$\Delta S^\circ = 38.2$ g/mole
$\Delta H^\circ = 20.3$ kcal/mole
$\Delta C^\circ_p = -1.9$ g/mole

log A	E	log k_T (700)	Conditions	System	Surface	References
11.34	39.0	-0.83	683–713 °K 4–40 torr	static	< 10%	[1] deM. Claude Fre-jacques, Compt. Rend. **231**, 1061 (1950).
11.05	39.0	-1.12	683–733 °K	flow		[2] K. A. Wilde, Ind. Eng. Chem. **48**, 769 (1956).
11.05	39.3	-1.07	523–610 °K 16 torr	static	negligible	[3] T. E. Smith and J. G. Calvert, J. Phys. Chem. **63**, 1305 (1959).
11.3	40	-1.09	800–1000 °K	VLPP		[4] G. N. Spokes and S. W. Benson, J. Am. Chem. Soc. **89**, 6030 (1967).

Preferred:
Rate constants are reliable; parameters seem low.
$\log k = 11.3 - 40/\theta$ (however, see below).

Comments: Arrhenius parameters appear unreasonably low. The minimum possible A-factor would correspond to total loss of two internal rotations. With symmetry corrections one obtains $\Delta S^\ddagger \simeq (-6.9-8.4+R \ln 12) = -10.3$ g/mole and $A^\ddagger_{min} = 10^{13.5-2.2} = 10^{11.3}$ sec^{-1}. More realistic estimates give $\Delta S^\ddagger \simeq 0$ and $\log A_{est} = 13.5$. See comments on nitroethane.

Experimental

[1] Rates by ΔP. Stoichiometry independent of initial pressure and almost independent of temperature.
[2] Rate by polarographic analysis on nitropropane.
[3] Rate by formation of propylene. Analysis by M.S. Identification of products by G.L.C. S/V large effect on overall 2-nitropropane decomposition but negligible effect on propylene production. Also neither the addition of propylene nor NO had any effect on the rate of propylene formation.

---

*Products: Propylene, NO, H_2O roughly equivalent amounts and approximately 65–70 percent of products; acetone, acetonitrile, and formaldehyde approximately 15–25 percent; hydrocarbons, nitroparaffins, CO, and CO_2 approximately 10 percent.

Reaction: Isopropyl ether

$$(CH_3)_2CHOCH(CH_3)_2 \ (I) \longrightarrow CH_2{=}CHCH_3 \ (II) + (CH_3)_2CHOH \ (III)$$

	I	II	III
$\Delta H^\circ_{f(298)}$	-77.0	4.9	-65.1
$S^\circ_{(298)}$	97.4	63.8	74.1
$C^\circ_{p(298)}$	37.8	15.3	21.5

$\Delta S^\circ = 40.5$ g/mole
$\Delta H^\circ = 16.8$ kcal/mole
$\Delta C^\circ_p = -1.0$ g/mole

log A	E	log k_T (730)	Conditions	System	Surface	References
14.62	63.5	-3.69	696–760 °K ~ 10–600 torr	static		[1] N. J. Daly and V. R. Stimson, Aust. J. Chem. **19**, 239 (1966).

Preferred:
   Suspect.

Comments: Evidence for first-order reaction is ambiguous. Until more definite evidence is available, it is preferable to treat this as a chain reaction.

Experimental

[1] Initial rates followed manometrically. Analysis by G.L.C. Major products were propylene and 2-propanol (70–90 percent), and propane and acetone (30–10 percent). No permanent gases were formed. In the presence of 2-methyl propene (20 cm), propane production was about 80 percent slower and propene production about 30 percent slower. Rates were not significantly surface sensitive. A complex free radical chain process was proposed to explain the minor reaction products and to account for the somewhat larger than overall first-order kinetics observed for the isopropanol and propene formation. The principal source of the latter, however, was thought to be unimolecular.

Reaction: 1,1-Dimethyl-1-ethanesulfonyl chloride (trimethylmethanesulfonyl chloride)

$$(CH_3)_3CSO_2Cl\ (I) \begin{array}{l} \xrightarrow{a} (CH_3)_3CCl\ (II) + SO_2\ (III) \\ \xrightarrow{b} (CH_3)_2C=CH_2\ (IV) + SO_2 + HCl\ (V) \end{array}$$

	I	II	III	IV	V
$\Delta H^\circ_{f(298)}$		-43.1	-70.9	-4.0	-22.1
$S^\circ_{(298)}$		77.4	59.3	70.2	44.6
$C^\circ_{p(298)}$		27.9	9.5	21.3	7.0

$\Delta S^\circ =$
$\Delta H^\circ =$
$\Delta C^\circ_p =$

log A	E	log k_T (470)	Conditions	System	Surface	References
4.88	$15.3 \pm .8$	-2.24	363–578 °K	static		[1] R. T. Van Aller, R. B. Scott, Jr., and E. L. Brockelbank, J. Org. Chem. **31**, 2357 (1966).

Preferred:
   Unreliable.

Comments: A low A-factor is inconsistent with any unimolecular reaction transition state proposed. The maximum entropy loss in activation would correspond to the entropy of two large internal rotations ($\Delta S_{max} \simeq -18$ g/mole). This reaction is probably heterogeneous.

Experimental

   [1] Static system. Rate was followed manometrically, and also by G.L.C. determinations of products. It was found that (isobutene/t-butyl chloride)$=2.0$ at all temperatures. There was no effect on the rates by added toluene or O_2. NO accelerated the decomposition. Absence of isobutyl chloride was taken as evidence against the presence of free radicals. Wall effects were observed and the possibility of a heterogeneous wall-catalyzed reaction was not excluded. The solution reaction was also studied and found to be strongly solvent dependent.

Reaction: 3-Butene-1-ol (allylcarbinol)

$$CH_2{=}CHCH_2CH_2OH \ (I) \longrightarrow CH_3CH{=}CH_2 \ (II) + H_2CO \ (III)$$

	I	II	III
$\Delta H^\circ_{f(298)}$	-36.3	4.9	-27.7
$S^\circ_{(298)}$	84.8	63.8	52.3
$C^\circ_{p(298)}$	23.7	15.3	8.5

$\Delta S^\circ = 31.3$ g/mole
$\Delta H^\circ = 13.5$ kcal/mole
$\Delta C^\circ_p = \ 0.1$ g/mole

log A	E	log k_T (665)	Conditions	System	Surface	References
11.65	41.0	-1.82	643–685 °K	static	None	[1] G. G. Smith and B. L. Yates, J. Chem. Soc., 7242 (1965).

Preferred:
   log $k = 11.65 - 41.0/\theta$.

Comments: Transition state estimate gives log $A_{est} = 11.7$ (see section II–4.0). Note that the back reaction has an A-factor of 10^7 l/mole-sec and an activation energy of 26.4 kcal/mole. It should be measurable at about 550 °K; so should H—D exchange between products.

Experimental

[1] Rates by ΔP. Analysis by G.L.C.

Reaction: 4-Pentene-2-ol (allylmethylcarbinol)

$$CH_2{=}CHCH_2(CH_3)CHOH \text{ (I)} \longrightarrow CH_3CH{=}CH_2 \text{ (II)} + CH_3CHO \text{ (III)}$$

	I	II	III
$\Delta H^\circ_{f(298)}$	-44.8	4.9	-39.8
$S^\circ_{(298)}$	92.8	63.8	63.2
$C^\circ_{p(298)}$	29.7	15.3	13.1

$\Delta S^\circ = 34.2$ g/mole
$\Delta H^\circ = 9.9$ kcal/mole
$\Delta C^\circ_p = -1.3$ g/mole

log A	E	log k_T (645)	Conditions	System	Surface	References
11.93	40.9	-1.93	625–663 °K	static	none	[1] G. G. Smith and B. L. Yates, J. Chem. Soc. 7242 (1965).

Preferred:
  log $k = 11.93 - 40.9/\theta$.

Comments: The activation energies for the elimination reactions of the alcohols do not change appreciably with β-(to the double bond)-alkyl substitution. This is in marked contrast to the sizable substituent effect found in the ester eliminations. However, reaction enthalpies decrease with methyl substitution (by about 4 kcal/mole) for both alcohols and ester eliminations. This means that the back reaction activation energies for the ester reactions are essentially constant with CH_3 substitution, but increase by about 4 kcal with successive CH_3 substitution in the β-hydroxy alcohol systems. Transition state estimates give log $A_{est} = 11.7$ (see section II–4.0).

Experimental

[1] Rates by ΔP. Analysis by G.L.C.

Reaction: 2-Methyl-4-pentene-2-ol (allyldimethylcarbinol)

$$CH_2=CHCH_2C(CH_3)_2OH \text{ (I)} \longrightarrow CH_3CH=CH_2 \text{ (II)} + CH_3COCH_3 \text{ (III)}$$

	I	II	III
$\Delta H^\circ_{f(298)}$	-54.1	4.9	-51.7
$S^\circ_{(298)}$	97.4	63.8	70.5
$C^\circ_{p(298)}$	35.4	15.3	17.9

$\Delta S^\circ = 36.9$ g/mole
$\Delta H^\circ = 7.3$ kcal/mole
$\Delta C^\circ_p = -2.2$ g/mole

log A	E	log k_T (625)	Conditions	System	Surface	References
12.14	40.7	-2.09	607–643 °K	static	none	[1] G. G. Smith and Brian L. Yates, J. Chem. Soc. 7242 (1965).

Preferred:
    log $k = 12.14$–$40.7/\theta$ (see comments on 4-pentene-2-ol).
Transition state estimate gives log $A_{est} = 11.9$ (see section II-4.0).

Experimental

[1] Rates by ΔP. Analysis by G.L.C.

Reaction: 3-Phenyl-3-butene-1-ol

$$CH_2=C(\emptyset)CH_2CH_2OH \text{ (I)} \rightarrow \emptyset(CH_3)C=CH_2 \text{ (II)} + CH_2O \text{ (III)}$$

	I	II	III
$\Delta H^\circ_{f(298)}$	-15.7	25.7	-27.7
$S^\circ_{(298)}$	109.4	88.2	52.3
$C^\circ_{p(298)}$	44.1	35.9	8.5

$\Delta S^\circ = 31.1$ g/mole
$\Delta H^\circ = 13.7$ kcal/mole
$\Delta C^\circ_p = 0.3$ g/mole

log A	E	log k_T (620)	Conditions	System	Surface	References
11.80	38.9	-1.91	605–631 °K	static	none	[1] G. G. Smith and B. L. Yates, J. Chem. Soc., 7242 (1965).

Preferred:
   log $k = 11.80 - 38.9/\theta$.
Transition state estimate gives log $A_{est} = 11.7$ (see section II–4.0).

Experimental

[1] Rates by ΔP. Analysis by G.L.C.

Reaction: 4-Phenyl-3-butene-1-ol

$$\text{ØCH}=\text{CHCH}_2\text{CH}_2\text{OH (I)} \longrightarrow \text{ØCH}_2\text{CH}=\text{CH}_2 \text{ (II)} + \text{CH}_2\text{O (III)}$$

	I	II	III
$\Delta H^{\circ}_{f(298)}$	-13.5	32.0	-27.7
$S^{\circ}_{(298)}$	112.3	93.6	52.3
$C^{\circ}_{p(298)}$	43.1	33.7	8.5

$\Delta S^{\circ} = 33.6$ g/mole
$\Delta H^{\circ} = 17.8$ kcal/mole
$\Delta C^{\circ} = -0.9$ g/mole

log A	E	log k_T (680)	Conditions	System	Surface	References
11.58	42.8	-2.17	661–700 °K	static	none	[1] G. G. Smith and B. L. Yates, J. Chem. Soc., 7242 (1965).

Preferred:
   log $k = 11.58 - 42.8/\theta$.
Transition state estimate gives log $A_{est} = 11.6$ (see section II–4.0).

Experimental

[1] Rates by ΔP. Analysis by G.L.C.

139

Reaction: 1-Phenyl-4-ethyl-4-hydroxyhex-l-ene

$$\text{ØCH}=\text{CHCH}_2\text{C}(\text{C}_2\text{H}_5)_2\text{OH} \quad (I) \longrightarrow \text{ØCH}_2\text{CH}=\text{CH}_2 \ (II) + \text{C}_2\text{H}_5\text{COC}_2\text{H}_5 \ (III)$$

	I	II	III
$\Delta H^\circ_{f(298)}$	-36.0	32.0	-62.2
$S^\circ_{(298)}$	143.3	93.6	88.4
$C^\circ_{p(298)}$	65.8	33.7	31.3

$\Delta S^\circ = 38.7$ g/mole
$\Delta H^\circ = 5.8$ kcal/mole
$\Delta C^\circ_p = -0.8$ g/mole

log A	E	log k_T (600)	Conditions	System	Surface	References
12.04	41.75	-3.16	579–607 °K	static		[1] G. G. Smith and R. Taylor, Chem. Ind. 949 (1961).
12.00	41.80	-3.22	650 °K	static	none	[2] G. G. Smith and B. L. Yates, J. Chem. Soc. 7242 (1965).

Preferred:
   log $k = 12.0 - 41.8/\theta$.
Transition state calculation gives log $A_{\text{est}} = 11.6$ (see section II–4.0).

Experimental

[1] Rates by ΔP unaffected by N_2. First-order kinetics were obtained to 99 percent reaction.

[2] Rates by ΔP. Analysis by G.L.C. Single temperature point used with prior data of [1] to obtain revised Arrhenius parameters.

Reaction: 3-Butenoic acid

$$CH_2=CHCH_2COOH \text{ (I)} \longrightarrow CH_3CH=CH_2 \text{ (II)} + CO_2 \text{ (III)}$$

	I	II	III
$\Delta H^\circ_{f(298)}$	-84.1	4.9	-94.1
$S^\circ_{(298)}$	84.4	63.8	51.1
$C^\circ_{p(298)}$	25.8	15.3	8.9

$\Delta S^\circ = 30.5$ g/mole
$\Delta H^\circ = -5.1$ kcal/mole
$\Delta C^\circ_p = -1.6$ g/mole

log A	E	log k_T (620)	Conditions	System	Surface	References
11.34	40.6	-2.97	587–651 °K	static	< 5%	[1] G. G. Smith and S. E. Blau, J. Phys. Chem. **68**, 1231 (1964).

Preferred:
log $k = 11.34 - 40.6/\theta$.
Transition state estimate gives log $A_{est} = 11.1$ (see section II-4.0).

Experimental

[1] Rate by ΔP. Analysis by G.L.C. No effect on rate with added cyclohexene.

Reaction: 2,2-Dimethyl-3-butenoic acid

	I	II	III
$\Delta H^\circ_{f(298)}$	-94.7	-10.3	-94.1
$S^\circ_{(298)}$	96.2	80.4	51.1
$C^\circ_{p(298)}$	35.8	25.5	8.9

$\Delta S^\circ = 35.3$ g/mole
$\Delta H^\circ = -9.7$ kcal/mole
$\Delta C^\circ_p = -1.4$ g/mole

log A	E	log k_T (530)	Conditions	System	Surface	References
11.13	36.6	-3.95	511–548 °K 150–250 torr	static		[1] D. B. Bigley and R. W. May, J. Chem. Soc. **B,** 557 (1967).

Preferred:
   log $k = 11.13 - 36.6/\theta$.

Comments: Transition states estimates for A of this and related reactions are all similar to that for 3-butenoic acid (i.e., $\sim A \simeq 10^{11.1}$ sec^{-1}); therefore, this reaction seems quite reasonable. Rate constants are reliable

Experimental

[1] Rates were followed by rates of CO_2 produced. Analysis of olefin was by G.L.C., using tetralin as an internal standard. Good mass balances. Relative rates to but-3-enoic acid at 500 °K were calculated.

Reaction: 2,2-Dimethyl-*trans*-3-pentenoic acid

	I	II	III
$\Delta H^\circ_{f(298)}$	-102.5	-15.1	-94.1
$S^\circ_{(298)}$	104.8	90.2	51.1
$C^\circ_{p(298)}$	41.1	30.6	8.9

$\Delta S^\circ = 36.5$ g/mole
$\Delta H^\circ = -6.7$ kcal/mole
$\Delta C^\circ_p = -1.6$ g/mole

log A	E	log k_T (545)	Conditions	System	Surface	References
11.74	40.3	-4.43	526–564 °K 150–250 torr	static		[1] D. B. Bigley and R. W. May, J. Chem. Soc. **B**, 557 (1967).

Preferred:
   Reliable.

Comments: Transition state estimates for A of this and related reactions are all similar to that for 3-butenoic acid (i.e., $\sim A \simeq 10^{11.1}$ sec^{-1}); therefore, this reaction seems quite reasonable. Rate constants are probably reliable.

Experimental

[1] Rates were followed by rates of CO_2 produced. Analysis of olefin was by G.L.C., using tetralin as an internal standard. Good mass balances. Relative rates to but-3-enoic acid at 500 °K were calculated.

Reaction: 2,2,3-Trimethyl-3-butenoic acid

$$\text{C=C}-\text{COOH (I)} \longrightarrow \text{C=C (II)} + CO_2 \text{ (III)}$$

	I	II	III
$\Delta H^\circ_{f(298)}$	-103.6	-16.7	-94.1
$S^\circ_{(298)}$	103.8	84.6	51.1
$C^\circ_{p(298)}$	41.9	33.0	8.9

$\Delta S^\circ = 31.9$ g/mole
$\Delta H^\circ = -7.2$ kcal/mole
$\Delta C^\circ_p = 0$ g/mole

log A	E	log k_T (465)	Conditions	System	Surface	References
10.85	32.9	-4.62	447–488 °K 150–250 torr	static		[1] D. B. Bigley and R. W. May, J. Chem. Soc. **B**, 557 (1967).

Preferred:
   Reliable.

Comments: Transition state estimates for A of this and related reactions are all similar to that for 3-butenoic acid (i.e., $\sim A \simeq 10^{11.1}$ sec^{-1}); therefore, this reaction seems quite reasonable. Rate constants are probably reliable.

Experimental

   [1] Rates were followed by rates of CO_2 produced. Analysis of olefin was by G.L.C., using tetralin as an internal standard. Good mass balances. Rates relative to but-3-enoic acid at 500 °K were calculated.

Reaction: 2,2-Dimethyl-3-ethyl-3-pentenoic acid

	I	II	III
$\Delta H^\circ_{f(298)}$	-113.3	-26.3	-94.1
$S^\circ_{(298)}$	123.0	105.6	51.1
$C^\circ_{p(298)}$	52.3	43.2	8.9

$\Delta S^\circ = 33.7$ g/mole
$\Delta H^\circ = -7.1$ kcal/mole
$\Delta C^\circ_p = 0.2$ g/mole

log A	E	log k_T (485)	Conditions	System	Surface	References
11.68	36.0	-4.54	468–502 °K 150–250 torr	static		[1] D. B. Bigley and R. W. May, J. Chem. Soc., **B,** 557 (1967)

Preferred:
   Reliable.

Comments: Transition state estimates for A of this and related reactions are all similar to that for 3-butenoic acid (i.e., $\sim A \simeq 10^{11.1}$ sec^{-1}), therefore, this reaction seems quite reasonable. Rate constants are probably reliable.

Experimental

[1] Rates were followed by rates of CO_2 produced. Analysis of olefin was by G.L.C., using tetralin as an internal standard. Good mass balances. Rates relative to but-3-enoic acid at 500 °K were calculated.

Reaction: 2-Methyl-2-(1-cyclopentyl) propionic acid

	I	II	III
$\Delta H^\circ_{f(298)}$	-100.0	-10.8	-94.1
$S^\circ_{(298)}$	110.7	93.3	51.1
$C^\circ_{p(298)}$	44.7	34.3	8.9

$\Delta S^\circ = 33.7$ g/mole
$\Delta H^\circ = -4.9$ kcal/mole
$\Delta C^\circ_p = -1.5$ g/mole

log A	E	log k_T (485)	Conditions	System	Surface	References
8.95	29.9	-4.52	470–502 °K 150–250 torr	static		[1] D. B. Bigley and R. W. May, J. Chem. Soc., **B** 557 (1967)

Preferred:
   Suspect.

Comments: Transition state estimates for A of this and related reactions are all similar to that for 3-butenoic acid (i.e., $\sim A \simeq 10^{11.1}$ sec^{-1}), therefore the A-factors seem too low by at least an order of magnitude. Rate constants are probably reliable.

Experimental

[1] Rates were followed by rates of CO_2 produced..

action: 2-Methyl-2-(1-cyclohexenyl) propionic acid

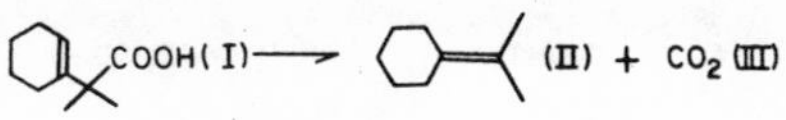

	I	II	III
$\Delta H^\circ_{f(298)}$	−110.7	−21.8	−94.1
$S^\circ_{(298)}$	114.3	96.3	51.1
$C^\circ_{p(298)}$	51.7	43.0	8.9

$^\circ = 33.1$ g/mole
$^\circ = -5.2$ kcal/mole
$^\circ_p = +0.2$ g/mole

og A	E	log k_T	Conditions	System	Surface	References
10.04	33.3	−4.51	487–517 °K 150–250 torr	static		[1] D. B. Bigley and R. W. May, J. Chem. Soc. **B**, 557 (1967).

eferred:
Suspect.

mments: Transition state estimates for A of this and related reactions are all similar to that for 3-butenoic id (i.e., $\sim A \simeq 10^{11.1}$ sec^{-1}). The A-factors seem too low by at least an order of magnitude. Rate constants probably reliable.

Experimental

[1] Rates were followed by rates of CO_2 produced.

Reaction: 2-Methyl-2-(1-cycloheptenyl) propionic acid

	I	II	III
$\Delta H^\circ_{f(298)}$	-110.4	-21.4	-94.1
$S^\circ_{(298)}$			51.1
$C^\circ_{p(298)}$			8.9

$\Delta S^\circ = (33)$ g/mole
$\Delta H^\circ = -4.1$ kcal/mole
$\Delta C^\circ_p = (\quad)$

log A	E	log k_T (485)	Conditions	System	Surface	References
8.50	28.6	-4.39	468–502 °K 150–250 torr	static		[1] D. B. Bigley and R. W May, J. Chem. Soc. 557 (1967).

Preferred:
   Suspect.

Comments: Transition state estimates for A of this and related reactions are all similar to that for 3-buten acid (i.e., $\sim A \simeq 10^{11.1}$ sec^{-1}). The A-factors seem too low by at least an order of magnitude. Rate consta are probably reliable.

Experimental

[1] Rates were followed by rates of CO_2 produced.

Reaction: Ethyl chloroethanoate (ethyl chloroformate)

$$ClCOOC_2H_5 \text{ (I)} \longrightarrow C_2H_5Cl \text{ (II)} + CO_2 \text{ (III)}$$

	I	II	III
$\Delta H_{f(298)}^{\circ}$	-108.3	-26.3	-94.1
$S_{(298)}^{\circ}$	90.4	66.0	51.1
$C_{p(298)}^{\circ}$	24.7	15.1	8.9

$\Delta S^{\circ} = 26.7$ g/mole
$\Delta H^{\circ} = -12.1$ kcal/mole
$\Delta C_p^{\circ} = -0.7$ g/mole

log A	E	log k_T (500)	Conditions	System	Surface	References
10.74	29.41	-2.11	383–473 °K 10–700 torr	static	none	[1] A. R. Choppin and G. F. Kirby, J. Am. Chem. Soc. **61**, 3176 (1939).
8.91	[a] 32.5	-5.29	513–552 °K	stirred flow	[b]	[2] E. S. Lewis and W. C. Herndon, J. Am. Chem. Soc. **83**, 1955 (1961).

Preferred:
Unreliable.

Comments: The Arrhenius parameters for this reaction are extremely low for a unimolecular elimination reaction. In addition, the mechanism proposed involves either pentavalent carbon or an appreciable development of a very polar (essentially ionic) transition state. Both seem quite unreasonable for a gas phase reaction. The large rate discrepancies (factor of 10^3) between the two experimental studies also suggest serious complications (probably surface catalysis) for this reaction. A free radical mechanism propagated by ethyl radicals with chlorine abstraction would lead to the observed products. Heterogeneous reactions are also supported by the abnormally low activation energies and A-factor.

Fast chains which produce the observed products:

$$\text{(1) } R + Cl\!-\!\overset{\displaystyle O}{\overset{\|}{C}}\!-\!OR \longrightarrow RCl + \cdot CO_2R$$

$$\cdot CO_2R + (M) \xrightarrow{\text{fast}} CO_2 + R + (M)$$

$$\text{(2) } Cl + Cl\overset{\displaystyle O}{\overset{\|}{C}}\!-\!OR \longrightarrow Cl_2 + \cdot CO_2R$$
$$\cdot CO_2R + (M) \longrightarrow CO_2 + R + (M) \left.\right\} \text{ Chain transfer.}$$

(Continued)

149

Ethyl chloroethanoate (*Continued*)

J. C. J. Thynne, Trans. Faraday Soc. **58**, 676 (1962) has shown that decomposition of the ·CO₂R radi
gives exclusively CO₂ and R·, not CO and ·OR. Thus the proposed chain accounts nicely for the produ
observed. The Cl abstraction by R· would also be favored relative to the H-abstraction by several pow
of 10 in the rate.

Experimental

[1] Rates by ΔP. Chemical analysis for CO_2 and ethyl chloride. No effect by the addition of a variety of forei
gases. (Choppin and Kirby, J. Am. Chem. Soc. **62**, 1592 (1940).)

[2][a] The Arrhenius factors have been recalculated from the rate constant data since the quoted transition st
parameters are not consistent with the rate constants. Rate by G.L.C. analysis of the products.

[b] The first runs in a series were often characterized by much faster rates. This was attributed to surface catalys

Reaction: Isopropyl chloromethanoate (isopropyl chloroformate)

$$\text{ClCOOCH(CH}_3)_2 \text{ (I)} \xrightarrow{a} \text{HCl (V)} + \text{CO}_2 + \text{CH}_2\!\!=\!\!\text{CHCH}_3 \text{ (II)}$$
$$\xrightarrow{b} \text{(CH}_3)_2\text{CHCl (III)} + \text{CO}_2 \text{ (IV)}$$

	I	II	III	IV	V
$\Delta H^\circ_{f(298)}$	-116.1	4.9	-33.0	-94.1	-22.1
$S^\circ_{(298)}$	96.8	63.8	74.1	51.1	44.6
$C^\circ_{p(298)}$	30.7	15.3	21.4	8.9	7.0

	a	b
$\Delta S^\circ =$	62.7	28.4 g/mole
$\Delta H^\circ =$	4.8	-11.0 kcal/mole
$\Delta C_p^\circ =$	0.5	-0.4 g/mole

Path	log A	E	log k_T (500)	Conditions	System	Surface	References
a	9.11	25.8	-2.21	453–493 °K	static and flow	some*	[1] A. R. Choppin and E. L. Compere, J. Am. Chem. Soc. **70**, 3797 (1948).
a	12.71	**39.2	-4.5	513–528 °K	stirred flow	——	[2] E. S. Lewis and W. C. Herndon, J. Am. Chem. Soc. **83**, 1955 (1961).
b	9.36	26.4	-2.21	453–493 °K	static, flow	some*	[1]
b	8.73	27.4	-3.3	513–528 °K	stirred flow reactor	——	[2]

Preferred:
  log $k_a = 12.9 - 39.7/\theta$ (see below).
  path b, unreliable.

Comments: Since such serious discrepancies in rates exist for these reactions, there must be serious complications with the reactions themselves. Surface effects observed by Choppin and Compere and fast initial rates observed by Lewis and Herndon strongly suggest heterogeneous catalysis. The unreasonably low A-factors in all cases except one also suggest wall catalysis. See ethyl chloroformate for a more complete discussion.

  Path a appears reasonable for the elimination reaction. The rate and rate parameters compare favorably with those of the substituted phenyl ethyl methyl carbonates, as one might expect. The transition state estimate (see section II–4.0) is: log $A_{(a)} = 10^{12.34}$; log $k_a = 12.34 - 38.3/\theta$. Path b is probably not a unimolecular reaction.

Experimental

[1] Rate by ΔP. Qualitative chemical analysis of the products.
[2] Rate by G.L.C. analysis of products.

---

*Packing the static reaction cell with glass wool doubled the observed rate of decomposition. Increased surface in the flow experiment *decreased* the reaction rate.
**Parameters were calculated from the rate constants reported.

Reaction: Isobutyl chloromethanoate (isobutyl chloroformate)

$$\text{ClCOOCH}_2\text{CH(CH}_3)_2 \text{ (I)} \longrightarrow \text{CH}_2\!\!=\!\!\text{C(CH}_3)_2 \text{ (II)} + \text{HCl (III)} + \text{CO}_2 \text{ (IV)}$$

	I	II	III	IV
$\Delta H^\circ_{f(298)}$	-119.5	-4.0	-22.1	-94.1
$S^\circ_{(298)}$	106.5	70.2	44.6	51.1
$\Delta C^\circ_{p(298)}$	35.7	21.3	7.0	8.9

$\Delta S^\circ = 59.4$ g/mole
$\Delta H^\circ = -0.7$ kcal/mole
$\Delta C^\circ_p = 1.5$ g/mole

log A	E	log k_T (560)	Conditions	System	Surface	References
13.0	40.0	-2.61	540–573 °K	static		[1] Calculated by A. R. Choppin and E. L. Compere, J. Am. Chem. Soc. **70**, 3797 (1948) from the data of E. T. Lessig, J. Phys. Chem. **36**, 2325 (1932).

Preferred:
    log $k = 11.9 - 37.2/\theta$.
Transition state estimate is preferred (see section II–4.0).

Experimental

[1] The rate constants were calculated from reported 3/4 lifetimes measured manometrically. It is inferred that the rate constants are representative of the above elimination reaction. Initial products are probably isobutene + ClCOOH.

Reaction: *sec*-Butyl chloromethanoate (*sec*-butyl chloroformate)

$$\xrightarrow{a} CH_2\!\!=\!\!CHCH_2CH_3 \ (II) + HCl + CO_2$$

$$\xrightarrow{b} cis\text{-}CH_3CH\!\!=\!\!CHCH_3 \ (III) + HCl + CO_2$$

$$ClCOOCH(CH_3)CH_2CH_3 \ (I) \xrightarrow{c} trans\text{-}CH_3CH\!\!=\!\!CHCH_3 \ (IV) + HCl \ (VI) + CO_2 \ (VII)$$

$$\xrightarrow{d} CH_3CHClCH_2CH_3 \ (V) + CO_2$$

	I	II	III	IV	V	VI	VII
$\Delta H^\circ_{f(298)}$	-120.3	0	-1.7	-2.7	-37.2	-22.1	-94.1
$S^\circ_{(298)}$	106.2	73.6	72.1	70.9	83.4	44.6	51.1
$C^\circ_{p(298)}$	36.5	20.5	18.9	21.0	26.7	7.0	8.9

a
$\Delta S^\circ = 63.1$ g/mole
$\Delta H^\circ = 4.1$ kcal/mole
$\Delta C_p^\circ = -0.1$ g/mole

Path	log A	E	log k_T (513)	Conditions	System	Surface	References
a	10.21	31.5	-3.19	513–528 °K	stirred flow	————	[1] E. S. Lewis and W. C. Herndon, J. Am. Chem. Soc. **83**, 1955 (1961).
c	13.7	40.0	-3.32	513–528 °K			
b	13.8	40.4	-3.34	513–528 °K			
d	9.7	28.6	-2.46	513–528 °K			
a+b+c	12.9	37.0	-2.80	513–528 °K			

Preferred:
  Path *a* log $k = 12.1 - 36.0/\theta$ log $A_{est} = 12.6$
  Path *b* log $k = 11.9 - 35.8/\theta$ log $A_{est} = 12.1$
  Path *c* log $k = 11.9 - 35.9/\theta$ log $A_{est} = 12.1$ (see section II–4.0).
  Path *d* Not reliable.

Comments: Paths *a*, *b*, and *c* are probably unimolecular elimination reactions, although the Arrhenius parameters appear somewhat unexpected by comparison with the formates. Path *d* is probably not a unimolecular reaction and probably has a heterogeneous component. (See discussion on ethyl chloroformate.) The small temperature range (i.e., $\Delta T \sim 15$ °K) would be quite conducive to large errors in the Arrhenius parameters. ($\Delta E \pm 4$ kcal.) The transition state calculation of the *A*-factors is preferred. Eliminations via primary and secondary H-atom transfers were almost statistical.

Experimental

[1] Nitrogen carrier. Analysis by G.L.C. Deuterium isotope effects have also been studied for this reaction by these authors (J. Am. Chem. Soc. **83**, 1959 (1959)).

Reaction: Ethyl methanoate (ethyl formate)

$$HCOOCH_2CH_3 \ (I) \longrightarrow C_2H_4 \ (II) + HCOOH \ (III)$$

	I	II	III
$\Delta H^\circ_{f(298)}$	-88.9	12.5	-88
$S^\circ_{(298)}$	82.0	52.5	60.1
$C^\circ_{p(298)}$	21.7	10.4	9.1

$\Delta S^\circ = 30.6$ g/mole
$\Delta H^\circ = 13.4$ kcal/mole
$\Delta C^\circ_p = -2.2$ g/mole

log A	E	log k_T (865)	Conditions	System	Surface	References
11.33	44.14	0.18	810–920 °K 15–21 torr	flow	———	[1] A. T. Blades, Can. J. Chem. **32**, 366 (1954).
9.41	40.01	(673) -3.58	648–698 °K	static	(see below)	[2] R. F. Makens and W. G. Eversole, J. Am. Chem. Soc. **61**, 3203 (1939).

Preferred:
  log $k = 12.4 - 48.3/\theta$.

Comments: Rate parameters for both studies are certainly low. In [2] surface effects were observed and it is possible that similar complications existed in the high-temperature flow experiments. If rate constants in the middle of the two temperature ranges are used to calculate the Arrhenius parameters, one obtains approximately log $k = 13.3 - 52.1/\theta$.

  If the calculated A-factor and the activation energy of ethyl acetate are adopted, then the calculated and observed rates of reaction at the higher temperature agree within 30 percent, while at the lower tempreatures, the observed rates are a factor of 5 slower. This could reflect an erroneous interpretation of the manometric data. The estimated parameters are preferred.

Experimental

  [1] Rates by acid titration. Toluene flow technique.
  [2] Rates by gasometric analysis for ethylene. Ethylene formation was not particularly surface sensitive, although subsequent decomposition of formic acid was strongly surface sensitive.

eaction: Propyl methanoate (*n*-propyl formate)

$$HCOOCH_2CH_2CH_3\ (I) \longrightarrow C_3H_6\ (II) + HCOOH\ (III)$$

	I	II	III
$\Delta H^\circ_{f(298)}$	−93.9	4.8	−88
$S^\circ_{(298)}$	91.4	63.6	60.1
$C^\circ_{p(298)}$	27.2	15.3	9.1

$S^\circ =$ 32.3 g/mole
$H^\circ =$ 10.7 kcal/mole
$C^\circ_p = -2.8$ g/mole

log *A*	*E*	log k_T (645)	Conditions	System	Surface	References
9.4	39.66	−4.04	613–673 °K	static		[1] R. B. Anderson and H. H. Rowley, J. Phys. Chem. **47,** 454 (1943).

referred:
log $k = 12.1 - 47.7/\theta$ (see below).

omments: Unreliable; Arrhenius parameters are much too low for the molecular elimination reaction. he estimated Arrhenius parameters are preferred. As in the ethyl formate system, the reported reaction tes are appreciably lower than the calculated rates. A systematic error in both studies is indicated.

Experimental

[1] Rates based on propene formation analyzed by absorption in sulfuric acid. Stoichiometry confirmed by a sub- quent surface decomposition of formic acid.

Reaction: Isopropyl methanoate (isopropyl formate)

$$HCOOCH(CH_3)_2 \; (I) \longrightarrow CH_2{=}CHCH_3 \; (II) + HCOOH \; (III)$$

	I	II	III
$\Delta H^\circ_{f(298)}$	-96.7	4.8	-88
$S^\circ_{(298)}$	88.4	63.6	60.1
$C^\circ_{p(298)}$	27.7	15.3	9.1

$\Delta S^\circ = 35.3$ g/mole
$\Delta H^\circ = 13.5$ kcal/mole
$\Delta C^\circ_p = -3.3$ g/mole

log A	E	log k_T (600)	Conditions	System	Surface	References
12.58	44.0	-3.44	721–811 °K 10.6–21.5 torr	flow	————	[1] A. T. Blades, Can. J. Chem. **32**, 366 (1954).
12.58	44.23	-3.53	596–608 °K	static		[2] R. B. Anderson and H. H. Rowley, J. Phys. Chem. **47**, 454 (1943).

Preferred:

   $\log k = 12.6 - 44.0/\theta$.

   Transition state estimate of A gives $\log A_{est} = 12.7$ (see section II–4.0).

Experimental

[1] Rates by acid titration. Toluene carrier technique.

[2] Rates determined on basis of propene formation analyzed by absorption in 83 percent sulfuric acid. Subsequent decomposition of the formic acid complicated the stoichiometry since (P_∞/P_0) was temperature and surface sensitive. Rate of propene formation was relatively insensitive to change of surface.

Reaction: *t*-Butyl methanoate (*t*-butyl formate)

$$HCOOC(CH_3)_3 \ (I) \longrightarrow CH_2{=}C(CH_3)_2 \ (II) + HCOOH \ (III)$$

	I	II	III
$\Delta H^\circ_{f(298)}$	-105.6	-4.0	-88
$S^\circ_{(298)}$	92.2	70.2	60.1
$C^\circ_{p(298)}$	33.4	21.3	9.1

$\Delta S^\circ = 38.1$ g/mole
$\Delta H^\circ = 13.6$ kcal/mole
$\Delta C^\circ_p = -3.0$ g/mole

log A	E	log k_T (550)	Conditions	System	Surface	References
11.1	34.6	(-2.65)	503–573 °K 38–103 torr	static	none	[1] E. Gordon, S. J. W. Price, and A. F. Trotman-Dickenson, J. Chem. Soc. 2813 (1957).

Preferred:
log $k = 12.9 - 39.2/\theta$. Rate constants are probably reliable around $\bar{T}$.

Comments: One would expect the *t*-butyl derivative to have an *A*-factor very close to the isopropyl derivative; the Arrhenius parameters are therefore probably low. A transition state estimate of the *A*-factor gives log $A_{est} = 12.9$ and is preferred (see section II–4.0).

Experimental

[1] Rates by ΔP were unaffected by added cyclohexene. The decomposition rates based on isobutene formation agreed with the observed pressure changes within (3–20 percent).

Reaction: Ethyl ethanoate (ethyl acetate)

$$CH_3COOC_2H_5 \ (I) \longrightarrow C_2H_4 \ (II) + CH_3COOH \ (III)$$

	I	II	III
$\Delta H^\circ_{f(298)}$	-103.4	12.5	-103.7
$S^\circ_{(298)}$	90.1	52.5	67.6
$C^\circ_{p(298)}$	26.7	10.4	16.0

$\Delta S^\circ = 30.0$ g/mole
$\Delta H^\circ = 12.2$ kcal/mole
$\Delta C^\circ_p = -0.3$ g/mole

log A	E	log k_T (830)	Conditions	System	Surface	References
12.48	47.75	-0.09	787–883 °K 11.9–18.8 torr	flow		[1] A. T. Blades, Can. J. Chem. **32**, 366 (1954).
12.59	48.0	-0.05	773–876 °K	flow		[2] A. T. Blades and P. W. Gilderson, Can. J. Chem. **38**, 1407 (1960).
12.54	48.0	-0.10	725–810 °K	flow		[3] J. C. Scheer, E. C. Kooyman, and F. L. J. Sixma, Rec. Trav. Chim. des Pays-Bas **82**, 1123 (1963).

Preferred:
log $k = 12.59 - 48.0/\theta$.
log $A_{est} \simeq 12.6$ (see section II-4.0).

Experimental

[1] Toluene carrier technique. Rate determined by titration of acetic acid.

[2] (as above) Ethyl (d_5) acetate decomposition also determined: $(k_H/k_d) \simeq 0.8 \times 10^{1.515/\theta}$ interpreted as a primary isotope effect with β (C—H) bond rupture playing a major role in the transition state. Other relative rate isotope studies on ethyl acetate include: ethyl acetate (d_3), [2] above; and 1,1,2,2(d_4) ethyl acetate, A. T. Blades and P. W. Gilderson, Can. J. Chem. **38**, 1401 (1960). In the isotope studies, the olefin products were determined by M. S.

[3] Rates by G. L. C. (see comments on t-butyl acetate).

Reaction: 1-Propyl ethanoate (*n*-propyl acetate)

$$CH_3COOCH_2CH_2CH_3 \text{ (I)} \longrightarrow CH_3COOH \text{ (II)} + CH_2{=}CHCH_3 \text{ (III)}$$

	I	II	III
$\Delta H^\circ_{f(298)}$	-108.4	-103.7	4.8
$S^\circ_{(298)}$	99.5	67.6	63.6
$C^\circ_{(298)}$	32.2	16.0	15.3

$\Delta S^\circ = 31.7$ g/mole
$\Delta H^\circ = 9.5$ kcal/mole
$\Delta C^\circ_p = -0.9$ g/mole

log A	E	log k_T (760)	Conditions	System	Surface	References
12.40	47.7	-1.29	725–810 °K	flow		[1] J. C. Scheer, E. C.
11.27	43.7	-1.27				Kooyman, and F. L. J.
12.27	48.3	-1.59				Sixma, Rec. Trav.
						Chim. des Pays-Bas **82**,
						1123 (1963).

Preferred:
    log $k = 12.4 - 47.7/\theta$
    log $A_{est} = 12.3$ $E \simeq 47.4$ kcal/mole (see section II–4.0).

Experimental

[1] Rates by G.L.C. analysis on product olefins and reactant. It is apparent that the experimental errors in the method of study are such that the Arrhenius parameters reported are not reliable to better than an order of magnitude. (For comments on the method see *t*-butyl acetate.)

Reaction: 1-Butyl ethanoate (n-butyl acetate)

$$CH_3COO(CH_2)_3CH_3 \; (I) \longrightarrow CH_3COOH \; (II) + CH_2{=}CHCH_2CH_3 \; (III)$$

	I	II	III
$\Delta H^\circ_{f(298)}$	-113.3	-103.7	0
$S^\circ_{(298)}$	108.9	67.6	73.6
$C^\circ_{p(298)}$	37.7	16.0	20.5

$\Delta S^\circ = 32.3$ g/mole
$\Delta H^\circ = 9.6$ kcal/mole
$\Delta C^\circ_p = -1.2$ g/mole

log A	E	log k_T (760)	Conditions	System	Surface	References
12.19	46.0	-1.01	725–810 °K	flow	————	[1] J. C. Scheer, E. C. Kooyman, and F. L. J. Sixma, Rec. Trav. Chim. des Pays-Bas **82** 1123 (1963).
13.28	49.3	*-0.89				

Preferred:
   $\log k = 12.19 - 46.0/\theta$
   $\log A_{est} = 12.2$ (see section II–4.0).

Comments: The rate constants should be very similar to those for n-propyl and n-pentyl acetates. Rather large experimental errors are evident.

Experimental

[1] Rates by G.L.C. analysis for 1-butene.

---

*Reported A-factor of $10^{11.2}$ sec^{-1} was assumed to be a misprint. Experimental errors were large. (See comments on t-butyl acetate.)

Reaction: Isobutyl ethanoate (2-methylpropyl acetate; isobutyl acetate)

$$CH_3COOCH_2CH(CH_3)_2 \text{ (I)} \longrightarrow CH_3COOH \text{ (II)} + CH_2{=}C(CH_3)_2 \text{ (III)}$$

	I	II	III
$\Delta H^\circ_{f(298)}$	-114.6	-103.7	-4.0
$S^\circ_{(298)}$	106.2	67.6	70.2
$C^\circ_{p(298)}$	37.5	16.0	21.3

$\Delta S^\circ = 32.6$ g/mole
$\Delta H^\circ = 6.9$ kcal/mole
$\Delta C^\circ_p = -0.2$ g/mole

log A	E	log k_T (760)	Conditions	System	Surface	References
11.06	44.1	(-1.59)	725–810 °K	flow		[1] J. C. Scheer, E. C. Kooyman, and F. L. J. Sixma, Rec. Trav. Chim. des Pays-Bas **82**, 1123 (1963).
12.38	48.8	(-1.64)				

Preferred:
Estimated Arrhenius parameters are preferred (see section II–4.0).
log $k = 11.9-47.3/\theta$.

Experimental

[1] Rates by G.L.C. analysis of isobutene. See comments on *t*-butyl acetate.

Reaction: 1-Pentyl ethanoate (*n*-pentyl acetate)

$$CH_3COO(CH_2)_4CH_3 \ (I) \longrightarrow CH_3COOH \ (II) + CH_2{=}CHCH_2CH_2CH_3 \ (III)$$

	I	II	III
$\Delta H^\circ_{f(298)}$	-118.3	-103.7	-4.9
$S^\circ_{(298)}$	118.3	67.6	82.8
$C^\circ_{p(298)}$	43.2	16.0	26.2

$\Delta S^\circ = 32.1$ g/mole
$\Delta H^\circ = 9.7$ kcal/mole
$\Delta C^\circ_p = -1.0$ g/mole

log *A*	*E*	log k_T (760)	Conditions	System	Surface	References
12.2	46.4	(-1.14)	725–810 °K	flow		[1] J. C. Scheer, E. C. Kooyman, and F. L. J. Sixma, Rec. Trav. Chim. des Pays-Bas **82**, 1123 (1963).

Preferred:
   $\log k = 12.2 - 46.4/\theta.$
   $\log A_{est} = 12.2$ (see section II–4.0).

Experimental

[1] Rates by G.L.C. analysis of 1-pentene. See comments on *t*-butyl acetate.

Reaction: 2-Methylbutyl ethanoate (2-methylbutyl acetate)

$$CH_3COOCH_2CH(CH_3)CH_2CH_3 \ (I) \longrightarrow CH_3COOH \ (II) + CH_2{=}C(CH_3)C_2H_5 \ (III)$$

	I	II	III
$\Delta H^\circ_{f(298)}$	-118.8	-103.7	-8.6
$S^\circ_{(298)}$	115.6	67.6	81.9
$C^\circ_{p(298)}$	43.0	16.0	26.7

$\Delta S^\circ = 33.9$ g/mole
$\Delta H^\circ = 6.5$ kcal/mole
$\Delta C^\circ_p = -0.3$ g/mole

log A	E	log k_T (760)	Conditions	System	Surface	References
12.61	49.0	(-1.48)	725–810 °K	flow		[1] J. C. Scheer, E. C. Kooyman, and F. L. J. Sixma, Rec. Trav. Chim. des Pays-Bas **82**, 1123 (1963).
11.60	45.7	(-1.52)				

Preferred:
    log $k = 11.9{-}46.7/\theta$. Rate constants are reliable.

Comments: Rate constants should be close to those for 2-methylpropyl acetate, as observed. The estimated Arrhenius parameters are preferred (see section II–4.0).

Experimental

[1] Rates by G.L.C. analysis. See comments on *t*-butyl acetate.

Reaction: 3-Methylbutyl ethanoate (γ-methylbutyl acetate)

$$CH_3COO(CH_2)_2CH(CH_3)_2 \ (I) \longrightarrow CH_3COOH \ (II) + CH_2{=\!\!=}CHCH(CH_3)_2 \ (III)$$

	I	II	III
$\Delta H^\circ_{f(298)}$	-119.5	-103.7	-6.9
$S^\circ_{(298)}$	115.6	67.6	79.7
$C^\circ_{p(298)}$	43.0	16.0	25.8

$\Delta S^\circ = 31.7$ g/mole
$\Delta H^\circ = 8.9$ kcal/mole
$\Delta C^\circ_p = -1.2$ g/mole

log A	E	log k_T (760)	Conditions	System	Surface	References
12.63	47.9	(-1.11)	$(725-810 \ ^\circ K)$	flow		[1] J. C. Scheer, E. C. Kooyman, and F. L. J. Sixma, Rec. Trav. Chim. des Pays-Bas **82**, 1123 (1963).

Preferred:
   log $k = 12.2 - 46.4/\theta$. Rate constants are reliable.

Comments: The Arrhenius parameters seem slightly high. Rate constant agrees with that of pentyl ethanoate, as one might expect.

Experimental

   [1] Rates by G.L.C. analysis. See comments on *t*-butyl acetate.

Reaction: 2-Ethylbutyl ethanoate (β-ethylbutyl acetate)

$$CH_3COOCH_2CH(C_2H_5)_2 \text{ (I)} \longrightarrow CH_3COOH \text{ (II)} + CH_2 = C(C_2H_5)_2 \text{ (III)}$$

	I	II	III
$\Delta H^\circ_{f(298)}$	-122.9	-103.7	-13.6
$S^\circ_{(298)}$	125.0	67.6	89.9
$C^\circ_{p(298)}$	48.5	16.0	32.2

$\Delta S^\circ = 32.5$ g/mole
$\Delta H^\circ = 5.6$ kcal/mole
$\Delta C^\circ_p = -0.3$ g/mole

log A	E	log k_T (760)	Conditions	System	Surface	References
13.04	49.7	(-1.23)	725–810 °K	flow		[1] J. C. Scheer, E. C. Kooyman, and F. L. J. Sixma, Rec. Trav. Chim. des Pays-Bas **82**, 1123 (1963).

Preferred:
    log $k = 11.9 - 45.8/\theta$. Rate constants are reliable.

Comments: Estimated Arrhenius parameters are preferred (see section II–4.0). Replacement of a methyl group by an ethyl group at the β-carbon position seems to produce a slight rate acceleration.

Experimental

[1] Rates obtained from G.L.C. analysis. See comments on *t*-butyl acetate.

Reaction: 2-Methoxyethyl ethanoate (β-methoxyethyl acetate)

$$CH_3COOCH_2CH_2OCH_3 \text{ (I)} \longrightarrow CH_3COOH \text{ (II)} + CH_2{=}CHOCH_3 \text{ (III)}$$

	I	II	III
$\Delta H^\circ_{f(298)}$	-135.4	-103.7	-25.1
$S^\circ_{(298)}$	109.3	67.6	71.1
$C^\circ_{p(298)}$	35.1	16.0	18.8

$\Delta S^\circ = 29.4$ g/mole
$\Delta H^\circ = 6.6$ kcal/mole
$\Delta C^\circ_p = -0.3$ g/mole

log A	E	log k_T (760)	Conditions	System	Surface	References
11.96	47.8	(-1.76)	725–810 °K	flow		[1] J. C. Scheer, E. C. Kooyman, and F. L. J. Sixma, Rec. Trav. Chim. des Pays-Bas, **82**, 1123 (1963).

Preferred:

log $k = 12.2 - 48.6/\theta$. Rate constants are reliable.
log $A_{est} = 12.2$ and is preferred (see section II–4.0).

Comments: The calculated Arrhenius A-factor is the same as that for *n*-butyl acetate.

Experimental

[1] Rates by G.L.C. analysis. See comments on *t*-butyl acetate.

Reaction: 2-Ethoxyethyl ethanoate (β-ethanoxyethyl acetate)

$$CH_3COOCH_2CH_2OC_2H_5 \text{ (I)} \longrightarrow CH_3COOH \text{ (II)} + CH_2\!\!=\!\!CHOC_2H_5 \text{ (III)}$$

	I	II	III
$\Delta H^\circ_{f(298)}$	-143.9	-103.7	-33.6
$S^\circ_{(298)}$	119.8	67.6	81.6
$C^\circ_{p(298)}$	40.1	16.0	23.8

$\Delta S^\circ = 29.4$ g/mole
$\Delta H^\circ = 6.6$ kcal/mole
$\Delta C^\circ_p = -0.3$ g/mole

log A	E	log k_T (760)	Conditions	System	Surface	References
12.09	47.9	(-1.67)	725–810 °K	flow		[1] J. C. Scheer, E. C. Kooyman, and F. L. J. Sixma, Rec. Trav. Chim. des Pays-Bas **82**, 1123 (1963).

Preferred:
  log $k = 12.09 - 47.9/\theta$.
  log $A_{est} = 12.2$ (see section II–4.0).

Comments: Rate constant should be similar to that for 2-methoxyethyl ethanoate.

Experimental

[1] Rates based on G.L.C. analysis. See comments on t-butyl acetate.

Reaction: 2-Arylethyl ethanoates (*meta-* or *para*-substituted 2-phenylethyl acetates)

$$X\!-\!\varnothing CH_2CH_2OCOCH_3 \text{ (I)} \longrightarrow X\!-\!\varnothing CH\!=\!CH_2 \text{ (II)} + CH_3COOH \text{ (III)}$$

	I (X=H)	II (X=H)	III
$\Delta H^\circ_{f(298)}$	-75.3	35.4	-103.7
$S^\circ_{(298)}$	120	82.5	67.6
$\Delta S^\circ_{p(298)}$	45.6	29.6	16.0

$\Delta S^\circ = 30.1$ g/mole
$\Delta H^\circ = 9.0$ kcal/mole
$\Delta C^\circ_p = 0$ g/mole

log A	E	log k_T (*380*)	Conditions	System	(X-substituents)	References
12.37	45.4	-2.82	343–409 °C	static	H	[1] R. Taylor, G. G.
12.27	44.8		344–409 °C		*m*-Cl	Smith, and W. H.
12.38	45.4		341–409 °C		*p*-Me	Wetzel, J. Am. Chem
12.46	45.9		343–405 °C		*p*-MeO	Soc. **84**, 4817 (1962).

Preferred:
  2-arylethyl acetate: log $k = 12.37 - 45.4/\theta$.

Comments: Transition state estimates of A for all compounds above gives log $A_{est} = 12.2$ (see section II–4.0)

Experimental

  [1] Rates were obtained from ΔP and initial slopes. These compounds fit a Hammett $\rho - \sigma^+$ plot (H. C. Brown and Y. Okamoto, J. Am. Chem. Soc. **80**, 4979 (1958)), giving a ρ factor of about 0.3. This ρ is numerically smaller than that obtained for the 1-arylethyl acetates, suggesting that substituents in the 2-aryl ring affect the rates of decomposition less than substituents in the 1-aryl ring.

Reaction: Isopropyl ethanoate (isopropyl acetate)

$$CH_3COOCH(CH_3)_2 \text{ (I)} \longrightarrow CH_3CH\text{=}CH_2 \text{ (II)} + CH_3COOH \text{ (III)}$$

	I	II	III
$\Delta H^\circ_{f(298)}$	-111.2	4.8	-103.7
$S^\circ_{(298)}$	96.5	63.6	67.6
$C^\circ_{p(298)}$	32.7	15.3	16.0

$\Delta S^\circ = 34.7$ g/mole
$\Delta H^\circ = 12.3$ kcal/mole
$\Delta C^\circ_p = -1.4$ g/mole

log A	E	log k_T (610)	Conditions	System	Surface	References
13.0	45.0	(-3.12)	715–801 °K 10.3–22.8 torr	flow		[1] A. T. Blades, Can. J. Chem. **32**, 366 (1954).
13.4	46.34	(-3.20)	586–635 °K 152–189 torr	static		[2] E. U. Emovan, Allan Maccoll, J. Chem. Soc. 335 (1962).
13.38	46.6	(-3.25)	650–710 °K	flow		[3] J. C. Scheer, E. C. Kooyman, and F. L. J. Sixma, Rec. Trav. Chim. des Pays-Bas **82**, 1123 (1963).

Preferred:
   log $k = 13.0 - 45.0/\theta$.

Comments: All studies agree within experimental error.
   log $A_{est} \simeq 12.9$ (see section II–4.0).

Experimental

[1] Toluene carrier technique. Rate by acid titration. No bibenzyl in products taken as evidence for the molecular nature of the elimination.

[2] Rate by ΔP. Stoichiometry confirmed by G.L.C. analysis.

[3] Rates by G.L.C. analysis. See comments on t-butyl acetate.

Reaction: *sec*-Butyl ethanoate (*sec*-butyl acetate)

$$CH_3COOCH(CH_3)CH_2CH_3 \text{ (I)}$$

$$\xrightarrow{a} cis\ CH_3CH{=}CHCH_3 \text{ (II)} + CH_3COOH \text{ (V)}$$
$$\xrightarrow{b} trans\ CH_3CH{=}CHCH_3 \text{ (III)} + CH_3COOH$$
$$\xrightarrow{c} CH_2{=}CHCH_2CH_3 \text{ (IV)} + CH_3COOH$$

	I	II	III	IV	V
$\Delta H^\circ_{f(298)}$	-115.4	-1.7	-2.7	0	-103.7
$S^\circ_{(298)}$	105.9	72.1	70.9	73.6	67.6
$C^\circ_{p(298)}$	38.2	18.9	21.0	20.5	16.0

b
$\Delta S^\circ = 35.3$ g/mole
$\Delta H^\circ = 11.7$ kcal/mole
$\Delta C^\circ_p = -1.7$ g/mole

Path	log A	E	log k_T (600)	Conditions	System	Surface	References
total	13.3	46.6	(-3.67)	576–632 °K 126–341 torr	static	none	[1] E. U. Emovan and A. Maccoll, J. Chem. Soc. **335** (1962).
total	14.15	48.6	(-3.58)	650–710 °K	flow		[2] J. C. Scheer, E. C. Kooyman, and F. L. J. Sixma, Rec Trav. Chim. des Pays-Bas **82**, 1123 (1963).

Preferred:
Estimated: log $k = 13.3 - 46.6/\theta$.
log $A_{\text{1-butene}} = 12.6$
log $A_{\text{2-butene}} = 12.4$ (see section II–4.0).

Experimental

[1] Rate by ΔP. Olefin analysis by G.L.C. indicating ~ 57 percent 1-butene, (*trans/cis*) 2-butenes $\simeq 0.64$. Wall conditioning was essential. Stoichiometry confirmed by titration of acid.

[2] Rates by G.L.C. Olefin product ratio was: 1-butene/2-butene $= 1.32$ or about 57 percent but-1-ene. See comments on *t*-butyl acetate.

Reaction: 1-Methyl-3-butenyl ethanoate

$$CH_3COOCH(CH_3)CH_2CH{=}CH_2 \text{ (I)} \xrightarrow{\ a\ } CH_2{=}CHCH_2CH{=}CH_2 \text{(II)} + CH_3COOH \text{ (IV)}$$

$$\xrightarrow{\ b\ } cis \text{ and } trans \ CH_2{=}CH{-}CH{=}CH{-}CH_3 \text{ (III)} + CH_3COOH$$

	I	II	III (cis)	III (trans)	IV
$\Delta H^\circ_{f(298)}$	−90.4	25.2	19.6	18.7	−103.7
$S^\circ_{(298)}$	113.7	79.7	76.4	76.4	67.6
$C^\circ_{p(298)}$	40.9	25.1	22.7	24.9	16.0

a

$\Delta S^\circ = 33.6$ g/mole
$\Delta H^\circ = 11.9$ kcal/mole
$\Delta C^\circ_p = 0.2$ g/mole

Path	log A	E	log k_T (600)	Conditions	System	Surface	References
$a+b$	13.0	44.41	−3.17	564–628 °K 82–245 torr	static	<5% (conditioned)	[1] A. Maccoll, J. Chem. Soc. 227 (1964).

Preferred: log $k = 13.0{-}44.4/\theta$
  Estimated: log $A = 12.6$
    log $A_b = 12.4$ (see section II–4.0).

Experimental

[1] Rates by ΔP. $(P_f/P_i) \sim 1.68 \rightarrow 1.88$ taken as an indication of olefin polymerization. G.L.C. analysis on olefin gave (*trans*/*cis*) $\sim 7/3$ and (1,4-pentadiene/1,3-pentadiene) $\simeq$ ½. The latter ratio changed (increased) with time after completion of the reaction indicating polymerization of the 1,3 diolefin.

Reaction: 1-Methylbutyl ethanoate (2-pentyl acetate)

$$\xrightarrow{\;a\;} CH_3COOH + (cis \text{ and } trans)\ CH_3CH{=}CHCH_2CH_3 \text{ (II)}$$

$$CH_3COOCH(CH_3)C_3H_7 \text{ (I)}$$

$$\xrightarrow{\;b\;} CH_3COOH \text{ (IV)} + CH_2{=}CH(CH_2)_2CH_3 \text{ (III)}$$

	I	II (cis)	III	IV
$\Delta H^\circ_{f(298)}$	-120.4	-6.7	-4.9	-103.7
$S^\circ_{p(298)}$	115.3	82.8	82.8	67.6
$C^\circ_{p(298)}$	43.7	24.2	26.2	16.0

b
$\Delta S^\circ = 35.1$ g/mole
$\Delta H^\circ = 11.8$ kcal/mole
$\Delta C^\circ = -1.5$ g/mole

Path	log A	E	log k_T (684)	Conditions	System	Surface	References
$a+b$	12.73	43.7	-1.21	650–710 °K	flow		[1] J. C. Scheer, E. C. Kooyman, and F. L. J. Sixma, Rec. Trav. Chim. des Pays-Bas **82**, 1123 (1963).

Preferred:
   log $k = 12.7 - 43.7/\theta$

Comments: Estimated: log $A_{(a)} = 12.35$
               log $A_{(b)} = 12.6$ (see section II–4.0).

Experimental

[1] See *t*-butyl acetate. The observed olefin product ratio was: (1-ene/2-ene) $\simeq 1.2$, or about 55 percent pent-1-ene.

Reaction: 1-Ethylpropyl ethanoate (3-pentyl acetate)

$$CH_3COOCH(C_2H_5)_2 \text{ (I)} \longrightarrow CH_3COOH \text{ (II)} + CH_3CH=CHCH_2CH_3 \text{ (III)} \text{ (cis or trans)}$$

	I	II	(trans) III
$\Delta H^\circ_{f(298)}$	−119.5	−103.7	−7.6
$S^\circ_{(298)}$	115.3	67.6	81.4
$C^\circ_{p(298)}$	43.7	16.0	25.9

trans
$\Delta S^\circ = $ 33.7 g/mole
$\Delta H^\circ = $ 8.2 kcal/mole
$\Delta C^\circ_p = -1.8$ g/mole

log A	E	log k_T (684)	Conditions	System	Surface	References
13.09	44.7	−1.20	650–710 °K	flow	————	[1] J. C. Scheer, E. C. Kooyman, and F. L. J. Sixma, Rec. Trav. Chim. des Pays-Bas **82**, 1123 (1963).

Preferred:
log $k = 13.09 - 44.7/\theta$
log $A_{est} = 12.9$ (see section II–4.0).

Experimental

[1] (see *t*-butyl acetate.) Rates based on G.L.C. analysis.

Reaction: Cyclohexyl ethanoate (cyclohexyl acetate)

$$CH_3COO—\hexagon\ (I) \longrightarrow CH_3COOH\ (II) + \hexagon\ (III)$$

	I	II	III
$\Delta H^\circ_{f(298)}$	-116.3	-103.7	-1.7
$S^\circ_{(298)}$	105.6	67.6	74.3
$C^\circ_{p(298)}$	40.7	16.0	25.3

$\Delta S^\circ = 36.3$ g/mole
$\Delta H^\circ = 10.9$ kcal/mole
$\Delta C^\circ_p = 0.6$ g/mole

log A	E	log k_T (700)	Conditions	System	Surface	References
11.56	40.3	-1.01	623–773 °K 7–70 torr	flow		[1] M. Kraus, N. Vavruska, and V. Băzant, Collection Czechoslov. Chem. Commun. **22**, 484 (1957).

Preferred:
    log $k = 13.0 - 44.9/\theta$. Rate constants are reliable.

Comments: The A-factor reported seems about an order of magnitude too low. Estimated parameters are preferred (see section II–4.0).

Experimental

[1] Rates by chemical analysis on cyclohexene.

Reaction: 1,2-Dimethylbutyl ethanoate (α,β-dimethyl-n-butyl acetate)

$$CH_3COOCH(CH_3)CH(CH_3)C_2H_5 \text{ (I)} \xrightarrow{\;a\;} CH_2{=}CHCH(CH_3)CH_2CH_3 \text{ (II)} + CH_3COOH$$

$$\xrightarrow{\;b\;} cis \text{ and } trans\text{-}CH_3CH{=}C(CH_3)C_2H_5 \text{ (III)} + CH_3COOH \text{ (IV)}$$

	I	II	III	IV
$\Delta H^\circ_{f(298)}$	-126.0	-11.0	-14.8	-103.7
$S^\circ_{(298)}$	122	90.1	91.0	67.6
$C^\circ_{p(298)}$	49.0	32.4	30.3	16.0

a

$\Delta S^\circ = 35.7$ g/mole
$\Delta H^\circ = 11.3$ kcal/mole
$\Delta C^\circ_p = -0.6$ g/mole

log A	E	log k_T (684)	Conditions	System	Surface	References
12.60	43.2	-1.21	650–710 °K	flow		[1] J. C. Scheer, E. C. Kooyman, and F. L. J. Sixma, Rec. Trav. Chim. des Pays-Bas **82**, 1123 (1963).

Preferred:
    log $k = 12.6$–$43.2/\theta$.

Estimated: log $A_{(a)} = 12.6$
        log $A_{(b)} = 12.0$ (see section II–4.0).

Experimental

[1] Rates based on G.L.C. analysis. Isomer ratio: $\left(\dfrac{\text{1-ene}}{\text{2-enes}}\right) \simeq 3.2$, or about 76 percent 3-methyl-1-pentene.

Reaction: 1-Isopropyl-2-methylpropyl ethanoate (α-isopropyl β-methyl-n-propyl acetate)

$$\begin{array}{c} \quad CH(CH_3)_2 \\ \quad \diagup \\ CH_3COOCH \qquad (I) \longrightarrow CH_3COOH \ (II) + (CH_3)_2C\!\!=\!\!CHCH(CH_3)_2 \ (III) \\ \quad \diagdown \\ \quad CH(CH_3)_2 \end{array}$$

	I	II	III
$\Delta H^\circ_{f(298)}$	-132.0	-103.7	-22.6
$S^\circ_{(298)}$	128.7	67.6	95.3
$C^\circ_{p(298)}$	54.3	16.0	38.6

$\Delta S^\circ = 34.2$ g/mole
$\Delta H^\circ = 5.7$ kcal/mole
$\Delta C^\circ_p = 0.3$ g/mole

log A	E	log k_T (684)	Conditions	System	Surface	References
12.84	44.7	-1.43	650–710 °K	flow		[1] J. C. Scheer, E. C. Kooyman, and F. L. J. Sixma, Rec. Trav. Chim. des Pays-Bas **82** 1123 (1963).

Preferred:
   log $k = 12.84$–$44.7/\theta$.
   log $A_{\text{est}} = 12.3$ (see section II–4.0).

Experimental

[1] Rates based on G.L.C. analysis (see t-butyl acetate).

Reaction: 1-Methylhexyl ethanoate (2-heptyl acetate)

$$CH_3COOCH(CH_3)(CH_2)_4CH_3 \text{ (I)} \xrightarrow{(a)} CH_3COOH + CH_2{=}CH(CH_2)_4CH_3 \text{ (II)}$$

$$\xrightarrow{(b)} CH_3COOH \text{ (IV)} + cis \text{ and } trans \ CH_3CH{=}CH(CH_2)_3CH_3 \text{ (III)}$$

	I	II	III *cis*	IV
$\Delta H^\circ_{f(298)}$	-130.5	-14.8	-16.6	-103.7
$S^\circ_{(298)}$	134.1	101.6	101.6	67.6
$C^\circ_{p(298)}$	54.7	37.2	35.2	16.0

a

$\Delta S^\circ = 35.1$ g/mole
$\Delta H^\circ = 12.0$ kcal/mole
$\Delta C^\circ_p = -1.5$ g/mole

Path	log A	E	log k_T (684)	Conditions	System	Surface	References
$a+b$	13.32	45.3	-1.15	650–710 °K	flow		[1] J. C. Scheer, E. C. Kooyman, and F. L. J. Sixma, Rec. Trav. Chim. des Pays-Bas **82**, 1123 (1963).

Preferred:
log $k = 12.73 - 43.7/\theta$. .
Estimated: log $A_{(a)} = 12.6$
log $A_{(b)} = 12.3$ (see section II–4.0).

Comments: Arrhenius parameters seem slightly high although the rate constant agrees well with 2-pentyl acetate as one would expect. The 2-pentyl actate parameters are preferred.

Experimental

[1] Rates and analysis by G.L.C. Isomer ratios: $\left(\dfrac{\text{1-heptene}}{\text{2-heptene}}\right) = 1.2$, or 58 percent 1-heptene. (See comments on -butyl acetate.)

Reaction: 1-Ethylpentyl ethanoate (3-heptyl acetate)

$$CH_3COOCH(C_2H_5)C_4H_9 \text{ (I)} \quad\begin{array}{c}\xrightarrow{(a)}\end{array}\quad CH_3COOH \text{ (IV)} + CH_3CH{=}CH(CH_2)_3CH_3 \text{ (II) } (cis, trans)$$

$$\xrightarrow{(b)} CH_3COOH + CH_3CH_2CH{=}CH(CH_2)_2CH_3 \text{ (III) } (cis, trans)$$

	I	II cis	III $trans$	IV
$\Delta H^\circ_{f(298)}$	-129.5	-16.6	-17.6	-103.7
$S^\circ_{(298)}$	134.1	101.6	100.6	67.6
$C^\circ_{p(298)}$	54.7	35.2	36.5	16.0

a, cis

$\Delta S^\circ = 35.1$ g/mole
$\Delta H^\circ = 9.2$ kcal/mole
$\Delta C^\circ_p = -3.5$ g/mole

log A	E	log k_T (684)	Conditions	System	Surface	References
13.93	46.9	-1.05	650–710 °K	flow		[1] J. C. Scheer, E. C. Kooyman, and F. L. J. Sixma, Rec. Trav. Chim des Pays-Bas **82**, 1123 (1963).

Preferred:
  log $k = 12.75 - 43.2/\theta$.
  Estimated: log $A_a = 12.35$
       log $A_b = 12.3$ (see section II–4.0).

Comments: Arrhenius parameters are certainly high.

Experimental

[1] Rates based on G.L.C. analysis. Isomer ratio $\left(\dfrac{3\text{-heptene}}{2\text{-heptene}}\right) \simeq 1.0$ or close to 50 percent 3-heptene (See t-but acetate).

178

Reaction: 1-Propylbutyl ethanoate (4-heptyl acetate)

$$CH_3COOCH(C_3H_7)_2 \text{ (I)} \longrightarrow CH_3COOH \text{ (III)} + \textit{cis and trans } CH_3CH_2CH{=}CH(CH_2)_2CH_3 \text{ (II)}$$

	I	II *cis*	II *trans*	III
$\Delta H^{\circ}_{f(298)}$	-129.4	-16.6	-17.6	-103.7
$S^{\circ}_{(298)}$	134.1	101.6	100.6	67.6
$C^{\circ}_{p(298)}$	54.7	35.2	36.5	16.0

trans

$\Delta S^{\circ} = 34.1$ g/mole
$\Delta H^{\circ} = 8.1$ kcal/mole
$\Delta C^{\circ}_p = -3.2$ g/mole

log A	E	log k_T (684)	Conditions	System	Surface	References
13.32	44.9	-1.01	650–710 °K	flow		[1] J. C. Scheer, E. C. Kooyman, and F. L. J. Sixma, Rec. Trav. Chim. des Pays-Bas **82**, 1123 (1963).

Preferred:

$\log k = 12.6 - 42.7/\theta$.

Comments: Arrhenius parameters are slightly high although the rate constant seems reasonable (compare with 3-heptyl acetate). The transition state estimate of log A is preferred (see section II–4.0).

Experimental

[1] Rates based on G.L.C. analysis. (See *t*-butyl acetate.)

179

Reaction: Endo-2-acetoxybornane (bornyl acetate)

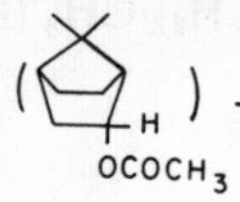

$\longrightarrow$ CH$_3$COOH + 1,7,7 trimethyltricyclo [2,2,1,0^{2,6}] heptane (22.3%)

2-bornene (61%)

camphene (14.8%)

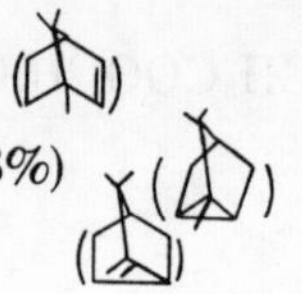

$$\left.\begin{array}{c} \Delta H^\circ_{f(298)} \\ S^\circ_{(298)} \\ C^\circ_{p(298)} \end{array}\right\} \text{see exo-2-acetoxybornane (isobornyl acetate)}$$

$\Delta S^\circ =$
$\Delta H^\circ =$
$\Delta C^\circ_p =$

log A	E	log k_T (620)	Conditions	System	Surface	References
11.99	45.3	-3.96	603–643 °K 132–242 torr	static	none	[1] E. U. Emovan, J. Chem. Soc. **(B)**, 588 (1966).

Preferred: (See exo-2-acetoxybornane, isobornyl acetate).

Experimental

[1] Products were analyzed by G.L.C. Rates were followed by ΔP measurements and the rate constants were based on titration of the acetic acid product. Added cyclohexene reduced the reaction rates by about 3–8 percent. Products were 61 percent bornylene, 23.3 percent tricyclene, and 14.8 percent camphene. See discussion for bornyl chloride

Reaction: Exo-2-acetoxybornane (isobornyl acetate)

$$(I) \longrightarrow CH_3COOH \ (II) + \begin{array}{l} (20\%) \text{ bornylene} \\ (32\%) \text{ tricyclene} \\ (48\%) \text{ camphene} \end{array} \quad (III)$$

	I	II	III
$\Delta H^\circ_{f(298)}$	-117.9	-103.7	0.2
$S^\circ_{(298)}$	125.4	67.6	92
$C^\circ_{p(298)}$	———	16.0	———

$\Delta S^\circ = 34.2$ g/mole
$\Delta H^\circ = 14.4$ kcal/mole
$\Delta C_p^\circ =$ ———

log A	E	log k_T (595.)	Conditions	System	Surface	References
11.64	42.02	-4.06	571–618 °K 104–216 torr	static	none	[1] E. U. Emovan, J. Chem. Soc. **(B)**, 588 (1966).

Preferred:
   Suspect.

Comments: The rate constant parameters appear much too low. A transition state calculation gives log $A_{est} = 13.0$ for the bornylene product. Heterogeneous effects may well be appreciable.

Experimental

   [1] Products were analyzed by G.L.C. and were about 20 percent bornylene, 32 percent tricyclene, and 48 percent camphene. Rate constants were obtained from titration of the acetic acid. Added cyclohexene lowered the rates by about 3 percent. See discussion for bornyl chloride.

Reaction: 1-Methyl-2-methoxyethyl ethanoate (1-methoxy-2-propyl acetate)

$$CH_3COOCH(CH_3)CH_2OCH_3 \ (I) \xrightarrow{\ a\ } CH_2{=}CHCH_2OCH_3 \ (II) + CH_3COOH \ (IV)$$

$$\xrightarrow{\ b\ } (cis \text{ and } trans) \ CH_3CH{=}CHOCH_3 \ (III) + CH_3COOH$$

	I	II	III cis	IV
$\Delta H^{\circ}_{f(298)}$	-142.4	-27.2	-31.4	-103.7
$S^{\circ}_{(298)}$	115.7	82.8	82.2	67.6
$C^{\circ}_{p(298)}$	41.1	23.7	22.3	16.0

a
$\Delta S^{\circ} = 34.7$ g/mole
$\Delta H^{\circ} = 11.5$ kcal/mole
$\Delta C^{\circ}_p = -1.4$ g/mole

log A	E	log k_T (648)	Conditions	System	Surface	References
13.05	46.6	-2.67	650–710 °K	flow		[1] J. C. Scheer, E. C. Kooyman, and F. L. J. Sixma, Rec. Trav. Chim. des Pays-Bas **82** 1123 (1963).

Preferred:
  log $k = 13.05{-}46.6/\theta$.
  Estimated: log $A_{(a)} = 12.6$
      log $A_{(b)} = 12.35$ (see section II–4.0).

Experimental

[1] Rates based on G.L.C. analysis. Isomer product ratios (unrecorrected for detector sensitivity) were

$$\left(\frac{\text{3-methoxypropene}}{\text{1-methoxypropene}}\right) \simeq 1.35 \text{ or about 58 percent 3-methoxypropene.}$$

Reaction: 1-Methyl-3-oxobutyl ethanoate

$$CH_3COOCH(CH_3)CH_2COCH_3 \text{ (I)} \longrightarrow CH_3COCH\!=\!CHCH_3 \text{ (II)} + CH_3COOH \text{ (III)}$$

	I	II	III
$\Delta H^\circ_{f(298)}$	-148.1	-41.4	-103.7
$S^\circ_{(298)}$	120.8	86.2	67.6
$C^\circ_{p(298)}$	45.0	26.8	16.0

$S^\circ = 33.0$ g/mole
$H^\circ = 3.0$ kcal/mole
$C^\circ_p = -2.2$ g/mole

$\log A$	E	$\log k_T$ (550)	Conditions	System	Surface	References
11.88	37.4	-3.00	529–570 °K 89–302 torr	static	< 5% (conditioned)	[1] A. Maccoll, J. Chem. Soc., 227 (1964).

Preferred:
   $\log k = 11.9 - 37.4/\theta.$

Comments: Transition state calculation (assuming appreciable enolic form (or conjugation) of the ketone in the transition state) gives $\log A_{\text{est}} \simeq 11.6$ (see section II–4.0).

Experimental

[1] Rates from ΔP. Analysis of olefin product by G.L.C. The low A-factor and exclusive secondary-H-elimination observed were taken as evidence for polarity enhancement in the transition state by the β-carbonyl group.*

*This conclusion is supported by the lowered A-factor (*i.e.*, relative to isopropyl acetate) and suggests the loss of one additional internal rotation in the transition state. The activation energy lowering of about 7 kcal/mole relative to *sec*-butyl acetate also supports the highly polar transition state proposed.

Reaction: 1-Phenylethyl ethanoate (α-phenylethyl acetate)

$$CH_3COOCHCH_3(\emptyset)(I) \longrightarrow \emptyset CH{=}CH_2 (II) + CH_3COOH (III)$$

	I	II	III
$\Delta H^\circ_{f(298)}$	-79.1	35.4	-103.7
$S^\circ_{(298)}$	116.5	82.5	67.6
$C^\circ_{p(298)}$	45.4	29.6	16.0

$\Delta S^\circ = 33.6$ g/mole
$\Delta H^\circ = 10.8$ kcal/mole
$\Delta C^\circ_p = 0.2$ g/mole

log A	E	log k_T (610)	Conditions	System	Surface	References
12.83	43.7	-2.83	585–641 °K 6–200 torr	static	————	[1] R. Taylor, G. G. Smith, W. H. Wetzel, J. Am. Chem. Soc. **84,** 4817 (1962).

Preferred:
  log $k = 12.8 - 43.7/\theta$.

Comments: Assuming no benzyl resonance in the transition state gives log $A_{est} = 12.6$. This is consistent with the fact that the activation energy has not been lowered appreciably from the ethyl acetate value by the phenyl substitution. The actual lowering is more comparable to that of alkyl substitution. (See ethyl and isopropyl acetate.)

Experimental

[1] Rates by ΔP. Identification of products by I.R.

Reaction: 1-Arylethyl ethanoates (1-phenylethyl derivatives)

$$\underset{\overset{|}{\underset{X-C_6H_4CHOCCH_3}{}}}{CH_3}\ \ \underset{\overset{||}{O}}{}\ \longrightarrow\ X-C_6H_4CH{=\!=}CH_2 + CH_3COOH$$

$$\Delta H^\circ_{f(298)}$$

$$S^\circ_{(298)}$$

$$C^\circ_{p(298)}$$

$\Delta S^\circ =$
$\Delta H^\circ =$
$\Delta C^\circ_p =$

log A	E	log k_T (600)	Conditions	X (substituents)	Surface	References
12.52	41.7	−2.80	571–617	p-MeO		[1] R. Taylor, G. G.
13.08	43.4	−2.34	588–638	3,4-C$_7$H$_6$*		Smith, and W. H.
13.03	43.6	−2.59	581–640	o-MeO		Wetzel, J. Am. Chem.
13.17	44.1	−2.50	591–642	o-Ph		Soc. **84,** 4817 (1962).
12.92	43.4	−2.50	589–642	p-t-Bu		
12.97	43.6	−2.52	587–642	o-Me		
12.80	43.2	−2.68	585–637	p-Me		
12.94	43.8	−2.63	587–642	2,3-C$_4$H$_4$**		
12.98	43.8	−2.59	587–642	p-Ø		
12.80	43.6	−2.33	603–657	p-F		
12.83	43.7	−2.33	603–658	m-Ø		
12.84	44.1	−2.96	585–637	p-Cl		
12.92	44.6	−2.56	603–658	p-I		
12.87	44.1	−2.43	603–659	p-Br		
12.84	44.4	−2.57	604–658	m-I		
12.83	44.4	−2.70	603–653	m-Cl		
12.89	44.7	−2.62	599–657	m-F		
12.69	44.5	−2.75	601–657	m-NO$_2$		

Preferred:
Reliable as reported.

Comments: The heterolytic nature of the transition state in the ester eliminations is strongly supported by these results. Transition state estimate of A for all the above compounds gives log $A_{est} = 12.7$ (see section II–4.0).

Experimental

[1] All rates obtained from ΔP measurements. *Meta* and *para* compounds were found to fit a linear free energy ρ-σ^+ plot very well, giving $\rho = -0.66$ at 600 °K, where the σ^+ constants are those given by H. C. Brown and Y. Okamoto, J. Am. Chem. Soc. **80,** 4979 (1958).

---

*1-(2-Fluorenyl)-ethyl acetate
**1-(α-Naphthyl)-ethyl acetate

Reaction: 1,2-Diarylethyl ethanoates (*meta* or *para* substituted 1,2-diphenylethyl acetates)

$$\left(\begin{array}{c}X\\ \bigcirc\end{array}\!\!-\!\!\underset{\underset{\underset{O}{\parallel}}{\underset{O-C-CH_3}{|}}}{CH-CH_2}\!\!-\!\!\bigcirc\!\!-Y\right)(I)\longrightarrow\left(\begin{array}{c}X\\ \bigcirc\end{array}\!\!-\!\!CH=CH\!\!-\!\!\bigcirc\!\!-y\right)(II)+\ CH_3COOH\ (III)$$

	I $X=Y=H$	*trans* II $X=Y=H$	III
$\Delta H^\circ_{f(298)}$	-56.6	58.6	-103.7
$S^\circ_{(298)}$	146.2	108.3	67.6
$C^\circ_{p(298)}$	64.4	48.9	16.0

$X=Y=H$
$\Delta S^\circ = 29.7$ g/mole
$\Delta H^\circ = 11.5$ kcal/mole
$\Delta C^\circ_p = 0.5$ g/mole

log A	E	log k_T (600)	Conditions	System	Substituents X	Y	References
13.05	43.3	-2.72	575–625 °K	static	H	H	[1] G. G. Smith, F. D.
12.56	40.6	-2.23	15–150 torr		*p*-MeO	*p*-Cl	Bagley, and R.
12.54	40.6	-2.25			*p*-MeO	H	Taylor, J. Am. Chem.
12.67	41.7	-2.52			*p*-Me	H	Soc. **83**, 3647 (1961).
13.07	43.3	-2.70			H	*m*-Cl	
13.06	43.3	-2.71			H	*p*-Cl	
12.94	43.0	-2.72			H	*p*-Me	
12.58	42.1	-2.76			H	*p*-MeO	
12.56	42.1	-2.78			*p*-Cl	H	
12.87	43.2	-2.87			*p*-Cl	*p*-MeO	
12.96	43.8	-3.00			*m*-Cl	H	

Preferred:
   Reliable as reported.

Comments: For 1,2-diarylethyl acetate: log $k = 13.05-43.3/\theta$. Transition state calculation of A for all the above compounds gives log $A_{est} = 12.4$ (see section II–4.0).

Experimental

   [1] Rates by ΔP. Analysis by N.M.R. Various linear free energy σ-ρ plots were made to show: (a) that substituents in the 1-aryl ring have a greater effect on the rate than do substituents in the 2-aryl ring; (b) that the rate is most strongly influenced by electron release to the (C—O) bond. Effects on the bonds being broken (i.e., the C—O and β—(C—H)) are not on those being formed (i.e., the olefinic double bond and the acid O—H) are most important in determining the rate of elimination.

Reaction: 1-Methyl-2-chloroethyl ethanoate (1-chloroisopropyl acetate)

$$CH_3COOCH(CH_3)CH_2Cl \ (I) \quad \xrightarrow{\ a\ } CH_3COOH \ (IV) + cis \text{ and } trans \ ClCH{=}CHCH_3 \ (II)$$

$$\xrightarrow{\ b\ } CH_3COOH + CH_2{=}CHCH_2Cl \ (III)$$

	I	II	III	IV
$\Delta H^\circ_{f(298)}$	-116.5	0.7	-1.3	-103.7
$S^\circ_{(298)}$	106.1	71.5	73.2	67.6
$C^\circ_{p(298)}$	35.7	18.3	18.7	16.0

	a	b	
$\Delta S^\circ =$	33.0	34.7	g/mole
$\Delta H^\circ =$	13.5	11.5	kcal/mole
$\Delta C^\circ_p =$	-1.4	-1.0	g/mole

log A	E	log k_T (684)	Conditions	System	Surface	References
11.90	43.8	-2.09	650–710 °K	flow		[1] J. C. Scheer, E. C. Kooyman, and F. L. J. Sixma, Rec. Trav. Chim. des Pays-Bas **82**, 1123 (1963).

Preferred:
   $\log k = 12.8 - 46.6/\theta$.

Comments: Estimated parameters are preferred (see section II–4.0).
   Estimated: $\log A_a = 12.6$
   $\log A_b = 12.6$.

Experimental

[1] Rates based on G.L.C. analysis. Ratio of isomers: $\left(\dfrac{\text{1-chloropropene}}{\text{3-chloropropene}}\right) \simeq 1.15$ or 53.4 percent 1-chloropropene (see t-butyl acetate).

Reaction: 1-Methyl-2-dimethylaminoethyl ethonoate (2-dimethylamino-1-methyl ethyl ethanoate β-dimethylamino-2-propylacetate)

$$CH_3COOCH(CH_3)CH_2N(CH_3)_2 \text{ (I)} \xrightarrow{\quad a \quad} CH_3COOH \text{ (IV)} + CH_2{=}CHCH_2N(CH_3)_2 \text{ (II)}$$
$$\xrightarrow{\quad b \quad} CH_3COOH + cis, trans\ CH_3CH{=}CHN(CH_3)_2 \text{ (III)}$$

	I	II	III *trans*	IV
$\Delta H^\circ_{f(298)}$	-101.9	13.5	11.6	-103.7
$S^\circ_{(298)}$	120.7	88.5	87.2	67.6
$C^\circ_{p(298)}$	47.2	30.1	32.6	16.0

a

$\Delta S^\circ = 35.4$ g/mole

$\Delta H^\circ = 11.7$ kcal/mole

$\Delta C^\circ_p = -1.1$ g/mole

log A	E	log k_T (684)	Conditions	System	Surface	References
12.14	42.2	-1.34	650–710 °K	flow		[1] J. C. Scheer, E. C. Kooyman, and F. L. J. Sixma, Rec. Trav. Chim. des Pays-Bas **82** 1123 (1963).

Preferred:

log $k = 12.8{-}44.2/\theta$.

Comments: Estimated parameters are preferred. Rate constants are taken as reliable.

Estimated: log $A_a = 12.6$

log $A_b = 12.35$ (see section II–4.0).

Experimental

[1] Rates based on G.L.C. analysis (see *t*-butyl acetate). No isomer product ratios reported.

Reaction: *t*-Butyl ethanoate (*t*-butyl acetate)

$$CH_3COOC(CH_3)_3 \text{ (I)} \longrightarrow CH_2 = C(CH_3)_2 \text{ (II)} + CH_3COOH \text{ (III)}$$

	I	II	III
$\Delta H^\circ_{f(298)}$	-120.1	-4.0	-103.7
$S^\circ_{(298)}$	100.3	70.2	67.6
$C^\circ_{p(298)}$	38.4	21.3	16.0

$\Delta S^\circ = 37.9$ g/mole
$\Delta H^\circ = 12.4$ kcal/mole
$\Delta C^\circ_p = -1.1$ g/mole

log A	E	log k_T (545)	Conditions	System	Surface	References
13.34	40.5	-2.90	516–576 °K 5–275 torr	static	none on conditioned surfaces.	[1] C. E. Rudi, Jr., and P. Fugassi, J. Phys. Chem. **52**, 357 (1948).
13.15	40.0	-2.89	514–564 °K 135–172 torr	static	————	[2] E. U. Emovan and A. Maccoll, J. Chem. Soc., 335 (1962).
14.52	43.6	-2.96	560–610 °K	flow		[3] J. C. Scheer, E. C. Kooyman, and F. L. J. Sixma, Rec. Trav. Chim. des Pays-Bas **82**, 1123 (1963).

Preferred:
   log $k = 13.15 - 40.0/\theta$
   log $A_{est} = 13.1$ (see section II–4.0).

Experimental

[1] Rates by titration of the acid.
[2] Rates by ΔP. Stoichiometry confirmed by G.L.C.
[3] Analysis by G.L.C. The experimental method for determining the reaction rates was unusual. The temperature of the reactor was allowed to cool slowly during which time 10–14 runs were performed. The first runs constituted ~ 80 percent decomposition in the period of contact, while at the lower temperatures, ~ 20 percent decomposition occurred. Constant-temperature conditions for the runs were assumed. The Arrhenius parameters obtained by the method would not be expected to be accurate to better than a power of 10 in A and about 3–4 kcal/mole in E. See for example *n*-propyl ethanoate, *n*-butyl ethanoate, and 2-methylbutyl ethanoate.

Reaction: *t*-Pentyl ethanoate (*t*-amyl acetate)

$$CH_3COOC(CH_3)_2CH_2CH_3 \ (I) \xrightarrow{\ a\ } CH_2{=}C(CH_3)CH_2CH_3 \ (II) + CH_3COOH \ (IV)$$

$$\xrightarrow{\ b\ } (CH_3)_2C{=}CHCH_3 \ (III) + CH_3COOH$$

	I	II	III	IV
$\Delta H^\circ_{f(298)}$	-123.5	-8.6	-10.2	-103.7
$S^\circ_{(298)}$	112.0	81.9	81.1	67.6
$C^\circ_{p(298)}$	43.9	26.7	25.1	16.0

	a	b
$\Delta S^\circ =$	37.5	36.7 g/mole
$\Delta H^\circ =$	11.2	9.6 kcal/mole
$\Delta C^\circ_p =$	-1.2	-2.8 g/mole

Path	log A	E	log k_T (530)	Conditions	System	Surface	References
$a+b$	13.43	40.26	-3.17	501–562 °K 127–284 torr	static	none. (conditioned)	[1] E. U. Emovan, A. Maccoll, J. Chem. 335 (1962).
$a+b$	15.17	44.3	-3.06	560–610 °K	flow		[2] J. C. Scheer, E. C. Kooyman, F. L. J. Sixma, Rec. Trav. Chim. des Pays-Ba **82**, 1123 (1963).

Preferred:

log $k = 13.4 - 40.3/\theta$
Estimated: log $A_{1\text{-ene}} = 12.95$
log $A_{2\text{-ene}} = 12.5$ (see section II–4.0).

Experimental

[1] Rates by ΔP. Olefin product analysis by G.L.C. gave 75 percent 2-methylbut-1-ene. Stoichiometry confirmed b acid titration.

[2] Rates by G.L.C. Product olefin ratio: $\frac{\text{but-1-ene}}{\text{but-2-ene}} = 3.2$ or about 75 percent 2-methylbut-1-ene (see comments fo

t-butyl ethanoate).

Reaction: 1,1,2-Trimethylpropyl ethanoate (2,3-dimethyl-2-butyl acetate)

$$CH_3COOC(CH_3)_2CH(CH_3)_2 \text{ (I)} \xrightarrow{\quad a \quad} (CH_3)_2C{=}C(CH_3)_2 \text{ (II)} + CH_3COOH \text{ (IV)}$$
$$\xrightarrow{\quad b \quad} CH_2{=}C(CH_3)CH(CH_3)_2 \text{ (III)} + CH_3COOH$$

	I	II	III	IV
$\Delta H^\circ_{f(298)}$	-128.9	-15.9	-14.8	-103.7
$S^\circ_{(298)}$	118.6	86.7	87.4	67.6
$C^\circ_{p(298)}$	49.1	30.5	32.5	16.0

a
$\Delta S^\circ = 35.7$ g/mole
$\Delta H^\circ = 9.3$ kcal/mole
$\Delta C^\circ_p = -2.6$ g/mole

log A	E	log k_T (584)	Conditions	System	Surface	References
14.22	41.3	-1.24	560–610 °K	flow		[1] J. C. Scheer, E. C. Kooyman, and F. L. J. Sixma, Rec. Trav. Chim. des Pays-Bas **82**, 1123 (1963).

Preferred:
   log $k = 13.1 - 37.9/\theta$.

Comments: Arrhenius parameters are certainly too high. Estimated parameters are preferred.
   Estimated: log $A_a = 12.0$
          log $A_b = 12.9$ (see section II–4.0).

Experimental

[1] Rates based on G.L.C. analysis (see comments on *t*-butyl ethanoate). Product isomer ratio: $\dfrac{\text{path } b}{\text{path } a} \simeq \dfrac{9}{1}$, or 90 percent 2,3-dimethyl-1-butene.

Reaction: 1,1-Dimethylbutyl ethanoate (1,1-dimethyl butyl acetate)

$$CH_3COOC(CH_3)_2CH_2CH_2CH_3 \ (I) \ \xrightarrow{\ a\ } CH_2{=}C(CH_3)CH_2CH_2CH_3 \ (II) + CH_3COOH \ (IV)$$
$$\xrightarrow{\ b\ } (CH_3)_2C{=}CHCH_2CH_3 \ (III) + CH_3COOH$$

	I	II	III	IV
$\Delta H^\circ_{f(298)}$	-128.5	-13.6	-15.2	-103.7
$S^\circ_{(298)}$	121.3	91.3	89.3	67.6
$C^\circ_{p(298)}$	49.4	32.2	30.2	16.0

a

$\Delta S^\circ = 37.6$ g/mole
$\Delta H^\circ = 11.2$ kcal/mole
$\Delta C^\circ_p = -1.2$ g/mole

log A	E	log k_T (584)	Conditions	System	Surface	References
13.85	40.6	-1.33	560–610 °K	flow		[1] J. C. Scheer, E. C. Kooyman, and F. L. J. Sixma, Rec. Trav. Chim. des Pays-Bas **82** 1123 (1963).

Preferred:
  log $k = 13.17 - 38.8/\theta$.
  Estimated: log $A_a = 12.9$
       log $A_b = 12.35$.

Comments: Estimated parameters are preferred (see section II–4.0).

Experimental

[1] Rates based on G.L.C. analysis (see *t*-butyl ethanoate). Olefin product ratio: (path *a*/path *b*) $\simeq 2.57$ or about 72 percent 2-methyl pent-1-ene.

Reaction: 1-Ethyl-1-methylpropyl ethanoate (1-ethyl-1-methylpropyl acetate)

$$\xrightarrow{a} cis \text{ and } trans \ CH_3CH=C(CH_3)CH_2CH_3 \ (II) + CH_3COOH$$

$$CH_3COOC(C_2H_5)_2CH_3 \ (I)$$

$$\xrightarrow{b} CH_2=C(CH_2CH_3)_2 \ (III) + CH_3COOH \ (IV)$$

	I	II *trans*	III	IV
$\Delta H^\circ_{f(298)}$	-127.0	-14.3	-13.6	-103.7
$S^\circ_{(298)}$	121.3	89.6	90.3	67.6
$C^\circ_{p(298)}$	49.4	30.3	31.8	16.0

a

$\Delta S^\circ = 35.9$ g/mole
$\Delta H^\circ = 9.0$ kcal/mole
$\Delta C^\circ_p = -3.1$ g/mole

Path	log A	E	log k_T (584)	Conditions	System	Surface	References
$a+b$	14.60	42.4	-1.27	560–610 °K	flow		[1] J. C. Scheer, E. C. Kooyman, and F. L. J. Sixma, Rec. Trav. Chim. des Pays-Bas **82**, 1123 (1963).

Preferred:
  log $k = 13.14 - 38.5/\theta$.

Comments: Arrhenius parameters are certainly too high. Estimated parameters are preferred.
  Estimated: log $A_{(a)} = 12.7$
       log $A_{(b)} = 12.6$ (see section II–4.0).

Experimental

[1] Rates based on G.L.C. analysis (see *t*-butyl ethanoate). Isomer product ratios: $\left(\dfrac{\text{path } b}{\text{path } a}\right) = 1.8$ or about 65 percent 2-ethylbut-1-ene.

Reaction: 1-Methylcyclohexyl ethanoate (1-methylcyclohexyl acetate)

	I	II	III	IV
$\Delta H^\circ_{f(298)}$	-124.4	-9.6	-8.2	-103.7
$S^\circ_{(298)}$	111.6	81.4	79.8	67.6
$C^\circ_{p(298)}$	46.4	30.4	28.5	16.0

a

$\Delta S^\circ = 37.4$ g/mole
$\Delta H^\circ = 11.1$ kcal/mole
$\Delta C^\circ_p = 0$ g/mole

log A	E	log k_T (584)	Conditions	System	Surface	References
15.36	45.2	-1.54	560–610 °K	flow		[1] J. C. Scheer, E. C. Kooyman, and F. L. J. Sixma, Rec. Trav. Chim. des Pays-Bas, **82**, 1123 (1963).

Preferred:
   log $k = 13.1 - 39.1/\theta$.

Comments: Arrhenius parameters are certainly high. Transition state estimates are preferred. Note that the isomer ratio is close to that predicted by the calculated A-factors.
Estimated: log $A_{(a)} = 13.0$
         log $A_{(b)} = 12.6$ (see section II–4.0).

Experimental

[1] Rates based on G.L.C. analysis (see *t*-butyl ethanoate). Product ratios: $\left(\dfrac{\text{path } a}{\text{path } b}\right) \simeq 3$ or about 75 percent 1-methyl cyclohexene.
   (See discussion of cyclohexyl acetate.)

Reaction: *t*-Butyl chloroethanoate (*t*-butyl chloroacetate)

$$CH_2ClCOOC(CH_3)_3 \text{ (I)} \longrightarrow CH_2{=}C(CH_3)_2 \text{ (II)} + CH_2ClCOOH \text{ (III)}$$

	I	II	III
$\Delta H^\circ_{f(298)}$	-124	-4.0	-106.5
$S^\circ_{(298)}$	109.7	70.2	76.6
$C^\circ_{p(298)}$	41.3	21.3	18.9

$\Delta S^\circ = 37.1$ g/mole
$\Delta H^\circ = 13.5$ kcal/mole
$\Delta C^\circ_p = -1.1$ g/mole

log A	E	log k_T (515)	Conditions	System	Surface	References
13.09	38.11	-3.08	489–540 °K 100–300 torr	static	(none when conditioned)	[1] E. U. Emovan, J. Chem. Soc., 1246 (1963).

Preferred:
  log $k = 13.09 - 38.11/\theta$
  log $A_{est} = 13.1$ (see section II–4.0).

Experimental

[1] Rates by ΔP. Stoichiometry confirmed by G.L.C. No effect on rate by added cyclohexene.

Reaction: *t*-Butyl dichloroethanoate (*t*-butyl dichloroacetate)

$$CHCl_2COOC(CH_3)_3 \ (I) \longrightarrow CH_2{=}C(CH_3)_2 \ (II) + CHCl_2COOH \ (III)$$

	I	II	III
$\Delta H^\circ_{f(298)}$	-125.7	-4.0	-109.3
$S^\circ_{(298)}$	115.8	70.2	83.4
$C^\circ_{p(298)}$	44.2	21.3	21.8

$\Delta S^\circ = 37.8$ g/mole
$\Delta H^\circ = 12.4$ kcal/mole
$\Delta C^\circ_p = -1.1$ g/mole

log A	E	log k_T (500)	Conditions	System	Surface	References
12.77	36.09	-3.00	487–520 °K 100–300 torr	static	(none when conditioned)	[1] E. U. Emovan, J. Chem. Soc., 1246 (1963).

Preferred:
  log $k = 12.8 - 36.1/\theta$
  log $A_{est} = 13.1$ (see section II–4.0).

Experimental

[1] Rates by ΔP. Stoichiometry confirmed by G.L.C. No effect on rate by added cyclohexene.

Reaction: Ethyl propanoate (ethyl propionate)

$$CH_3CH_2COOC_2H_5 \text{ (I)} \longrightarrow C_2H_4 \text{ (II)} + CH_3CH_2COOH \text{ (III)}$$

	I	II	III
$\Delta H^\circ_{f(298)}$	-108.7	12.5	-109.8
$S^\circ_{(298)}$	99.1	52.5	76.6
$C^\circ_{p(298)}$	33.4	10.4	22.7

$\Delta S^\circ = 30.0$ g/mole
$\Delta H^\circ = 11.4$ kcal/mole
$\Delta C^\circ_p = -0.3$ g/mole

log A	E	log k_T (830)	Conditions	System	Surface	References
12.72	48.5	-0.05	778–875 °K 15–20 torr	flow	——————	[1] A. T. Blades and P. W. Gilderson, Can. J. Chem. **38**, 1412 (1960).

Preferred:
   log $k = 12.72 - 48.5/\theta$.
   log $A_{est} \simeq 12.6$ (see section II–4.0).

Experimental

[1] Rates by titration of the acid. Toluene carrier technique. Copyrolysis of ethylpropionate with ethyl d_5 acetate and comparison of the ethyl d_5 acetate to the unlabeled acetate gave an activation energy difference between propionate and acetate esters of 20 ± 65 cal/mole.

Reaction: *t*-Butyl propanoate (*t*-butyl propionate)

$$CH_3CH_2COOC(CH_3)_3 \text{ (I)} \longrightarrow CH_2{=}C(CH_3)_2 \text{ (II)} + CH_3CH_2COOH \text{ (III)}$$

	I	II	III
$\Delta H^\circ_{f(298)}$	-125.4	-4.0	-109
$S^\circ_{(298)}$	109.2	70.2	76.6
$C^\circ_{p(298)}$	45.1	21.3	22.7

$\Delta S^\circ = 37.6$ g/mole
$\Delta H^\circ = 12.4$ kcal/mole
$\Delta C^\circ_p = -1.1$ g/mole

log *A*	*E*	log k_T (540)	Conditions	System	Surface	References
12.79	39.16	-3.06	513–569 °K 17–125 torr	static	none	[1] E. Warrick, P. Fugassi, J. Phys. Chem. **52**, 1314 (1948).

Preferred:
   $\log k = 12.8 - 39.2/\theta$.

Comments: Note that *t*-butyl acetate and *t*-butyl propionate have identical rates of reaction, as do ethyl acetate and ethyl propionate.
   $\log A_{est} = 13.1$ (see section II–4.0).

Experimental

[1] Rates by ΔP and titration of the acid. Surface conditioning required.

Reaction: Ethyl 2,2-dimethylpropanoate (ethyl trimethylacetate)

$$(CH_3)_3CCOOC_2H_5 \ (I) \longrightarrow (CH_3)_3CCOOH \ (II) + C_2H_4 \ (III)$$

	I	II	III
$\Delta H^\circ_{f(298)}$	-121.4	-121.7	12.5
$S^\circ_{(298)}$	109.2	86.7	52.5
$C^\circ_{p(298)}$	43.5	32.8	10.4

$\Delta S^\circ = \ \ 30.0$ g/mole
$\Delta H^\circ = \ \ 12.2$ kcal/mole
$\Delta C^\circ_p = -0.3$ g/mole

log A	E	log k_T	Conditions	System	Surface	References
11.24	44.00		635–694 °K 30–370 torr	static	none	[1] J. T. D. Cross and V. R. Stimson, Aus. J. Chem. **20**, 177 (1967).

Preferred:
  $\log k = 12.6 - 48.1/\theta.$
  $\log A_{est} = 12.6.$

Comments: The parameters are somewhat low in terms of transition state theory. They should correspond closely to those of ethylacetate. The authors checked their experimental conditions by studying also the ethylacetate decomposition. Although rate constants were not greatly different from those of previous workers, an Arrhenius plot of their data gives $E \simeq 44.2$ kcal/mole. Since the accepted value is 48.0 kcal/mole, one may conclude that the reported parameters of the ethyl trimethylacetate reaction entail a similar systematic error.

Experimental

Rates were followed manometrically and agreed well with product analysis (i.e., titration of the acid). Identification of ethylene by G.L.C. Rates were unaffected by additions of cyclohexene and isobutene.

Reaction: (−)Menthyl benzoate

	I	II	III	IV
$\Delta H^\circ_{f(298)}$	−115.6	−24.8	−26.1	−79.1
$S^\circ_{(298)}$	155.8	106.2	106.4	87.8
$C^\circ_{p(298)}$	75.5	46.5	47.0	28.7

	a	b
$\Delta S^\circ =$	38.2	38.4 g/mole
$\Delta H^\circ =$	11.7	10.4 kcal/mole
$\Delta C^\circ_p =$	−0.3	0.2 g/mole

Path	log A	E	log k_T (595)	Conditions	System	Surface	References
a + b	11.0	38.1	−2.99	569–615 °K 2.7–27.1 torr	static	none	[1] D. H. R. Barton, A. J Head, and R. J. Williams, J. Chem. Soc. 1715 (1953).

Preferred:
  Rate constants are reliable; however, the parameters look low (see below).

Comments: Transition state estimates give for (+)p-menth-2-ene: log $A \simeq 13.0$; (+)p-menth-3-ene: log $A = 12.7$. The authors were unwilling to attach error limits to the reported Arrhenius parameters due to the difficulty of working with a compound of such low volatility. The calculated parameters are therefore preferred.

Experimental

  [1] Rates by benzoic acid titration. Flow experiments were also made which gave slightly faster rates but the same activation energy. p-menth-2-ene $\simeq$ const $\simeq$ 35 percent from 628 $\longrightarrow$ 647 °K in flow experiments.

Reaction: Methylene diethanoate (methylene diacetate)

$$CH_2(OCOCH_3)_2 \text{ (I)} \longrightarrow CH_2O \text{ (II)} + (CH_3CO)_2O \text{ (III)}$$

	I	II	III
$\Delta H^\circ_{f(298)}$	-187.3	-27.7	-141.8
$S^\circ_{(298)}$	111.9	52.3	93.2
$C^\circ_{p(298)}$	36.6	8.5	27.6

$\Delta S^\circ = 33.6$ g/mole
$\Delta H^\circ = 17.8$ kcal/mole
$\Delta C^\circ_p = -0.5$ g/mole

log A	E	log k_T (535)	Conditions	System	Surface	References
9.23	33.0	-4.25	493–578 °K ~ 0.4–4 atm	static	none	[1] C. C. Coffin and W. B. Beazley, Can. J. Res. **B15,** 229 (1937).

Preferred:
  log $k = 10.7 - 36.4/\theta$. Rate constants around $\bar{T}$ are probably reliable.

Comments: At 550 °K, the equilibrium constant for methylene diacetate from the thermodynamics is about $K_{eq} = 1.9$ atm. Thus equilibrium would be reached at about 80 percent decomposition (at $P_t \sim 1$ atm). This agrees with observation. Arrhenius parameters seem too low. Prefer calculated values of log $A = 10.7$.

Experimental

[1] Rates were followed manometrically and also by titration of the hydrolised anhydride. The reactions were believed to proceed to an equilibrium condition since, with increasing initial pressures (i.e., up to 5 atm), the reaction rate decreased. Because of a secondary reaction, the equilibrium condition could not be reached.

Reaction: Ethylidene diethanoate (ethylidene diacetate)

$$CH_3CH \Big\langle \begin{matrix} OCOCH_3 \\ OCOCH_3 \end{matrix} \;(I) \longrightarrow CH_3COOCOCH_3\;(II) + CH_3CH_3CHO\;(III)$$

	I	II	III
$\Delta H^\circ_{f(298)}$	-196.2	-141.8	-39.8
$S^\circ_{(298)}$	120	93.2	63.2
$C^\circ_{p(298)}$	42.1	27.6	13.1

$\Delta S^\circ = 36.4$ g/mole
$\Delta H^\circ = 14.6$ kcal/mole
$\Delta C^\circ_p = -1.4$ g/mole

log A	E	log k_T (520)	Conditions	System	Surface	References
10.27	32.9	-3.55	493–541 °K 110–460 torr	static	none	[1] C. C. Coffin, Can. J. Res. **5**, 636 (1931).

Preferred:
   log $k = 10.27 - 32.9/\theta$.

Comments: It has been noted (S. W. Benson, Foundations of Chemical Kinetics, McGraw-Hill Book Co., New York (1960), p. 257) that the acetic anhydride product decomposes at a rate of about an order of magnitude faster than the diacetate at the temperatures of study. This interesting observation can be resolved by examining the thermodynamics of the acetic anhydride decomposition. The estimated equilibrium constant for decomposition at 520 °K is $K_{eq} \simeq 0.8$ torr.

For initial diacetate pressures of 300 torr, this K_{eq} gives about 5 percent decomposition of the anhydride at 100 percent reaction.

The errors in K_{eq} would accommodate about a factor of three in these estimates. The stoichiometry and products observed are therefore consistent with the thermodynamics. The limited temperature range of study will allow errors of 2–3 kcal/mole in E and about one log unit in A. Thus the very low A-factor reported for this reaction (and the other diacetates) definitely rules out the four-center transition states that have been proposed (see S. W. Benson, loc. cit. and A. F. Trotman-Dickenson, Gas Kinetics, Butterworths Scientific Publications, London (1955), p. 130). Two transition states are consistent with the large negative entropy of activation. An eight-center transition state

leading to $CH_3COOH + CH_2CO + CH_3CHO$, followed by rapid equilibration of ketene and acetic acid to form the anhydride; and a six-center transition state

(Continued)

proceeding directly to the observed products. The latter seems the more reasonable because of the insensitivity of the reaction activation energies to varied R group substitution. A-factor estimates for both transition states are about a factor of ten higher than observed. At the higher temperatures the formation of vinyl acetate undoubtedly arises from the "normal" six-center elimination where the reactive β-hydrogens are those of the central alkyl group.

Experimental

[1] Rates were by ΔP with an assumed stoichiometry of $P_f/P_o \simeq 2.0$. Chemical analysis showed the major products to be acetic anhydride and CH_3CHO in a 1/1 ratio. At higher temperatures acetic acid and vinyl acetate were also formed.

Reaction: Butylidene diethanoate (butylidene diacetate)

$$CH_3(CH_2)_2CH \begin{matrix} OCOCH_3 \\ \\ OCOCH_3 \end{matrix} \text{(I)} \longrightarrow CH_3(CH_2)_2CHO \text{ (II)} + CH_3COOCOCH_3 \text{ (III)}$$

	I	II	III
$\Delta H^\circ_{f(298)}$	-205.4	-50.9	-141.8
$S^\circ_{(298)}$	138.8	82.0	93.2
$C^\circ_{p(298)}$	53.1	24.0	27.6

$\Delta S^\circ = 36.4$ g/mole
$\Delta H^\circ = 12.7$ kcal/mole
$\Delta C^\circ_p = -1.5$ g/mole

log A	E	log k_T (510)	Conditions	System	Surface	References
10.47	32.9	-3.63	484–538 °K 50–560 torr	static	none	[1] C. C. Coffin, Can. J. Res. **6**, 417 (1932).

Preferred:
Probably reliable. See comments on ethylidene diacetate.
log $A_{est} = 11.0$.

Experimental

[1] Rates by ΔP. Quantitative analysis of products. Brown film deposits observed presumed to be polymer formation. Always somewhat less than 100 percent of anhydride obtained.

Reaction: Heptylidene diethanoate (heptylidene diacetate)

$$CH_3(CH_2)_5CH(OCOCH_3)_2 \text{ (I)} \longrightarrow (CH_3CO)_2O \text{ (II)} + CH_3(CH_2)_5CHO \text{ (III)}$$

	I	II	III
$\Delta H^\circ_{f(298)}$	-220	-141.8	-65.9
$S^\circ_{(298)}$	167	93.2	109.8
$C^\circ_{p(298)}$	69.6	27.6	41.8

$\Delta S^\circ = 36.0$ g/mole
$\Delta H^\circ = 12.3$ kcal/mole
$\Delta C^\circ_p = 0.1$ g/mole

log A	E	log k_T (520)	Conditions	System	Surface	References
10.48	33.0	-3.37	473–573 °K 88–185 torr	static	none	[1] C. C. Coffin, J. R. Dacey, and N. A. D. Parlee, Can. J. Res. **B15**, 247 (1937).

Preferred:

Probably reliable. See comments on ethylidene diacetate.
log $A_{est} = 11.0$.

Experimental

[1] Rates were obtained from pressure measurements.

Reaction: Crotonylidene diethanoate (crotonylidene diacetate)

$$CH_3CH{=}CHCH\ (O\overset{\overset{O}{\|}}{C}CH_3)_2\ (I) \longrightarrow cis{-}CH_3CH{=}CHCHO\ (II) + (CH_3CO)_2O\ (III)$$

	I	II	III
$\Delta H^\circ_{f(298)}$	-178.5	-25.5	-141.8
$S^\circ_{(298)}$	135.5	75.5	93.2
$C^\circ_{p(298)}$	50.4	22.9	27.6

$\Delta S^\circ = 33.2$ g/mole
$\Delta H^\circ = 11.2$ kcal/mole
$\Delta C^\circ_p = \ 0.1$ g/mole

log A	E	log k_T (510)	Conditions	System	Surface	References
11.1	33.0	-3.00	492–533 °K 44–420 torr	static		[1] J. R. Dacey and C. C. Coffin, Can. J. Res. **B15**, 260 (1937).

Preferred:
Probably reliable. log $A_{est} = 11.0$. See comments on ethylidene diacetate.

Experimental

[1] Rates obtained manometrically.

Reaction: Furfurylidene diethanoate (furfurylidene diacetate)

	I	II	III
$\Delta H^\circ_{f(298)}$	-187	-38.5	-141.8
$S^\circ_{(298)}$	129.8	70.7	93.2
$C^\circ_{p(298)}$	53	21.9	27.6

$\Delta S^\circ = 34.1$ g/mole
$\Delta H^\circ = 6.7$ kcal/mole
$\Delta C^\circ_p = -3.5$ g/mole

log A	E	log k_T (520)	Conditions	System	Surface	References
11.1	33.0	-2.75	493–553 °K ~ 20–175 torr	static		[1] J. R. Dacey and C. C. Coffin, Can. J. Res. **B15,** 260 (1937).

Preferred:
    Probably reliable.
    log $A_{est} = 11.0$. See comments on ethylidene diacetate.

Experimental

[1] Rates followed manometrically.

Reaction: 2,2,2-Trichloro-1-ethylidene diethanoate

$$CCl_3CH(OCOCH_3)_2 \ (I) \longrightarrow CCl_3CHO \ (II) + (CH_3CO)_2O \ (III)$$

	I	II	III
$\Delta H^\circ_{f(298)}$	-203	-49.7	-141.8
$S^\circ_{(298)}$	140.0	83.2	93.2
$C^\circ_{p(298)}$	52.2	23.2	27.6

$\Delta S^\circ = 36.4$ g/mole
$\Delta H^\circ = 11.3$ kcal/mole
$\Delta C^\circ_p = -1.4$ g/mole

log A	E	log k_T (530)	Conditions	System	Surface	References
10.11	33.0	-3.52	503–563 °K 50–360 torr	static		[1] N. A. D. Parlee, J. R. Dacey, and C. C. Coffin, Can. J. Res. **B15,** 254 (1937).

Preferred:

Probably reliable.

log $A_{est} = 11.0$. See comments on ethylidene diacetate.

Experimental

[1] Rates were obtained from ΔP measurements. Solution decompositions gave rate constants in agreement with the gas phase results.

Reaction: Methylene dipropanoate

$$CH_2(OCOC_2H_5)_2 \ (I) \longrightarrow CH_2O \ (II) + (C_2H_5CO)_2O \ (III)$$

	I	II	III
$\Delta H_{f(298)}^\circ$	-197.3	-27.7	-151.8
$S_{(298)}^\circ$	131.1	52.3	112.4
$C_{p(298)}^\circ$	49.0	8.5	40.0

$\Delta S^\circ = 33.6$ g/mole
$\Delta H^\circ = 17.8$ kcal/mole
$\Delta C_p^\circ = -0.5$ g/mole

log A	E	log k_T (535)	Conditions	System	Surface	References
9.23	33.0	-4.25	493–578 °K 0.4–4 atm	static	none	[1] C. C. Coffin and W. B. Beazley, Can. J. Res. **B15,** 229 (1937).

Preferred:
   log $k = 10.7 - 36.4/\theta$.

Comments: See methylene and ethylidene diacetates.

Experimental

   [1] See methylene diacetate.

Reaction: Ethylidene dipropanoate

$$\begin{array}{c} \text{OCOC}_2\text{H}_5 \\ \diagup \\ \text{CH}_3\text{CH} \qquad\qquad (I) \longrightarrow \text{CH}_3\text{CHO (II)} + \text{C}_2\text{H}_5\text{COOCOC}_2\text{H}_5 \text{ (III)} \\ \diagdown \\ \text{OCOC}_2\text{H}_5 \end{array}$$

	I	II	III
$\Delta H^\circ_{f(298)}$	-206.7	-39.8	-152.3
$S^\circ_{(298)}$	137.9	63.2	111.0
$C^\circ_{p(298)}$	55.5	13.1	40.8

$\Delta S^\circ = 36.3$ g/mole
$\Delta H^\circ = 14.6$ kcal/mole
$\Delta C^\circ_p = -1.6$ g/mole

log A	E	log k_T (510)	Conditions	System	Surface	Reference
10.4	32.9	-3.63	484–538 °K	static	none	[1] C. C. Coffin, Can. J. Res. **6**, 417 (1932).

Preferred:
Probably reliable. log $A_{\text{est}} = 11.0$.

Comments: See ethylidene diacetate.

Experimental

[1] Rates by ΔP. Products analyzed chemically. Always less than 100 percent yield of the anhydride was realized. Stoichiometry of $1 \to 2$ within ± 2 percent fairly well established.

Reaction: Methylene dibutanoate

$$CH_2(OCO(CH_2)_2CH_3)_2 \text{ (I)} \longrightarrow CH_2O \text{ (II)} + (C_3H_7CO)_2O \text{ (III)}$$

	I	II	III
$\Delta H^\circ_{f(298)}$	-207.3	-27.7	-161.8
$S^\circ_{(298)}$	149.9	52.3	131.2
$C^\circ_{p(298)}$	60.0	8.5	51.0

$\Delta S^\circ = 33.6$ g/mole
$\Delta H^\circ = 17.8$ kcal/mole
$\Delta C^\circ_p = -0.5$ g/mole

log A	E	log k_T (535)	Conditions	System	Surface	References
9.23	33.0	-4.25	493–578 °K 0.4–4 atm	static	none	[1] C. C. Coffin and W. B. Beazley, Can. J. Res. **B15,** 229 (1937).

Preferred:
   $\log k = 10.7 - 36.4/\theta.$.

Comments: See methylene and ethylidene diacetates.

Experimental

[1] See methylene diacetate.

Reaction: Ethylidene dibutanoate

$$CH_3CH(OCO(CH_2)_2CH_3)_2 \; (I) \longrightarrow (CH_3(CH_2)_2CO)_2O \; (II) + CH_3CHO \; (III)$$

	I	II	III
$\Delta H^\circ_{f(298)}$	-216.7	-162.3	-39.8
$S^\circ_{(298)}$	156.7	130	63.2
$C^\circ_{p(298)}$	66.5	52	13.1

$S^\circ = 36.5$ g/mole
$H^\circ = 14.6$ kcal/mole
$C^\circ_p = -1.4$ g/mole

log A	E	log k_T (520)	Conditions	System	Surface	References
10.25	33.0	-3.60	473–573 °K 27–103 torr ($\sim$ 100 torr)	static	none	[1] C. C. Coffin, J. R. Dacey, and N. A. D. Parlee, Can. J. Res. **B15,** 247 (1937).

Preferred:
   Probably reliable.
   log $A_{est} = 11.0$.

Comments: See ethylidene diacetate.

Experimental

[1] Rates obtained from ΔP measurements.

Reaction: 2,2,2-Trichloro-1-ethylidene dibutanoate

$$CCl_3CH(OCO(CH_2)_2CH_3)_2 \text{ (I)} \longrightarrow CCl_3CHO \text{ (II)} + (CH_3(CH_2)_2CO)_2O \text{ (III)}$$

	I	II	III
$\Delta H^\circ_{f(298)}$	-223.5	-49.7	-162.3
$S^\circ_{(298)}$	176.7	83.2	130
$C^\circ_{p(298)}$	76.6	23.2	52

$\Delta S^\circ = 36.5$ g/mole
$\Delta H^\circ = 11.5$ kcal/mole
$\Delta C^\circ_p = -1.4$ g/mole

log A	E	log k_T (540)	Conditions	System	Surface	References
10.11	33.0	-3.77	514–563 °K 53–253 torr (~ 200 torr)	static		[1] N. A. D. Parlee, J. R. Dacey, and C. C. Coffin Can. J. Res. **B15**, 254 (1937).

Preferred:
    Probably reliable.
    log $A_{est} = 11.0$.

Comments: See ethylidene diacetate.

Experimental

[1] Rates followed by ΔP. Rate constants in solution (obtained from the titration of the hydrolized anhydric agreed with the gas phase results.

Reaction: Methyl ethyl carbonate

$$CH_3OCOC_2H_5 \text{ (I)} \longrightarrow CO_2 \text{ (II)} + C_2H_4 \text{ (III)} + CH_3OH \text{ (IV)}$$

(with O double-bonded above the first C)

	I	II	III	IV
$\Delta H^\circ_{f(298)}$		−94.1	12.5	−48.1
$S^\circ_{(298)}$		51.1	52.5	57.3
$C^\circ_{p(298)}$		8.9	10.4	10.5

$S° =$
$H° =$
$C_p° =$

log A	E	log k_T (610)	Conditions	System	Surface	References
13.7	46±2	−2.78	573–648 °K 20 torr	static	none	[1] A. S. Gordon and W. P. Norris, J. Phys. Chem. **69**, 3013 (1965).

Preferred:
log k = 12.6−43.0/θ. Rate constants are reliable.

Comments: The Arrhenius parameters are certainly high. Transition state estimate of A gives log A = 12.6, which is supported by the experimental values found for the methyl-1-aryl ethyl carbonates.

Experimental

[1] Analysis by M.S. and G.L.C. Added CO_2 had no effect on the rate.

Reaction: Diethyl carbonate

$$C_2H_5O\overset{\overset{\displaystyle O}{\|}}{C}OC_2H_5 \text{ (I)} \longrightarrow CO_2 \text{ (II)} + C_2H_4 \text{ (III)} + C_2H_5OH \text{ (IV)}$$

	I	II	III	IV
$\Delta H^\circ_{f(298)}$		-94.1	12.5	-56.5
$S^\circ_{(298)}$		51.1	52.5	67.6
$C^\circ_{p(298)}$		8.9	10.4	15.5

$\Delta S^\circ =$
$\Delta H^\circ =$
$\Delta C^\circ_p =$

log A	E	log k_T (610)	Conditions	System	Surface	References
13.9	46	-2.58	573–648 °K	static	none	[1] A. S. Gordon and W. P. Norris, J. Phys. Chem. **69**, 3013 (1965).

Preferred:

log $k = 12.9$–$43.3/\theta$. Rate constants $\bar{T}$ reliable.

Comments: As in the methyl ethyl carbonate decomposition, the Arrhenius parameters are high. A negative entropy of activation is more reasonable. Transition state estimates of A are therefore preferred.

Experimental

[1] Analysis by M.S. and G.L.C. No effect on the rate by CO_2. The unimolecular path probably forms

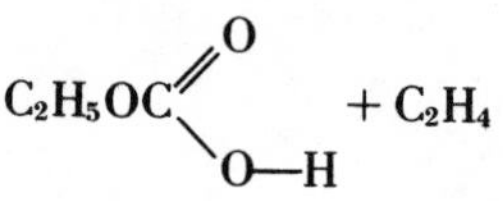

$$C_2H_5OC\overset{\overset{\displaystyle O}{\diagup}}{\diagdown}_{O—H} + C_2H_4$$

as initial products and the semi-carbonate probably rearranges at the wall.

Reaction: *X*-1-phenylethyl methyl carbonates, *X = ortho, meta,* or *para* substitution

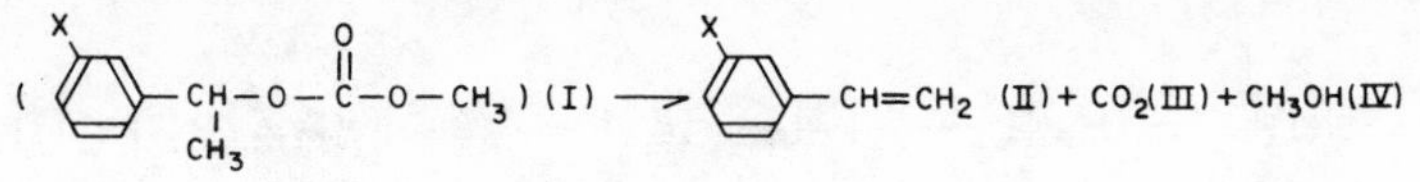

$$(\bigcirc\!\!\!\!\!\!\!\! \overset{X}{} \!\!\!\!\!\!- CH-O-\overset{\overset{O}{\|}}{C}-O-CH_3)\,(I) \longrightarrow \bigcirc\!\!\!\!\!\!\!\! \overset{X}{} \!\!\!\!\!\!- CH=CH_2 \; (II) + CO_2(III) + CH_3OH(IV)$$

	I(X = H)	II(X = H)	III	IV
$\Delta H^\circ_{f(298)}$		35.4	−94.1	−48.1
$S^\circ_{(298)}$		82.5	51.1	57.3
$C^\circ_{p(298)}$		29.6	8.9	10.5

$\Delta S^\circ =$

$\Delta H^c =$

$\Delta C^\circ_p =$

log A	E	log k_T (600)	Conditions	System	(substituent X =)	References
12.33	39.9	−2.20	307–341.4 °C	static	H	[1] G. G. Smith and B. L.
12.71	41.9	−2.55			o—Cl	Yates, J. Org. Chem.
12.66	41.5	−2.46			m—Cl	**30,** 434 (1965).
12.22	38.8	−1.91			p—Me	

Preferred:

All reliable as reported. Transition state calculation of *A* for all compounds gives log $A_{est} = 12.6$ (see section II–4.0).

Experimental

[1] Rates by ΔP. Analysis by G.L.C.

Reaction: Ethanoic anhydride (acetic anhydride)

$$\overset{\overset{\displaystyle O}{\|}}{CH_3C}\overset{\overset{\displaystyle O}{\|}}{OCCH_3}\ (I) \longrightarrow \text{ketene } (CH_2{=}C{=}O)\ (II) + CH_3COOH\ (III)$$

	I	II	III
$\Delta H^\circ_{f(298)}$	-141.8	-14.6	-103.7
$S^\circ_{(298)}$	93.2	57.1	67.6
$C^\circ_{p(298)}$	27.6	11.4	16.0

$\Delta S^\circ = 31.5$ g/mole
$\Delta H^\circ = 23.5$ kcal/mole
$\Delta C^\circ_p = -0.2$ g/mole

log A	E	log k_T (600)	Conditions	System	Surface	References
12.0	34.5	-2.56	553–646 °K (6–13 torr total pressure)	flow	~10%	[1] J. Murawski and M. Szwarc, Trans. Faraday Soc. **47**, 269 (1951).

Preferred:
   log $k = 12.0-34.5/\theta$
   log $A_{est} = 12.6$ (see section II–4.0).

Experimental

[1] Rates based on ketene formation. Stoichiometry confirmed by titration of the acid. Toluene carrier technique. If the lowest temperature points of the data are used, the "best" line for the Arrhenius plot gives log $A_{est} = 12.3$.

Reaction: 4-Hydroxy-4-methyl-2-pentanone

$$\underset{\text{(I)}}{\overset{\text{O} \quad \text{OH}}{\underset{||}{\text{CH}_3\text{CCH}_2\text{C(CH}_3)_2}}} \longrightarrow 2[\overset{\text{O}}{\underset{||}{\text{CH}_3\text{CCH}_3}}] \text{ (II)}$$

	I	II
$\Delta H^\circ_{f(298)}$	-110.2	-51.7
$S^\circ_{(298)}$	104.5	70.5
$C^\circ_{p(298)}$	39.5	17.9

$\Delta S^\circ = 36.5$ g/mole
$\Delta H^\circ = 6.8$ kcal/mole
$\Delta C^\circ_p = -3.7$ g/mole

log A	E	log k_T (510)	Conditions	System	Surface	References
11.63	32.3	-2.21	495–528 °K	static	none	[1] G. G. Smith and B. L. Yates, J. Org. Chem. **30**, 2067 (1965).

Preferred:
   log $k = 11.63 - 32.3/\theta$.

Transition state estimate gives log $A = 11.7$ (see section II–4.0).

Experimental

[1] Rates by ΔP. Analysis by G.L.C., n_r and I.R.

Reaction: 1-Ethoxyethene (ethyl vinyl ether)

$$CH_2{=}CHOCH_2CH_3 \text{ (I)} \longrightarrow C_2H_4 \text{ (II)} + CH_3CHO \text{ (III)}$$

	I	II	III
$\Delta H^\circ_{f(298)}$	-33.6	12.5	-39.8
$S^\circ_{(298)}$	82.6	52.5	63.2
$C^\circ_{p(298)}$	23.8	10.4	13.1

$\Delta S^\circ = 33.1$ g/mole
$\Delta H^\circ = 6.3$ kcal/mole
$\Delta C^\circ_p = -0.3$ g/mole

log A	E	log k_T (750)	Conditions	System	Surface	References
11.43	43.8	-1.30	770–859 °K	flow		[1] A. T. Blades and G. W. Murphy, J. Am. Chem. Soc. **74**, 1039 (1952).
11.60	44.4	-1.31	640–721 °K 66–754 torr	static		[2] S. Wang and C. A. Winkler, Can. J. Res. **21B**, 97 (1943).

Preferred:
   log $k = 11.6$–$44.4/\theta$ (see below).

Comments: The Arrhenius parameters of both studies seem slightly low, particularly when compared to the vinyl isopropyl ether decomposition. The transition state calculation of A gives log $A_{\text{est}} = 12.2$. However both studies are in excellent agreement over a large temperature range, which makes it difficult not to accept the parameters reported.

Experimental

   [1] Toluene carrier technique. Rates based on U.V. analysis for acetaldehyde. Above 810 °K, some free radical split was evident.
   [2] Rates by ΔP and by chemical analysis of the products. Subsequent decomposition of acetaldehyde producing CH_4, C_2H_6, and CO was observed.

Reaction: Isopropoxyethene (vinyl isopropyl ether)

$$CH_2\!=\!CHOCH(CH_3)_2 \ (I) \longrightarrow CH_2\!=\!CHCH_3 \ (II) + CH_3CHO \ (III)$$

	I	II	III
$\Delta H^\circ_{f(298)}$	-41.4	4.9	-39.8
$S^\circ_{(298)}$	88.9	63.8	63.2
$C^\circ_{p(298)}$	29.8	15.3	13.1

$\Delta S^\circ = 38.1$ g/mole
$\Delta H^\circ = 6.5$ kcal/mole
$\Delta C^\circ_p = -1.4$ g/mole

log A	E	log k_T (755)	Conditions	System	Surface	References
12.58	43.56	-0.03	720–794 °K 17.4–21.5 torr	flow	————	[1] A. T. Blades, Can. J. Chem. **31**, 418 (1953).

Preferred:
   log $k = 12.58 - 43.56/\theta$
Transition state estimate of A gives log $A_{est} = 12.5$ (see section II–4.0).

Experimental

[1] Toluene flow technique. Rates based on U.V. analysis for acetaldehyde. Above 843 °K a minor free radical induced decomposition was evident.

Reaction: *n*-Butyl vinyl ether

$$CH_2{=}CHOC_4H_9 \text{ (I)} \longrightarrow CH_3CHO \text{ (II)} + CH_2{=}CHCH_2CH_3 \text{ (III)}$$

	I	II	III
$\Delta H^\circ_{f(298)}$	-43.5	-39.8	0
$S^\circ_{(298)}$	102.2	63.2	73.6
$C^\circ_{p(298)}$	34.8	13.1	20.5

$\Delta S^\circ = 34.6$ g/mole
$\Delta H^\circ = 3.7$ kcal/mole
$\Delta C^\circ_p = 1.2$ g/mole

$\log A$	E	$\log k_T$ (620)	Conditions	System	Surface	References
11.15	42.38	-3.79	590–650 °K 60–345.5 torr (in presence of cyclohexene)	static	None in an aged reaction vessel	[1] T. O. Bamkole and E. U. Emovon, J. Chem. Soc. **B,** 523 (1967).

Preferred:
$\log k = 11.15 - 42.38/\theta$
$\log A_{est} = 11.0$.

Experimental

Products were analyzed by G.L.C. and titrimetric determination of the aldehyde. Rates by ΔP. Stoichiometry was confirmed ($\Delta P = \Delta(CH_3CHO)$). Addition of cyclohexene resulted in a significant rate suppression, suggesting the presence of a chain reaction. Reaction products in the presence of HBr and acetaldehyde were complex, confirming the importance of free radicals in the *uninhibited* system.

2. Cyclic Compound Reactions

Reaction: Cyclopropane

$$C_3H_6 \ (\bigtriangledown) \ (I) \longrightarrow CH_2{=}CHCH_3 \ (II) \ (\diagup\!\!\diagup)$$

	I	II
$\Delta H^\circ_{f(298)}$	12.7	4.8
$S^\circ_{(298)}$	56.8	63.6
$C^\circ_{p(298)}$	13.3	15.3
$C^\circ_{p(700)}$	28.8	28.4

$\Delta S^\circ = \ 6.8$ g/mole
$\Delta H^\circ = -7.9$ kcal/mole
$\Delta C^\circ_p = \ 2.0$ g/mole

log A	E	log k_T (750)	Conditions	System	Surface	References
15.17	65	−3.77	772 ± 29 °K 1.27–76.5 torr	static	none	[1] T. S. Chambers and G. B. Kistiakowsky, J. Am. Chem. Soc. **56**, 399 (1934).
14.89	65.2	−4.11	753 ± 40 °K 10–900 (600)	static		[2] E. S. Corner and R. N. Pease, J. Am. Chem. Soc. **67**, 2067 (1945).
15.45	65.6	−3.67	750 ± 57 °K (30)	static		[3] W. E. Falconer, T. F. Hunter, and A. F. Trotman-Dickenson, J. Chem. Soc. 609 (1961).

Preferred:
   log $k = 15.2 - 65.5/\theta$.

Comments: Transition state estimates for the biradical mechanism are in good agreement with the kinetics.

Mechanism: $\triangle \ \underset{2}{\overset{1}{\rightleftharpoons}} \ \wedge \ \overset{3}{-\!-\!-} \ \diagup\!\!\diagup \ ; \ k_2 \gg k_3$

Estimates give: log $k = \log \left(\dfrac{k_1 k_3}{k_2} \right) = 15.16 - 65.4/\theta$. (See discussion on small ring compounds, section III–4.0, and also 1,2-dideuteriocyclopropane.)

Experimental

   [1] Rate determined by chemical analysis on propylene; k_∞ obtained by extrapolation of k_{uni} versus $1/P$.
   [2] Rate determined by chemical analysis on propylene. Added H_2, C_2H_4, and C_3H_6 had no effect on the rate in the high-pressure region.

   [3] Rate based on G.L.C. analysis. Used the Slater equation (log $p = \dfrac{n}{2} \log T_2/T_1$) to determine k_∞.

Reaction: *Trans*-1,2-dideuterocyclopropane

	I	II	III
$\Delta H^\circ_{f(298)}$	10.9	3.0	10.9
$S^\circ_{(298)}$	59.0	65.0	60.4
$C^\circ_{p(298)}$	13.9	15.9	13.9

	a	b	
$\Delta S^\circ =$	6.0	1.4	g/mole
$\Delta H^\circ =$	−7.9	0	kcal/mole
$\Delta C^\circ_p =$	2.0	0	g/mole

Path	log A	E	log k_T (717)	Conditions	System	Surface	References
a	15.12	65.4	−4.82	723 ± 48 °K 0.01 ⟶ 630 torr (100)	static		[1] E. W. Schlag and B. S. Rabinovitch, J. Am. Chem. Soc. **82**, 5996 (1960).
a	15.20	65.5	−4.77	717 ± 30 °K 0.03 ⟶ 76 torr (56)	static		[2] E. W. Schlag, B. S. Rabinovitich, and K. Wiberg, J. Chem. Phys. **28**, 504 (1958).
b	16.11	65.1	−3.57	(as in [1])			[1]
b	15.7	64.2	−3.87	(as in [2])			[2]

Preferred:
    log $k_a = 15.2 - 65.5/\theta$.
    log $k_b = 15.8 - 64.1/\theta$.

Comments: By the biradical mechanism (see cyclopropane), the rate-determining step for geometric (*trans* ⟶ *cis*) isomerization is ring opening. We estimate log $A_1 =$ log $A_b = 15.8$ (see section III–4.0). Individual rate constants of the mechanism have also been deduced (see discussion on small ring compound reactions). Activation energies for ring closing and 1,2-H-migration from the biradical are estimated to be $E_{2(C_3 \text{ ring close})} = 9.3$ kcal/mole and $E_{3(\text{H-migration})} = 10.7$ kcal/mole respectively.

Experimental

[1] Analysis by G.L.C. Falloff occurred near 200 torr for path (a); $n \simeq 14$. Falloff near 1000 torr for path (b); $n \simeq 14$. Rates were not affected by 0.2 torr of O_2. The shift in falloff with temperature was not consistent with the Slater theory.
[2] Analysis by I.R.

Reaction: Methylcyclopropane

$$\xrightarrow{a} CH_2{=}C(CH_3)_2 \ (II)$$

$$\xrightarrow{b} CH_2{=}CHCH_2CH_3 \ (III)$$

$$\xrightarrow{c} cis \ CH_3CH{=}CHCH_3 \ (IV)$$

$$\xrightarrow{d} trans \ CH_3CH{=}CHCH_3 \ (V)$$

(I)

	I	II	III	IV	V
$\Delta H^\circ_{f(298)}$	5.7	−3.7	0	−1.7	−2.7
$S^\circ_{(298)}$	67.1	70.4	73.6	72.1	70.9
$C^\circ_{p(298)}$	18.5	21.3	20.5	18.9	21.0

a

$\Delta S^\circ = 3.3$ g/mole
$\Delta H^\circ = -9.4$ kcal/mole
$\Delta C^\circ_p = 2.8$ g/mole

Path	log A	E	log k_T (738)	Conditions	System	Surface	References
a	14.62	66.0	−4.93	738 ± 25 °K	static		[1] D. W. Placzek and
b	14.95	64.3	−4.10	0.01–20(10)			B. S. Rabinovitch,
c	14.59	63.9	−4.34				J. Chem. Phys. **69**,
d	15.49	68.1	−4.68				2141 (1965).
a	14.06	64.3	−4.99	(as above)	static		[2] D. W. Setzer and
b	14.14	62.0	−4.22				B. S. Rabinovitch,
c	13.97	61.9	−4.37				J. Am. Chem. Soc.
d	14.32	64.4	−4.76				**86**, 564 (1964).
total	15.45	65.0	−3.80	(as above)	static		[3] J. P. Chesick, J. Am. Chem. Soc. **82**, 3277 (1960).

Preferred:
Rate constant parameters of [1] are preferred.

Comments: The range of values reported in the two studies for any single process are of the order of the experimental errors associated with the data. The agreement between observed Arrhenius parameters and those obtained by transition state estimates for a biradical mechanism similar to that for cyclopropane is therefore good.

Estimates are log $k_a = 14.4 - 65.8/\theta$
log $k_b = 14.7 - 63.0/\theta$
log $k_c = 14.3 - 63.0/\theta$
log $k_d = 14.5 - 63.0/\theta$ (see section III–4.0).

Experimental

[1] and [2] Calculated from the data of [3].
[3] Analysis by G.L.C. ($C_2 + C_3 + C_5$ compounds represented less than 2 percent of products.) Falloff observed near 100 torr. Relative collision efficiencies determined for He, Ar, N_2, CH_4, C_2H_6, and toluene. Pressure and temperature dependencies in the butene isomer product distributions were reported.

Reaction: *cis* or *trans*-1,2-Dideutero-3-methylcyclopropane

$$\left(\begin{array}{c} \text{D} \hspace{2mm} \text{CH}_3 \\ \text{or} \end{array} \text{D} \hspace{2mm} \text{CH}_3 \right)_{(I)}$$

$$\xrightarrow{\ a\ } (\rightangle)_{d2}\ (II) \quad \text{2-methylpropenes}(d_2)$$

$$\xrightarrow{\ b\ } (\diagup\!\!\diagup)_{d2}\ (III) \quad \text{1-butenes}(d_2)$$

$$\xrightarrow{\ c\ } (\diagdown\!\!\diagup)_{d2}\ (IIII) \quad cis\text{-2-butenes}(d_2)$$

$$\xrightarrow{\ d\ } (\diagdown\!\!\diagdown)_{d2}\ (V) \quad trans\text{-2-butenes}(d_2)$$

	I(*cis*)	II	III	IV	V
$\Delta H^\circ_{f(298)}$	3.9	−5.8	−1.8	−3.5	−4.5
$S^\circ_{(298)}$	68.5	71.6	75.0	73.5	72.3
$C^\circ_{p(298)}$	19.1	21.9	21.1	19.5	21.6

a

$\Delta S^\circ = \ 3.1$ g/mole
$\Delta H^\circ = -9.7$ kcal/mole
$\Delta C^\circ_p = \ 2.8$ g/mole

Path	log A	E	log k_T (725)	Conditions	System	Surface	References
a	13.98	64.1	−5.34	725 ± 35 °K (10) torr	static		[1] D. W. Setzer and B. S. Rabinovitch, J. Am. Chem. Soc. **86,** 564 (1964).
b	13.87	61.6	−4.70				
c	13.76	61.5	−4.78				
d	14.26	64.5	−5.19				
total	14.43	62.3	−4.35				

Preferred:

Within experimental error, all parameters are reliable as reported. (Compare to methylcyclopropane results.)

Experimental

[1] Analysis by G.L.C. Rates are very comparable to those of methylcyclopropane as calculated by these authors. Primary and secondary deuterium isotope effects for the formation of the various olefins were measured. All products expected on the basis of a biradical mechanism were observed.

Reaction: *Cis*-1,2-dideutero-3-methylcyclopropane

            Trans-1,2-dideutero-3-methylcyclopropane

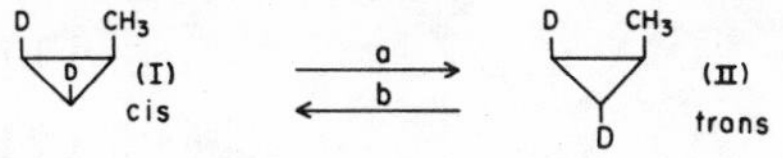

	I *cis*	II *trans*
$\Delta H^\circ_{f(298)}$	3.9	3.9
$S^\circ_{(298)}$	68.5	68.5
$C^\circ_{p(298)}$	19.1	19.1

a

$\Delta S^\circ = 0$ g/mole
$\Delta H^\circ = 0$ kcal/mole
$\Delta C^\circ_p = 0$ g/mole

Path	log A	E	log k_T (725)	Conditions	System	Surface	References
a	15.35	60.5	-2.89	725 ± 35 °K 10 torr	static		[1] D. W. Setzer and B. S. Rabinovitch, J. Am. Chem. Soc. **86,** 564 (1964)
b	15.35	60.5	-2.89				

Preferred:

    log $k_a = $ log $k_b = 15.35-60.5/\theta$.

    Transition state estimates give: log $k_{est} = 15.4 - 62.1/\theta$ (see section III–4.0).

Experimental

[1] Analysis by I.R.

Reaction: *cis*-1,2-Dimethylcyclopropane

$$\text{(I)} \xrightarrow{g} \text{(II)} \quad \textit{trans}\text{-1,2-dimethylcyclopropane}$$
$$\xrightarrow{a} \text{(III)} \quad 2\text{-methyl-1-butene}$$
$$\xrightarrow{b} \text{(IV)} \quad 2\text{-methyl-2-butene}$$
$$\xrightarrow{c} \text{(V)} \quad \textit{cis}\text{-2-pentene}$$
$$\xrightarrow{d} \text{(VI)} \quad \textit{trans}\text{-2-pentene}$$

	I	II	III	IV	V	VI
$\Delta H^\circ_{f(298)}$	-0.3	-1.3	-8.6	-10.2	-6.7	-7.6
$S^\circ_{(298)}$	75.2	72.6	81.9	81.1	82.8	81.4
$C^\circ_{p(298)}$	22.6	23.9	26.7	25.1	24.2	25.9

	g	a
$\Delta S^\circ =$	-2.6	6.7 g/mole
$\Delta H^\circ =$	-1.0	-8.3 kcal/mole
$\Delta C^\circ_p =$	1.3	4.1 g/mole

Path	log A	E	log k_T	Conditions	System	Surface	References
			(689)				
g	15.52	59.42	-3.60	689 ± 36 °K 0.1–105 torr (25)	static		[1] M. C. Flowers and H. M. Frey, Proc. Roy. Soc. (London) **A257**, 122 (1960).
			(727)				
a	13.93	61.9	-4.68	727 ± 20 °K (25) torr	static		[2] M. C. Flowers and H. M. Frey, Proc. Roy. Soc. (London) **A260**, 424 (1961).
b	14.08	62.3	-4.65				
c	13.92	61.4	-4.54				
d	13.96	61.2	-4.44				

Preferred:
   All rate constants are reliable as reported.

Comments: Transition state estimates for the biradical mechanism (see section III–4.0) are in reasonable agreement with the observed parameters.
   Estimated: $\log k_g = 15.5 - 61.2/\theta$
   $\log k_c = 14.1 - 61.7/\theta$.

(See also *trans*-1,2-dimethylcyclopropane.)

Experimental

   [1] Analysis by G.L.C. Falloff observed near 16 torr.
   [2] Analysis by G.L.C. Structural isomerization is slow relative to geometric isomerization at 727 ± 20 °K. All the products expected are observed. Paths c and d by α(C—C) rupture; paths a and b by β(C—C) rupture.

Reaction: *trans*-1,2-Dimethylcyclopropane

$\xrightarrow{\text{a}}$ (II) *cis*-1,2-Dimethylcyclopropane

$\xrightarrow{\text{g}}$ (III) 2-methyl-1-butene

(I) $\xrightarrow{\text{b}}$ (IV) 2-methyl-2-butene

$\xrightarrow{\text{c}}$ (V) *cis*-2-pentene

$\xrightarrow{\text{d}}$ (VI) *trans*-2-pentene

	I	II	III	IV	V	VI
$\Delta H^\circ_{f(298)}$	−1.3	−0.3	−8.6	−10.2	−6.7	−7.6
$S^\circ_{(298)}$	72.6	75.2	81.9	81.1	82.8	81.4
$C^\circ_{p(298)}$	23.9	22.6	26.7	25.1	24.2	25.9

	b	c
$\Delta S^\circ =$	8.5	10.2 g/mole
$\Delta H^\circ =$	−8.9	−5.4 kcal/mole
$\Delta C^\circ_p =$	1.2	0.3 g/mole

Path	log A	E	log k_T	Conditions	System	Surface	References
			(689)				
g	15.97	60.49	−3.22	689±36 °K 0.1−105 (25)	static		[1] M. C. Flowers and H. M. Frey, Proc. Roy. Soc. (London) **A257**, 122 (1960).
			(727)				
a	13.93	61.9	−4.68	727±20 °K (25)	static		[2] M. C. Flowers and H. M. Frey, Proc. Roy. Soc. (London) **A260**, 424 (1961).
b	14.08	62.3	−4.65				
c	14.40	63.6	−5.02				
d	14.30	62.9	−4.61				

Preferred:
   All rate constants are reliable as reported.

Comments: Estimated Arrhenius parameters (see section III–4.0) for the biradical mechanism are in reasonable agreement with observations: log $k_g = 15.8 − 62.2/\theta$; log $k_c = 14.3 − 62.7/\theta$. A comparison of the *cis* and *trans*-1,2-dimethylcyclopropane parameters for the various reaction paths shows quite clearly that the rate-determining steps for the structural isomerizations are H-migrations and that internal rotation and ring closing in the biradical are fast. Thus paths *a* and *b* involving β(C—C) rupture for both *cis* and *trans* reactants have identical parameters, indicating rapid equilibrium between rotational conformations in the biradical. Also, paths *c* and *d* involving α(C—C) rupture are in the same ratio to one another in both systems and differ absolutely only by the differences in entropy and heats of formation of the reactants (i.e., by a *cis* methyl effect).

Experimental

[1] and [2] See comments on *cis*-1,2-dimethylcyclopropane.

Reaction: 1,1-Dimethylcyclopropane

$$\text{(I)} \xrightarrow[b]{a} \begin{cases} a \to \text{(II)} & \text{3-methyl-1-butene} \\ b \to \text{(III)} & \text{2-methyl-2-butene} \end{cases}$$

	I	II	III
$\Delta H^\circ_{f(298)}$	-1.9	-6.9	-10.2
$S^\circ_{(298)}$	70.9	79.7	81.1
$C^\circ_{p(298)}$	24.7	28.1	25.1

	a	b
$\Delta S^\circ =$	8.8	10.2 g/mole
$\Delta H^\circ =$	-5.0	-8.3 kcal/mole
$\Delta C^\circ_p =$	3.4	0.4 g/mole

Path	log A	E	log k_T (750)	Conditions	System	Surface	References
a	14.75	62.6	-3.49	752 ± 32 °K	static	none	[1] M. C. Flowers and
b	14.75	62.6	-3.49	0.1–550 torr			H. M. Frey, J.
				(100)			Chem. Soc., 3953
$a+b$	15.05	62.6	-3.13				(1959).
$a+b$	15.37	63.6	-3.13	735 ± 20 °K	static		[2] M. C. Flowers and
				0.0075–35 torr			H. M. Frey, J.
				(35)			Chem. Soc., 1157
							(1962).

Preferred:
Rate constants are reliable as reported.

Comments: All products expected by the biradical mechanism were observed: α(C—C) split, 3-methyl-1-butene and 2-methyl-2-butene; β(C—C) split cannot lead to products. Transition state estimates are in excellent agreement with the observed parameters.

Estimated: $\log A_a = 14.7$
$\log A_b = 14.7$
$\log E_a = E_b = 61.3$ kcal/mole (see section III–4.0).

Experimental

[1] Analysis by G.L.C. Falloff observed near 4-8 torr (743 °K). 2-methyl-1-butene amounted to 1–2 percent of products. Slight rate acceleration with added NO.

[2] Analysis by G.L.C. Temperature dependence of falloff gave $n \simeq 19$ from the Slater equation ($\log P = n/2 \log T_2/T_1$) gave $n \simeq 29$. Thus the Slater equation is not consistent with the data. Relative third-body collision efficiencies determined for CH_4, H_2, N_2, Ar, He, C_2H_4, CF_4, SF_6, CO_2, and toluene. In another pertinent study, M. C. Flowers and H. M. Frey [J. Phys. Chem. **65**, 373 (1961)] found that k_∞ did not decrease at very high pressures, contrary to theoretical predictions. [See D. J. Wilson, J. Phys. Chem. **64**, 323 (1960).]

Reaction: Ethylcyclopropane

$$\xrightarrow{a}\ cis \text{ and } trans\text{-CH}_3\text{CH}\!\!=\!\!\text{CHCH}_2\text{CH}_3 \text{ (II)}$$

$$\xrightarrow{b}\ \text{CH}_2\!\!=\!\!\text{C(CH}_3)\text{CH}_2\text{CH}_3 \text{ (III)}$$

(I)

$$\xrightarrow{c}\ \text{CH}_2\!\!=\!\!\text{CHCH}\!\!=\!\!\text{CH}_2 \text{ (IV)} + \text{CH}_4 \text{ (V)}$$

$$\xrightarrow{d}\ \text{CH}_2\!\!=\!\!\text{CH(CH}_2)_2\text{CH}_3 \text{ (VI)}$$

	I	(cis) II	(trans) II	III	IV	V	VI
$\Delta H^\circ_{f(298)}$	0.7	-6.7	-7.6	-8.6	26.3	-17.9	-5.0
$S^\circ_{(298)}$	76.5	82.8	81.4	81.9	66.6	44.5	83.3
$C^\circ_{p(298)}$	24.0	24.2	25.9	26.7	19.0	8.5	26.3

b

$\Delta S^\circ =\ 5.4$ g/mole
$\Delta H^\circ = -9.3$ kcal/mole
$\Delta C^\circ_p =\ 2.7$ g/mole

Path	log A	E	log k_T	Conditions	System	Surface	References
total	14.40	61.6	-3.74	742 ± 15 °K 0.05–84 torr (25)	static	$< 10\%$	[1] M. L. Halberstadt and J. P. Chesick, J. Phys. Chem. **69**, 429 (1965).

Preferred:
   Paths a, b, and d are reliable; path c is highly suspect.

Comments: Path a, b, and d, by analogy with other cyclopropane ring isomerization reactions, are undoubtedly unimolecular and surface independent reactions. The surface dependence observed in the pentene/butadiene ratio probably comes from path c. Reaction c is not likely to be unimolecular since any reasonable transition state to products involves a highly concerted process with pentavalent carbon (i.e.,). A heterogeneous free radical mechanism seems more plausible. (See comments on 1,1-diethylcyclopropane.) The calculated Arrhenius parameters for the various structural isomerization reactions are the same as those obtained for methylcyclopropane except that all activation energies are lower by 0.8 kcal/mole. This is a result of the gauche repulsion of the ethyl group with the ring which is relieved in the biradical and transition states.
   Estimated: log $k_{est} = 15.1 - 63.2/\theta$ (see section III–4.0).

Experimental

   [1] Analysis by G.L.C. Rates of pentenes/butadiene increased with increasing (s/v). Fallout observed near 2 torr (740 °K). An RRK–$s \simeq 22$ fit the falloff. The lifetime of the activated molecule was found to be a factor of 10 longer than that for methylcyclopropane.

Reaction: *cis*-1-Ethyl-2-methylcyclopropane (*a*)
    trans-1-Ethyl-2-methylcyclopropane (*b*)

	I	II
$\Delta H^\circ_{f(298)}$	-5.3	-6.3
$S^\circ_{(298)}$	82.8	83.2
$C^\circ_{p(298)}$	28.1	29.4

a
$\Delta S^\circ = 0.4$ g/mole
$\Delta H^\circ = -1.0$ kcal/mole
$\Delta C^\circ_p = 1.3$ g/mole

Path	log A	E	log k_T (694)	Conditions	System	Surface	References
a	15.08	58.87	-3.46	694 ± 25 °K 3–100 torr	static	none	[1] C. S. Elliot and H. M. Frey, J. Chem. Soc. 900 (1964).
b	15.08	60.07	-3.84				

Preferred:
    log $k_a = 15.08 - 58.87/\theta$; log $k_b = 15.08 - 60.07/\theta$

Comments: Transition state estimates for the biradical mechanism (see section III–4.0) with ring opening as rate determining give: log A_a = log A_b = 15.5; E_a = 60.4, E_b = 61.4.

Experimental

[1] Analysis by G.L.C. Slow structural isomerizations to C_6 olefins were also observed. Olefin products identified were *cis* and *trans*-2-hexene, 3-emthyl-2-pentene, and 2-methyl-1-pentene. Measurement of the *cis* $\rightleftharpoons$ *trans* equilibrium over the temperature range of study gave $K_{eq} = 10^{0.5/4.575 - 1.2/\theta}$.

Reaction: (a) *cis,cis*-1,2,3-Trimethylcyclopropane
(b) *cis,trans*-1,2,3-Trimethylcyclopropane

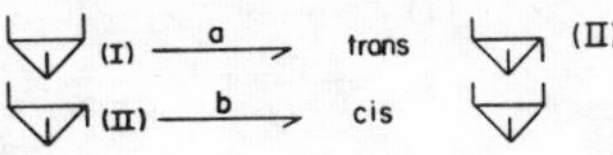

	I	II
$\Delta H^\circ_{f(298)}$	-5.3	-7.3
$S^{\circ*}_{(298)}$	82.5	81.7
$C^\circ_{p(298)}$	25.2	28.0

a
$\Delta S^\circ = -0.8$ g/mole
$\Delta H^\circ = -2.0$ kcal/mole
$\Delta C^\circ_p = 2.8$ g/mole

Path	log A	E	log k_T (696)	Conditions	System	Surface	References
a	15.78	60.95	-3.36	696 ± 28 °K 0.5–12.5 (2.5)	static	none	[1] H. M. Frey and D. C. Marshall, J. Chem. Soc. 5717 (1963).
b	15.30	63.25	-4.56				

Preferred:
   $\log k_a = 15.78 - 60.95/\theta$;
   $\log k_b = 15.30 - 63.25/\theta$.

Comments: The agreement between the observed Arrhenius parameters and those calculated by transition state methods for a biradical mechanism (see section III–4.0) is acceptable.

Estimated: *log A_a = 16.0
      *log A_b = 16.2
      E_a = 61.3
      E_b = 63.3.

Experimental

[1] Analysis by G.L.C. A concurrent slow structural isomerization produced *cis* and *trans*-3-methyl-2-pentene. Small yields of 2-ethyl-1-butene were observed at runs carried to near completion. Falloff observed near 1 torr.

---

*Entropy estimates (which do not agree with the kinetics) are not considered to be particularly accurate (i.e., ± 2 g/mole).

Reaction: 1,1-Diethylcyclopropane

	I	II	III	IV	V
$\Delta H^\circ_{f(298)}$	-11.8	-16.0	-19.3	13.1	-17.9
$S^\circ_{(298)}$	89.7	98.5	100.3	85.2	44.5
$C^\circ_{p(298)}$	35.7	37.5	37.2	30.1	8.5

a

$\Delta S^\circ = 8.8$ g/mole
$\Delta H^\circ = -4.2$ kcal/mole
$\Delta C^\circ_p = 1.8$ g/mole

Path	log A	E	log k_T (723)	Conditions	System	Surface	References
a	14.95	63.8	-4.34	723 $\pm$ 25 °K 0.2–16 torr (4.5)	static	< 10%	[1] H. M. Frey and D. C. Marshall, J. Chem. Soc. 191 (1965).
b	14.84	63.4	-4.33				
c	15.44	65.9	-4.48				

Preferred:
Reactions a and b are reliable as reported; reaction c is unreliable.

Comments: By the biradical mechanism one would expect the parameters of paths a and b to be the same as those for 1,1-dimethylcyclopropane (which is the case within experimental error). The unimolecularity of path c is suspect. The observed Arrhenius parameters imply a large entropy increase ($\Delta S^\ddagger = +9$ g/mole) in going to the transition state. However, the concerted process required would, by transition state estimates, involve a zero or negative entropy of activation. Thus, path c would appear to be most reasonably explained in terms of a surface sensitive free radical process propagated by the reactions:

(See also comments on ethylcyclopropane.)

Experimental

[1] Analysis by G.L.C. Rate falloff observed near 1 torr.

234

Reaction: 1,1,2,2-Tetramethylcyclopropane

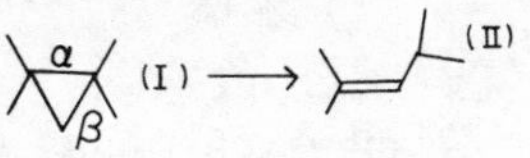

(I) $\longrightarrow$ (II) 2,4-dimethyl-2-pentene

	I	II
$\Delta H^\circ_{f(298)}$	-14.7	-22.3
$S^\circ_{(298)}$	85.1	95.3
$C^\circ_{p(298)}$	36.0	38.6

a

$\Delta S^\circ = \;9.2$ g/mole
$\Delta H^\circ = -7.6$ kcal/mole
$\Delta C^\circ_p = \;2.6$ g/mole

log A	E	log k_T (733)	Conditions	System	Surface	References
15.83	*64.4	-3.38	$733 \pm 25\ ^\circ$K 2–22.5 torr (5)	static	none	[1] H. M. Frey and D. C. Marshall, J. Chem. Soc. 3052 (1962).

Preferred:
   log $k = 14.4 - 59.6/\theta$. Rate constants around $\bar{T}$ are probably reliable.

Comments: The single product expected on the basis of the free radical mechanism (i.e., by α(C—C) rupture) was the only primary product reported. By comparison to the Arrhenius parameters of other alkyl substituted cyclopropanes, the values for tetramethylcyclopropane appear high. The rather narrow temperature range of study and the probable errors in E tend to confirm this suspicion. We prefer the transition state estimate of the A-factor and have adjusted the activation energy accordingly (see section III–4.0).

Experimental

[1] Analysis by G.L.C. Falloff observed near 0.5 torr. A slow subsequent isomerization and decomposition of the product was observed.

---

*Estimated error in E is ± 2.4 kcal/mole.

Reaction: Bicyclopropyl

$$\beta \; \triangleright\!\!\triangleleft \;\text{(I)} \quad \xrightarrow{a} \quad \text{cyclohexene} \; \bigcirc \; \text{(II)}$$
$$\xrightarrow{b} \quad \text{all products (see below)}$$

	I	II
$\Delta H^\circ_{f(298)}$	31.6	−1.7
$S^\circ_{(298)}$	76.3	74.3
$C^\circ_{p(298)}$	25.0	25.1

$\Delta S^\circ = -2.0$ g/mole
$\Delta H^\circ = -33.3$ kcal/mole
$\Delta C^\circ_p = 0.1$ g/mole

Path	log A	E	log k_T (714)	Conditions	System	Surface	References
a	16.8	70.8	−4.87	$714 \pm 33\,°K$	static	———	[1] M. C. Flowers and H. M. Frey, J. Chem. Soc., 1689 (1962).
b	15.36	60.71	−3.22				

Preferred:
Reliable as reported.

Comments: The biradical mechanism is able to identify the 17 products formed. Thus, α(C—C) split leads to four primary products, three of which may decompose to give eight more products.

β(C—C) split leads to only one primary product which has four secondary products.

Thus we have five primary products and 12 secondary products for a total of 17 products (as observed).

Quantitatively, all primary processes involve H-migrations with the exception of that forming cyclohexene. Parameters similar to those reactions producing olefins from methylcyclopropane are therefore predicted from transition state calculations. Thus log $k_{b(est)} = 15.5 - 64.2/\theta$. A factor of 2 in A has been used to account for isomerization from each cyclopropane ring. Since $E_{b(obs)} = 60.4$ (i.e., ~4 kcal/mole lower than the methylcyclopropane reaction activation energy), a resonance energy of this size could exist in the 1-cyclopropyl-1,3-n-propyl biradical ( ).

Experimental

[1] Analysis by G.L.C. Secondary decomposition produced C_6 dienes. At least 17 products were formed. The most important were: 1,3-butadiene, ethylene, isopropenylcyclopropane, *cis* and *trans*-1-cyclopropylpropene.

236

Reaction: Vinylcyclopropane

	I	II	III	IV	V
$\Delta H^\circ_{f(298)}$	30.0	7.9	25.2	19.7	18.6
$S^\circ_{(298)}$	74.2	69.2	79.7	76.5	76.4
$C^\circ_{p(298)}$	24.0	18.1	25.1	22.6	24.4

	a	b
$\Delta S^\circ =$	-5.0	5.5 g/mole
$\Delta H^\circ =$	-22.1	-4.8 kcal/mole
$\Delta C_p^{\circ\prime} =$	-5.9	1.1 g/mole

Path	$\log A$	E	$\log k_T$ (630)	Conditions	System	Surface	References
a	13.61	49.7	-3.61	631 ± 33 °K	static	$< 10\%$	[1] C. A. Wellington, J. Phys. Chem. **66,** 1671 (1962).
b	14.43	57.3	-5.42	0.14–24.7 (10)			
c	13.90	56.2	-5.57	—same as above—			
d	13.00	53.6	-5.57				
a	13.50	49.6	-3.67	639 ± 26 °K			[2] M. C. Flowers and H. M. Frey, J. Chem. Soc. 3547 (1961).

Preferred:
Reliable as reported with the experimental error limits noted below.

Comments: Mechanism:

with $k_2 > k_a + k_b + k_c + k_d$.

Transition state estimates (see discussion on small ring compound reactions, section III–4.2) give:

$$\log k_a = 13.8 - 49.7/\theta$$
$$\log k_b = 14.5 - 63.8(-)/\theta \quad (57.5 \text{ with half allylic resonance})$$
$$\log k_c = 13.9 - 57.5/\theta$$
$$\log k_d = 13.3 - 51.2/\theta.$$

The activation energy for C_5 ring closing in vinylcyclopropane systems is estimated to be: $E_a = E_{C_5 r.c.} = 8.3$ kcal/mole.

Experimental

[1] Analysis by G.L.C. Product identification with I.R. Falloff observed near 8 torr. No effect on the rate with added NO.

[2] Analysis by G.L.C. Other olefin products less than 1 percent. Products are those predicted by the biradical mechanism. Since products other than cyclopentene are minor ones, their rate constant parameters are not exceptionally reliable (i.e., $\Delta E \simeq 2$–4 kcal/mole).

Reaction: *cis*-1-Methyl-2-vinylcyclopropane

(I) → (II) *cis*-1,4-hexadiene

	I	II
$\Delta H^{\circ}_{f(298)}$	24.2	19.0
$S^{\circ}_{(298)}$	80.5	89.3
$C^{\circ}_{p(298)}$	28.0	29.2

$\Delta S^{\circ} = 7.3$ g/mole
$\Delta H^{\circ} = -5.2$ kcal/mole
$\Delta C^{\circ}_{p} = 1.2$ g/mole

log A	E	log k_T (457)	Conditions	System	Surface	References
11.03	31.2	−3.89	457±28 °K 3–40 (3) torr	static	none	[1] R. J. Ellis and H. M. Frey, Proc. Chem. Soc., 221 (1964) (preliminary). [2] R. J. Ellis and H. M. Frey, J. Chem. Soc. 5578 (1964).

Preferred:
Reliable as reported.

Comments: The Arrhenius parameters are extraordinarily low and indicate that this reaction cannot be a biradical process. If the parameters are compared to those for the "ene" type isomerization of 4-methyl-1,3-pentadiene and its inverse (; log $k_1 = 11.72 - 36.19/\theta$; log $k_2 = 11.24 - 32.76/\theta$) it is apparent that the *cis*-1-methyl-2-vinylcyclopropane reaction is concerted and proceeds through a six-centered transition state.

Experimental

[1] and [2] Analysis by G.L.C. Identification of products by I.R. The *trans* isomer was not formed.

Reaction: *trans*-1-Methyl-2-vinylcyclopropane

(I) →a→ (II) *cis*-1,4-hexadiene
(I) →b→ (III) 3-methylcyclopentene*

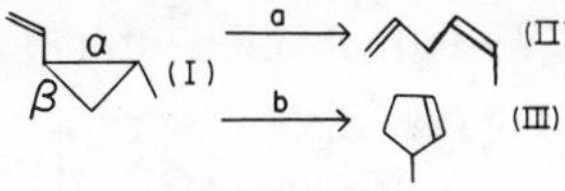

	I	II	III
$\Delta H_{f(298)}^{\circ}$	23.0	19.0	0.0
$S_{(298)}^{\circ}$	80.9	89.3	79.0
$C_{p(298)}^{\circ}$	29.3	29.2	25.9

	a	b
$\Delta S^{\circ} =$	6.9	-3.4 g/mole
$\Delta H^{\circ} =$	-4.0	-23.0 kcal/mole
$\Delta C_p^{\circ} =$	-0.1	-3.4 g/mole

Path	log A	E	log k_T (585)	Conditions	System	Surface	References
a	14.78	48.64	-3.40	585 ± 16 °K 3–40 (3)	static	none	[1] R. J. Ellis and H. M. Frey, J. Chem. Soc., 5578 (1964).
b	13.67	48.64	-4.51	←——— same as above ———→			

Preferred:
Both reactions reliable as reported.

Comments: Reaction *a* undoubtedly involves geometric isomerization to the *cis* isomer (with ring opening as rate determining) followed by the rapid concerted isomerization of *cis*-1-methyl-2-vinylcyclopropane to *cis*-1,4-hexadiene. By the biradical mechanism reaction, *b* must proceed via β(C—C) cleavage and have as its rate-determining step C_5 ring closing. 4-methyl-1-cyclopentene was not observed; therefore, α(C—C) cleavage (which would be expected to be the favored reaction path) leads to hexadiene formation, and not C_5 ring formation.*

Mechanism:

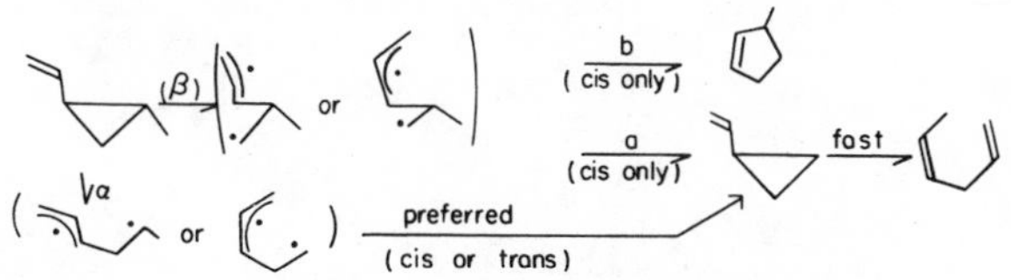

Experimental

[1] Analysis by G.L.C. Identification confirmed with I.R.

---

*NOTE added in proof: The cyclopentene product was incorrectly reported and should be 4-methylcyclopentene (private communication, H. M. Frey). Thus the "expected" product via the energetically favored α (C — C) rupture *was* the product formed. The discussion of this reaction in section III–4.3 is consistent with the "real" facts.

239

Reaction: 1-Methyl-1-vinylcyclopropane

(I) ⟶ (II)   1-methylcyclopentene

	I	II
$\Delta H^\circ_{f(298)}$	23.0	−0.3
$S^\circ_{(298)}$	79.4	78.0
$C^\circ_{p(298)}$	26.2	24.2

$\Delta S^\circ = -1.4$ g/mole
$\Delta H^\circ = -23.3$ kcal/mole
$\Delta C^\circ_p = -2.0$ g/mole

log A	E	log k_T (608)	Conditions	System	Surface	References
14.11	49.35	−3.64	608 ± 22 2–30 torr	static	none	[1] R. J. Ellis and H. M. Frey, J. Chem. Soc., 959 (1964).

Preferred:

Reliable as reported.

Transition state estimate gives, log A_{est} = 14.1 (see section III—4.2).

Experimental

[1] Analysis by G.L.C. Rate constants were not pressure dependent.

Reaction: Isopropenylcyclopropane

(I) $\longrightarrow$ (II)   1-methylcyclopentene

	I	II
$\Delta H^\circ_{f(298)}$	22.0	−0.3
$S^\circ_{(298)}$	81.7	78.0
$C^\circ_{p(298)}$	30.1	24.2

$\Delta S^\circ = -3.7$ g/mole
$\Delta H^\circ = -22.3$ kcal/mole
$\Delta C^\circ_p = -5.9$ g/mole

log A	E	log k_T (605)	Conditions	System	Surface	References
13.89	50.9	−3.72	605–659 °K 0.5–21 torr (5)	static	none	[1] H. M. Frey and D. C. Marshall, J. Chem. Soc., 3981 (1962).

Preferred:
   Reliable as reported.

Comments: Transition state estimates based on the biradical mechanism (see vinylcyclopropane) are in good agreement with the observed parameters: log A_{est}=14.1; E=49.7 kcal/mole.

Experimental

[1] Analysis by G.L.C.

Reaction: *trans*-1-Cyclopropyl-1-butene

(I) ⟶ (II) 3-ethylcyclopentene

	I	II
$\Delta H^\circ_{f(298)}$	17.5	−3.3
$S^\circ_{(298)}$	92.6	88.4
$C^\circ_{p(298)}$	34.2	29.4

$\Delta S^\circ = -4.2$ g/mole
$\Delta H^\circ = -20.8$ kcal/mole
$\Delta C^\circ_p = -4.8$ g/mole

log A	E	log k_T (626)	Conditions	System	Surface	References
13.79	49.98	−3.60	626 ± 20 °K 2–25 torr	static	none	[1] R. J. Ellis and H. M. Frey, J. Chem. Soc., 4188 (1964).

Preferred:
   Reliable as reported.

Comments: Biradical mechanism transition state estimates give: log $k_{est} = 13.8 - 49.7/\theta$ (see section III–4.2).

Experimental

   [1] Analysis by G.L.C. The rate constants were independent of pressure. At the highest temperatures very small yields of various dienes were also detected.

Reaction: 1-Cyclopropyl-2-methyl-1-propene

$$\xrightarrow{\;a\;}\; \text{3,3-dimethylcyclopentene} \quad \text{(II)}$$

$$\xrightarrow{\;b\;}\; \text{5-methyl-1,4-hexadiene} \quad \text{(III)}$$

(I) $\xrightarrow{\;c\;}\;$ *cis*-2-methyl-2,4-hexadiene (IV)

$$\xrightarrow{\;d\;}\; \textit{trans}\text{-2-methyl-2,4-hexadiene} \quad (V)$$

	I	II	III	IV	V
$\Delta H^{\circ}_{f(298)}$	15.4	−6.8	10.7	5.0	4.0
$S^{\circ}_{(298)}$	89.9	83.1	96.8	91.9	92.3
$C^{\circ}_{p(298)}$	34.0	29.4	35.3	33.4	34.7

	a	b
$S^{\circ} =$	−6.8	6.9 g/mole
$H^{\circ} =$	−22.2	−4.7 kcal/mole
$C^{\circ}_p =$	−4.6	1.3 g/mole

Path	log A	E	log k_T (643)	Conditions	System	Surface	References
	14.0	54.6	−4.56	643 ± 20 °K 2–17 torr	static	< 10%	[1] C. S. Elliott and H. M. Frey, J. Chem. Soc., 345 (1965).
	14.61	56.65	−4.65				
	13.33	53.0	−4.68				
	13.25	52.1	−4.46				

Preferred:
Reliable as reported.

Comments: Transition state estimates:

$$\log k_a = 14.0 - 49.7/\theta$$
$$\log k_b = 14.6 - 57.2/\theta \quad \text{(half-allylic resonance)}$$
$$\log k_c = 13.0 - 51.2/\theta$$
$$\log k_d = 13.2 - 51.2/\theta.$$

The discrepancy between the estimated and observed activation energy in the cyclopentene formation could be a result of steric effects caused by the methyl substitutions at the position for ring closing and in the *cis* form of the biradical. (See the discussion on vinylcyclopropane and section III–4.2).

Experimental

[1] Analysis by G.L.C. Identification with M.S. and I.R. The diene products are those predicted by the biradical mechanism. Absence of 2,4-dimethyl-1,3-pentadiene in the products would be expected on the bsais of energy considerations (i.e., no allylic resonance stabilization of the biradical intermediate formed via $\beta(C\!-\!C)$ rupture).

Reaction: 1-Isopropenyl-1-methylcyclopropane

(I) $\longrightarrow$ 1,2-dimethylcyclopentene (II)

	I	II
$\Delta H^\circ_{f(298)}$	14.7	-8.5
$S^\circ_{(298)}$	87.2	84.0
$\Delta C^\circ_{p(298)}$	32.1	30.3

$\Delta S^\circ = -3.2$ g/mole
$\Delta H^\circ = -23.2$ kcal/mole
$\Delta C^\circ_p = -1.8$ g/mole

log A	E	log k_T (620)	Conditions	System	Surface	References
14.14	50.5	-3.64	620 ± 22 °K 0.5–3.2 torr (5)	static	none	[1] C. S. Elliott and H. M. Frey, J. Chem. Soc., 4289 (1965).

Preferred:
  Reliable as reported.

Comments: Transition state estimates for the biradical mechanism (see vinylcyclopropane) give: log A_e = 14.1; E = 48.1 kcal/mole. (See discussion on small ring compound reactions, section III–4.2.

Experimental

[1] Analysis by G.L.C. Identification with M.S. At the highest temperatures a diene was formed in small yield ($\sim 1.5\%$).

Reaction: 1,1-Dicyclopropylethene

(I) ⟶ (II)   1-cyclopropylcyclopentene

	I	II
$\Delta H^\circ_{f(298)}$	51.0	26.6
$S^\circ_{(298)}$	93.6	88.7
$C^\circ_{p(298)}$	38.6	32.8

$\Delta S^\circ = -4.9$ g/mole
$\Delta H^\circ = -24.4$ kcal/mole
$\Delta C^\circ_p = -5.8$ g/mole

log A	E	log k_T (640)	Conditions	System	Surface	References
14.29	51.06	−3.15	615–663 °K (1–5 mm Hg)	static	none	[1] G. R. Branton and H. M. Frey, J. Chem. Soc. **A**, 1342 (1966).

Preferred:
  log $k = 14.29 - 51.06/\theta$.

Comments: Transition state estimates on the basis of a biradical mechanism give $A_{est} = 10^{14.1}$ sec^{-1} and $E_{est} = 49.7$ kcal/mole in good agreement with the reported parameters.

Experimental

[1] Rates were based on G.L.C. analysis of the products. Added N_2 up to 200 mm Hg did not affect the kinetics. 1-cyclopropylcyclopentene never exceeded 53 percent of the products because of its own subsequent decomposition. Reaction paths:

⟶ ⟶   (bicyclo[3,3,0]oct-1-ene)

Other products were less than 2 percent.

Reaction: 1-Cyclopropyl-1-cyclopentene

(I) ⟶ (II)   [3,3,0-bicyclo-1-octene]

	I	II
$\Delta H^\circ_{f(298)}$	26.6	4.2
$S^\circ_{(298)}$	88.7	85.3
$C^\circ_{p(298)}$	32.8	28.3

$\Delta S^\circ = -\ 3.4$ g/mole
$\Delta H^\circ = -22.4$ kcal/mole
$\Delta C^\circ_p = -\ 4.5$ g/mole

$\log A$	E	$\log k_T$ (640)	Conditions	System	Surface	References
14.01	51.29	−3.51	615–663 °K 1–15 torr	static	none	[1] G. R. Branton and H. M Frey, J. Chem. Soc. A 1342 (1966).

Preferred:
   $\log k = 14.01 - 51.29/\theta$.

Comments: Transition state estimates based on a biradical mechanism give $A_{est} = 10^{14.1}$ and $E \simeq 49.9$ kca mole (see 1,1-dicyclopropylethene for related reaction and section III–4.2 for estimation methods).

Experimental

[1] (See 1,1-dicyclopropylethene.)

Reaction: Fluorocyclopropane

$$\overset{F}{\underset{\beta}{\triangledown}}{\scriptstyle\alpha}\;(I) \longrightarrow \left(\!\!\nearrow\!\!\searrow\right)_{F_1}\;(II)\;\;\text{monofluoropropenes (see below)}$$

	I	II
$\Delta H^\circ_{f(298)}$	-30.9	-44.3
$S^\circ_{(298)}$	65.4	69.8
$C^\circ_{p(298)}$	15.5	16.9

$\Delta S^\circ = \quad 4.4$ g/mole
$\Delta H^\circ = -13.4$ kcal/mole
$\Delta C^\circ_p = \quad 1.4$ g/mole

log A	E	log k_T (730)	Conditions	System	Surface	References
14.58	61.01	-3.69	730 ± 45 °K 0.017–46 torr (46)	static	none	[1] F. Casas, J. A. Kerr, and A. F. Trotman-Dickinson, J. Chem. Soc., 3655 (1964).

Preferred:
Reliable: $\log k = 14.58 - 61.01/\theta$.

Comments: S. Pavlou and B. S. Rabinovitch (private communication) report some heterogeneity for this reaction. Thus the (*cis/trans*) 1-propene ratio was found to be total pressure dependent at low pressures. Comparison of the activation energy with that for cyclopropane suggests a destabilization of the C_3 ring of about 4 kcal/mole by the F atom substitution.

Experimental

[1] Analysis by G.L.C. Fluoropropene distribution: *cis*-1-propene ~ 18.5 percent, *trans*-1-propene ~ 60.9 percent, 2-propene ~ 9.1 percent, 3-propene ~ 11.4 percent. Falloff observed near 100 torr at 748 °K. RRK–$s \approx$ 12–14.

Reaction: 1,1-Difluorocyclopropane

$$\xrightarrow{\ a\ } C_2H_4 \text{ (III)} + CF_2 \text{ (IV)}$$

(I)

$$\xrightarrow{\ b\ } \text{propylene } (F_2) \text{ (II)}$$

	I	II	III	IV
$\Delta H^\circ_{f(298)}$	(-71.4)		12.5	-39.7
$S^\circ_{(298)}$	67.1	73.8	52.5	57.5
$C^\circ_{p(298)}$	17.8		10.4	9.1

Path a
$\Delta S^\circ = 42.9$ g/mole
$\Delta H^\circ = 44.2$ kcal/mole
$\Delta C^\circ_p = 1.7$ g/mole

Path	log A	E	log k_T (696)	Conditions	System	Surface	References
$a+b$	14.09	56.35	-3.61	696 ± 22 °K 0.007–280 torr (280)	static	none	[1] F. P. Herbert, J. A. Kerr, and A. F. Trotman-Dickenson, J. Chem. Soc., 5710 (1965).

Preferred:
    Parameters and rate constants are probably reliable. Proposed products and reaction path b are suspect

Comments: Atkinson and McKeagan (see perfluorocyclopropane) report that CF_2: addition to C_2H_4 (530 °K is slow but detectable relative to its addition to perfluoropropylene. The latter has an activation energy of 8 kcal/mole (for k in pressure units); therefore a reasonable guess for the former would be about 11–12 kcal mole. Thus for a total strain of 35.6 kcal/mole (i.e., a normal C_3 ring strain (27.6) plus an additional 8 kcal/mole destabilization for the two F atom substitutions) one obtains, ( ) $=-71.4$ kcal/mole, $\Delta H^\circ_a = 44.2$ kcal/mole, and an estimated $E_a = 44.2 + 12.0 = 56.2$ kcal/mole, in very good agreement with the observed activation energy. The extensive polymerization of the product olefins would then also be readily understandable in terms of polymerization initiated by CF_2:. Olefin formation via H-migration from the biradical (path b) according to these thermodynamics, should probably be competitive. The enthalpy change for ring opening to the biradical is estimated to be, ( ) $= DH^\circ(C-C) - E$ strain $= 81.6 - 35.6 = 46$ kcal/mole

Thus, $E_b \simeq 46.0 + 10.8$ (H-mig) $= 56.8$ kcal/mole. The A-factor for decomposition of the biradical to CF_2 would be expected to be slightly favored over H-migration. If our estimates are correct, paths a and b should have similar Arrhenius parameters and should be competitive processes. Path a could also be a concerted elimination without proceeding via a biradical.

Experimental

    [1] Analysis by G.L.C. Falloff observed near 100 torr; RRK–$s \sim 17$. Olefin products polymerized and therefore were not analyzed. Rates were determined from the disappearance of reactant. The reaction proposed was path b.

Reaction: 1,1,2-Trifluorocyclopropane

$$\overset{F}{\underset{F}{\diagdown}} \overset{F}{\diagup} \; (I) \quad \overset{a}{\longrightarrow} \; \ddot{C}F_2 \;\; (III) + CH_2\!\!=\!\!CFH \; (IV)$$
$$\overset{b}{\longrightarrow} \; \text{propylene } (F_3) \; (II)$$

	I	II	III	IV
$\Delta H^\circ_{f(298)}$	-110.8		-39.7	-31.4
$S^\circ_{(298)}$	74.7		57.5	60.4
$C^\circ_{p(298)}$	20.0		9.1	11.9

a

$\Delta S^\circ = 43.2$ g/mole
$\Delta H^\circ = 39.7$ kcal/mole
$\Delta C^\circ_p = 1.0$ g/mole

Path	log A	E	log k_T (*602*)	Conditions	System	Surface	References
total	14.43	50.52	-3.91	$602 \pm 12\ °K$ 0.007–200 torr (200)	static	none	[1] F. P. Herbert, J. A. Kerr, and A. F. Trotman-Dickenson, J. Chem. Soc., 5710 (1965).

Preferred:
 Rate constants and parameters are reliable. Reaction products and path are suspect (see also 1,1-difluorocyclopropane).

Comments: The observed activation energy and estimated reaction enthalpy are consistent with a reverse activation energy of $E_{-a} = 11$ kcal/mole, which is close to that estimated for $CF_2: + C_2H_4$. A total strain energy of 39.6 kcal/mole has been used for $(\nabla)_{F_3}$. By our thermodynamics, ring opening to the biradical is estimated as: $DH^\circ(C\!-\!C) - E$ strain $= 81.6 - 39.6 = 42.0$ kcal/mole endothermic. With $E_{H\text{-mig}} = 10.8$ kcal/mole, one obtains $E_b \simeq 52.8$ kcal/mole. Paths *a* and *b* should therefore be competitive processes, with path *a* slightly favored.

Experimental

 [1] Analysis by G.L.C. Falloff observed near 100 torr; RRK$-s \sim 18$. Olefin products polymerized. The reaction assumed was that of path *b*.

Reaction: 1,1,2,2-Tetrafluorocyclopropane

$$\text{(I)} \quad \xrightarrow{a} \quad CF_2: \text{(III)} + CH_2{=}CF_2 \text{ (IV)}$$
$$\xrightarrow{b} \quad \text{propylene (F}_4) \text{ (II)}$$

	I	II	III	IV
$\Delta H^\circ_{f(298)}$	(-155.5)		-39.7	-80.8*
$S^\circ_{(298)}$	75.3		57.5	
$C^\circ_{p(298)}$	22.2		9.1	

$$\Delta S^\circ = \left.\begin{array}{c} \\ \\ \\ \end{array}\right.$$
$$\Delta H^\circ = \left(35.0\right)$$
$$\Delta C^\circ_p = $$

Path	log A	E	log k_T (543)	Conditions	System	Surface	References
total	15.27	48.48	-4.25	543 ± 18 °K 0.005–210 torr (210)	static	none	[1] F. P. Herbert, J. A. Kerr, and A. F. Trotman-Dickenson, J. Chem. Soc., 5710 (1965).

Preferred:
Rate constants and parameters are reliable. Reaction path b and products are suspect (see also 1,1 difluorocyclopropane).

Comments: There is considerable uncertainty in the thermodynamics. Additivity gives $\Delta H^\circ_f(CH_2{=}CF_2)$ $= -70.7$ kcal/mole. We have used a total ring strain of 43.6 kcal/mole, although this could well be larger (see perfluorocyclopropane). However, with the strain indicated, we estimate:

$$\text{path } a: E_a = \Delta H^\circ_a + E_{-a} \simeq 35 + 10 = 45 \text{ kcal/mole}$$

$$\text{path } b: E_b = DH^\circ(C{-}C) - E_{st} + E_{H\text{-mig}} = 81.6 - 43.6 + 10.8 = 48.8 \text{ kcal/mole}.$$

Both processes, therefore, seem possible and are probably competitive.

Experimental

[1] Analysis by G.L.C. Falloff observed near 100 torr; RRK–$s \sim 21$. Olefin product polymerized. The reaction assumed was that of path b.

---

*An experimental value.

Reaction: Hexafluorocyclopropane (perfluorocyclopropane)

$$(\bigtriangledown)_{F_6} \longrightarrow C_2F_4 \ (II) + CF_2\text{: (III)}$$

	I	II	III
$\Delta H^\circ_{f(298)}$	[228]	−155.0	−39.6
$S^\circ_{(298)}$	80.2	71.8	57.5
$C^\circ_{p(298)}$	26.6	19.4	9.1

$S^\circ = 49.1$ g/mole
$H^\circ = 33.4$ kcal/mole
$C^\circ_p = 1.9$ g/mole

log A	E	log k_T (535)	Conditions	System	Surface	References
13.25	38.6	−4.50	526–549 °K 2–16 mm Hg	static	—————	[1] B. Atkinson and D. McKeagan, Chem. Comm. 189 (1966)

referred:
   log $k = 15.0 - 43.0/\theta$. Rate constants are reliable.

Comments: The temperature range of study was only 23 °C, and with a 2-percent error in the rate constants, could produce an error in E of ±2.6 kcal/mole. By analogy with the similar reaction, perfluoroallylcyclopropane. and as a result of transition state estimates of the A-factor, slightly higher than observed parameters are preferred. With the activation energy suggested for the back reaction ($E_{b(p)} = 8.0$ kcal/mole). the heat of formation of perfluorocyclopropane in brackets is obtained. This is consistent with a strain energy in $(\bigtriangledown)_{F_6}$ of 3 kcal/mole. By the biradical mechanism, decomposition of the biradical is rate determining with an activation energy about 23 kcal/mole.

Mechanism: $(\bigtriangledown)_{F_6} \underset{2}{\overset{1}{\rightleftharpoons}} (\dot{\vee}\dot{})_{F_6} \xrightarrow{3} C_2F_4 + CF_2\text{:}$

$$\Delta H^\circ_{1.2} = 18.6 \text{ kcal/mole} \qquad E_3 \simeq 23 \text{ kcal/mole}$$
$$E_{-3} = 8.0 \text{ kcal/mole.}$$

Since some addition of CF_2: to C_2H_4 did occur. although very slow relative to the addition to $(\bigwedge)_{F_6}$ an activation energy for addition to ethylene of around 12 kcal/mole seems reasonable.

Experimental

   [1] Rates were obtained from ΔP measurements. Material balance ($2C_3F_6 \longrightarrow 3C_2F_4$) was checked by analysis (U.V., I.R., G.L.C.). With added perfluoropropene, perfluoromethylcyclopropane was formed. With added ethylene. small amounts of $(\bigtriangledown)_{F_2}$ were formed. Thus CF_2: adds more rapidly to $(\bigwedge)_{F_6}$ than to (C_2H_4). The mechanism proposed as,

$$(\bigtriangledown)_{F_6} \underset{2}{\overset{1}{\rightleftharpoons}} C_2F_4 + CF_2\text{:}$$

$$2CF_2\text{:} \xrightarrow{3} C_2F_4$$

Values of $k_2/k_3^{1/2}$ were combined with low-temperature data to give $k_2/k_3^{1/2} = 10^{2.8}T^{1/2}10^{-7.9/\theta}$ (1/mole)$^{1/2}$sec$^{-1/2}$. Using $= 10^{6.57}T^{1/2} \times 10^{-1.2/\theta}$ 1/mole-sec [F. W. Dalby, J. Chem. Phys. **41**, 2297 (1964)], the authors obtained $k_2 = 10^{6.09}$ $^{1/2} \times 10^{-8.5/\theta}$ 1/mole-sec.

Reaction: Trifluoromethylcyclopropane

	I	II	III	IV	V
$\Delta H^\circ_{f(298)}$	-138.5	-148.2	-145.8	-147.5	-148.5
$S^\circ_{(298)}$	79.3	83.7	85.7	84.4	84.4
$C^\circ_{p(298)}$	25.0	27.8	27.0	25.4	27.5

a

$\Delta S^\circ = 4.4$ g/mole
$\Delta H^\circ = -9.7$ kcal/mole
$\Delta C^\circ_p = 2.8$ g/mole

Path	log A	E	log k_T (758)	Conditions	System	Surface	References
a	13.87	69.5	-6.17	758±45 °K (82) torr	static		[1] D. W. Placzek and B. S. Rabinovitch, J. Phys. Chem. **69**, 2141 (1965).
b	14.38	67.3	-5.03				
c	14.17	65.2	-4.63				
d	13.95	65.0	-4.79				
total	14.61	65.6	-4.31				

Preferred:
   All rate constants reliable as reported. (Compare with results on methylcyclopropane.)

Comments: The biradical mechanism is consistent with the kinetics. The products observed are those expected. Paths b, c, and d occur by α(C—C) rupture and path a by β(C—C) rupture. Transition state estimates (see section III–4.0) are the same as those for methylcyclopropane and predict somewhat higher A-factors. It is apparent that the fluorine substitution outside the ring produces a rate decrease. It is not clear whether the effect is a result of increased activation energies or (as the overall parameters imply) lowered A-factors. We favor an activation energy increase with fluorine substitution.

Experimental

[1] Analysis by G.L.C.; N.M.R. used for identification purposes.

252

Reaction: 2-2-2-Trifluoro-1-ethylcyclopropane

	I	II	III	IV
$\Delta H^\circ_{f(298)}$	-145.1	-151	-152.5	-153.5
$S^\circ_{(298)}$	88.7	95.1	94.2	94.2
$C^\circ_{p(298)}$	30.5	33.5	30.5	32.6

$\Delta S^\circ = 6.4$ g/mole
$\Delta H^\circ = -5.9$ k/cal/mole
$\Delta C^\circ_p = 3.0$ g/mole

Path	log A	E	log k_T (747)	Conditions	System	Surface	References
a	13.88	63.4	-4.67	$747 \pm 68\,°K$ (82) torr	static		[1] D. W. Placzek and B. S. Rabinovitch, J. Phys. Chem. **69**, 2141 (1965)
b	13.84	63.3	-4.68				
c	13.69	63.1	-4.77				
total	14.39	63.6	-4.22				

Preferred:
Rate constants are reliable as reported.

Comments: All products expected by the biradical mechanism were observed. The reactions are analogous to those of ethylcyclopropane. As in the trifluoromethyl cyclopropane reaction, it is apparent that fluorine substitution decreases the reaction rate and comparison of the parameters for the two overall reactions suggests that the rate decrease is a result of generally higher activation energies.

Experimental

[1] Analysis by G.L.C. N.M.R. used for identification. Rate constant parameters for 2-trifluoroethylpropene (path d) were not obtained. However, it was estimated that $(k_d/k_a + k_b) = 0.1$.

Reaction: Octafluorovinylcyclopropane (perfluorovinylcyclopropane)

$$\left(\bigtriangledown\right)_{F_8}{}^{(I)} \longrightarrow \left(\bigcirc\right)_{F_8}{}^{(II)} \quad \text{perfluorocyclopentene}$$

	I	II
$\Delta H^\circ_{f(298)}$	( )	( )
$S^\circ_{(298)}$	108.7	103.4
$C^\circ_{p(298)}$	41.6	37.9

$\Delta S^\circ = -5.3$ g/mole
$\Delta H^\circ =$
$\Delta C^c_p = -3.7$ g/mole

log A	E	log k_T (430)	Conditions	System	Surface	References
13.9	34.6	−3.69	404–456 °K 1–90 torr	static	none	[1] R. A. Mitsch and E. W. Neuvar, J. Phys. Chem. **70**, 546 (1966).

Preferred:
Reliable. log $k = 13.9 - 34.6/\theta$.

Comments: The A-factor should be similar to that for vinylcyclopropane, and this is as observed. With strain energy of 46.5 kcal/mole (see perfluoroallylcyclopropane) and a "normal" allyl resonance, an enthalpy of ring opening to the biradical of $\Delta H^\circ_{1,2} = 21.1$ kcal/mole (at 298 °K) is obtained. An activation energy for C₅ ring closing of about 13.5 kcal/mole is therefore suggested by the observed activation energy. [Compare to $E_{C_5} = 8.3$ kcal/mole $\left(\bigtriangledown\right)$ and $E_{C_5} = 13.2$ kcal/mole $\left(\diagup\!\!\bigtriangledown\right)$.] Steric effects of the fluorine could be responsible for this higher value.

Experimental

[1] Analysis by G.L.C. First-order plots were linear to 97 percent reaction. Rates were unaffected by 10 percent NO. The decrease in activation energy for the perfluoro compound relative to the hydrocarbon analogue was attributed to increased ring strain, a reasonable conclusion.

Reaction: Decafluoroallycyclopropane (perfluoroallylcyclopropane)

	I	II	III
$\Delta H^\circ_{f(298)}$	-397.1	-320.5	-39.7
$S^\circ_{(298)}$			57.5
$C^\circ_{p(298)}$	52.5	43.5	9.1

$\Delta S^\circ = 49.9$ g/mole
$\Delta H^\circ = [33.7$ kcal/mole$]$
$\Delta C^\circ_p = 0.1$ g/mole

log A	E	log k_T (496)	Conditions	System	Surface	References
14.8	42.7	-4.02	469–523 °K 1–40 torr	static	none	[1] R. A. Mitsch and E. W. Neuvar, J. Phys. Chem. **70,** 546 (1966).

Preferred:
  log $k = 14.8 - 42.7/\theta$.

Comments: If an activation energy of CF$_2$: addition to the olefin product of 9.0 kcal/mole is assumed [see $\langle\triangledown\rangle$F$_6$], the reaction enthalpy in brackets is obtained. This gives a ring strain in perfluoroallylcyclopropane of 46.5 kcal/mole.

Experimental

[1] Analysis and rate by G.L.C. C$_2$F$_4$ was added in order to quantitatively trap CF$_2$: [as $\langle\triangledown\rangle$F$_6$]. NO had no effect on the reaction rate.

Reaction: Chlorocyclopropane

(I) $\longrightarrow$ Cl (II)   3-chloropropene

	I	II
$\Delta H_{f(298)}$	4.9	-0.7
$S^\circ_{(298)}$	68.5	73.4
$C^\circ_{p(298)}$	17.0	18.2

$\Delta S^\circ = \quad 4.9$ g/mole
$\Delta H^\circ = -5.5$ kcal/mole
$\Delta C_p = \quad 1.2$ g/mole

log A	E	log k_T	Conditions	System	Surface	References
14.8	56.2		613–693 °K			[1] R.C.S. Grant and E. S.
			35–440 torr			Swinbourne, Chem.
						Comm. 620 (1966).

Preferred:
Unimolecularity of this reaction needs verification.

Comments: Transition state estimates of log A for the normal biradical mechanism of a cyclopropane isomerization give log $A_{est} = 14.7$ in good agreement with the value observed. However, the low activation energy suggests either an appreciable increase in ring strain, due to the chlorine substitution, or an unexpected radical stabilization by chlorine. Thus from E_{act} one can estimate that $DH^\circ(RCHCl—H) = 91$ kcal/mole compared to $DH^\circ(RCH_2—H) = 98$ kcal/mole.

A 7-kcal stabilization (or increased ring strain) is not very reasonable. A more plausible explanation of the experimental results is that the reaction is a free radical process with a β-μ radical recombination termination (see bromocyclopropane for the proposed mechanism). Estimated parameters are slightly lower than those observed (giving faster predicted rates) suggesting that the radical process is certainly feasible. With estimates:

$$\log k_i \simeq 13.5 - 80.2/\theta$$
$$\log k_t \simeq 11.2$$
$$\log k_1 \simeq 10.7 - 4/\theta$$
$$\log k_3 \simeq 13.5 - 14/\theta$$

one obtains, log $k_{est} \simeq 13.2 - 49.2/\theta$.

Experimental

[1] Analysis by G.L.C. The only product, 3-chloropropene, decomposed at $T > 400$ °C.

Reaction: 1,1-Dichlorocyclopropane

$$\text{CH}_2 \overset{\overset{\displaystyle CCl_2}{\diagup \diagdown}}{\underline{\hspace{2cm}}} \text{CH}_2 \text{ (I)} \longrightarrow \text{CH}_2 \text{=CClCH}_2\text{Cl (II)}$$

	I	II
$\Delta H^{\circ}_{f(298)}$	4.2	-4.6
$S^{\circ}_{(298)}$	63.2	80.8
$C^{\circ}_{p(298)}$	20.0	21.3

$\Delta S^{\circ} = 17.6$ g/mole
$\Delta H^{\circ} = -8.8$ kcal/mole
$\Delta C^{\circ}_p = 1.3$ g/mole

log A	E	log k_T (700)	Conditions	System	Surface	References
15.13	57.8	-2.95	615–714 °K 20–120 torr	static	No effect	[1] K. A. W. Parry and P. J. Robinson, Chem. Comm. 1083 (1967).

Preferred:

log $k = 15.13-57.8/\theta$ (sec^{-1}) seems reasonable.

Comments: There is about 5 percent secondary decomposition of product at one half-life. Although the authors suggest that the mechanism does not involve biradicals and propose a concerted path, it seems much more plausible that the biradical path is operative. The $\dot{C}H_2CH_2\dot{C}Cl_2$ biradical is favored over the $\dot{C}H_2 CCl_2\dot{C}H_2$ biradical by only 1.8 ± 2 kcal, but the Cl migration in the latter is undoubtedly faster than the H migration in the former and so makes the observed path the favored one. A low activation energy for 1-2-Cl migration makes ring opening the rate-determining step. A_{est} from transition state theory is $10^{15.5}$ sec^{-1}. If each Cl introduces 3.0 kcal of additional ring strain, $E_{est} = 58$ kcal/mole.

Experimental

[1] Analysis by G.L.C. No effect on the rates with NO, C_3H_6, or the product. S/V increased a factor of sixteen.

Reaction: 2,2-Dichloro-1-methyl-1-vinylcyclopropane (1-methyl-1-vinyl-2,2-dichlorocyclopropane)

(I) $\longrightarrow$ (II) 2-methyl-4,4-dichlorocyclopentene

	I	II
$\Delta H^{\circ}_{f(298)}$	10.5	-14.7
$S^{\circ}_{(298)}$	92.6	91.2
$C^{\circ}_{p(298)}$	32.2	30.2

$$\Delta S = \begin{pmatrix} -1.4 \end{pmatrix} \text{ g/mole}$$
$$\Delta H^{\circ} = \begin{pmatrix} -25.2 \end{pmatrix} \text{ kcal/mole}$$
$$\Delta C_p = \begin{pmatrix} -2.0 \end{pmatrix} \text{ g/mole}$$

log A	E	log k_T (510)	Conditions	System	Surface	References
11.7	34.6	-3.13	473–548 °K	static		[1] A. D. Ketley, A. J. Berlin, E. Gorman, and L. P. Fisher, J. Org. Chem. 31, 305 (1966).

Preferred:
  Suspect.

Comments: Transition state estimates give log $k = 13.9-39.7/\theta$. The parameters are too low. The badly behaved Arrhenius plot (with high rates at the lower temperatures) suggests some surface catalysis.

Experimental

[1] Static system. Analysis by G.L.C. 0.5-ml samples were sealed in 2.5-ml pyrex ampules. Parameters above are maximum values calculated from reported rate constants at 200, 212, and 234 °C. The Arrhenius plot showed bad curvature. The β(C—C) split product expected from a biradical mechanism was not observed. A number of other decompositions were also studied [(A), (B), and (C)] but no rate constant data for these were reported. However, the exclusive products formed were from A and and from C.

Reaction: Bromocyclopropane

$$\text{(I)} \xrightarrow{\;a\;} CH_2\!=\!CHCH_2Br \;\text{(II)}$$
$$\xrightarrow{\;b\;} BrCH\!=\!CHCH_3 \;\text{(III)}$$

	I	II	III
$\Delta H^\circ_{f(298)}$	18.7	9.5	11.2
$S^\circ_{(298)}$	70.2	76.4	74.5
$C^\circ_{p(298)}$	16.8	19.4	18.5

a
$\Delta S^\circ = 6.2$ g/mole
$\Delta H^\circ = -9.2$ kcal/mole
$\Delta C_p = 2.6$ g/mole

Path	log A	E	log k_T (610)	Conditions	System	Surface	References
$a+b$	13.5	47.3	−3.45	583–633 °K 120–320 torr	static	———————	[1] R.C.S. Grant and E. S. Swinborne, Chem. Comm. 620 (1966).

Preferred:
   Suspect.

Comments: Both Arrhenius parameters are low in terms of transition state estimates for a biradical three-membered ring isomerization. However, they are very similar to those for the *sec*-butyl bromide four-center elimination reaction (i.e., $k_{elim} = 10^{13.5-46.5/\theta}$ which is known to have an appreciable free radical component in the uninhibited system. It is most likely, then, that this reaction is a free radical process with the following mechanism:

Estimates: *Units:*
   $k_i' = 10^{13.6-58/\theta}$ k_i, k_3 sec^{-1}
   $\log k_i \simeq 14.6-70/\theta$ k_1, k_t (1/mole-sec)
   $\log k_t \simeq 11.0$
   $\log k_1 \simeq 10.7-16.2/\theta$

allyl Br $\overset{i'}{\rightleftarrows}$ allyl · + Br ·   } initiations

Br· + $\underset{}{\overset{Br}{\triangledown}}$ $\underset{2}{\overset{1}{\rightleftarrows}}$ $\left(\overset{Br}{\triangledown}\right)^{*}_{-H}$ + HBr

R · $\xrightarrow[3]{\text{fast}}$ allyl radical (R′ ·)   } chain

R′ · + HBr $\overset{4}{\rightleftarrows}$ R′H + Br (product)

R′· + Br · $\xrightarrow{t}$ $\overset{Br}{\triangledown}$ termination

(Continued)

————————
*Alternatively, the ring-opening reaction:

$$Br + c\text{-}C_3H_5Br \overset{1'}{\rightleftarrows} \dot{C}H_2CHBrCH_2Br \xrightarrow{\text{fast}} CH_2\!=\!CHCH_2Br + Br$$

Bromocyclopropane (*Continued*)

Experimental

[1] Static experiment. Analyses by G.I..C. The ratio of products $\frac{\text{3-bromo}}{\text{1-bromo}}$ decreased with time. 3-bromopropene was found to isomerize to 1-bromopropene at roughly (1/2) the rate of the bromocyclopropane isomerization. The olefin isomerization was catalyzed by HBr. Surface effects were not studied.

Reaction: Dimethyldiazirine

$$\left(\begin{array}{c} CH_3 \\ CH_3 \end{array} C \begin{array}{c} N \\ \| \\ N \end{array} \right) (I) \longrightarrow N_2 + \diagup\!\!\diagup \diagdown (III)$$

		I	II	III
$\Delta H^\circ_{f(298)}$		72.0	0	4.8
$S_{(298)}$		69.0	45.8	63.6
$C^\circ_{p(298)}$		23.2	7.0	15.3

$\Delta S^\circ = -40.4$ g/mole
$\Delta H^\circ = -68.2$ kcal/mole
$\Delta C^\circ_p = -0.9$ g/mole

log A	E	log k_T (*422*)	Conditions	System	Surface	References
13.89	33.17	-3.31	422 ± 25 °K 2.3 $-$ 100 torr (4)	static		[1] H. M. Frey and I. D. R. Stevens, J. Chem. Soc., 3865 (1962).

Preferred:
   Reliable. log $k = 13.89$–$33.17/\theta$

Comments: The reaction very likely proceeds through a hot diazo compound intermediate.

Mechanism: $\begin{array}{c} CH_3 \\ CH_3 \end{array} C \begin{array}{c} N \\ \| \\ N \end{array} \rightleftarrows \left(\begin{array}{c} CH_3 \\ CH_3 \end{array} C : \begin{array}{c} N \\ \diagdown N \end{array} \rightleftarrows \begin{array}{c} CH_3 \\ CH_3 \end{array} C = N \equiv N \right) \xrightarrow{E_{H-mig} = 10.8} \diagup\!\!\diagup \diagdown + N_2$

If the DH°(C—N) bond is taken as the activation energy observed for the decomposition of 2.2′-azobutane ($\diagdown$ N=N $\diagdown$) (see section V–7.0) and a normal cyclopropane strain is assumed, then $E_{est} \simeq 47.5 - 27.6 + 10.8 = 30.7$ kcal/mole, in reasonable agreement with the observed value.

Experimental

[1] Analysis by G.L.C. ($\Delta N_2 = \Delta P$) Falloff observed below 100 torr. The rate constant parameters in the falloff region at 4 torr; therefore, in the high-pressure region somewhat higher values would pertain. Propylene did not affect the rate.

Reaction: 3,3-Diethyldiazirine

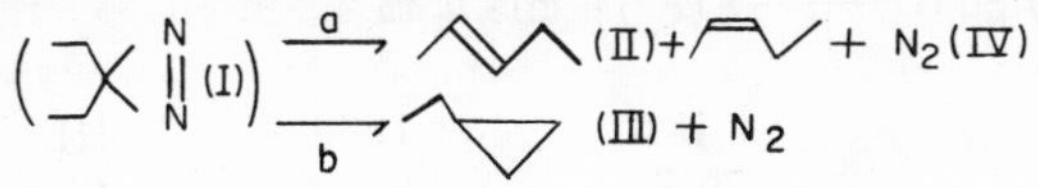

	I	II	III	IV
$\Delta H^\circ_{f(298)}$	63.1	−7.7	0.7	0.
$S^\circ_{(298)}$	87.8	82.2	76.5	45.8
$C^\circ_{p(298)}$	33.2	25.8	24.0	7.0

a(trans)
$\Delta S^\circ =$ 40.2 g/mole
$\Delta H^\circ = -70.8$ kcal/mole
$\Delta C_p =$ 0.4 g/mole

Path	log *A*	*E*	log k_T *(405)*	Conditions	System	Surface	References
(*a*+*b*)	13.73	31.89	−3.48	391–422 °K 1–20 torr (10 torr)	static		[1] H. M. Frey and A. W. Scaplehorn, J. Chem. Soc. **A,** 968 (1966).

Preferred:
Reliable. $\log k = 13.73 - 31.89/\theta$.

Comments: Transition state estimates give, $E \simeq DH^\circ(\text{C—N}) - \Delta_{st} + E_{r.c.} \simeq 47.5 - 27.6 + 10.8 = 30.7$ kcal/mole and $A_{est} \simeq 10^{13.9}$ sec^{-1} (see dimethyldiazirine). The ethylcyclopropane product probably forms from a 1,3–H atom shift in an intermediate hot olefin:

$$CH_3CH_2\ddot{C}C_2H_5 \xrightarrow{\text{1,2-H shift}} CH_3\dot{C}H\dot{C}HC_2H_5 \longrightarrow \text{2-pentene}$$

$$\downarrow \text{1,4-H shift}$$

$$CH_3CH_2\ddot{C}C_2H_5 \xrightarrow{\text{1,3-H shift}} \dot{C}H_2CH_2\dot{C}HC_2H_5 \longrightarrow$$

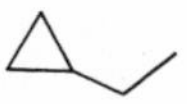

Experimental

[1] Static system. Analysis by G.L.C. The ratio of products was (*cis*/*trans*/ (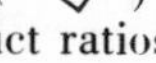) = (30.6/67.5/1.6) independent of temperature and percent decomposition. The problem of differences in product ratios between thermal and photochemical diazirine systems is discussed relative to hot carbene intermediates in the photochemical systems. Results are inconclusive.

Reaction: 3,3-Tetramethylenediazirine

$$(\langle\!\!\!\backslash\!\!\!\backslash N \rangle) \,(\mathrm{I}) \longrightarrow (\langle\!\!\!\backslash \rangle) \;\; (\mathrm{II}) + N_2 \,(\mathrm{III})$$

	I	II	III
$\Delta H^{\circ}_{f(298)}$	79.7	8.6	0
$S^{\circ}_{(298)}$	77.6	69.2	45.8
$C^{\circ}_{p(298)}$	25.3	18.1	7.0

$\Delta S^{\circ} = -37.4$ g/mole
$\Delta H^{\circ} = -71.1$ kcal/mole
$\Delta C^{\circ}_{p} = -\ 0.2$ g/mole

log A	E	log k_T (390)	Conditions	System	Surface	References
13.4	30.5	−3.70	373–412 °K $P_T \sim 1$–150 torr (7 torr)	static no (SN) effect	None	[1] H. M. Frey and A. W. Scaplehorn, J. Chem. Soc. **A**, 968 (1966).

Preferred:
   $\log k = 13.4$–$30.5/\theta$.

Comments: Transition state estimates for a biradical mechanism (see dimethyldiazirine) are in good agreement with the observed parameters.

Experimental

[1] Analysis by G.L.C.

Reaction: 3,3-Pentamethylenediazirine

	I	II	III
$\Delta H^\circ_{f(298)}$	68.4	−0.8	0
$S^\circ_{(298)}$	78.5	74.3	45.8
$C^\circ_{p(298)}$	31.9	25.3	7.0

$\Delta S = 41.6$ g/mole
$\Delta H^\circ = -69.2$ kcal/mole
$\Delta C^\circ_p = 0.4$ g/mole

log A	E	log k_T (390)	Conditions	System	Surface	References
13.34	30.87	−3.96	374–410 °K $P \sim 1$–150 torr (5 torr)	static		[1] H. M. Frey and A. W. Scaplehorn, J. Chem. Soc. **B**, 968 (1966).

Preferred:
   log $k = 13.34 - 30.87/\theta$.

Comments: A biradical mechanism is consistent with the observed parameters (see dimethyldiazirine).

Experimental

[1] Analysis by G.L.C. on cyclohexene.

Reaction: Difluorodiazirine

$$\underset{F}{\overset{F}{\diagdown}}C\underset{N}{\overset{N}{\diagup}}\!\!\parallel (I) \longrightarrow CF_2\colon (II) + N_2 \ (III)$$

	I	II	III
$\Delta H^\circ_{f(298)}$		-39.7	0
$S^\circ_{(298)}$	69	57.5	45.8
$C^\circ_{p(298)}$		9.1	7.0

$\Delta S^\circ = (34.3)$ g/mole
$\Delta H^\circ =$
$\Delta C_p^\circ =$

log A	E	log k_T (424)	Conditions	System	Surface	References
13.1	32.2	-3.12	400–447 °K 100–800 torr (200)	static	none	[1] E. W. Neuvar and R. A. Mitsch, J. Phys. Chem. **71**, 1229 (1967).

Preferred:
   $\log k = 13.9 – 33.2/\theta$.

Comments: Since the reaction was in its falloff region, the reported parameters are probably low. (See, for comparison, dimethyldiazirine decomposition.) We have assumed $k_{exp} \simeq 1/2 \ k_\infty$ and raised A to the calculated value.

Experimental

   [1] Analysis by G.L.C. on CF_2N_2 disappearance. Pyrolysis performed in excess C_2F_4 to trap CF_2: as $(\nabla)_{F6}$. Reaction is in its falloff region; therefore parameters are slightly low; however, it was estimated that $E_{200 \ mm} \simeq E_\infty$.

Reaction: Ethylidenecyclopropane (I)
2-Methyl-1-methylenecyclopropane (II)

	I	II
$\Delta H^\circ_{f(298)}$	39.1	38.3
$S^\circ_{(298)}$	74.7	74.5
$C^\circ_{p(298)}$	21.6	24.2

$\Delta S^\circ = -0.2$ g/mole
$\Delta H^\circ = -0.8$ kcal/mole
$\Delta C^\circ_p = 2.6$ g/mole

Path	$\log A$	E	$\log k_T$ (488)	Conditions	System	Surface	References
a	14.0	40.76	−4.25	488 ± 18 °K (25 torr)	static	<10%	[1] J. P. Chesick, J. Am. Chem. Soc. **85**, 2720 (1963).
b	13.9	40.26	−4.13				

Preferred:
Reliable as reported.

Comments: The observed kinetics are consistent with the biradical mechanism with ring opening (assisted by one allylic resonance) rate determining. Transition state estimates give:

$$\log k_a = 14.1 - 39.3/\theta$$
$$\log k_b = 14.2 - 38.8/\theta \text{ (see section III-4.2)}.$$

Experimental

[1] Analysis by G.L.C. Both reactions proceeded to the equilibrium state. The equilibrium constant for the isomerization was:

$$K_{a,b} = 10^{0.64/4.575 - 0.57/\theta}$$
$$K_{a,b} = 0.77 \text{ at } 210 \text{ °C}.$$

Reaction: Oxirane (ethylene oxide)

$$\triangle^{\!\!\!o}\,(\mathrm{I}) \;\rightarrow\; \mathrm{CH_3CHO^*\ (II)} \xrightarrow{\text{fast}} \text{acetaldehyde decomposition products } [\mathrm{CH_4 + CO}]$$

	I	II
$\Delta H^\circ_{f(298)}$	-13.2	-39.8
$S^\circ_{(298)}$	59.4	63.2
$C^\circ_{p(298)}$	11.4	13.1

$\Delta S^\circ = \quad 3.8$ g/mole
$\Delta H^\circ = -26.6$ kcal/mole
$\Delta C^\circ_p = \quad 1.7$ g/mole

log A	E	log k_T (670)	Conditions	System	Surface	References
14.13	56.9	-4.39	673 ± 30 °K (30) torr	static		[1] M. L. Neufeld and A. T. Blades, Can. J. Chem. **41**, 2956 (1963).
14.34	57.4	-4.34	668 ± 45 °K 180–440 torr	static	< 10%	[2] K. H. Mueller and W. D. Walters, J. Am. Chem. Soc. **73**, 1458 (1951); J. Am. Chem. Soc. **76**, 330 (1954).
———	55.2		1050 ± 50 °K	flow		[3] L. Crocco, I. Glassman, and I. E. Smith, J. Chem. Phys. **31**, 506 (1959).

Preferred:
    log $k = 14.34 - 57.4/\theta$.

Comments: The "hot" acetaldehyde intermediate decomposes to $\mathrm{CH_4 + CO}$ at low pressures and is stabilized at high pressures. For a biradical mechanistic interpretation and review of this reaction, see S. W. Benson, J. Chem. Phys. **40**, 105 (1964). The H-migration activation energy from the kinetics is estimated to be about 4.4 kcal/mole (i.e., appreciably lower than the 1,2-H-migration in cyclopropane). Transition state estimate gives: log $A_{\mathrm{est}} = 14.5$ (see section III–4.0).

Experimental

[1] Analysis by G.L.C. Rates obtained from initial rates under maximum inhibition with propylene.
[2] Analysis by G.L.C. Rates obtained under "maximum inhibition" conditions with propylene.
[3] Rates determined by "temperature profile history." Short chain mechanism proposed from which the activation energy was deduced.

---

*Indicates vibrationally excited acetaldehyde.

Reaction: β,β-Dimethylcyclopropyl methyl ketone (2,2-dimethylcyclopropyl-1-ethanone)

	I	II
$\Delta H^\circ_{f(298)}$	-40.8	-46.7
$S^\circ_{(298)}$	93.9	105.5
$C^\circ_{p(298)}$	36.0	39.0

$\Delta S^\circ = 11.6$ g/mole
$\Delta H^\circ = -5.9$ kcal/mole
$\Delta C^\circ_p = 3.0$ g/mole

log A	E	log k_T (430)	Conditions	System	Surface	References
12.6	33	-4.15	425–436 °K 0.1 mm Hg	static		[1] R. M. Roberts and R. G. Landolt, J. Am. Chem. Soc. **87**, 2281 (1965).

Preferred:
   log $k = 12.6 - 33/\theta$.

Comments: Note the similarity in mechanism between the diolefin isomerization, *cis*-2-methyl penta-1,3-diene ⟶ 4-methyl penta-1,3-diene. The initial product is probably enol which rearranges on the walls to the ketone.

Experimental

   [1] Rates based on G.L.C. analysis. 1-Acetyl-*trans*-2-methylcyclopropane was stable up to 460 °K, indicating a six-center, concerted, "ene" reaction.

Reaction: Perfluorooxirane (tetrafluorooxirane; tetrafluoroethylene oxide)

$$CF_2\text{---}CF_2 \ (I) \longrightarrow CF_2O \ (II) + CF_2: (III)$$
$$\diagdown O \diagup$$

	I	II	III
$\Delta H^\circ_{f(298)}$			-39.7
$S^\circ_{(298)}$	74.6		57.5
$C^\circ_{p(298)}$			9.1

$\Delta S^\circ =$
$\Delta H^\circ =$
$\Delta C^\circ_{pr} =$

log A	E	log k_T (363)	Conditions	System	Surface	References
13.7	31.6	-5.32	363 ± 50 °K 0.13 − 785 torr (785)	static	< 10%	[1] M. Lenzi and A. Mele. J. Chem. Phys. **43**, 1974 (1965).

Preferred:
Reliable. log $k = 13.7 - 31.6/\theta$

Experimental

[1] Rate and analysis by G.L.C. and I.R. A free radical non-chain mechanism was proposed with the above initiation rate determining step. Falloff observed near 780 torr. The RRK-$s \simeq 8.9$ fit the falloff data. The CF_2: biradicals gave C_2F_4 (low percent conversion) and perfluorocyclopropane (high percent conversions). An isomerization on the walls leading to trifluoroacetylfluoride was also observed.

Reaction: Cyclobutane

$$\square \xrightarrow{(I)} 2(C_2H_4) \ (II)$$

	I	II
$\Delta H_{f(298)}$	6.3	12.5
$S^\circ_{(298)}$	63.5	52.5
$C^\circ_{p(298)}$	17.4	10.4

$\Delta S^\circ = 41.5$ g/mole
$\Delta \dot{H}^\circ = 18.7$ kcal/mole
$\Delta C^\circ_p = 3.4$ g/mole

log A	E	log k_T (717)	Conditions	System	Surface	References
15.6	62.5	-3.45	717 ± 24 °K 1–996 torr (120)	static		[1] C. T. Genaux, F. Kern, and W. D. Walters, J. Am. Chem. Soc. **75,** 6196 (1953).
15.62	62.5	-3.47	728 ± 45 °K 240–1500 torr (650–790) °K (1250–1500) torr	static	none	[2] R. W. Carr, Jr., and W. D. Walters, J. Phys. Chem. **67,** 1370 (1963).

Preferred:
$\log k = 15.6 - 62.5/\theta$.

Comments: By the biradical mechanism, $\log k_{est} = 15.6 - 63.2/\theta$ (see section III–5.0).

Mechanism: $\square \underset{2}{\overset{1}{\rightleftarrows}} \diagdown\!\!\!\!\diagup\! \xrightarrow{3} 2(=) \quad k_2 \simeq k_3$ and $E_2 \simeq E_3$

Experimental

[1] Analysis by M.S. Rate by ΔP. Confirmed stoichiometry. Falloff observed near 20 torr. Cyclobutane decomposition did not sensitize the decomposition of H_2CO or the polymerization of C_2H_4 indicating the absence of free radicals.

[2] Analysis by M.S. Rate by ΔP. No evidence for a decrease in the k_x with increasing pressure for the two pressure ranges studied. (See D. J. Wilson, J. Phys. Chem. **64,** 323 (1960).)

General: For preliminary studies with regard to surface and inhibitor effects see F. Kern and W. D. Walters, Proc. Natl. Acad Sci. **38,** No. 16, 937 (1952). For relative collision efficiencies of various third bodies, see H. O. Pritchard. R. G. Sowden, and A. F. Trotman-Dickinson, Proc. Roy. Soc. **A218,** 416 (1953). For falloff characteristics, see C. T. Genaux and W. D. Walters, J. Am. Chem. Soc. **73,** 4497 (1951); J. N. Butler and R. B. Ogawa, J. Am. Chem. Soc. **85,** 3346 (1963); and R. W. Vreeland and D. F. Swinehart, J. Am. Chem. Soc. **85,** 3349 (1963).

Reaction: Methylcyclobutane

$$\square\!\!\!/\ {\scriptstyle (\mathrm{I})}\longrightarrow\ C_3H_6\ (\mathrm{II}) + C_2H_4\ (\mathrm{III})$$

	I	II	III
$\Delta H^\circ_{f(298)}$	-0.7	4.8	12.5
$S^\circ_{(298)}$	74.4	63.6	52.5
$C^\circ_{p(298)}$	22.6	15.3	10.4
$C^\circ_{p(700)}$	49.0	28.4	18.8

$\Delta S^\circ = 31.7$ g/mole
$\Delta H^\circ = 18.0$ kcal/mole
$\Delta C^\circ_p = 3.1$ g/mole

log A	E	log k_T (703)	Conditions	System	Surface	References
15.38	61.2	-3.65	703 ± 20 °K 7–417 torr (10), (200)	static	none	[1] M. N. Das and W. D. Walters, Zeit. fur Physik. Chemie **N.F.15,** 23 (1958).

Preferred:
Reliable as reported.

Comments: By the biradical mechanism (see cyclobutane) products are those expected and log $k_{est} = 15.5-62.1/\theta$ (see section III–5.0).

Experimental

[1] Analysis by I.R. and M. S. Rate by ΔP. Rate unaffected by added NO, toluene, and propylene and by KCl surface. Falloff observed near 10 torr (700 °K) with an RRK–$s \simeq 23$. (See A. F. Pataracchia and W. D. Walters, J. Phys. Chem. **68,** 3894 (1964).)

Reaction: *trans*-1,2-Dimethylcyclobutane

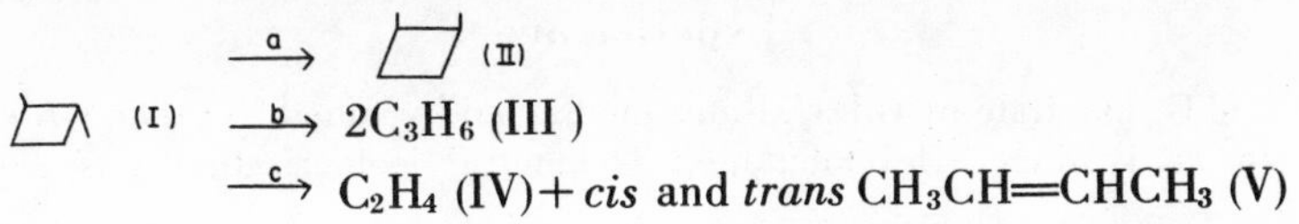

	I	II	III	IV	V *cis*	V *trans*
$\Delta H^\circ_{f(298)}$	-7.7	-6.7	4.8	12.5	-1.7	-2.7
$S^\circ_{(298)}$	81.1	82.3	63.6	52.5	72.1	70.9
$C^\circ_{p(298)}$	27.9	26.5	15.3	10.4	18.9	21.0
$C^\circ_{p(700)}$	59.4	58.9	28.4	18.8	37.6	38.4

	a	b
$\Delta S^\circ =$	1.2	46.1 g/mole
$\Delta H^\circ =$	1.0	17.3 kcal/mole
$\Delta C^\circ_p =$	-1.4	2.7 g/mole

Path	log A	E	log k_T	Conditions	System	Surface	References
a	14.57	61.3	-4.90	688±25 °K 13–375 torr (15–19)	static	none	[1] H. R. Gerberich and W. D. Walters, J. Chem. Soc. **83**, 4884 (1961).
b	15.45	61.6	-4.12	(as above)			
c	15.46	63.4	-4.68	(as above)			

Preferred:
Reliable as reported.

Comments: Products are those expected by the biradical mechanism. The biradical mechanism is shown below.

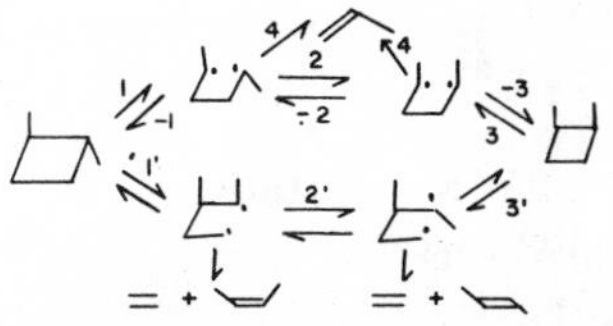

Rates of the competitive reactions from the biradical intermediates (i.e., internal rotations, ring closings, and decompositions) must all be competitive processes with comparable rate constants and rate constant parameters. Since the (*cis/trans*) but-2-ene ratios differ depending on the starting isomer, these reactions are rotationally controlled.

By applying steady state considerations to the above mechanism and by making reasonable assumptions regarding the relative rates of three of the pertinent reactions, it has been possible to obtain estimates of the rate constants for decomposition, internal rotation, and C_4 ring closing from the biradical intermediates. (See E. O'Neal and S. W. Benson, J. Phys. Chem. **72**, 1866 (1968).)

Activation energies for ring closing and decomposition in the analysis are both comparable. $E_{r.c.} \simeq E_{dec} \simeq 7.4$ kcal/mole.

Estimated:

log $k_a = 14.4$–$61.1/\theta$
log $k_b = 14.9$–$61.4/\theta$
log $k_c = 15.3$–$63.2/\theta$ (see secton III–5.0).

Continued

Experimental

[1] Analysis by I.R. and G.L.C. Rate by G.L.C. Rates unaffected by added NO. The (*trans/cis*) but-2-ene ratio ≃ 9 (See also results on *cis*-1,2-dimethylcyclobutane.) Geometric isomerization was slow relative to structural isomerization.

Reaction: *cis*-1,2-Dimethylcyclobutane

$$\square_{(I)} \begin{array}{l} \xrightarrow{a} \square_{(II)} \\ \xrightarrow{b} 2C_3H_6 \ (III) \\ \xrightarrow{c} cis \ \text{and} \ trans \ CH_3CH{=}CHCH_3 \ (IV) + C_2H_4 \ (V) \end{array}$$

	I	II	III	IV *cis*	IV *trans*	V
$\Delta H^\circ_{f(298)}$	−6.7	−7.7	4.8	−1.7	−2.7	12.5
$S^\circ_{(298)}$	82.3	81.1	63.6	72.1	70.9	52.5
$C^\circ_{p(298)}$	26.5	27.9	15.3	18.9	21.0	10.4
$C^\circ_{p(700)}$	58.9	59.4	28.4	37.6	38.4	18.8

	a	$c(cis)$
$\Delta S^\circ =$	−1.2	42.3 g/mole
$\Delta H^\circ =$	−1.0	17.5 kcal/mole
$\Delta C^\circ_p =$	1.4	2.8 g/mole

Path	log A	E	log k_T (688)	Conditions	System	Surface	References
a	14.81	60.1	−4.28	688 ± 25 °K 13–375 torr (15–19)	static	none	[1] H. R. Gerberich and W. D. Walters, J. Am Chem. Soc. **83**, 4884 (1961).
b	15.48	60.4	−3.51	678 ± 25 °K 5.8–393 torr (15)	static	none	[2] H. R. Gerberich and W. D. Walters, J. Am. Chem. Soc. **83**, 3935 (1961).
c	15.57	63.4	−4.57	(as above)			Ref. [2]

Preferred:
    Reliable as reported. (see also *trans*-1,2-dimethylcyclobutane)
Comments: Compare reported parameters to transition state estimates which give:
    log $k_a = 14.7 − 60.1/\theta$
    log $k_b = 15.2 − 60.4/\theta$
    log $k_c = 15.3 − 62.2/\theta$ (see section III–5.0).

Experimental

[1] Analysis by I.R. and G.L.C. Rate by G.L.C.
[2] Analysis by I.R. and G.L.C. Rates by G.L.C. Rates were not affected by added NO and propylene. The ratio of (*cis/trans*) but-2-ene was ≃ 1.8. The geometric isomerization to *trans*-1,2-dimethylcyclobutane was slow relative to the structural isomerizations.

Reaction: Ethylcyclobutane

$$\text{(I)} \longrightarrow C_2H_4 \text{ (II)} + CH_2\!\!=\!\!CHCH_2CH_3 \text{ (III)}$$

	I	II	III
$\Delta H^\circ_{f(298)}$	-5.2	12.5	0
$S^\circ_{(298)}$	83.8	52.5	73.6
$C^\circ_{p(298)}$	28.1	10.4	20.5
$C^\circ_{p(700)}$	59.2	18.8	38.7

$\Delta S^\circ = 42.3$ g/mole
$\Delta H^\circ = 17.7$ kcal/mole
$\Delta C^\circ_p = 2.8$ g/mole

log A	E	log k_T (713)	Conditions	System	Surface	References
15.56	62.0	-3.45	713 ± 20 °K 7–400 torr (10, 70, 200)	static	none	[1] R. E. Wellman and W. D. Walters, J. Am. Chem. Soc. **79,** 1542 (1957).

Preferred:
    log $k = 15.56 - 62.0/\theta$.

Comments: By the biradical mechanism, the parameters should be about the same as those for methylcyclo-butane. Products are those expected. Transition state estimates for the biradical mechanism (see section II–5.0) give: log $k_{\text{est}} = 15.3 - 61.6/\theta$.

Experimental

[1] Analysis by I.R., M.S. Rates by ΔP. Rates were unaffected by added NO, propylene, and toluene.

Reaction: *n*-Propylcyclobutane

(I) $\longrightarrow$ $CH_2=CHCH_2CH_3$ (II) + C_2H_4 (III)

	I	II	III
$\Delta H^\circ_{f(298)}$	-10.1	-4.9	12.5
$S^\circ_{(298)}$	93.2	82.8	52.5
$C^\circ_{p(298)}$	33.6	26.2	10.4
$C^\circ_{p(700)}$	69.4	49.1	18.8

$\Delta S^\circ = 42.1$ g/mole
$\Delta H^\circ = 17.7$ kcal/mole
$\Delta C^\circ_p = 3.0$ g/mole

log A	E	log k_T (710)	Conditions	System	Surface	References
15.53	61.6	-3.68	701 ± 28 °K 5.4–495 torr (5.4, 117)	static	none	[1] S. M. E. Kellner and W. D. Walters, J. Phys. Chem. **65**, 466 (1961)

Preferred:
   Reliable.

Comments: Transition state estimates are the same as those for ethylcyclobutane (see section III–5.0)

Experimental

[1] Analysis by I.R., M.S., G.L.C. Rates by ΔP; unaffected by added NO, propylene, and toluene. Side product less than 2 percent of total products.

Reaction: Isopropylcyclobutane

$$\diagup\!\!\!\!\square\text{ (I)} \longrightarrow C_2H_4\text{ (II)} + CH_2{=}CHCH(CH_3)_2\text{ (II)}$$

	I	II	III
$\Delta H^\circ_{f(298)}$	-11.1	12.5	-6.9
$S^\circ_{(298)}$	90.5	52.5	79.7
$C^\circ_{p(298)}$	33.4	10.4	28.5
$C^\circ_{p(700)}$	69.6	18.8	50.2

$^\circ = 41.7$ g/mole
$^{\prime\circ} = 16.7$ kcal/mole
$^{\circ}_p = 5.5$ g/mole

og A	E	log k_T (708)	Conditions	System	Surface	References
15.63	62.6	-3.70	708 ± 25 °K 9–55 torr (12)	static	none	[1] M. Zupan and W. D. Walters, J. Phys. Chem. **67**, 1845 (1963).

eferred:
    Reliable.

mments: Transition state estimates for the biradical mechanism give: $\log k = 15.3 - 61.4/\theta$, in good agreement with the observed parameters (see section III–5.0).

Experimental

[1] Analysis by I.R., M.S., G.L.C. Rate by ΔP. Less than 1 percent side products.

Reaction: Isopropenylcyclobutane

	I	II	III	IV
$\Delta H_{f(298)}$	16.9	12.5	18.1	−10.5
$S^\circ_{(298)}$	89.0	52.5	75.4	82.3
$C^\circ_{p(298)}$	34.0	10.4	25.0	31.4
$C^\circ_{p(600)}$	59.4	17.1	41.4	40.1

	a	b
$\Delta S^\circ =$	38.9	−6.7 g/mole
$\Delta H^\circ =$	13.7	−27.4 kcal/mole
$\Delta C^\circ_p =$	1.4	−2.6 g/mole

Path	log A	E	log k_T (599)	Conditions	System	Surface	References
a	14.64	51.03	−3.98	599 ± 24 °K 1–40 torr (3.5)	static	none	[1] R. J. Ellis and H. M Frey, Trans Faraday Soc. **59,** 2076 (1963).
b	14.53	51.03	−4.09	←——— as above ———→			

Preferred:

$\log k_a = 14.64 - 51.03/\theta$; $\log k_b = 14.53 - 51.03/\theta$

Comments: Products are those expected from the biradical mechanism (see section III–5.2). We estima log k_a = log k_b = 14.2 − 49.3/θ. If the rate constant parameters are compared to those of isopropylcyc butane (i.e., $k = 10^{15.6-62.6/\theta}$sec^{-1}), it appears that close to a full allylic resonance (i.e., $E_{res} \simeq 12.6$ kcal/mo is achieved in the transition state.

Experimental

[1] Analysis by G.L.C. In clean reaction cells (unconditioned walls) other products were produced. The ratio paths *a* and *b* products was essentially temperature independent.

Reaction: Oxetane (trimethylene oxide)

$$\square^{\alpha\,(I)}_{\beta} \longrightarrow C_2H_4(II) + CH_2O (III)$$

	I	II	III
$\Delta H^\circ_{f(298)}$	-19.3	12.5	-27.7
$S^\circ_{(298)}$	63.5	52.5	53.7
$C^\circ_{p(298)}$	14.3	10.4	8.5

$\Delta S^\circ = 42.7$ g/mole
$\Delta H^\circ = 4.1$ kcal/mole
$\Delta C^\circ_p = 4.6$ g/mole

log A	E	log k_T (713)	Conditions	System	Surface	References
14.78	60	-3.61	713 ± 20 °K 54–330 torr (100)	static	< 10%	[1] D. A. Bittker and W. D. Walters, J. Am. Chem. Soc. **77**, 1429 (1955).

Preferred:
  $\log k = 14.78 - 60/\theta$.

Comments: Transition state estimates for the biradical mechanism (see cyclobutane and section III–5.0). Path ring opening via an α (C—O) split gives: $\log A_{est} = 14.7$; $E_{est} = 59.0$ kcal/mole. The activation energy for β C—C) split is estimated to be more than 3 kcal/mole higher and is therefore probably not important.

Experimental

[1] Analysis by I.R., M.S., Chem., P.O.L. Stoichiometry confirmed in the initial stages. Rates were determined by in the presence of added NO, propylene, or toluene. The uninhibited rate was 10 percent faster. The origin of the free radical component to the decomposition was attributed to the subsequent decomposition of the formaldehyde product.

Reaction: 3,3-Dimethyloxetane (3,3-dimethylketane)

$$\beta\,\boxed{}^{\alpha}\ (\mathrm{I}) \rightarrow (CH_3)_2C{=}CH_2\,(\mathrm{II}) + CH_2O\,(\mathrm{III})$$

	I	II	III
$\Delta H^\circ_{f(298)}$	−34.0	−4.0	−27.7
$S^\circ_{(298)}$	75.4	70.2	53.7
$C^\circ_{p(298)}$	25.6	21.4	8.5

$\Delta S^\circ = 48.5$ g/mole
$\Delta H^\circ = 2.3$ kcal/mole
$\Delta C^\circ_p = 4.3$ g/mole

log A	E	log k_T (700)	Conditions	System	Surface	References
15.58	60.7	−3.37	698 ± 25 °K 6–70 torr	static	none	[1] G. F. Cohoe and W. D. Walters, J. Phys. Chem. **71**, 2326 (1967).

Preferred:
   Reliable. log $k = 15.58 - 60.7/\theta$.

Comments: Transition state calculations indicate that the reaction should proceed almost exclusively ▼
β (C−C) cleavage rather than by an α (C−C) split as in trimethylene oxide. Thus one estimates (for
mechanism like cyclobutane):

$$\beta\ (C\text{--}C)\ \text{split:}\quad \log k = 16.2 - 60.3/\theta$$

$$\alpha\ (C\text{--}C)\ \text{split:}\quad \log k = 14.7 - 59.8/\theta$$

Experimental

   [1] Analysis by G.L.C. Good mass balances were obtained. Rates were unaffected by additions of C_3H_6, and up
50 percent NO.

Reaction: Cyclobutane carboxaldehyde

$$\square_{CH=O} \; (I) \longrightarrow C_2H_4 \; (II) + CH_2{=}CH{-}CH{=}O \; (III)$$

	I	II	III
$\Delta H^\circ_{f(298)}$	-19.6	12.5	-16.6
$S^\circ_{(298)}$	80.7	52.5	(67.3)
$C^\circ_{p(298)}$	23.9	10.4	17.1
$C^\circ_{p(600)}$	42.4	17.1	26.0

$\Delta S^\circ = 39.1$ g/mole
$\Delta H^\circ = 15.5$ kcal/mole
$\Delta C^\circ_p = 3.6$ g/mole

log A	E	log k_T (653)	Conditions	System	Surface	References
14.43	53.3	-3.41	653 ± 20 °K 9–35 torr (9–12)	static	none	[1] B. C. Roquitte and W. D. Walters, J. Am. Chem. Soc. **84**, 4049 (1962).

Preferred:
Reliable as reported. log $k = 14.43 - 53.3/\theta$

Comments: A resonance energy of 8.7 kcal/mole for $\text{(} \overset{O}{\underset{H}{\text{C}}}{<} \text{)}$ is inferred. (See also ethanoylcyclobutane.)
Transition state estimates give: log $A_{est} = 14.2$.

Experimental

[1] Analysis by I.R., M.S., G.L.C., P.O.L., U.V. Rates by ΔP. Rates were unaffected by additions of NO, propylene, toluene, and by a KCl surface.

Reaction: Ethanoylcyclobutane (methyl cyclobutyl ketone)

$$CH_3CO—\square \ (1) \longrightarrow C_2H_4 \ (II) + CH_3CO—CH{=}CH_2 \ (III)$$

	I	II	III
$\Delta H^\circ_{f(298)}$	-30.9	12.5	-28.6
$S^\circ_{(298)}$	89.3	52.5	76.0
$C^\circ_{p(298)}$	28.7	10.4	21.5
$C^\circ_{p(600)}$	52.7	17.1	36.9

$\Delta S^\circ = 39.2$ g/mole
$\Delta H^\circ = 14.8$ kcal/mole
$\Delta C^\circ_p = 3.2$ g/mole

log A	E	log k_T (658)	Conditions	System	Surface	References
14.53	54.5	-3.56	658 ± 25 °K 10–65 torr (5C)	static	none	[1] L. G. Daignault and W. D. Walters, J. Am. Chem. Soc. **80**, 541 (1958).

Preferred:
   $\log k = 14.53 - 54.5/\theta$.

Comments: Biradical mechanism estimates: $\log k = 14.4 - 54.4/\theta$. Comparison of the rate constant parameters with those of isopropyl cyclobutane suggest a carbonyl resonance $\left(\overset{O}{\underset{}{\lambda}\!\!\!\diagdown} \right)$ stabilization of about 7.9 kcal/mole.

Experimental

[1] Analysis by I.R., M.S., U.V. Rates by ΔP. Rates were unaffected by NO, toluene, and propylene.

Reaction: Propionylcyclobutane (ethyl cyclobutyl ketone)

$$C_2H_5\overset{\overset{O}{\|}}{C}\!\!-\!\!\square \quad (I) \longrightarrow C_2H_4 \ (II) + CH_3CH_2\overset{\overset{O}{\|}}{C}CH=\!\!CH_2 \ (III)$$

	I	II	III
$\Delta H^\circ_{f(298)}$	-36.3	12.5	-33.9
$S^\circ_{(298)}$	98.3	52.5	85.0
$C^\circ_{p(298)}$	35.4	10.4	28.2
$C^\circ_{p(600)}$	62.5	17.1	46.7

$\Delta S^\circ = 39.2$ g/mole
$\Delta H^\circ = 14.9$ kcal/mole
$\Delta C^\circ_p = 3.2$ g/mole

log A	E	log k_T (663)	Conditions	System	Surface	References
14.51	54.2	-3.36	663 ± 20 °K 5.48–17.47 torr (5.4–7.4)	static	none	[1] B. C. Roquitte and W. D. Walters, J. Phys. Chem. **68**, 1606 (1964).

Preferred:
Reliable as reported. log $k = 14.51 - 54.2/\theta$.

Comments: The products are those expected on the basis of the biradical mechanism. The activation energy suggest a resonance energy for [structure] of 7.6 kcal/mole. (See also ethanoylcyclobutane.) Transition state estimates give log $A_{est} = 14.5$.

Experimental

[1] Analysis by U.V., I.R., G.L.C. Rates by ΔP. Rates unaffected by NO and propylene additions.

Reaction: Methyl cyclobutanecarboxylate

$$\text{(I)} \longrightarrow C_2H_4 \text{ (II)} + CH_2\!\!=\!\!CH\!-\!\overset{\displaystyle O}{\overset{\|}{C}}\!-\!O\!-\!CH_3 \text{ (III)}$$

	I	II	III
$\Delta H^\circ_{f(298)}$	-74.2	12.5	-70.5
$S^\circ_{(298)}$	97.2	52.5	(84.4)
$C^\circ_{p(298)}$	32.6	10.4	26.0
$C^\circ_{p(700)}$	64.4	18.8	44.8

$\Delta S^\circ = 39.7$ g/mole
$\Delta H^\circ = 16.2$ kcal/mole
$\Delta C^\circ_p = 3.8$ g/mole

log A	E	log k_T (673)	Conditions	System	Surface	References
14.84	57.3	-3.77	673 ± 20 °K 6–12 torr (10)	static	none	[1] M. Zupan and W. D. Walters, J. Am. Chem. Soc. **86,** 173 (1964).

Preferred:
Reliable. log $k = 14.84 - 57.3/\theta$.

Comments: Transition state estimates for the biradical mechanism coupled with the observed activation energy suggest a carboxylic resonance stabilization of the free radical. ( ) of about 4.7 kcal/mole. (See also ethanoylcyclobutane.)

Experimental

[1] Analysis by M.S., G.L.C. Rates by ΔP. Rates were unaffected by NO and propylene.

eaction: Cyclobutanone

$$\beta\ \underset{\alpha}{\boxed{}}{}^{O}\ \text{(I)} \longrightarrow C_2H_4\ \text{(II)} + CH_2{=}C{=}O\ \text{(III)}$$

	I	II	III
$\Delta H^\circ_{f(298)}$	-20.5	12.5	-14.6
$S^\circ_{(298)}$	71.3	52.5	57.1
$C^\circ_{p(298)}$	20.0	10.4	11.4
$C^\circ_{p(600)}$	33.2	17.1	(17.2)

$S^\circ = 38.3$ g/mole
$H^\circ = 18.4$ kcal/mole
$C^\circ_p = 1.8$ g/mole

log A	E	log k_T (626)	Conditions	System	Surface	References
14.56	52.0	-3.60	626 ± 20 °K 10–88 torr (15–30)	static	$< 10\%$	[1] M. N. Das, F. Kern, T. D. Coyle, and W. D. Walters, J. Am. Chem. Soc. **76**, 6271 (1954).

referred:
Reliable as reported. $\log k = 14.56 - 52.0/\theta$.

omments: The biradical mechanism is consistent with the kinetics with ring opening being rate deter-
ining (see section III–5.2).

Estimated parameters are: $\log A_{est} = 14.7$; $E_{act} = 52.6$ kcal/mole. The activation energy was calculated
sing the resonance energy obtained in the ethanoylcyclobutane reaction and the normal C_4 ring closing
ctivation energy. Evidently the resonance energy of the biradical need not be lost in the decomposition
ep (see for comparison, methylene cyclobutane). The two paths, α(C—C) fission and β(C—C) fission have
bout the same parameters.

Experimental

[1] Analysis by I.R., M.S., Chem. Rates by ΔP. Rates were unaffected by NO, toluene, and propylene.

Reaction: Methylenecyclobutane

(I) $\longrightarrow$ C$_2$H$_4$ (II) + CH$_2$=C=CH$_2$ (III)

	I	II	III
$\Delta H^\circ_{f(298)}$	29.8	12.5	45.9
$S^\circ_{(298)}$	72.5	52.5	58.3
$C^\circ_{p(298)}$	20.3	10.4	14.1
$C^\circ_{p(700)}$	43.2	18.8	23.8

$\Delta S^\circ = 38.3$ g/mole
$\Delta H^\circ = 28.6$ kcal/mole
$\Delta C^\circ_p = 4.2$ g/mole

log A	E	log k_T (723)	Conditions	System	Surface	References
15.08	61.5	−3.52	708 ± 25 °K 2.3–10.4	static		[1] R. L. Brandaur. B. Short, and S. M. E. Kellner, J. Phys. Chem. **65**, 2269 (1961).
15.68	63.3	−3.46	723 ± 20 °K 0.1–25 torr (6)	static		[2] J. P. Chesick, J. Phys. Chem. **65**, 2170 (1961).
15.8	63.5	−3.40	683–763 °K 10^{-3}–10 torr	static		[3] P. J. Burkhardt, Ph. D. Diss., Univ. of Oregon (1962).

Preferred:
   log $k = 15.8 - 63.5/\theta$.

Comments: Comparison of these kinetics with those of dideuteromethylenecyclobutane (unpublishe
results of W. von E. Doering) provides a very forceful argument for biradical intermediates in small rin
compound reactions. The latter reaction proceeds readily at about 600 °K with an activation energy o
49.5 kcal/mole. Thus ring closing from the biradical is very fast relative to decomposition (see below), an
ring opening occurs with an allylic resonance assist (see also methylenecyclopropane). Apparently decom
position of methylenecyclobutane has an activation energy close to that of cyclobutane because in twistin
of the biradical toward the allenic π bond conformation, the allylic resonance is lost.

Mechanism:

Transition state estimates give: $\log k = \log \left(\dfrac{k_1 k_3}{k_2}\right) = 15.7 - 61.9/\theta$ (decomposition)

$\log k_1 = 14.5 - 48.3/\theta$ (isomerization)

Experimental

[1] Analysis by G.L.C., I.R., and M.S. Rates by ΔP.
[2] Analysis and rates by G.L.C. Falloff observed near 6 torr (732 °K). Added nitrogen accelerated the rate in t
low-pressure region.
[3] Analysis by M.S. and G.L.C. Falloff over the entire pressure range was observed and high-pressure rate co
stants were obtained from fits of the data to the Kassel integral.

eaction: Cyclobutene

$$\square \;(I) \longrightarrow \;\diagdown\!\diagup\!\diagdown \;(II)$$

	I	II
$\Delta H^\circ_{f(298)}$	36.0	26.3
$S^\circ_{(298)}$	63.0	66.6
$C^\circ_{p(298)}$	16.0	19.0
$C^\circ_{p(400)}$	21.6	24.3

$\Delta S^\circ = \quad 3.6$ g/mole
$\Delta H^\circ = -9.7$ kcal/mole
$\Delta C^\circ_p = \quad 3.0$ g/mole

log A	E	log k_T (426)	Conditions	System	Surface	References
13.08	32.5	−3.60	425 ± 22 °K 5–50 torr (8–14)	static	< 10%	[1] W. Cooper and W. D. Walters, J. Am. Chem. Soc. **80**, 4220 (1958).
13.18	32.7	−3.60	426 ± 23 °K 0.01–23 torr (0.055, 0.22, 5.4)	static	< 10%	[2] W. P. Hauser and W. D. Walters, J. Phys. Chem. **67**, 1328 (1963).
13.40	32.9	−3.48	426 ± 23 °K 48–1521 torr (100, 1500)	static	< 10%	[3] R. W. Carr, Jr., and W. D. Walters, J. Phys. Chem. **69**, 1073 (1965).

Preferred:
  All reliable. $\log k = 13.4 - 32.9/\theta$.

Comments: A biradical mechanism would require a resonance energy in the transition state of about 26 cal/mole which is greater than two allylic resonances. The reaction is therefore "concerted." For a review of cyclobutene isomerizations see R. Criegie, D. Seeback, R. E. Winter, B. Börretzen, and H. A. Brune. Chemische Berichte **98**, 2339 (1965).

Experimental

  [1] Analysis by I.R., M.S., U.V. Rate by U.V. No inhibition with NO and propylene. At 0.5 torr, rate constant was about 0.7 k_x.
  [2] Analysis and rate by U.V. Falloff observed near 10 torr at 423 °K. Collision efficiencies of He. N_2, H_2, CO_2, CH_4, C_2H_2, C_2H_6. and C_3H_8 were determined.
  [3] Rates by U.V.

Reaction: 1-Methyl-1-cyclobutene

	I	II
$\Delta H^{\circ}_{f(298)}$	27.8	18.1
$S^{\circ}_{(298)}$	72.0	75.4
$C^{\circ}_{p(298)}$	22.2	25.0
$C^{\circ}_{p(500)}$	33.0	37.1

$\Delta S^{\circ} = \quad 3.4$ g/mole
$\Delta H^{\circ} = -9.7$ kcal/mole
$\Delta C^{\circ}_p = \quad 2.8$ g/mole

log A	E	log k_T (446)	Conditions	System	Surface	References
13.79	35.1	−3.42	446 ± 25 °K 5–150 torr	static	< 10%	[1] H. M. Frey, Trans. Faraday Soc. **58**, 957 (1962).

Preferred:
Reliable. (see cyclobutene) log $k = 13.79 - 35.1/\theta$.

Experimental

[1] Analysis by G.L.C. Not inhibited by added NO and propylene. Rate constants were pressure independent.

Reaction: 3-Methyl-1-cyclobutene

$$\square \ (I) \longrightarrow \diagup\!\!\diagdown\!\!\diagup\!\!\diagdown \ (II)$$

	I	II
$\Delta H^\circ_{f(298)}$	28.2	18.6
$S^\circ_{(298)}$	70.5	76.4
$C^\circ_{p(298)}$	23.9	24.7
$C^\circ_{p(400)}$	30.7	31.2

$\Delta S^\circ = 5.9$ g/mole
$\Delta H^\circ = -9.6$ kcal/mole
$\Delta C^\circ_p = 0.8$ g/mole

log A	E	log k_T (408)	Conditions	System	Surface	References
13.53	31.55	-3.37	408 ± 22 °K 0.4→ 25 torr (7)	static	< 10%	[1] H. M. Frey, Trans. Faraday Soc. **60**, 83 (1964).

Preferred:
Reliable. (see cyclobutene) log $k = 13.53-31.55/\theta$.

Comments: Note that the intrinsic A-factors of all the "cyclobutene" reactions are the same (i.e., very close to normal with $\Delta S^\ddagger = 0$).

Experimental

[1] Analysis by G.L.C. Rates unaffected by added propylene. Falloff observed near 25 torr and k_∞ (reported) was obtained from a log k versus $P^{-1/2}$ plot. Falloff curve fit by RRK $- s \simeq 15$. (See H. M. Frey and D. C. Marshall, Trans. Faraday Soc. **61**, 1715 (1965).

Reaction: 1-Ethyl-1-cyclobutene

$$\text{(I)} \longrightarrow CH_2\!=\!C(C_2H_5)CH\!=\!CH_2 \text{ (II)}$$

	I	II
$\Delta H^\circ_{f(298)}$	22.8	13.1
$S^\circ_{(298)}$	81.8	85.2
$C^\circ_{p(298)}$	27.3	30.1
$C^\circ_{p(400)}$	35.9	38.7

$\Delta S^\circ = \quad 3.4$ g/mole
$\Delta H^\circ = -9.7$ kcal/mole
$\Delta C^\circ_p = \quad 2.8$ g/mole

log A	E	log k_T (446)	Conditions	System	Surface	References
13.76	34.83	−3.34	446 ± 22 1–20 torr (2)	static	< 10%	[1] H. M. Frey and R. F. Skinner, Trans. Farada Soc. **61**, 1918 (1965).

Preferred:
Reliable. (see cyclobutene) log $k = 13.76 - 34.88/\theta$.

Experimental

[1] Analysis by G.L.C. Rate constants were pressure independent.

Reaction: 1,2-Dimethyl-1-cyclobutene

$$\square\!\!\!\!\triangleleft \;(I) \longrightarrow CH_2\!\!=\!\!C(CH_3)C(CH_3)\!\!=\!\!CH_2 \;(II)$$

	I	II
$\Delta H^\circ_{f(298)}$	20.6	11.8
$S^\circ_{(298)}$	79.4	81.4
$C^\circ_{p(298)}$	27.1	30.8
$C^\circ_{p(500)}$	38.7	41.0

$\Delta S^\circ = \;\;2.0$ g/mole
$\Delta H^\circ = -8.8$ kcal/mole
$\Delta C^\circ_p = \;\;3.7$ g/mole

log A	E	log k_T (446)	Conditions	System	Surface	References
13.84	36.04	−3.83	446±240 °K 1–100 torr (3)	static	none	[1] H. M. Frey, Trans. Faraday Soc. **59**, 1619 (1963)

Preferred:

Reliable. (see cyclobutene) log $k = 13.84 - 36.04/\theta$.

Experimental

[1] Analysis by G.L.C. No inhibition of the rates with added NO and propylene.

Reaction: 1,3-Dimethyl-1-cyclobutene

	I	II
$\Delta H^\circ_{f(298)}$	20.0	11.5
$S^\circ_{(298)}$	78.1	86.1
$C^\circ_{p(298)}$	30.0	30.5

$\Delta S^\circ = 8.0$ g/mole
$\Delta H^\circ = -8.5$ kcal/mole
$\Delta C'_p = 0.5$ g/mole

log A	E	log k_T (420)	Conditions	System	Surface	References
13.65	33.0	−3.52	420 ± 27 °K 0.25 − 140 torr (3)	static	none	[1] H. M. Frey, D. C. Marshall, and R. F. Skinner, Trans. Faraday Soc. **61**, 861 (1965).

Preferred:
   Reliable. (see cyclobutene) log $k = 13.65{-}33.0/\theta$.

Experimental

   [1] Analysis by G.L.C. The vapor pressure of 1,3-dimethyl-1-cyclobutene was found to be log $p_{mm} = 7.856{-}1633/T$ °K between −4.35 and 22.25 °C.

Reaction: 2,3-Dimethyl-1-cyclobutene

	I	II
$\Delta H^{\circ}_{f(298)}$	20.0	12.5
$S^{\circ}_{(298)}$	78.0	87.3
$C^{\circ}_{p(298)}$	30.0	29.2

$\Delta S^{\circ} = 9.3$ g/mole
$\Delta H^{\circ} = -7.5$ kcal/mole
$\Delta C^{\circ}_{p} = -0.8$ g/mole

log A	E	log k_T (433)	Conditions	System	Surface	References
13.52	33.39	-3.34	433 ± 21 °K 0.7–32.5 torr (3)	static	none	[1] H. M. Frey, D. C. Marshall, and R. F. Skinner, Trans. Faraday Soc. **61**, 861 (1965).

Preferred:
   Reliable. (see cyclobutene). log $k = 13.52 - 33.39/\theta$.

Experimental

[1] Rates and analysis by G.L.C.

Reaction: *trans*-1,2,3,4-Tetramethyl-1-cyclobutene

	I	II
$\Delta H^\circ_{f(298)}$	5.0	1.0
$S^\circ_{(298)}$	91.6	105.2
$C^\circ_{p(298)}$	42.5	36.1

$\Delta S^\circ = 13.6$ g/mole
$\Delta H^\circ = -4.0$ kcal/mole
$\Delta C^\circ_p = -6.4$ g/mole

log A	E	log k_T (419)	Conditions	System	Surface	References
13.85	33.59	−3.67	398–440 °K 1–76 torr	static		[1] G. R. Branton, H. M. Frey, and R. F. Skinner, Trans. Faraday Soc. **62**, 1546 (1966).
13.99	33.2	−3.37	408–428 °K	(see below)		[2] R. Criegie, D. Seebach, R. E. Winter, B. Börretzen, and H. A. Brune, Chemische Berichte **98**, 2339 (1965).

Preferred:
    log $k = 13.85 - 33.59/\theta$.

Comments: Absence of the *trans-cis*-3,4-dimethyl-2,4-hexadiene indicates that the mechanism does not involve biradicals, but rather is a conrotary concerted process.

Experimental

[1] Rates were obtained by G.L.C. analysis on the cyclobutene remaining. The product was observed to polymerize rapidly presumably on the surface. Reaction in solution gave exclusively and quantitatively the indicated product.
[2] Reaction was studied in neat and in solution and the rate was followed by U.V. absorption of the diene.

Reaction: *cis*-1,2,3,4-Tetramethyl-1-cyclobutene

	I	II
$\Delta H^\circ_{f(298)}$	7.7	1.0
$S^\circ_{(298)}$	94.2	103.6
$C^\circ_{p(298)}$	41.3	36.1

$\Delta S^\circ = 9.4$ g/mole
$\Delta H^\circ = -6.7$ kcal/mole
$\Delta C^\circ_p = -5.2$ g/mole

log A	E	log k_T (452)	Conditions	System	Surface	References
14.1	37.36	−3.95	431–474 °K 1–76 torr	static	< 5%	[1] G. R. Branton, H. M. Frey, and R. F. Skinner, Trans. Faraday Soc. **62,** 1546 (1966).

Preferred:
   Reliable. (see *trans*-1,2,3,4-tetramethyl-1-cyclobutene)

Experimental

   [1] Rates based on G.L.C. analysis on remaining cyclobutene. Only *one* product was obtained and cited as proof for a conrotary concerted mechanism.

Reaction: Perfluorocyclobutene

$$(\square)_{F_6} (I) \longrightarrow \diagup\!\!\!\diagdown\!\!\!\diagup F_6 \, (III)$$

	I	II
$\Delta H^\circ_{f(298)}$	-234	-223
$S^\circ_{(298)}$	88.2	98.6
$C^\circ_{p(298)}$	29.6	32.6

$\Delta S^\circ = 10.4$ g/mole
$\Delta H^\circ = 11.0$ kcal/mole
$\Delta C^\circ_p = 3.0$ g/mole

log A	E	log k_T (503)	Conditions	System	Surface	References
14.12	47.08	-6.34	503 $\pm$ 36 °K 1–18 torr	static	< 10%	[1] E. W. Schlag and W. B. Peatman, J. Am. Chem. Soc. **86**, 1676 (1964).

Preferred:
   Reliable. log $k = 14.12 - 47.08/\theta$.

Experimental

[1] Analysis and rate by G.L.C. The reverse reaction was also studied: $K_{eq} = 10^{2.07} \times 10^{-11.7/\theta}$. The equilibrium constant parameters [$\Delta S^\circ = 9.5$ g/mole and $\Delta H^\circ = -11.7$ kcal/mole] are in reasonably good agreement with the thermodynamic estimates.

Reaction: Perfluorocyclobutane

$$(\Box)_8(I) \xrightarrow[\substack{b \\ \longleftarrow}]{a} \begin{array}{l} 2[C_2F_4] \ (II) \\ C_3F_6 \ (III) + CF_2: (IV) \end{array}$$

	I	II	III	IV
$\Delta H^\circ_{f(298)}$	-361.5	-155		-39.6
$S^\circ_{(298)}$	93.5	71.8		59.6
$C^\circ_{p(298)}$	38.2	19.4		9.1

a
$\Delta S^\circ = 50.1$ g/mole
$\Delta H^\circ = 51.5$ kcal/mole
$\Delta C^\circ_p = 0.6$ g/mole

Path	log A	E	log k_T (830)	Conditions	System	Surface	References
a	15.95	74.1	-3.53	828 ± 35 °K 200–550 torr	static	(see below)	[1] B. Atkinson and A. B. Trenwith, J. Chem. Soc., 2082 (1953); B. Atkinson and V. Atkinson, J. Chem. Soc., 2086 (1957).
b	16.59	79.0	-4.16				
a	16.0	74.3	-3.53	683 ± 50 °K 0.01–300 torr (10–100)	static		[2] J. N. Butler, J. Am. Chem. Soc. **84**, 1393 (1962).
b	17.2	87.0	-5.67	787 ± 51 °K 20–600 torr	static		
a	16.32	74.3	-3.21	1343 ± 300 °K 1% in 500 torr of Ar	S.P. shock		[3] A. Lifshitz, H. F. Carroll, and S. H. Bauer, J. Chem. Phys. **39**, 1661 (1963).

Preferred:
   log $k_a = 16.0 - 74.3/\theta$; process *b* — suspect.

Comments: The observed equilibrium constant for reaction (*a*) is in good agreement with the estimated thermodynamics. From K_{eq}, $\Delta S^\circ = 49.5$ g/mole. Reaction path (*b*) is probably not a unimolecular first-order process. With the parameters reported in either [1] or [2], one would expect path (*b*) to dominate at the temperatures of the S.P. shock study. This was not the case. In addition, the fluorine migration required is not very probable.

Mechanism, path *a*:

$$\Box \ \underset{\frac{1}{2}}{\rightleftharpoons} \ [\cdot \Box \cdot] \xrightarrow{3} 2C_2F_4 \qquad E_{act} \simeq \Delta H^\circ_{1,2} + E_3 \simeq DH^\circ(\text{C—C}) - E_{est} + E_3 \simeq 81.6 - 28 + E_3$$

$E_3 \simeq 20.7$ kcal/mole. The high value of E_3 compared to that for cyclobutane ($E_3 \simeq 5.8$ kcal/mole) is probably

(Continued)

Perfluorocyclobutane (*Continued*)

a result of the lower exothermicity of step 3 for the fluorocarbon caused by fluorine destablization of the $(C\pi\text{---}C\pi)$ bond.

Experimental

[1] Analysis by I.R. Rates by ΔP. Surface effects apparent in pyrex cell, but well-behaved kinetics in steel cell. Kinetics of the reverse reaction also studied. ($\log k_{rec} = 8.01 - 25.4/\theta$, with k in l/mole-sec.)

[2] Analysis and rates by G.L.C. Falloff (path a) observed near 10 torr with an RRK-$s \simeq 20$. At pressures below 0.05 mm, the rate was pressure independent due to a slow heterogeneous reaction. Path (b) rate unaffected by O_2. Reaction (a) catalyzed by O_2. The equilibrium constant for path (a) was found to be $K_a = 10^{8.6-49.9/\theta}$ moles/l.

[3] Analysis by G.L.C.

Reaction: *cis*-1,2-Dichlorohexafluorocyclobutane

	I	II
$\Delta H^{\circ}_{f(298)}$	-265	-265
$S^{\circ}_{(298)}$	101.3	99.9
$C^{\circ}_{p(298)}$	40.8	40.8

$\Delta S^{\circ} = -1.4$ g/mole
$\Delta H^{\circ} = 0$ kcal/mole
$\Delta C^{\circ}_p = 0$ g/mole

Path	log A	E	log k_T (720)	Conditions	System	Surface	References
a	15.1	60.2	-3.18	698–742 °K 60 torr	static	none	[1] B. Atkinson and M. Stedman, J. Chem. Soc., 512 (1962).
b	14.88	60.2	-3.40	(as above)		none	(as above)

Preferred

Reliable. $\log k_a = 15.1 - 60.2/\theta$
$\log k_b = 14.88 - 60.2/\theta$.

Experimental

[1] Analysis by G.L.C. A slow formation of dichlorohexafluorobut-2-ene occurred at the higher temperatures. The equilibrium constant for the reaction was temperature-independent and given by $K_{a,b} = 1.67$.

Reaction: (*cis* or *trans*)-1,2-Dichlorohexafluorocyclobutane

$$(\substack{Cl \quad Cl \\ \square})_{F_6} \, (I) \longrightarrow 2[CFCl = CF_2] \, (II)$$

	I	II
$\Delta \bar{H}^\circ_{f(298)}$	-267.7	-113.5
$\bar{S}^\circ_{(298)}$	104 ± 2	77.1
$\bar{C}^\circ_{p(298)}$	37.6	20.0

$\Delta S^\circ = 50.2$ g/mole
$\Delta H^\circ = 40.7$ kcal/mole
$\Delta C_p^\circ = 2.4$ g/mole

log A	E	log k_T (743)	Conditions	System	Surface	References
15.4	65.3	-3.82	698–787 °K 30–140 torr	static		[1] B. Atkinson and M. Stedman, J. Chem. Soc., 512 (1962).

Preferred:
   Reliable. log $k = 15.4 - 65.3/\theta$.

Experimental

   [1] Rates by ΔP. Analysis by G.L.C. The reverse reaction kinetics were also studied giving: $k_b = 4.3 \times 10^7 \times 10^{-26.6/\theta}$ 1/mole-(sec), from which $K_{a,\, b} = 10^{7.76-38.7/\theta}$ moles/1. The observed equilibrium data do not agree very well with the entropy estimates. (From K_{eq}, $\Delta S^\circ \simeq 45.7$ g/mole.)

Reaction: *cis*-Hexafluoro-1,2-*bis*-trifluoromethylcyclobutane

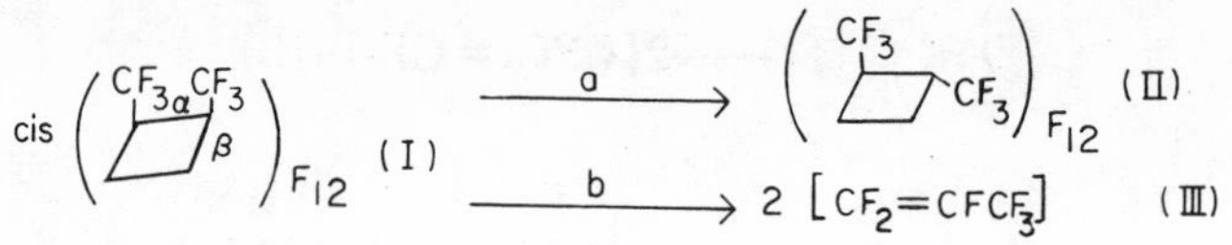

$$\Delta H^{\circ}_{f(298)}$$
$$S^{\circ}_{(298)}$$
$$C^{\circ}_{p(298)}$$

$\Delta S^{\circ} =$
$\Delta H^{\circ} =$
$\Delta C_p =$

Path	log A	E	log k_T	Conditions	System	Surface	References
a	15.36	64.2	−3.86	683–773 °K 25–125 torr	static	none	[1] B. Atkinson and P. B. Stockwell, J. Chem. Soc. **B**, 984 (1966).
b	15.08	64.2	−4.14				

Preferred:
Reliable, as reported. log $k_a = 15.36 - 64.2/\theta$
log $k_b = 15.08 - 64.2/\theta$

Comments: Parameters are consistent with a biradical mechanism (see cyclobutane and perfluorocyclobutane) with $k_2 \approx k_3$ and $E_2 \simeq E_3$. Absence of β(C—C) split products is understandable since from the perfluorocyclo-butane results and those above, one can guess that

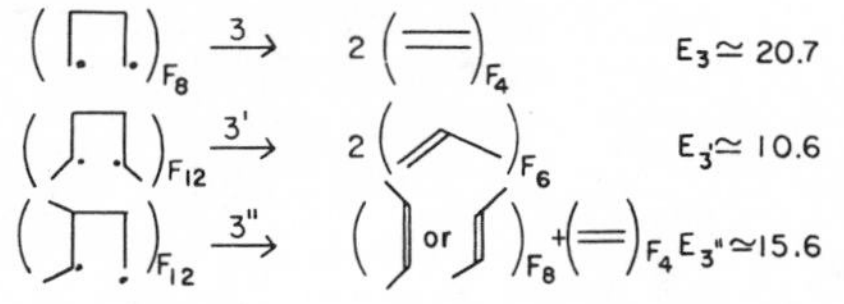

This is consistent with a decrease in olefin stability with increasing fluorine atom substitution at the Pi bond centers.

Experimental

[1] Analysis by G.L.C. and by NMR (for isomers). No (S/V) ratio effect in aged pyrex or nickel vessels. Dissociation to C_2F_4 and 2-butenes was not observed. In the temperature range studied, $K_{eq}\left(\dfrac{trans}{cis}\right) \simeq 0.28$. (See also *trans* isomer results.)

Reaction: *Trans*-Hexafluoro-1,2-*bis*-trifluoromethylcyclobutane

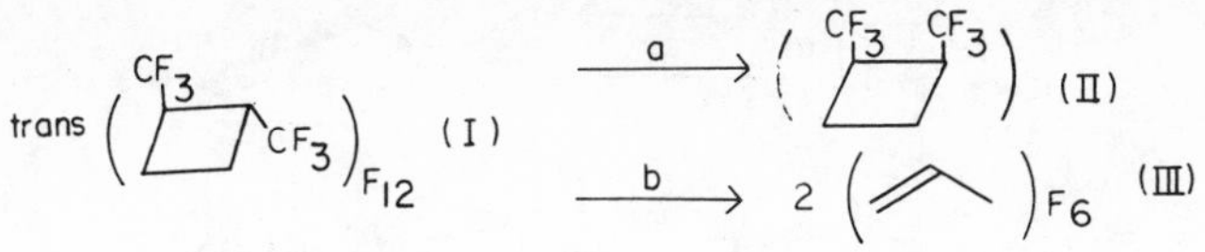

$$\Delta S^\circ =$$
$$\Delta H^\circ =$$
$$\Delta C_p^\circ =$$

Path	log A	E	log k_T (730)	Conditions	System	Surface	References
a	15.77	64.2	-3.45	683–773 °K 25–125 torr	static	none	[1] B. Atkinson and P. B. Stockwell, J. Chem. Soc. **B** 984 (1966).
b	15.63	64.2	-3.59				

Preferred:

$$\log k_a = 15.77 - 64.2/\theta$$
$$\log k_b = 15.63 - 64.2/\theta.$$

Experimental

[1] See *cis*-isomer.

Reaction: Decafluoro-1,2-dimethylcyclobutene

$$
\begin{array}{ccc}
 & \text{I} & \text{II} \\
\Delta H^\circ_{f(298)} & -454.4 & -454.0 \\
S^\circ_{(298)} & 119.7 & 124.6 \\
C^\circ_{p(298)} & & 53.6
\end{array}
$$

$\Delta S^\circ = 4.9$ g/mole
$\Delta H^\circ = 0.40$ kcal/mole
$\Delta C^\circ_p =$

Path	log A	E	log k_T (595)	Conditions	System	Surface	References
a	13.64	46.0	−3.26	563–625 °K 40–1500 mm Hg	static	none	[1] J. P. Chesick, J. Am. Chem. Soc. **88**, 4800 (1966).
b	12.57	45.6	−4.18				

Preferred:

$\log k_a = 13.64 - 46.0/\theta$
$\log k_b = 12.57 - 45.6/\theta$.

Comments: Conclusions regarding the effect of fluorine atom on the stability of $(C_\pi - C_\pi)$ bonds also seem valid.

Experimental

[1] Analysis on product and reactant by G.L.C. The equilibrium constant was measured over the temperature range of 564–658 °K and found to be, $\log K_{a,b} = 1.06 - 0.40/\theta$. Also, from the method of opposing reaction rates, the data gave $\log (k_a + k_b) = 13.62 - 45.8 \pm 0.6/\theta$. In view of the greater exothermicity of this isomerization, as opposed to the perfluorocyclobutene isomerization (i.e., , $\Delta H^\circ_{1,2} = 11.7$ kcal/mole), the data support the theory of

Pi bond destabilization by fluorine atom substitution (E. W. Schlag and E. W. Kaiser, Jr., J. Am. Chem. Soc. **87**, 1171 (1965)).

Reaction: Cyclopentene

$$\text{(I)} \longrightarrow \text{(II)} + H_2\text{(III)}$$

	I	II	III
$\Delta H^\circ_{f(298)}$	7.9	32.5	0
$S^\circ_{(298)}$	69.2	67	31.2
$C^\circ_{p(298)}$	18.1	17.5	7.0

$\Delta S^\circ = 29.0$ g/mole
$\Delta H^\circ = 24.6$ kcal/mole
$\Delta C^\circ_p = 6.4$ g/mole

$\log A$	E	$\log k_T$ (790)	Conditions	System	Surface	References
13.04	58.8	−3.23	789 ± 33 °K 38–249 mm Hg	static	none	[1] D. W. Vanas and W. D. Walters, J. Am. Chem. Soc. **70**, 4035 (1948)

Preferred:
$\log k = 13.04 - 58.8 / \theta$; $\log A_{est} \simeq 13.4$

Comments: The entropy of the transition state should be close to that of the product. The mechanism appears to be a 1,4 H_2 elimination.

Experimental

[1] Chemical and U.V. analysis. Rates by ΔP. Stoichiometry confirmed in the initial stages of reaction. No inhibition by added propylene.

Reaction: 1,5,5-Trimethyl-1,3-cyclopentadiene

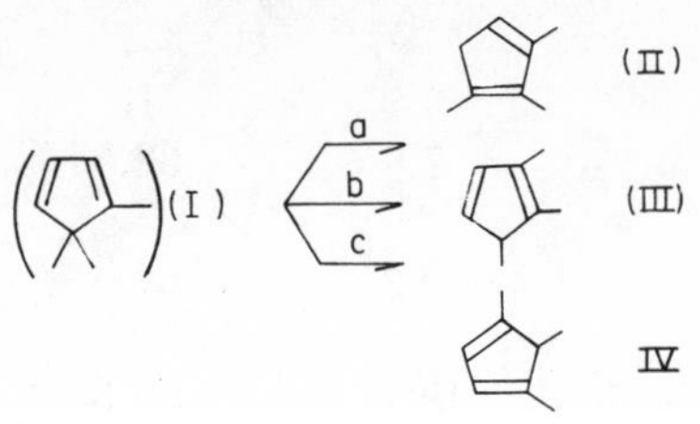

	I	II
$\Delta H^\circ_{f(298)}$	10.9	8.7
$S^\circ_{(298)}$	85.5	87.5
$C^\circ_{p(298)}$	35.3	33.6

$\Delta S^\circ = 2.0$ g/mole
$\Delta H^\circ = -2.2$ kcal/mole
$\Delta C^\circ_p = -1.7$ g/mole

Path	log A	E	log k_T (650)	Conditions	System	Surface	References
(a+b+c)	12.7	41.6	−1.29	623–673 °K not reported	flow, $t_c \simeq 5$–50 sec	not studied	[1] J. W. DeHaan and H. Kloosterziel, Rec. des Trav. Chim. des Pays-Bas **84**, 1594 (1965)

Preferred: Probably not reliable as unimolecular process! (see note).

Comments: This appears to be one of the very few examples (see MeNC pyrolysis) of a CH_3 migration which could involve pentavalent carbon. For this reason the interpretation must remain tentative. The test for radicals with *dt*BP was not reliable since its half-life at these temperatures would be a few milliseconds. A possible radical path is:

(all isomers)

The initiation step i has E_{act} between 50–56 kcal. The chain is:

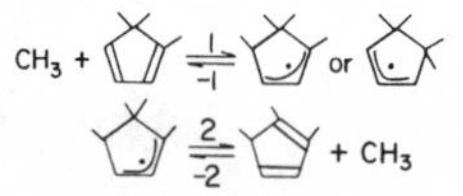

The other isomers could also be formed from 1,5 concerted H-shifts in the 1,2,3 product. Also, mitigating against a CH_3 shift is the absence of isomers, such as

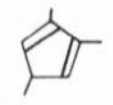

If termination is by Me + allyl, this leads to a first order rate constant $\sim 10^{14-47/\theta}$ sec^{-1} in good agreement with the reported rate constant. Alternatively, Me − Me termination yields a 3/2 order rate law $\sim 10^{11-30/\theta}$ $1^{1/2}$/mole$^{1/2}$-sec. At 10 torr of cyclopentadiene, this also gives rates very close to the reported values.

Experimental

[1] Analysis on products by M.S., U.V., IR, and N.M.R. Products were also hydrogenated and compared to known samples of trimethylcyclopentanes. A 1,5-intramolecular shift of the methyl group followed by rapid equilibration of product pentadienes by intramolecular H-shifts was postulated. A free radical catalyzed reaction path was excluded since the rate was not accelerated by the addition of di-*t*-butyl peroxide.

Reaction: 2,5,5-Trimethyl-1,3-cyclopentadiene

	I	II
$\Delta H^\circ_{f(298)}$	10.3	8.7
$S^\circ_{(298)}$	85.5	87.5
$C^\circ_{p(298)}$	35.3	34.6

$\Delta S^\circ = 2.0$ g/mole
$\Delta H^\circ = -1.6$ kcal/mole
$\Delta C^\circ_p = -0.7$ g/mole

Path	log A	E	log k_T (650)	Conditions	System	Surface	References
a	14.88	45.5	−0.42	623–673 °K, $\bar{P}$ not reported	static and flow	—————	[1] J. W. DeHaan and H. Kloosterzeil, Rec. des Trav. Chim. des Pays-Bas **84**, 1594 (1965).
b	14.22	45.7	−1.15				

Preferred:
    Suspect. Probably chain.

Comments and Experimental:
    (See 1,5,5-trimethylcyclopenta-1,3-diene).

Reaction: 2,5-Dihydrofuran*

$$\text{(I)} \longrightarrow \text{(II)} + H_2 \text{(III)}$$

	I	II	III
$\Delta H^\circ_{f(298)}$	-17.8	-1.2	0
$S^\circ_{(298)}$	67.7	66.1	31.2
$C^\circ_{p(298)}$	16.2	12.5	7.0

$\Delta S^\circ = 29.6$ g/mole
$\Delta H^\circ = 16.6$ kcal/mole
$\Delta C^\circ_p = 3.3$ g/mole

log A	E	log k_T (650)	Conditions	System	Surface	References
12.72	48.5	-3.59	649 ± 34 5–46 mm Hg (10)	static	none	[1] C. A. Wellington and W. D. Walters, J. Am. Chem. Soc. **83**, 4888 (1961)

Preferred:
Reliable as reported. log $k = 12.72 - 48.5/\theta$.

Experimental

[1] Analysis by M.S., G.L.C., I.R. Rates by ΔP. No effect on the rates with added NO, propylene or toluene. Rate constants were pressure independent.

---

*Note that 2,3-dihydrofuran does not eliminate H_2 to go to furan, but rather decomposes to $CO + C_3H_6$ via a complex biradical path. This is consistent with the Woodward Hoffman rule predictions. (See also 1,3 cyclohexadiene and 1,4-cyclohexadiene.)

Reaction: Pyrazoline

$$\text{(I)} \xrightarrow[\ b\ ]{\ a\ } \begin{array}{l} N_2 \ (\text{II}) + \triangle \ (\text{III}) \\ N_2 + C_3H_6 \ (\text{IV}) \end{array}$$

	I	II	III	IV
$\Delta H^\circ_{f(298)}$	56.3	0	12.7	4.8
$S^\circ_{(298)}$	68.7	45.8	56.8	63.6
$C^\circ_{p(298)}$	17.7	7.0	13.3	15.3

	a	b
$\Delta S^\circ =$	33.9	40.7 g/mole
$\Delta H^\circ =$	-43.6	-51.5 kcal/mole
$\Delta C^\circ_p =$	2.1	4.6 g/mole

log A	E	log k_T	Conditions	System	Surface	References
15.9	42.4		443–563 °K 100–200 torr	static	none	[1] R. J. Crawford, R. J. Dummel, and A. Mishra, J. Am. Chem. Soc. **87**, 3024 (1965)

Preferred:
   log $k = 15.9 - 42.4/\theta$.

Comments: The kinetics are consistent with a biradical mechanism. (See methyl substituted pyrazolines and section V–7.0.)

$$\underset{N=N}{\square} \underset{2}{\overset{1}{\rightleftarrows}} \left(\underset{N=N^\circ}{\square^\circ} \right) \xrightarrow[\text{fast}]{3} N_2 + \triangle$$

$$E_\text{est} \simeq DH^\circ(\text{C—N}_\text{A}) - E_\text{strain} + E_2 = (50.0 - 1.0) - 6.0 + 1.0 = 44.0 \text{ kcal/mole}.$$

Transition state estimates of the A-factor give log $A_\text{est} = 16.0$.

Experimental

[1] Rates were followed by pressure change. First order kinetics observed to better than 95 percent conversion.

Reaction: Methyl-substituted pyrazolines

$$\left(\begin{smallmatrix} x \\ x \end{smallmatrix}\!\!\times\!\!\diagdown\!\!\!\diagup\!\!\times\!\!\begin{smallmatrix} x \\ x \end{smallmatrix}\right) \quad \xrightarrow[\;b\;]{\;a\;} \quad \begin{matrix} N_2 + (\triangle)_{x_n} \\ N_2 + (\triangleright\!\!\!-)_{x_n} \end{matrix}$$

$\Delta S^\circ =$
$\Delta H^\circ =$
$\Delta C_p^\circ =$

Path	log A^*	E^*	log k_T	Conditions	System	Compounds	References
				443–563 °K	static		[1] R. J. Crawford,
				100–200 mm Hg			R. J. Dummel, and
							A. Mishra, J. Am.
							Chem. Soc. **87**,
							3023 (1965).

			log A_{est}	E_{est}	
$a+b$	15.67	41.0		41.6	3-methyl
	15.83	42.2		44.1	4-methyl
	15.83	40.0		37.8	3,3-dimethyl
	15.53	40.3		41.6	3,5-dimethyl (*cis*)
	15.66	40.2		41.6	3,5-dimethyl (*trans*)
	15.42	38.9		37.8	3,3,5-trimethyl
	14.48	37.7	14.6	37.8	3,3,5,5-tetramethyl

Preferred:
   Reliable: all values as reported.

Comments: The biradical mechanism (see estimates above) and the observed kinetic parameters tend to support the single-bond rupture hypothesis in alkyl azo compound decompositions (see section V–7.0).

Experimental

   [1] Rates were obtained from ΔP measurements. Change in surface from stainless steel to glass did not affect the rates. First-order plots were obtained to greater than 95 percent reaction.

---

   *Calculated on the basis that the reported entropies and energies of activation were obtained from Arrhenius parameters such that $k = \left(\dfrac{ekT}{h} e^{\Delta S^*_T/R}\right) \times 10^{-E/\theta}$.

   A study of the products in the thermal decomposition of 4-methyl diazirene gave isobutene $+ N_2$ *only*, which was taken as evidence for a biradical intermediate as opposed to a "hot" methylcyclopropane intermediate. The latter would give other olefin products preferentially (e.g., $\diagup\!\!\!\diagdown$, $\diagdown\!\!\!\diagup$, and $\triangleright\!\!\!- + N_2$).

Reaction: Cyclohexene

	I	II	III
$\Delta H^\circ_{f(298)}$	-1.7	26.3	12.5
$S^\circ_{(298)}$	74.3	66.6	52.5
$C^\circ_{p(298)}$	25.1	19.0	10.4

$\Delta S^\circ = 44.8$ g/mole
$\Delta H^\circ = 40.5$ kcal/mole
$\Delta C^\circ_p = 4.3$ g/mole

log A	E	log k_T (860)	Conditions	System	Surface	References
12.95	57.5	-1.67	798 ± 40 °K 10–200 torr	static	< 10%	[1] L. Küchler, Trans. Faraday Soc. **35**, 874 (1939).
12.13	55.1	-1.88	938–1018 °K 7–70 mm Hg	flow		[2] M. Kraus, M. Vavruska and V. Bazant, Collection Czech. Chem. Commun. **22**, 484 (1957).
17.15	72.7	-1.33	753 ± 55 °K	static	< 10%	[3] S. R. Smith and A. S. Gordon, J. Phys. Chem. **65**, 1124 (1961).
15.18	66.2	-1.65	858 ± 44 °K 25 mm Hg $t_c = 0.57$–5.4 sec.	flow	none	[4] M. Uchiyama, T. Tomioka and A. Amano, J. Phys. Chem. **68**, 1878 (1964).
15.02	66.7	-1.93	1025 ± 125 °K 1% in Ar	S. P. Sh.	none	[5] W. Tsang, J. Chem. Phys. **42**, 1805 (1961).

Preferred:
   log $k = 15.18 - 66.2/\theta$.*

Comments: $k_{back} = 10^{7.19 - 27.5/\theta}$ l/mole-sec [D. Rowley and H. Steiner, Disc. Faraday Soc. **10**, 198 (1951)]. The reaction is probably concerted.

Experimental

[1] Rate by ΔP. No effect on the rate by added NO and H_2.
[2] Rates were based on butadiene formation.
[3] Analysis by G.L.C. and M.S. Decomposition in D_2 produced no D incorporation in the products.
[4] Analysis by G.L.C.
[5] Method of comparative rates with 2-chloropropane decomposition as the internal standard.

---

*Reaction is undoubtedly unimolecular and homogeneous. The large discrepancies in Arrhenius parameters apparently arise from large systematic errors since rate constants in the middle of the experimental temperature ranges are in good agreement. Only the latter two sets of results agree thermodynamically with the rate constant for the association reaction.

Reaction: Cyclohexene

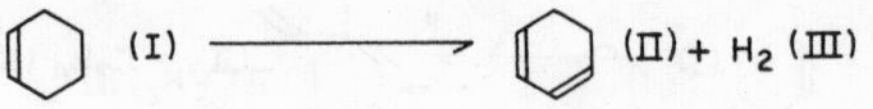

	I	II	III
$\Delta H^\circ_{f(298)}$	-1.7	26.3	0
$S^\circ_{(298)}$	74.2	72.1	31.2
$C^\circ_{p(298)}$	25.1	23.4	7.0

$\Delta S^\circ = 29.1$ g/mole
$\Delta H^\circ = 28.0$ kcal/mole
$\Delta C^\circ_p = 5.3$ g/mole

log A	E	log k_T (755)	Conditions	System	Surface	References
16.28	71.2	-4.33	753 ± 55	static	$< 10\%$	[1] S. R. Smith and A. S. Gordon, J. Phys. Chem. **65**, 1124 (1961)

Preferred:

log $k = 13.5 - 62.0/\theta$. Rate constants around $\bar{T}$ are probably reliable; however, see comments.

Comments: Absence of D in the products with added D_2 does not exclude the possibility of a free radical mechanism for the above reaction since $H \cdot +$ $\longrightarrow$  $+ H_2$ is very fast and $H + D_2 \longrightarrow HD + D$ has a kcal/mole activation energy. If the reaction is molecular, the A-factor should be closer to normal, possibly with a slightly negative $\Delta S^\ddagger$.

Experimental

[1] Analysis by G.L.C. and M.S. No incorporation of D in products with added D_2.

Reaction: 1-Methyl-1,4-cyclohexadiene

$$\left(\bigcirc, I\right) \longrightarrow \bigcirc (II) + H_2 (III)$$

	I	II	III
$\Delta H^\circ_{f(298)}$	16.0	12.0	0
$S^\circ_{(298)}$	81.8	76.4	31.2
$C^\circ_{p(298)}$	29.5	24.8	7.0

$\Delta S^\circ = 25.8$ g/mole
$\Delta H^\circ = -4.0$ kcal/mole
$\Delta C^\circ_p = 2.3$ g/mole

log A	E	log k_T (610)	Conditions	System	Surface	References
12.69	44.69	−3.32	587–635 °K 1–20 torr	static	none in aged reactor	[1] H. M. Frey and D. H. Lister, J. Chem. Soc. A, 509 (1967)

Preferred:

log $k = 12.69 - 44.69/\theta$. (See also 1,4-cyclohexadiene.)

Experimental

[1] It was demonstrated that the reaction was molecular and did not involve free radical chains (as does the thermal decomposition of 1,3-cyclohexadiene) by pyrolyzing a mixture of the reactant and di-*t*-butyl peroxide (30 percent) at 619 °K. Rates of decomposition were the same as in the absence of the peroxide sensitizer. Molecular elimination is also consistent with the Woodward-Hoffmann rules. The peroxide test is not a useful one, since the peroxide half-life is only 3 milliseconds at 619 °K.

Reaction: 4-Methylcyclohexene

$$\text{(I)} \longrightarrow CH_2{=}CHCH{=}CH_2 \text{ (II)} + CH_2{=}CHCH_3 \text{ (III)}$$

	I	II	III
$\Delta H^\circ_{f(298)}$	-8.8	26.3	4.8
$S^\circ_{(298)}$	81.0	66.6	63.6
$C^\circ_{p(298)}$	30.3	19.0	15.3

$\Delta S^\circ = 49.2$ g/mole
$\Delta H^\circ = 39.9$ kcal/mole
$\Delta C^\circ_p = 4.0$ g/mole

log A	E	log k_T (1025)	Conditions	System	Surface	References
15.13	66.6	$+1.03$	1025 ± 125 ~ 1% in Ar	S.P.Sh.		[1] W. Tsang, J. Chem. Phys. **42**, 1805 (1965)

Preferred:
   Reliable as reported. log $k = 15.13{-}66.6/\theta$.

Comments: The reaction is probably concerted.

Experimental

   [1] Analysis by G.L.C. Comparative rate study with the decomposition of 2-chloropropane as the internal standard. Small amounts of methane and ethylene were also detected.

Reaction: 4-Vinylcyclohexene

(I) $\longrightarrow 2[CH_2{=}CHCH{=}CH_2]$ (II)

	I	II
$\Delta H^\circ_{f(298)}$	15.6	26.3
$S^\circ_{(298)}$	88.6	66.6
$C^\circ_{p(298)}$	35.6	19.0

$\Delta S^\circ = 44.6$ g/mole
$\Delta H^\circ = 37.0$ kcal/mole
$\Delta C^\circ_p = 2.4$ g/mole

log A	E	log k_T (1025)	Conditions	System	Surface	References
15.20	62.0	+1.98	1025 ± 125 $\sim 1\%$ in Ar	S.P.Sh.		[1] W. Tsang, J. Chem. Phys. **42**, 1805 (1965)
8.37	36.0		783–978 °K 760 mm Hg	flow		[2] T. F. Doumani, R. F. Deering, and A. C. McKinnis, Ind. Eng. Chem. **39**, 89 (1947)

Preferred:
  $\log k = 15.20{-}62.0/\theta$.

Comments: The thermodynamics and the forward rate constant parameters, with an average $\langle \overline{\Delta C^\circ_p} \rangle \simeq 1.0$ g/mole, gives an estimate of the back reaction: $k_{back} = 10^{7.5-25.4/\theta}$ 1/mole-sec (800 °K). The observed addition rate constants are: $k_{back} = 10^{8.14-26.8/\theta}$ 1/mole-sec and $k_{back} = 10^{6.95-23.69/\theta}$ 1/mole-sec obtained by D. Rowley and H. Steiner, Disc. Faraday Soc. **10**, 198 (1951) and G. B. Kistiakowsky and W. W. Ransom, J. Chem. Phys. **7**, 725 (1939), respectively. The rate constant for association is predicted well by the thermodynamics, but no decision with regard to the parameters can be made since the estimated value is an intermediate one. The reaction is consistent with a biradical mechanism (see 1,5-cyclooctadiene).

Experimental

[1] Analysis by G.L.C. Comparative rate method with 2-chloropropane decomposition as standard.
[2] Rates were based on the "volume" of gases produced. No detailed analyses were made.

Reaction: 1,4-Cyclohexadiene

	I	II	III
$\Delta H^\circ_{f(298)}$	26.3	19.8	0
$S^\circ_{(298)}$	72	64.3	31.2
$C^\circ_{p(298)}$	23.4	19.5.	7.0

$\Delta S^\circ = 23.5$ g/mole
$\Delta H^\circ = -6.5$ kcal/mole
$\Delta C^\circ_p = 3.1$ g/mole

log A	E	log k_T (635)	Conditions	System	Surface	References
12.02	42.69	−2.68	576–616 °K	static	none	[1] R. J. Ellis and H. M. Frey, J. Chem. Soc. **A,** 553 (1966).
12.36	43.8	−2.72	603–663 °K	static flow	< 15%	[2] S. W. Benson and R. Shaw, Trans. Faraday Soc. **63,** 985 (1967).

Preferred:
    Reliable. log $k = 12.36 - 43.8/\theta$.

Experimental

[1] Rates were based on G.L.C. analysis. Propylene had no effect on the reaction rate. Cyclohexa-1,3-diene does not eliminate H_2 molecularly, but rather decomposes via a free radical chain process. (See also S. W. Benson and R. Shaw, J. Am. Chem. Soc. **89,** 5351 (1967).)

[2] Rates were based on G.L.C. analysis of C_6 products and mass-spectrometric analysis of H_2. No H, D exchange was observed with an equal amount of added hexadeuterobenzene and no methane was produced with added toluene; therefore no H-atoms are involved in the reaction.

Reaction: 1,4-Dioxane

$$\text{(I)} \longrightarrow 2[CH_2O]\ \text{(II)} + C_2H_4\ \text{(III)}$$

	I	II	III
$\Delta H^\circ_{f(298)}$	-76.0	-27.7	12.5
$S^\circ_{(298)}$	76.5	52.3	52.5
$C^\circ_{p(298)}$	19.4	8.5	10.4

$\Delta S^\circ = 80.6$ g/mole
$\Delta H^\circ = 43.1$ kcal/mole
$\Delta C^\circ_p = 8.0$ g/mole

log A	E	log k_T	Conditions	System	Surface	References
	71					[1] L. Küchler and J. D. Lambert, Z. Physik. Chemie **B42**, 359 (1939).

Preferred:
  Suspect. A free radical chain process is likely.

Experimental

[1] Reaction rates were strongly inhibited by NO, but were not catalyzed by acetaldehyde decomposition. No para-ortho hydrogen conversion.
  Products: $CH_2O + C_2H_4$.

Reaction: 1,3,5-Trioxane

$$\text{(I)} \longrightarrow 3(CH_2O) \ \text{(II)}$$

	I	II
$\Delta H^\circ_{f(298)}$	-120.8	-27.7
$S^\circ_{(298)}$	73.8	52.5
$C^\circ_{p(298)}$	18.4	8.5

$\Delta S^\circ = 83.7$ g/mole
$\Delta H^\circ = 37.7$ kcal/mole
$\Delta C^\circ_p = 7.1$ g/mole

log A	E	log k_T (585)	Conditions	System	Surface	References
15.0	47.4	-2.71	583 ± 38 °K 0.1–100 mm Hg (100)	static	$< 10\%$	[1] W. Hogg, D. M. McKinnon, and A. F. Trotman-Dickenson, and G. J. O. Verbeke, J. Chem Soc., 1403 (1961).
14.8	47.4	-2.91	582 ± 37 °K 0.1–600 mm Hg	static	none	[2] R. LeG. Burnett, R. P. Bell, Trans. Faraday Soc. **34,** 420 (1938).

Preferred:
  log $k = 15.0 - 47.4/\theta$.

Comments: The reaction must be concerted. The enthalpy of ring opening can be estimated at $\Delta H^\circ \approx 80$ kcal/mole.

Experimental

[1] Rates by ΔP. Falloff observed over the entire pressure range. Arrhenius parameters also obtained at 0.1, 1 and 10mm Hg. At 100 mm Hg the reaction was close to its high-pressure limit. Falloff was too severe to be attributable to a normal unimolecular reaction pressure dependence.

[2] Rates by ΔP. Pressure dependent below 15 mm Hg.

Reaction: 2,4,6-Trimethyl-1,3,5-trioxane (paraldehyde)

(I) $\longrightarrow 3[CH_3CHO]$ (II)

	I	II
$\Delta H^\circ_{f(298)}$	-152	-39.8
$S^\circ_{(298)}$	94.8	63.2
$C^\circ_{p(298)}$	34.9	13.1

$\Delta S^\circ = 94.8$ g/mole
$\Delta H^\circ = 32.6$ kcal/mole
$\Delta C^\circ_p = 4.4$ g/mole

log A	E	log k_T (515)	Conditions	System	Surface	References
15.1	44.16	-3.64	482–543 °K 11.8–520 mm Hg	static	none	[1] C. C. Coffin, Can. J. Res. **7**, 75 (1932).

Preferred:
Reliable. (see 1,3,5-trioxane) log $k = 15.1 - 44.16/\theta$.

Experimental

[1] Rates by ΔP measurements. In the packed reaction vessel, polymerization of the product aldehyde was observed.

Reaction: 2,4,6-Tri-n-propyl-1,3,5-trioxane (para-n-butyraldehyde)

(I) $\longrightarrow$ $3[CH_3(CH_2)_2CH{=}O]$ (II)

	I	II
$\Delta H^\circ_{f(298)}$	-179.6	-49.8
$S^\circ_{(298)}$	151.2	82.0
$C^\circ_{p(298)}$	67.9	24.1

$\Delta S^\circ = 94.8$ g/mole
$\Delta H^\circ = 30.2$ kcal/mole
$\Delta C^\circ_p = 4.4$ g/mole

log A	E	log k_T (510)	Conditions	System	Surface	References
14.35	42.0	-3.65	488–534 °K 13–550 mm Hg	static		[1] C. C. Coffin, Can. J. Res. **9**, 603 (1933)

Preferred:
Reliable. (see 1,3,5-trioxane) log $k = 14.35 - 42.0/\theta$

Experimental

[1] Rates followed manometrically. $\Delta P_\infty = 2P_0$; therefore, no side reactions occurred.

Reaction: 2,4,6-Tri-isopropyl-1,3,5-trioxane (*para*-isobutyraldehyde)

$$\text{(I)} \longrightarrow 3[(CH_3)_2CHCH{=}O]\ \text{(II)}$$

	I	II
$\Delta H^\circ_{f(298)}$	-183.2	-51.8
$S^\circ_{(298)}$	143.5	79.3
$C^\circ_{p(298)}$	67.0	23.8

$\Delta S^\circ = 94.4$ g/mole
$\Delta H^\circ = 27.8$ kcal/mole
$\Delta C^\circ_p = 4.4$ g/mole

log A	E	log k_T (510)	Conditions	System	Surface	References
14.75	42.8	-3.60	488–534 °K 13–550 mm Hg	static	◄—————	[1] C. C. Coffin Can. J. Res. **9**, 603 (1933).

Preferred:

   Reliable (see 1,3,5-trioxane).
   log $k = 14.75 - 42.8/\theta$.

Experimental

[1] Rates followed manometrically. The reaction stoichiometry was accurately 1 mole to 3 moles; therefore, side reactions were not important.

Reaction: Cycloheptatriene

	I	II
$\Delta H^\circ_{f(298)}$	44.1	12.0
$S^\circ_{(298)}$	75.4	76.4
$C^\circ_{p(298)}$	24.2	24.8

$\Delta S^\circ = 1.0$ g/mole
$\Delta H^\circ = -32.1$ kcal/mole
$\Delta C^\circ_p = 0.6$ g/mole

log A	E	log k_T	Conditions	System	Surface	References
13.54	51.1		658±23 °K 0.9–19.7 mm Hg	static	<10%	[1] K. N. Klump and J. P. Chesick, J. Am. Chem. Soc. **85,** 130 (1963).
13.90	52.2		661±44 °K	stirred flow		[2] W. C. Herndon and L. L. Lowey, J. Am. Chem. **86,** 1922 (1964).

Preferred:
   $\log k = 13.90 - 52.2/\theta$.

Comments: Results agree within experimental error and are reliable as reported. The conclusion regarding the biradical mechanism (see below) seems valid since the enthalpy of ring opening alone is estimated to be about 79 kcal/mole. Norcaradiene is formed, which then converts to toluene via biradical.

Experimental

[1] Analysis by G.L.C. No effect by NO on the rate, or by a 20-fold increase in the pressure through added nitrogen. A transition state similar to norcaradiene, or (0,1,4) bicyclohepta-2-4-diene, was suggested, and the biradical mechanism was dismissed on energy considerations.
[2] Analysis by G.L.C.

Reaction: 1,5-Cyclooctadiene

		I	II	III
	$\Delta H^\circ_{f(298)}$	(22.7)	15.6	26.3
	$S^\circ_{(298)}$	83.4	88.1	66.6
a	$C^\circ_{p(298)}$	30.1	35.6	19.1

$\Delta S^\circ = 4.7$ g/mole
$\Delta H^\circ = -7.1$ kcal/mole
$\Delta C^\circ_p = 5.5$ g/mole

Path	log A	E	log k_T (585)	Conditions	System	Surface	References
a	14.46	49	−3.85	586 ± 14 °K 1.2 mm Hg	static	< 10%	[1] R. Srinivasan and A. A. Levi, J. Am. Chem. Soc. **86**, 3756 (1964).
b	*15.7	*55	−4.85				

Preferred:
   Reliable. log $k_a = 14.46 - 49/\theta$; log $k_b = 15.7 - 55/\theta$.

Comments: A biradical mechanism has been proposed for this reaction which unites the kinetics and thermo-dynamics of three reactions: the decomposition of 4-vinyl-cyclohexene, the decompositions of 1,2-divinyl-cyclobutanes, and the dimerization of butadiene. (See S. W. Benson, J. Chem. Phys. **46**, 4920 (1967).)

Experimental

[1] Analysis by G.L.C. Surface effects appreciable at $T > 327$ °C. No effect on the rate by added propylene.

---

*Only the activation energy for path b was reported.

Reaction: Spiropentane

$$\bowtie\text{(I)} \longrightarrow \square\!\!\!\!/\text{(II)}$$

	I	II
$\Delta H^\circ_{f(298)}$	44.2	29.7
$S^\circ_{(298)}$	67.5	72.5
$C^\circ_{p(298)}$	21.1	20.3

$\Delta S^\circ = 5.0$ g/mole
$\Delta H^\circ = -14.5$ kcal/mole
$\Delta C^\circ_p = -0.8$ g/mole

log A	E	log k_T (675)	Conditions	System	Surface	References
15.86	57.57	−2.78	658±25 °K 25–350 mm Hg	static		[1] M. C. Flowers and H. M. Frey, J. Chem. Soc., 5550 (1961).
15.2	55.5	−2.77	643–703 °K 10^{-3}–5 mm Hg	static		[2] P. J. Burkhardt and D. F. Swinehart, Ph.D. diss., University of Oregon, 1962.

Preferred:
   $\log k = 15.2 - 55.5/\theta$.

Comments: The reaction is consistent with a biradical mechanism.

$$E_{(strain)} \simeq 63.5 \text{ kcal/mole}$$

Experimental

   [1] Analysis by G.L.C. Falloff observed near 13.5 mm Hg. A decomposition to allene + ethylene was also observed (~ 9 percent of reaction at 408 °C) with an activation energy in excess of 58 kcal/mole. Allene did not seem to be formed from the subsequent decomposition of methylenecyclobutane. Estimated error was ±0.6 kcal/mole.
   [2] Analysis by G.L.C. and M.S. Falloff observed over the entire pressure range. High pressure rate constants were obtained from a fit of the data to the Kassel integral.

Reaction: Bicyclo[1,1,0]butane

$$\text{(diagram)} \quad (1) \longrightarrow \quad \text{(diagram)} \,(II)$$

	I	II
$\Delta H^{\circ}_{f(298)}$	(55.3)	26.3
$S^{\circ}_{(298)}$	62.4	66.6
$C^{\circ}_{p(298)}$	16.0	19.1

$\Delta S^{\circ} = \quad 4.2$ g/mole
$\Delta H^{\circ} = -29.0$ kcal/mole
$\Delta C^{\circ}_p = \quad 3.1$ g/mole

log A	E	log k_T (490)	Conditions	System	Surface	References
14.23	40.58	−3.87	496 ± 28 °K 6 − 100 torr (20)	static	< 10%	[1] H. M. Frey and I. D. R. Stevens, Trans. Faraday Soc. **61**, 90 (1965).
14.52	41.4	−3.95	489 ± 13 °K 6 − 14 torr	static	10–20%	[2] R. Srinivasan, A. A. Levi and I. Haller, J. Phys. Chem. **69**, 1775 (1965).

Preferred:
 Reliable. log $k = 14.5 - 41.4/\theta$; log $A_{est} = 14.9$.

Comments: It has been shown that bicyclo[1,1,0]butane-2-exo-d_1 does not isomerize to the d_1 endo form at reaction temperatures (K. B. Wiberg and J. M. Lavanish, J. Am. Chem. Soc. **88**, 5272 (1966)). In terms of a biradical mechanism, this means that the rate-determining step must be ring opening.
 A concerted mechanism has been proposed for this reaction because of its low activation energy and because of its similarity to the cyclobutene reaction which is known to be concerted.
 However, the biradical mechanism cannot be ruled out on the basis of the energetics. For the mechanism,

$$\text{(diagram)} \;\underset{2}{\overset{1}{\rightleftharpoons}}\; \text{(diagram)} \;\overset{3}{\underset{\text{fast}}{\longrightarrow}}\; \text{(diagram)}$$

$$E = \Delta H^{\circ}_{1,2} + E_2 = DH^{\circ}(\text{C—C}) - \Delta E_{1,2\,\text{strain}} - (E_{\text{resonance}}) + E_2$$
$$= 80.1 - 69.2 + 27.6 - (4) + 9.3 = 43.8 \text{ kcal/mole.}$$

This estimate of E (which is within experimental error) depends critically on a 4 kcal/mole resonance energy in the ($\triangleright\!\!\cdot$) radical. This value comes from the kinetics of the bicyclopropyl reaction.
 If the reaction is concerted, then the reported A-factor will be the highest of its kind known. For this reason, we favor a biradical mechanism.

Experimental

[1] Analysis by G.L.C. Falloff observed near 20 mm Hg (estimated to be within 5 percent of the high-pressure region).
[2] Analysis by G.L.C.

Reaction: 1,3-Dimethylbicyclo[1,1,0]butane

$$\bowtie \;(\text{I}) \;\longrightarrow\; \rtimes\kern-0.3em\ltimes \;(\text{II})$$

	I	II
$\Delta H^\circ_{f(298)}$	39.3	11.0
$S^\circ_{(298)}$	75.0	80.4
$C^\circ_{p(298)}$	26.8	30.1

$\Delta S^\circ = \;\;\;\; 5.4$ g/mole
$\Delta H^\circ = -29.3$ kcal/mole
$\Delta C^\circ_p = \;\;\;\; 3.3$ g/mole

log A	E	kog k_T (550)	Conditions	System	Surface	References
14.45	43.3	-2.76	547 ± 24 °K 0.2–15 (2–4)	static	$< 10\%$	[1] J. P. Chesick, J. Phys. Chem. **68**, 2033 (1964).

Preferred:
   $\log k = 14.45 - 43.3/\theta$.

Comments: The reported parameters are consistent with a biradical mechanism,

$$\bowtie \;\underset{\text{slow}}{\overset{1}{\underset{2}{\rightleftharpoons}}}\; (\cdot\triangle\cdot) \;\overset{3}{\underset{\text{fast}}{\longrightarrow}}\; \rtimes\kern-0.3em\ltimes$$

$$E_{\text{est}} = DH^\circ\text{C—C} - \Delta E_{\text{strain}} - E_{\text{res}} + E_2$$

$$= 77.3 - (67.4\text{–}27.6) - (4) + 9.3 = 42.8 \text{ kcal/mole}.$$

$\log A_{\text{est}} = 14.6$ (see bicyclo[1,1,0](butane)

Experimental

   [1] Analysis by G.L.C. Heterogeneity was significant at $T < 531$ °K. Rates were unaffected by high pressures of
Side product production at the walls decreased with increasing temperature (i.e., from 5.4 percent (250 °C) to 1.3
percent (279 °C)).

Reaction: Bicyclo[1,1,1]pentane

(I) → (II)

	I	II
$\Delta H^\circ_{(298)}$	(34.3 to 44.3)	25.4
$S^\circ_{(298)}$	67.1	79.7
$C^\circ_{p(298)}$		24.2

$\Delta S^\circ = 12.6$ g/mole
$\Delta H^\circ =$
ΔC°_p

log A	E	log k_T (565)	Conditions	System	Surface	References
15.24	49.0	−3.72	553–582 °K 0.25–35 torr (5 torr)	static	none	[1] R. Srinivasan, J. Am. Chem. Soc. **90**, 2752 (1968).

Preferred:
Reliable as reported.
log $k = 15.24 - 49.0/\theta$.

Comments: Parameters at P_∞ may be slightly higher. Although the A-factor is "high," suggesting a biradical mechanism, the activation energy is low and favors a concerted process. Thus, for the biradical mechansim,

Mech.

$$E_{\text{biradical}} \simeq DH^\circ(\text{C—C}) - \Delta E_{\text{strain}} + E_2; \; 49 \simeq 77 - (E_{\text{st}} - 26) + 8$$

This suggests $\epsilon_{\text{st}} \left(\text{} \right) \simeq |62$ kcal/mole, which seems a bit too high.

Experimental

[1] Analysis by G.L.C. No effect by change in (S/V) ratio. The decomposition was total pressure dependent and $k_{(2.5 \text{ torr})} \simeq 1/2k_{(35 \text{ torr})}$.

Reaction: 1,3-Dimethylbicyclo[1,1,1]pentane

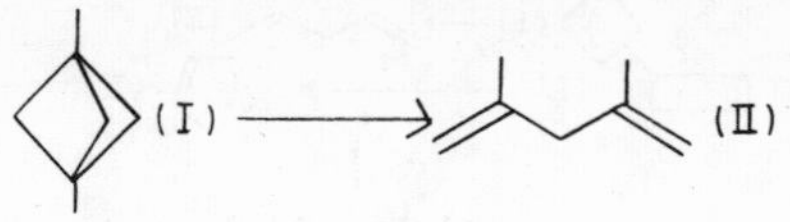

	I	II
$\Delta H^\circ_{f(298)}$	(24.0)	9.8
$S^\circ_{(298)}$	76.8	94.9
$C^\circ_{p(298)}$		36.4

$\Delta S^\circ = $ 18.1 g/mole
$\Delta H^\circ = (-14.2)$ kcal/mole
ΔC°_p

log A	E	log k_T (580)	Conditions	System	Surface	References
16.2	53.0	−3.77	568–594 °K 3 torr	static	none	[1] R. Srinivasan, J. Am. Chem. Soc. **90**, 2752 (1968).

Preferred:
    Reliable, as reported.   log $k = 16.2 - 53.0/\theta$.

Comments: The high *A*-factor suggests a biradical mechanism, and the observed activation energy is in fair agreement with thermodynamic estimates (see bicyclo[1,1,1] for the mechanism).

$$E_{act} \simeq DH^\circ(C\!-\!C) - \Delta E_{strain} + E_2$$
$$\simeq 77.3 - (58(?) - 26) + 8 \simeq 53.3 \text{ kcal/mole}$$
$$A_{est} \simeq 10^{15.6} \text{ sec}^{-1}; \ E_{st} \sim 58 \text{ kcal/mole}.$$

Experimental

[1] Analysis by G.L.C. No S/V dependence.

324

Reaction: Bicyclo[2,1,0]pent-2-ene

	I	II
$\Delta H^\circ_{f(298)}$	67.6	32.5
$S^\circ_{(298)}$	67.7	67.0
$C^\circ_{p(298)}$	(18.6)	17.5

$\Delta S^\circ = -0.7$ g/mole
$\Delta H^\circ = -35.1$ kcal/mole
$\Delta C^\circ_p = -1.1$ g/mole

log A	E	log k_T (340)	Conditions	System	Surface	References
14.2	26.9	-2.83	299–381 °K 0.2–760 torr			[1] D. M. Golden and J. I. Brauman, J. Am. Chem. Soc., **90,** 1920 (1968).

Preferred:
  log $k = 14.2 - 26.9/\theta$.

Comments: Transition state estimates based on the biradical mechanism give log $A \simeq 14.2$; $\Delta H^\circ_{1,2} = 26.3 - E_{\text{resonance}}$.

Experimental

[1] Analysis by G.L.C. Pressure falloff observed at temperatures above 346 °K. $M_{1/2}$ (382 °K) ~ 25 torr. High-pressure rates obtained with added Ar or C_3H_8. An RRK-$s \simeq 10$ fit the data.

Reaction: Bicyclo[2,1,0,]pentane

	I	II	III
$\Delta H^\circ_{f(298)}$	36.0	7.9	25.2
$S^\circ_{(298)}$	68.5	69.2	79.7
$C^\circ_{p(298)}$	17.9	18.1'	25.1

	a	b
$\Delta S^\circ =$	0.7	11.2 g/mole
$\Delta H^\circ =$	-28.1	-10.8 kcal/mole
$\Delta C^\circ_p =$	0.2	7.2 g/mole

Path	log A	E	log k_T (530)	Conditions	System	Surface	References
a	14.58	46.6	−4.64	572 ± 11 °K 0.04–66.7	static	< 10%	[1] M. L. Halberstadt and J. P. Chesick, J. Am. Chem. Soc. **84**, 2688 (1962)
a	14.1	45.6	−4.70	531 ± 35°K 400 mm Hg	static-	none	[2] C. Steel, R. Zand, P. Hurwitz, and S. G. Cohen, J. Am. Chem. Soc. **86**, 679 (1964)
b	14.4	52.3	−6.39	547 ± 42 °K 400 torr	static	none	

Preferred:

$\log k_a = 14.1 - 45.6/\theta$; $\log k_b = 14.4 - 52.3/\theta$.

Comments: The kinetics are in reasonable agreement with a biradical mechanism.

From the *cis, trans* isomerization of 2-methyl [2,1,0] bicyclopentane, $k_2 > (k_3 + k_4)$.

$$\Delta H^\circ_{1,2} = DH^\circ(C-C) - \Delta E_{strain} = 78.7 - 53.8 + 6.3 = 31.2 \text{ kcal/mole}$$
$$\log A_{a(est)} = 14.0; \ \log A_{b(est)} = 14.5$$

The H-migration and ring opening activation energies obtained from the observed activation energies (i.e., 14.4 kcal/mole and 21.1 kcal/mole, respectively) seem high, but not unreasonably so.

Experimental

[1] Analysis by G.L.C. Falloff observed near 3 mm Hg. An RRK−$s \simeq 18 \pm 2$ fit the falloff behaviour. Added nitrogen increased the rates in the low-pressure region with a collision efficiency of 0.1 relative to the reactant.

[2] Analysis by G.L.C. Reaction performed in sealed ampoules with estimated pressures of about 400 mm Hg. The energetics of the reaction and others are discussed in detail with regard to the biradical intermediates.

Reaction: *cis* 2-Methyl [2,1,0] bicyclopentane

trans-2-Methyl [2,1,0] bicyclopentane

$$\square\!\!\!\!\triangle \; \text{(I)} \; \underset{b}{\overset{a}{\rightleftharpoons}} \; \square\!\!\!\!\triangle\text{(II)}$$

	I(*cis*)	II(*trans*)
$\Delta H^{\circ}_{f(298)}$	28.3	28.8
$S^{\circ}_{(298)}$	74.9	75.3
$C^{\circ}_{p(298)}$	22.7	24.0

$\Delta S^{\circ} = 0.4$ g/mole
$\Delta H^{\circ} = 0.5$ kcal/mole
$\Delta C_p = 1.3$ g/mole

Path	log A	E	log k_T (490)	Conditions	System	Surface	References
a	14.36	39.15	−3.10	491 ± 15 °K 0.08 − 1.7	static	< 10%	[1] J. P. Chesick, J. Am. Chem. Soc. **84**, 3250 (1962).
b	13.90	38.65	−3.34				

Preferred:

$\log k_a = 14.36 - 39.15/\theta$
$\log k_b = 13.90 - 38.65/\theta$

Comments: The kinetics are consistent with a biradical mehcanism:

$$\square\!\!\!\!\triangle \; \underset{2}{\overset{1}{\rightleftharpoons}} \; (\diamondsuit\cdot) \; \underset{4}{\overset{3}{\rightleftharpoons}} \; \square\!\!\!\!\square$$

$\log A_{a(\text{est})} = 14.3$; $\log A_{b(\text{est})} = 14.0$.
$E_{\text{est}} = \Delta H_{1,2} + E_2 = 31.2 + E_2$; $E_2 \simeq 8$ kcal/mole.

Experimental

[1] Analysis by I.R. and G.L.C. Rates from G.L.C. analysis. A clear distinction between the identity of the two isomers could not be made. Tentatively, the *cis* isomer was identified as the one of lower energy and entropy.

Reaction: Bicyclo[2,2,0]hexane

(I) $\longrightarrow$ (II)

	I	II
$\Delta H^\circ_{f(298)}$	29.6	19.8
$S^\circ_{(298)}$	72.6	89.4
$C^\circ_{p(298)}$	24.6	28.8

$\Delta S^\circ = 16.8$ g/mole
$\Delta H^\circ = -9.8$ kcal/mole
$\Delta C^\circ_p = 4.2$ g/mole

log A	E	log k_T (445)	Conditions	System	Surface	References
13.4	36.0	−4.28	443 ± 40 °K 400 mm Hg	static		[1] C. Steel, R. Zand, P. Hurwitz, and S. G. Cohen, J. Am. Chem. Soc. **86,** 679 (1964).

Preferred:
   $\log k = 13.4 - 36.0/\theta$.

Comments: The kinetics are in agreement with a biradical mechanism. It seems quite likely that $k_2 \simeq k_3$.

   $\log A_{est} = 13.0$; $\Delta H^\circ_{1,2} \simeq 27$; $E_{r.c.} \simeq 9$ kcal/mole (see section III–6.0).

Experimental

[1] Analysis by G.L.C. Reaction performed in sealed ampoules at estimated pressures of about 400 mm Hg.

Reaction: Bicyclo[3,1,0]hex-2-ene

	I	II	III
$\Delta H^\circ_{f(298)}$	37.6	26.0	26.3
$S^\circ_{(298)}$	73.0	72.1	72
$C^\circ_{p(298)}$	19.9	23.4	23.4

a

$\Delta S^\circ = -0.9$ g/mole
$\Delta H^\circ = -11.6$ kcal/mole
$\Delta C_p^\circ = +3.5$ g/mole

Path	log A	E	log k_T (605)	Conditions	System	Surface	References
$a+b$	14.5	50.2	−3.64	586–620 °K 3–30 mm Hg	static	none	[1] R. J. Ellis and H. M. Frey, J. Chem. Soc. **A**, 553 (1966).
a	14.28	50.2	−3.86				
b	14.10	50.2	−4.04	(as above)			(as above)

Preferred:
Reliable.

Comments: Reactions fit a biradical mechanism with H-migration as rate determining. Transition state estimates give, $A_{(a+b)} = 10^{14.3}$ sec^{-1} and $E \simeq 48.5$ kcal/mole (see section III–6.0).

Experimental

[1] Rates were based on G.L.C. analysis of products. A subsequent decomposition of cyclohexa-1,4-diene to benzene and hydrogen was also observed (see cyclohexa-1,3-diene). The following added gases had no effect on the reaction rates: propylene (8 fold excess), nitric oxide, *t*-butyl peroxide. Product ratios were constant over the temperature range of study, ( ) / ( ) = 1.5.

Reaction: Bicyclo[3,1,0]hexane

	I	II	III
$\Delta H^\circ_{f(298)}$	10.3	-1.7	-0.3
$S^\circ_{(298)}$	73.0	74.3	78.0
$C^\circ_{p(298)}$	23.9	25.3	24.2

	a	b
$\Delta S^\circ =$	1.3	5.0 g/mole
$\Delta H^\circ =$	-12.0	-10.6 kcal/mole
$\Delta C^\circ_p =$	1.4	0.3 g/mole

Path	log A	E	log k_T (730)	Conditions	System	Surface	References
a	13.29	57.4	-3.90	728 ± 37 °K 5–70 mm Hg	static	< 10%	[1] H. M. Frey and R. C. Smith, Trans. Faraday Soc. **58**, 697 (1962).
b	13.89	61.17	-4.42	(as above)			(as above).

Preferred:

$\log k_a = 13.29 - 57.4/\theta$; $\log k_b = 13.89 - 61.17/\theta$.

Comments: The kinetics favor biradical mechanisms (see section III–6.0).

$\log A_{a(est)} = 13.5$; $\Delta H^\circ_{1,2(est)} \simeq 46$ kcal/mole; $E_{a(est)} = 56.5$
$\log A_{b(est)} = 14.2$; $\Delta H_{(1',2)est} \simeq 52$ kcal/mole; $E_{b(est)} = 62.5$.

Experimental

[1] Analysis by G.L.C. At the highest temperatures, small amounts (~ 1–4 percent) of methylenecyclopentane and benzene were detected. Yields increased with increasing (S/V).

Reaction: Bicyclo[2,1,1]hexane

	I	II
$\Delta H^\circ_{f(298)}$	15.4	20.2
$S^\circ_{(298)}$	69.4	88.4
$C^\circ_{p(298)}$	23.8	28.8

$\Delta S^\circ = 19.0$ g/mole
$\Delta H^\circ = 4.8$ kcal/mole
$\Delta C^\circ_p = 5.0$ g/mole

log A	E	log k_T (620)	Conditions	System	Surface	References
15.17	55	−4.21	618 ± 18 °K 0.2 − 20 mm Hg	static	< 10%	[1] R. Srinivasan and A. A. Levi, J. Am. Chem. Soc. **85**, 3363 (1963).

Preferred:
   $\log k = 15.17 - 55.0/\theta$.

Comments: The kinetics favor a biradical mechanism (see III−6.0).

Very likely $k_2 \simeq k_3$. With a strain energy for the reactant of 39 kcal/mole,

$$E \simeq DH^\circ(\text{C—C}) - \Delta E_{\text{strain}} + E_2 \text{ (or } E_3)$$
$$55 \simeq 80.1 - 39 + 6.3 + E_2; \; E_2 \simeq 7.6 \text{ kcal/mole}$$
$$\log A_{\text{est}} \simeq 15.2$$

Experimental

[1] Analysis by G.L.C. NO and propylene had no effect on the reaction rates.

Reaction: Bicyclo[3,2,0]heptane

	I	II	III	IV
$\Delta H^{\circ}_{f(298)}$	3.8	12.5	7.9	14.8
$S^{\circ}_{(298)}$	78.9	52.5	69.2	98.8
$C^{\circ}_{p(298)}$	24.5	10.4	17.5	34.3

	a	b
$\Delta S^{\circ} =$	42.8	19.9 g/mole
$\Delta H^{\circ} =$	16.6	11.0 kcal/mole
$\Delta C^{\circ}_p =$	3.4	9.8 g/mole

Path	log A	E	log k_T (735)	Conditions	System	Surface	References
a	14.84	60.74	−3.22	737 ± 38 °K 2–20 mm Hg	static	< 10%	[1] R. J. Ellis and H. M. Frey, J. Chem. Soc., 4184 (1964).
b	15.40	63.97	−3.62				

Preferred:
   log $k_a = 14.84 - 60.74/\theta$; log $k_b = 15.40 - 63.97/\theta$.

Comments: The kinetics favor biradical mechanisms (see section III–6.0).

Probably, $k_2 \simeq k_3$; $k_{2'} \simeq k_{3'}$ as in cyclobutane decompositions.
   Transition state estimates give:

$$\log A_{a(est)} \simeq 15.0; \ \Delta H^{\circ}_{1,2} \simeq 55 \text{ kcal/mole}; \quad E_{a(est)} = 61 \text{ kcal/mole}$$
$$\log A_{b(est)} \simeq 15.3; \ \Delta H^{\circ}_{1',2'} \simeq 56.5 \text{ kcal/mole}; \ E_{b(est)} = 62.5 \text{ kcal/mole}.$$

Experimental

   [1] Analysis by G.L.C. Rates were corrected for subsequent decomposition of 1,6-heptadiene to butadiene and propylene.

Reaction: Bicyclo[3,2,0]hept-6-ene

$$\text{I} \quad (1) \longrightarrow \quad \text{II}$$

	I	II
$\Delta H^\circ_{f(298)}$	33.3	20.8
$S^\circ_{(298)}$	74.6	77.3
$C^\circ_{p(298)}$	23.0	25.1

$\Delta S^\circ = \quad 2.7$ g/mole
$\Delta H^\circ = -12.5$ kcal/mole
$\Delta C^\circ_p = \quad 2.1$ g/mole

log A	E	log k_T (575)	Conditions	System	Surface	References
14.31	45.51	-2.99	547–600 °K 0.5–6 mm Hg	static	none	[1] G. R. Branton, H. M. Frey, D. C. Montague, and I. D. R. Stevens, Trans. Faraday Soc. **62**, 659 (1966).

Preferred:
   log $k = 14.31 - 45.51/\theta$.

Comments: The reaction may be compared to cyclobutene decompositions which proceed with "normal" A-factors, much lower activation energies, and are concerted processes. The exclusive con-rotary isomerizations of the cyclobutenes as predicted by the Woodward-Hoffman rules is here sterically inhibited. The result is a disrotary (or biradical) mechanism.

$$\text{I} \underset{2}{\overset{1}{\rightleftharpoons}} \text{(biradical)} \xrightarrow[\text{fast}]{3} \text{II}$$

Transition state estimates give,

   log $A_{\text{est}} = 14.3$; $\Delta H^\circ_{1.2} \simeq 35$ kcal/mole; $E_2 \simeq 10.5$ kcal/mole; $E_{\text{strain}} \simeq (6.3 + 29.8)$ kcal/mole

Experimental

[1] Analysis and rate by G.L.C. Reaction in solution gave log $k = 14.65 - 45.86/\theta$.

Reaction: Bicyclo[4,2,0]oct-7-ene

	I	II
$\Delta H^\circ_{f(298)}$	21.0	19.7
$S^\circ_{(298)}$	82.2	83.7
$\Delta C^\circ_{p(298)}$	33.9	(31)

$\Delta S^\circ = 1.5$ g/mole
$\Delta H^\circ = -1.3$ kcal/mole
$\Delta C^\circ_p = -2.9$ g/mole

log A	E	log k_T (535)	Conditions	System	Surface	References
14.13	43.18	−3.51	509–558 °K 0.5–4.0 mm Hg	static	none	[1] G. R. Branton, H. M. Frey, and R. F. Skinner, Trans. Faraday Soc. **62**, 1546 (1966).

Preferred:
   log $k = 14.13 - 43.18/\theta$.

Comments: The activation energy for this reaction is lower than one would expect for a biradical mechanism (i.e., $\Delta H^\circ_{\text{to biradical}} \simeq 42$ kcal/mole). However, the observed A-factor is quite close to the estimated value log $A_{\text{est}} = 13.9$. (See bicyclo[3,2,0]hept-6-ene.)

Experimental

[1] Rates were obtained from G.L.C. analysis on reactant and product.

Reaction: Bicyclo[2,2,1]hepta-2,5-diene

	I	II	III	IV	V
$\Delta H^\circ_{f(298)}$	57.1	44.1	54.2	32.5	12.0
$S^\circ_{(298)}$	71.3	75.4	48.0	66.2	76.4
$C^\circ_{p(298)}$	26.1	24.2	10.5	17.5	24.8

a

$\Delta S^\circ = 4.1$ g/mole

$\Delta H^\circ = -13$ kcal/mole

$\Delta C^\circ_p = -1.9$ g/mole

Path	log A	E	log k_T (660)	Conditions	System	Surface	References
a	14.68	50.61	−2.08	661 ± 44 °K	S. Flow	———	[1] W. C. Herndon and
b	14.62	50.19	−2.00				and L. L. Lowry,
c	14.23	53.14	−3.37				J. Am. Chem. Soc. **86**, 1922 (1964).
a	14.91	51.6	−2.18	615 ± 15 °K	static	~10%	[2] J. H. Birely and J. P.
b	14.72	50.5	−2.00	0.8–2 torr		<10%	Chesick, J. Phys. Chem **66**, 568 (1962).
a	13.94	49.8	−2.55	613 ± 20 °K	static	<10%	[3] B. C. Roquite, Can.
b	14.30	49.8	−2.19	4.4–24.7 torr		< 10%	J. Chem. **42**, 2134 (1964).

Preferred:

log $k_a = 14.68 - 50.61/\theta$

log $k_b = 14.62 - 50.19/\theta$

log $k_c = 14.23 - 53.14/\theta$.

Comments: The estimated enthalpy for ring opening, α(C—C) split — path b, is about 57 kcal/mole, therefore path b must be a concerted process. The estimated enthalpy of ring opening, β(C—C) split — paths a and c, is about 38 kcal/mole, thus paths a and c are consistent with the biradical mechanism.

$\Delta H^\circ_{1,2} = DH^\circ(\text{C—C}) - \Delta E_{\text{strain}} - R_{\text{allyl}} = 80.1 - (31.5 - 2) - 12.6 = 38$ kcal/mole

log $A_{c(\text{est})} = 14.2$

log $A_{a(\text{est})} = 14.5$.

(*Continued*)

Bicyclo[2,2,1]hepta-2,5-diene (*Continued*)

Experimental

[1] Analysis by I.R. and G.L.C. Rates by G.L.C. Toluene was also believed to be a product of the subseque decomposition of cycloheptatriene. This is consistent with the observations of [3].

[2] Analysis by G.L.C. Source of toluene was uncertain.

[3] Analysis by G.L.C. Toluene yields were very low in the initial stages. No effect on reaction rates by add O_2 and NO. The ratio of toluene to cycloheptatriene increased with increasing percent decomposition (see [1]).

Reaction: Bicyclo[2,2,1]hept-2-ene:

	I	II	III
$\Delta H^\circ_{f(298)}$	22.3	12.5	32.5
$S^\circ_{(298)}$	76.0	52.5	67.0
$C^\circ_{p(298)}$	27.3	10.4	17.5

$\Delta S^\circ = 43.5$ g/mole
$\Delta H^\circ = 22.7$ kcal/mole
$\Delta C^\circ_p = 0.6$ g/mole

log A	E	log k_T (560)	Conditions	System	Surface	References
13.84	43.47	−3.13	558 ± 19 °K 5–43 mm Hg	static	< 10%	[1] B. C. Roquite, J. Phys. Chem. **69**, 1351 (1965).
13.78	42.75	−2.91	625 ± 48 °K 673 ± 43 °K	stirred flow flow	< 10%	[2] W. C. Herndon, W. B. Cooper, Jr., and M. J. Chambers, J. Phys. Chem. **68**, 2016 (1964).

Preferred:
    log $k = 13.84$–$43.47/\theta$.

Comments: A biradical mechanism gives $\Delta H^\circ_{1,2} = DH^\circ(C-C) - E_{stra}$
$- R_{allyl} = 80.1 - 24.5 + 6 - 12.5 = 49.1$ kcal/mole. This *exceeds* the experimental activation energy by muc more than experimental error. There seems to be little chance of extra stabilization of the transition stat for ring closing in this system (as opposed to endo-dicyclopentadiene), thus the reaction is undoubtedly concerted process.

Experimental

[1] Analysis by G.L.C. Rates were unaffected by added O_2, NO, propylene and toluene. A reaction product est mated as less than 2 percent of the total was not identified.

[2] Analysis by G.L.C. Both flow methods were consistent and the data from both were combined to obtain th reported Arrhenius parameters.

336

Reaction: 2,3-Diazobicyclo[2,2,1]hept-2-ene

$(I) \longrightarrow$ (II) + N_2 (III)

	I	II	III
$\Delta H^\circ_{f(298)}$	(62)	36.0	0
$S^\circ_{(298)}$	75.9	70.4	45.8
$C^\circ_{p(298)}$	27.3	17.9	7.0

$\Delta S^\circ = 40.3$ g/mole
$\Delta H^\circ = -26$ kcal/mole
$\Delta C^\circ_p = -2.4$ g/mole

log A	E	log k_T	Conditions	System	Surface	References
14.86	37.3		429 ± 25 °K (35 mm Hg)	static	< 10%	[1] S. G. Cohen, R. Zand, and C. Steel, J. Am. Chem. Soc. **83**, 2895 (1961).
14.78	36.9		443–563 °K 100–200 mm Hg	static	none	[2] R. J. Crawford, R. J. Dummel, and A. Mishra, J. Am. Chem. Soc. **87**, 3023 (1965).

Preferred:
Reliable, log $k = 14.78 - 36.9/\theta$.

Comments: Using the activation energy for azoisopropane (~ 47.5 kcal/mole) as a measure of the (C—N$_{azo}$) bond energy, and assuming the same strain as in norbornane [, $E_{st} \simeq 17.6 \pm 2.5$ kcal/mole], one obtains an enthalpy of ring opening to the biradical of, $\Delta H^\circ_{1,2} = 30.0$ kcal/mole. A biradical mechanism, therefore, is consistent with the kinetics with $E_2 = 7.0$ kcal/mole. Also, log $A_{est} = 14.4$ (see section III–7.0).

Mechanism:

Experimental

[1] Analysis by G.L.C. Reactions performed in sealed tubes at approximate pressure reported and in the presence of 1 atm pressure of isooctane.

[2] Rates followed by pressure change. First order kinetics observed to greater than 95 percent reaction.

Reaction: 2,3-Diazobicyclo[2,2,2]oct-2-ene

	I	II	III
$\Delta H^\circ_{f(298)}$	(45.6)	19.8	0
$S^\circ_{(298)}$	81.8	88.4	45.8
$C^\circ_{p(298)}$	32.8	28.8	7.0

$\Delta S^\circ = \ \ 52.4$ g/mole
$\Delta H^\circ = -25.8$ kcal/mole
$\Delta C^\circ_p = \ \ \ 3.0$ g/mole

log A	E	log k_T	Conditions	System	Surface	References
15.3	44.6		503 ± 30 °K 25 mm Hg	static	< 10%	[1] S. G. Cohen and R. Zand, J. Am. Chem. Soc. **84,** 586 (1962)

Preferred:
   $\log k = 15.3 - 44.6/\theta.$

Comments: The kinetics are consistent with a biradical process. The activation energy suggests a strain energy of about 7 kcal/mole in the reactant if there is a 4 kcal back activation energy for the biradical (boat form of cyclohexane). This seems reasonable. $\log A_{\text{est}} = 15.5$. (See section III–7.0.)

Experimental

[1] Analysis by U.V. Reaction performed in sealed tubes at 1 atm pressure of isooctane or toluene.

Reaction: Bicyclo[5,1,0]oct-2-ene
Cycloocta-1,4-diene

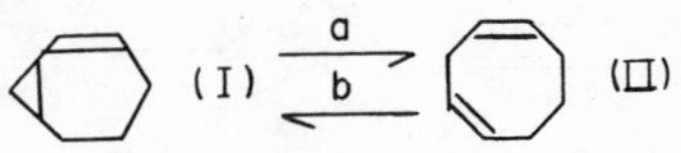

$(I) \xrightleftharpoons[b]{a} (II)$

	I	II
$\Delta H^\circ_{(298)}$	25 ± 2	25.0
$S^\circ_{(298)}$	77.0	83.4
$C^\circ_{p(298)}$	29.3	30.0

$S^\circ = (6.4)$ g/mole
$H^\circ = (0)$ kcal/mole
$C^\circ_p = 0.7$ g/mole

Path	log A	E	log k_T (480)	Conditions	System	Surface	References
	13.36	38.6	-4.22	468–489 °K	static		[1] W. Grimme. Chem. Ber. **98,** 756 (1965).
	11.80	38.6	-5.76				

Preferred:
$\log k_a = 13.36 - 38.6/\theta.$
$\log k_b = 11.80 - 38.6/\theta.$

Experimental

[1] Rates were followed by G.L.C. analysis. The equilibrium constant for the reaction was found to be about $K_{eq} \simeq 37$ t 473 °K with a temperature dependence $\Delta H^\circ_R = 0 \pm 0.3$ kcal/mole. The sum of rate constants was reported $(k_a + k_b)$ $= 2.2 \times 10^{13-38.6 \pm .6/\theta}$ sec^{-1}. Parameters above have been calculated from these data. Above 325 °C equilibrium is dis-
placed irreversibly to form 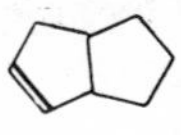 from (II) in a "vinylcyclopropane type" reaction.

Reaction: Tricyclo[3,3,0,0^{2,6}]octane

(I) $\longrightarrow$ (II)

	I	II
$\Delta H^\circ_{f(298)}$	(14.2)	(23)
$S^\circ_{(298)}$	74.6	83.4
$C^\circ_{p(298)}$	30.1	30.1

$\Delta S^\circ = 8.8$ kcal/mole
$\Delta H^\circ = 8.8$ kcal/mole
$\Delta C^\circ_p = 0$ g/mole

log A	E	log k_T (615)	Conditions	System	Surface	References
15.51	55.9	−4.35	616±16 1.5 torr	static	~10%	[1] R. Srinivasan and A. A. Levi, J. Am. Chem. 8(3756 (1964).

Preferred:
   log $k = 15.51 - 55.9/\theta$.

Comments: Transition state estimates based on a biradical mechanism give $\Delta S^\ddagger = 7.3$ g/mole and log A. $= 15.2$. A total strain of about 40 kcal/mole is estimated.

Experimental

[1] Analysis by I.R. and G.L.C. Rate by G.L.C. 1,5-cyclo-octadiene was an unstable product which decompos(by two paths to butadiene and to 4-vinyl cyclohexane. The rates were unaffected by propylene and decreased slight with increased (S/V).

	I	II	III
$\Delta H^\circ_{f(298)}$	4.0	17.5	−1.2
$S^\circ_{(298)}$	94.2	118.5	101.8
$C^\circ_{p(298)}$	41.3	49.9	45.1

	a	b
$\Delta S^\circ =$	24.3	7.6 g/mole
$\Delta H^\circ =$	13.5	−5.2 kcal/mole
$\Delta C^\circ =$	8.6	3.8 g/mole

Path	log A	E	log k_T (650)	Conditions	System	Surface	References
a	17.7	49.9	+1.09	648±25 °C 20–80 tor	flow	————	[1] E. Hawkins and J. Vogh, J. Phys. Chem. **57**, 902 (1953).
b	15.3	45.1	+0.14				

Preferred:
    log $k_a = 17.7 − 49.9/\theta$
    log $k_b = 15.3 − 45.1/\theta$.

Comments: A biradical mechanism is consistent with both processes.

he enthalpy for biradical formation is about, $\Delta H^\circ_{1,2} = 39$ kcal/mole using $E_{strain} = 26.2$ kcal/mole. log A_{est} 16.9.

Experimental

[1] Analysis and rate by ρ and O.R. Two minor products were also formed, but were not identified.

Reaction: Endo-dicyclopentadiene

$$(\text{I}) \longrightarrow 2 \quad (\text{II})$$

	I	II
$\Delta H^\circ_{f(298)}$	45.4	32.5
$S^\circ_{(298)}$	86.3	67.0
$C^\circ_{p(298)}$	36.1	17.5

$\Delta S^\circ = 47.7$ g/mole
$\Delta H^\circ = 19.6$ kcal/mole
$\Delta C^\circ_p = -1.1$ g/mole

log A	E	log k_T (455)	Conditions	System	Surface	References
13.0	33.7	−3.19	462 ± 33 °K 17–106 mm Hg	static	none	[1] J. B. Harkness, G. B. Kistiakowsky, and W. H. Mears, J. Chem. Phys. **5**, 682 (1937)
13.01	33.97	−3.31	426–484 °K N₂ carrier	(stirred flow)		[2] W. C. Herndon, C. R. Grayson, and J. M. Manion, J. Org. Chem. **32**, 526 (1967)

Preferred:
   log $k = 13.01 - 33.97/\theta$.

Comments: The estimated thermodynamics are in good agreement with the parameters of Kistiakowsky et al. There is considerable literature on the subject of the mechanism of the cyclopentadiene decomposition and dimerization (see [2] for other references). Generally a concerted process has been favored because of the low activation energy. However, the biradical mechanism cannot be excluded on this basis. Thus for the process,

$$(\text{endo}) \quad \underset{2}{\overset{1}{\rightleftharpoons}} \quad (\quad) \quad \xrightarrow[\text{fast}]{3} \quad 2 \quad$$

$$E = DH^\circ(\text{C—C}) - \Delta E_{\text{strain}} - 2R_{\text{allyl}} - (R_{\text{overlap}}) + E_2$$
$$= 78.7 - (24.5 + 6 - 2(6)) - 2(12.6) - R_0 + 2(?)$$
$$34 = 37.0 - R_0$$

   If in the transition state for ring closing some allylic overlap between rings leads to extra stabilization (i.e. ~ 3 kcal/mole is required), then the biradical process would be possible. The low A-factor observed would also be expected with such an interaction. Note that the activation energy observed for the exo dimer decomposition is just about what would be expected with no allylic overlap stabilization.

Experimental

   [1] Analysis by ΔP and η_r. Rates by ΔP. Rates unaffected by small amounts of O₂. The association reaction was also studied. Rate constant parameters were log k_b (1/mole-sec) $= 4.93 - 14.9/\theta$.*
   [2] Analysis was by G.L.C. Rates were unaffected by addition of propylene or by surface conditioning. Isomerization to the exo form was not detectable even at 95 percent conversion suggesting that the rate constant for isomerization at least a factor of 10^4 times slower than decomposition.

---

   *The back reaction has also been studied by G. A. Benford and A. Wasserman, J. Chem. Soc. 362 (1939) and by Schultze (Oel. Kohle, **6**, 113 (1938), who obtained, respectively, log $k_b = 6.1 - 16.7/\theta$ and log $k_b = 6.8 - 16.9/\theta$.

Reaction: Exo-dicyclopentadiene

$$(I) \longrightarrow 2 \left[\text{(II)} \right]$$

	I	II
$\Delta H^\circ_{f(298)}$	45.4	32.5
$S^\circ_{(298)}$	86.3	67.0
$C^\circ_{p(298)}$	36.1	17.5

$\Delta S^\circ = 47.7$ g/mole
$\Delta H^\circ = 19.6$ kcal/mole
$\Delta C^\circ_p = -1.1$ g/mole

log A	E	log k_T (550)	Conditions	System	Surface	References
13.72	38.49	−1.58	474–625 °K N$_2$ carrier	stirred flow	none	[1] W. C. Herndon, C. R. Grayson, and J. M. Manion, J. Org. Chem. **32**, 526 (1967).

Preferred:
   Reliable.   log $k = 13.72 - 38.49/\theta$.

Comments: An estimate of the activation energy for the exo decomposition via the biradical mechanism gives $E = 37.5$ kcal/mole (see endo-dicyclopentadiene).

Experimental

   [1] Analysis by G.L.C. Rates were unaffected by added propylene or the nature of the surface. Isomerization to the endo form was not observed to compete with the decomposition to cyclopentadiene.

Reaction: Quadricyclo[2,2,1,0,^{2,6}0^{3,5}]heptane

$$\text{(I)} \longrightarrow \text{(II)}$$

	I	II
$\Delta H^\circ_{f(298)}$	( )	57.1
$S^\circ_{(298)}$	71.8	71.3
$C^\circ_{p(298)}$	26	26.1

$\Delta S^\circ = -0.5$ g/mole
$\Delta H^\circ =$ kcal/mole
$\Delta C^\circ_p =$ 0.1 g/mole

log A	E	log k_T (445)	Conditions	System	Surface	References
12.81	33.51	−3.65	443 ± 20 °K 1–18 torr (3–4)	static	< 10%	[3] H. M. Frey, J. Chem., 365 (1964).

Preferred:
 log = 12.81−33.5/θ.

Experimental

[1] Analysis by G.L.C. Rates unaffected by propylene and other added third bodies.

Reaction: Endo-bicyclo[2,2,1]hept-5-ene-2-carboxaldehyde (endo-5-norbornene-2-carboxaldehyde) (endo-methylene-2,5-tetrahydrobenzaldehyde)

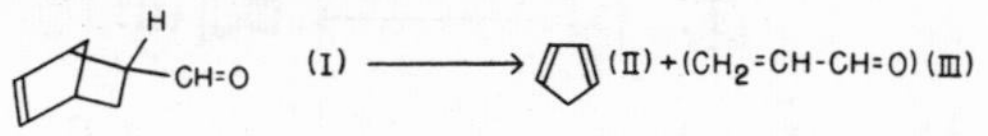

	I	II	III
$\Delta H^\circ_{f(298)}$	-4.2	32.5	-18.1
$\bar{S}^\circ_{(298)}$	89.7	67.0	(65.9)
$C^\circ_{p(298)}$	35.3	17.5	15.7

$\Delta S^\circ = 43.2$ g/mole
$\Delta H^\circ = 18.6$ kcal/mole
$\Delta C^\circ_p = -2.1$ g/mole

log A	E	log k_T (490)	Conditions	System	Surface	References
12.34	33.6	-2.65	490 ± 26	static	none	[1] G. B. Kistiakowsky and J. R. Lacher, J. Am. Chem. Soc. **58**, 123 (1936).

Preferred:
   log $k = 13.3 - 35.8/\theta$.

Comments: The forward and reverse rate constants give $\Delta H^\circ = 19.4$ kcal/mole and $\Delta S^\circ = 37.2$ g/mole, ignoring heat capacity effects. This is not in very good agreement with the estimated entropy. We prefer a slightly higher A-factor analogous to endo-dicyclopentadiene.

   The low activation energy reported favors a concerted mechanism for this reaction *unless* some stabilization of overlapping allylic centers in the transition state occurs. (See dicyclopentadiene.) For the biradical mechanism:

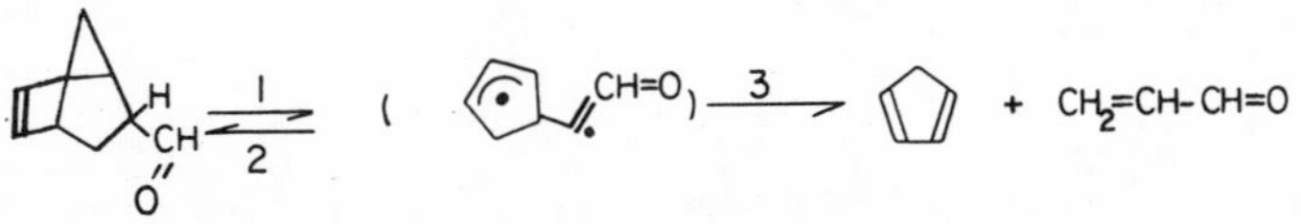

$E = DH^\circ(\text{C—C}) - R_{\text{allyl}} - R_{\text{carbonyl}} - \Delta E_{\text{strain}} - R_0 + E_2 = 77.9 - 12.6 - 8.7 - 24.5 + 6.0 - R_0 + 2 = 40.1 - R_0$. It would be necessary to have an overlap stabilization of about 5 kcal/mole in order for the reaction to involve biradicals.

Experimental

[1] Rate by ΔP. Reverse reaction was studied in detail. Rate constant parameters were, $k_b = 10^{6.18 - 15.2/\theta}$ 1/mole-sec.

3. Isomerization Reactions
(Other Than Cyclic Compound Reactions)

Reaction: *cis*-1,2-Dideuteroethene

$$
\begin{array}{ccc}
\text{D} \quad \text{D} & & \text{D} \quad \text{H} \\
\quad \text{C=C} \quad \text{(I)} \longrightarrow & & \quad \text{C=C} \quad \text{(II)} \\
\text{H} \quad \text{H} & & \text{H} \quad \text{D}
\end{array}
$$

	I	II
$\Delta H^{\circ}_{f(298)}$	10.3	10.3
$S^{\circ}_{(298)}$	55.3	55.3
$C^{\circ}_{p(298)}$	11.0	11.0

$\Delta S^{\circ} = 0$ g/mole
$\Delta H^{\circ} = 0$ kcal/mole
$\Delta C^{\circ}_{p} = 0$ g/mole

log A	E	log k_T (775)	Conditions	System	Surface	References
12.48	61.3	−4.80	723–823 °K 9–310 torr	static	(a)	[1] B. S. Rabinovitch, J. E. Douglas, and F. S. Looney, J. Chem. Phys. **20**, 1807 (1952).
~13.0	~65.0	−5.32	723–823 °K 9–310 torr	static	< 2%	[2] J. E. Douglas, B. S. Rabinovitch, and F. S. Looney, J. Chem. Phys. **23**, 315 (1955).

Preferred:
  log $k = 13.0 - 65.0/\theta$.
  log $A_{\text{est}} = 13.6$ (see section IV–3.0).

Comments: A classical calculation of the pressure at which this reaction is halfway into the falloff region gives $M_{1/2} = {}^1/_3$ atm. An effective $s=6$ can be estimated from the heat capacity of dideuteroethene.

Experimental

[1] Analysis by I.R.
[2] Analysis by I.R. Rate was pressure dependent over the entire pressure range. No effect on the rate by traces of O_2.

---

a Appreciable polymerization observed at high pressures. At low pressures the reaction was relatively free from surface effects.

Reaction: *trans*-1,2-Dichloroethene

	I	II
$\Delta H^\circ_{f(298)}$	5.4	6.4
$S^\circ_{(298)}$	69.2	69.2
$C^\circ_{p(298)}$	15.8	14.4

$\Delta S^\circ = 0$ g/mole
$\Delta H^\circ = 1.0$ kcal/mole
$\Delta C^\circ_p = -1.4$ g/mole

Path	log A	E	log k_T (826)	Conditions	System	Surface	References
a	12.69	41.9	+1.60	560–608 °K 200–760 mm Hg	static	(a)	[1] J. L. Jones and R. L Taylor, J. Am. Chem. Soc. **62**, 3480 (1940).
b	2.32	16.0	−1.90	473–523 °K 40 mm Hg	static		[2] B. Tamamuski, H. Akiyama, and Ishii, Zeit. Elektro chem. **47**, 340 (1941).
a	12.68	55.3	−2.12	806–846 °K 39 mm Hg	flow	(b)	[3] L. D. Hawton and G. P. Semeluk, Can. J. Chem. **44** 2143 (1966).
b	12.76	56.0					

Preferred:
   log $k = 12.68 - 55.3/\theta$; log $k_b = 12.76 - 56.0/\theta$.
   log $A_{\text{est}} = 13.0$ (see section IV–3.0).

Comments: The extreme sensitivity of this isomerization to impurities, free radical catalysis, and heter geneity has been shown in other studies (see B. S. Rabinovitch and M. J. Hulatt, J. Chem. Phys. **27**, 5 (1957); C. Steel, J. Phys. Chem. **64**, 1588 (1960)). It is possible that some catalysis still exists in the preferr study, although the low parameters could well indicate a pressure falloff. From C°_v, $s \approx 8$ one can calcula an $M_{1/2} \approx 20$ mm Hg.

Experimental

   [1] Analysis by refractive index.[a]
   [2] Analysis by dielectric constant measurements. High-pressure region above 150 mm Hg.
   [3] Toluene carrier technique. Analysis by G.L.C.[b]

---

   [a] Rates showed some surface dependence and also some variation with total pressure. The reverse reaction was highly surf. sensitive and could not be studied. A side reaction was detected which increased with (S/V).
   [b] The reaction was surface sensitive. Extrapolation of the rate constants to zero (S/V) ratio was made to obtain the homogene component rate constant of the reaction.

Reaction: *cis*-2-Butene

$$\text{(I)} \longrightarrow \text{(II)}$$

	I	II
$\Delta H^\circ_{f(298)}$	-1.7	-2.7
$S^\circ_{(298)}$	72.1	70.9
$C^\circ_{p(298)}$	19.4	20.7
$C^\circ_{p(700)}$	37.6	38.4

$\Delta S^\circ = -1.2$ g/mole
$\Delta H^\circ = -1.0$ kcal/mole
$\Delta C^\circ_p = 1.3$ g/mole

log A	E	log k_T (700)	Conditions	System	Surface	References
0.3	18	-5.32	663–690 °K 102–1440 torr	static	$S/V \times 6$ "Essentially homogeneous"	[1] G. B. Kistiakowsky and W. R. Smith, J. Am. Chem. Soc. **58**, 766 (1936).
11.0	52.0	-5.23	665–690 °K 200–400 torr	static	([a])	[2] W. F. Anderson, J. A. Bell, J. M. Diamond, and K. R. Wilson, J. Am. Chem. Soc. **80**, 2384 (1958).
13.78	62.8	-5.82	686–742 °K $10^{-3}-2 \times 10^3$ torr (N_2) (2–12 torr)	static	none	[3] B. S. Rabinovitch and K. W. Michel, J. Am. Chem. Soc. **81**, 5065 (1959).
14.00	62.4	-5.48	683–749 °K 0.015–400 torr	static	([a])	[4] R. B. Cundall and T. F. Palmer, Trans. Faraday Soc. **57**, 1936 (1961).
14.54	65.0	-5.76	1000–1250 °K 1–6% in Ar	S.P.Sh.	———	[5] A. Lifshitz, S. H. Bauer, and E. L. Resler, Jr., J. Chem. Phys. **38**, 2056 (1963).

Preferred:
   $\log k = 13.78 - 62.8/\theta$
   $\log A_{\text{est}} \simeq 13.3$ (see section IV–3.0).

Experimental

[1] Analysis by M.P. of mixture. Because of the unreasonably low A-factor, authors postulated a chain mechanism. Each run was first order, but the rate was dependent on initial pressure.

[2] Analysis by I.R. In falloff region; RRK–$M_{1/2} \simeq 310$ torr at 400 °C.

(*Continued*)

---

[a] Propane observed as a side product probably formed heterogeneously.

Cis-2-butene (*Continued*)

[3] Analysis by G.L.C. Identification by M.S. Falloff below 2 torr, at high pressures (above 10 torr) an autocatalytic reaction occurred. Side products increased with decreasing temperature and increased S/V.

[4] Analysis by G.L.C. Confirmed autocatalytic high-pressure reaction and pressure falloff region (i.e., ~ 4 torr) reported in [3].

[5] Analysis by G.L.C. The parameters were obtained from the low-temperature rate constants and those obtained at the shock temperatures. Parameters could not be obtained from the shock tube results alone because of a rather sizable scatter in the data.

Reaction: Perfluorobutadiene (hexafluorobutadiene)

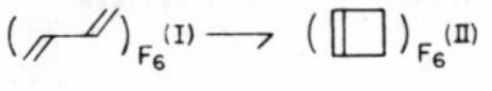

$$(\text{—})_{F_6}^{(I)} \longrightarrow (\text{—})_{F_6}^{(II)}$$

	I	II
$\Delta H^\circ_{f(298)}$	-225	-237
$S^\circ_{(298)}$	101	93.8
$C^\circ_{p(298)}$	32.6	29.6

$\Delta S^\circ = -7.2$ g/mole
$\Delta H^\circ = -12$ kcal/mole
$\Delta C^\circ_p = -3.0$ g/mole

log A	E	log k_T (500)	Conditions	System	Surface	References
12.03	35.38	-3.43	467–539 °K 1.0–18 torr	static	none	[1] E. W. Schlag and W. B. Peatman, J. Am. Chem. Soc. **86**, 1676 (1964).

Preferred:
Reliable as reported.
$A_{est} = 10^{12.6}$ sec^{-1}.

Experimental

[1] Analysis by G.L.C. Added O_2 and NO had no effect on the rate. The equilibrium constant for the above reaction was determined to be: $K_{eq} = 10^{-2.07} \times 10^{11.70/\theta}$. This is in reasonably good agreement with the estimated thermodynamics

Reaction: *trans*-Perfluoro-2-butene

	I	II
$\Delta H^\circ_{f(298)}$	(−382.6)	(−381.8)
$S^\circ_{(298)}$	107.5	107.0
$C^\circ_{p(298)}$	31.6	30.3

a

$\Delta S^\circ = -0.5$ g/mole
$\Delta H^\circ = 0.8$ kcal/mole
$\Delta C^\circ_p = -1.3$ g/mole

Path	log A	E	log k_T (740)	Conditions	System	Surface	References
a	13.53	56.4	−3.12	698–783 °K 5 torr	static	none	[1] E. W. Schlag and E. W. Kaiser, Jr., J. Am. Chem. Soc. **87**, 1171 (1965).
b	13.64	55.6	−2.78	← same as above →			

Preferred:
   Reliable as reported.
   log $A_{est} \simeq 13.3$ (see section IV–3.0).

Experimental

   [1] Analysis by G.L.C. No effect on the rate by added NO. Reaction proceeds to an equilibrium state with K_{eq} $(trans \rightarrow cis) = 10^{-0.107} \times 10^{-0.817/\theta}$. The lower activation energy observed relative to the corresponding hydrocarbon isomerization (i.e., $\sim \Delta E_{act} \sim 6$–8 kcal/mole) was attributed to the destabilization of the double bond by fluorine substitution.*

---

*This conclusion appears to be a reasonable one and is supported by the lower activation energies produced by fluorine substitution in some cyclopropane isomerizations.

Reaction: *cis*-1,2-Diphenylethene (isotilbene)

	I	II
$\Delta H^\circ_{f(298)}$	59.7	58.7
$S^\circ_{(298)}$	106.9	108.3
$C^\circ_{p(298)}$	47.9	49.2
$C^\circ_{p(600)}$	86.9	87.5

$\Delta S^\circ = 1.4$ g/mole
$\Delta H^\circ = -1.0$ kcal/mole
$\Delta C^\circ_p = 1.3$ g/mole

log A	E	log k_T (585)	Conditions	System	Surface	References
12.78	42.8	−3.21	553–615 °K 4–3588 mm Hg	static	none	[1] G. B. Kistiakowsky and W. R. Smith, J. Am. Chem. Soc. **56**, 638 (1934).

Preferred:
   Reliable as reported.
   $\log k = 12.78 - 42.8/\theta$.

Comments: The reaction is undoubtedly unimolecular. Transition state estimates give $\log A_{est} = 12.5$ (see section IV–3.0).

Experimental

   [1] Analysis by miscibility of product in Nujol (*trans* form was more soluble). The equilibrium constant (*cis* ⇌ *trans*) was found to be about 13.3 at 614 °K, from which a heat of reaction of $\Delta H^\circ_{eq} \simeq -3$ kcal/mole was inferred assuming $\Delta S^\circ_{eq} = 0$.*

---

   *These gas phase equilibrium measurements imply that the *cis* repulsion is somewhat larger than additivity predictions, but should not exceed 3 kcal/mole. R. B. Williams (J. Am. Chem. Soc. **64**, 1395 (1942)), has measured the ΔH° (hydrogenation) of *cis* stilbene to be $\Delta H^\circ_{(H_2)} \simeq 26.3$ kcal/mole, which gives ΔH° (*cis* ⟶ *trans*) stilbene = −5.7 kcal/mole. The discrepancy can be rationalized as follows. Styrene is flat in solid and in solution while it is not flat in the gas phase. This is due to H . . . H repulsions:

The result is that ΔH°_f (gaseous styrene) does not show a butadiene type stabilization. *Cis*-stilbene cannot be flat even in solution and as a result it probably cannot solvate as well as *trans*-stilbene (which is flat in solution). Thus it is quite feasible that ΔH°_{isom} (sol'n) = −5.7 kcal/mole (as measured by Williams) while $\Delta H^\circ_{gas} \simeq -3.0$ kcal/mole as estimated by Kistiakowsky and Smith.

Reaction: Dimethyl-*cis*-1,2-ethenedioate (dimethyl maleate)

	I	II
$\Delta H^\circ_{f(298)}$	-147.2	-148.2
$S^\circ_{(298)}$	109.6	111.0
$C^\circ_{p(298)}$	39.3	40.6

$\Delta S^\circ = \ \ 1.4$ g/mole
$\Delta H^\circ = -1.0$ kcal/mole
$\Delta C^\circ_p = \ \ 1.3$ g/mole

log A	E	log k_T (583)	Conditions	System	Surface	References
5.11	26.5	-4.82	573–593 °K 732–4060 torr	static		[1] M. Nelles and G. B. Kistiakowsky, J. Am. Chem. Soc. **54**, 2208 (1932); Zeit. physik. Chemie. (Bodenstein Festband) **152**, 369 (1931).

Preferred:
   Unreliable.

Comments: Arrhenius parameters are much too low to be reasonable. It is likely that similar complications occurred in this reaction as those sometimes found in the *cis → trans* but-2-ene reaction (i.e., heterogeneity and autocatalysis) probably promoted by·small amounts of free acid.

Experimental

[1] Analysis of mixture by M.P. Rate constants were pressure dependent. A slow decomposition of the fumaric ester was observed.

Reaction: Methyl *cis*-2-butenoate (methyl-*cis*-crotonate)

$$cis \ CH_3CH{=}CHCOOCH_3 \ (I) \underset{b}{\overset{a}{\rightleftharpoons}} trans \ CH_3CH{=}CHCOOCH_3 \ (II)$$

	I	II
$\Delta H^\circ_{f(298)}$	-74.4	-75.4
$S^\circ_{(298)}$	$(91.9)^*$	92.3
$C^\circ_{p(298)}$	29.4	30.7

$\Delta S^\circ = 0.4$ g/mole
$\Delta H^\circ = -1.0$ kcal/mole
$\Delta C^\circ_p = 1.3$ g/mole

Path	$\log A$	E	$\log k_T$ (750)	Conditions	System	Surface	References
a	13.2	57.8 ± 1.5	-3.64	673–833 °K 0.1 → 10 mm (10)	static	none	[1] J. N. Butler and G. J. Small, Can. J. Chem. **41**, 2492 (1963).
b	12.6	58.0	-4.30	(as above)			(as above)

Preferred:

Reliable as reported. $\log A_{est} = 13.2$; est $E_{act} = 57.6$ kcal/mole using a resonance stabilization in the biradical of 4 kcal/mole (see section IV–3.0).

Experimental

[1] Analysis by G.L.C. Equilibrium parameters (*cis* ⇌ *trans*) were found to be $\Delta H^\circ = -0.2$ kcal; $\Delta S^\circ = +2.7$ g/mole. Up to 1 percent added oxygen did not affect the rate. Simultaneous free radical reactions were also detected leading to vinylacetate, CO_2, butenes, CO, CH_4, and propylene.

---

*The estimated thermodynamics are in poor agreement with the observed equilibrium constant. There are obviously some poorly understood steric effects here. (See also *cis*-2-methyl penta-1,3-diene.)

Reaction: Methyl-*cis*-cinnamate

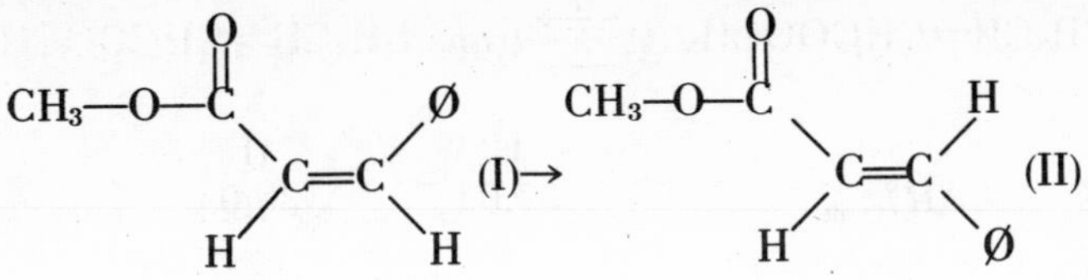

	I	II
$\Delta H^\circ_{f(298)}$	-43.0	-44.0
$S^\circ_{(298)}$	109.6	111.0
$C^\circ_{p(298)}$	43.5	44.8

$\Delta S^\circ = 1.4$ g/mole
$\Delta H^\circ = -1.0$ kcal/mole
$\Delta C^\circ_p = 1.3$ g/mole

log A	E	log k_T (610)	Conditions	System	Surface	References
10.54	41.6 ±2.0	-4.36	563–660 °K 5–500 torr	static	none	[1] G. B. Kistiakowsky and W. R. Smith, J. Am. Chem. Soc. **57**, 269 (1935).

Preferred:
   log $k = 12.6 - 47.4/\theta$. (see section IV–3.0).

Comments:
   Arrhenius parameters seem too low. Experimental errors were fairly large; therefore the calculated parameters are preferred. They are compatible with a 6 kcal resonance energy in the carbonyl system:

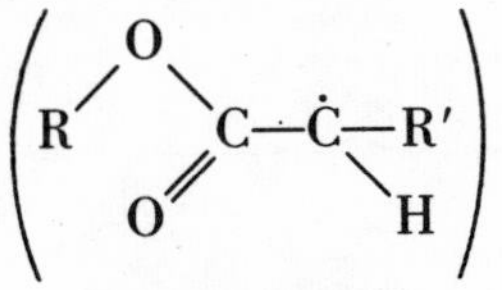

Experimental

[1] Analysis by mixed M.P. Some falling off of the rate constant at pressures below 5 torr appeared to occur.

357

Reaction: *cis*-2-Butenenitrile(*cis*-crotonitrile)

$$cis\text{-}CH_3CH{=\!=}CHCN \ (I) \longrightarrow trans\text{-}CH_3CH{=\!=}CHCN \ (II)$$

	I	II
$\Delta H^\circ_{f(298)}$	37.0	36.0
$S^\circ_{(298)}$	72.4	72.8
$C^\circ_{p(298)}$	19.3	20.6

*$\Delta S^\circ = +0.4$ g/mole
$\Delta H^\circ = -1.0$ kcal/mole
$\Delta C^\circ_p = \quad 1.3$ g/mole

log A	E	log k_T (750)	Conditions	System	Surface	References
11.0	51.3	-3.96	573–633 °K 0.2–20 torr	static	(a)	[1] J. N. Butler and R. D. McAlpine, Can. J. Chem. **41**, 2487 (1963).

Preferred:
    log $k = 12.7 - 55.7/\theta$ (see section IV–3.0).

Comments: Both rate constant parameters seem low, A possibly by as much as 2 orders of magnitude. Transition state calculations are preferred and are consistent with a $(>C\!-\!C{\equiv}N)$ resonance energy of about 9 kcal/mole.

Experimental

    [1] Analysis by G.L.C.

---

*Predicted thermodynamics are slightly different from those observed.

a The only appreciable side reaction was surface polymerization. Experimental equilibrium parameters between 573–633 °K were $\Delta H^\circ = 0.17$ kcal and $\Delta S^\circ = -0.39$ g/mole. Rate constants showed small pressure dependences. Error limits for the activation energy were placed at ± 3.7 kcal/mole.

Reaction: *cis-β*-Cyanostyrene

	I	II
$\Delta H^\circ_{f(298)}$	68.4	67.4
$S^\circ_{(298)}$	90.0	91.4
$C^\circ_{p(298)}$	33.5	34.8

$\Delta S^\circ = 1.4$ g/mole
$\Delta H^\circ = -1.0$ kcal/mole
$\Delta C^\circ_p = 1.3$ g/mole

log A	E	log k_T (615)	Conditions	System	Surface	References
11.6	46.0	−4.74	581–651 °K 17.5–458 torr	static	(a)	[1] G. B. Kistiakowsky and W. R. Smith, J. Am. Chem. Soc. **58**, 2428 (1936).

Preferred:
   log $k = 12.3 - 48.0/\theta$.

Comments: Wall effects were indicated both from the (S/V) dependence and the initial pressure dependence. However the reported parameters are in reasonable agreement with transition state estimates. The latter are preferred.

A 10 kcal resonance energy for ($> \dot{C}-C\equiv N$) is calculated from E.

Experimental

[1] Analysis by refractive index (N_r). The equilibrium constant was found to be $K(trans/cis) = 1.7$ and temperature independent.

---

a A marked increase in rate at the low pressures was observed with increased (S/V). Rates also increased at the lower pressures.

Reaction: 1,1′,6,6′-d_4-1,5-Hexadiene

	I	II
$\Delta H^\circ_{f(298)}$	16.5	16.5
$S^\circ_{(298)}$	92.2	92.2
$C^\circ_{p(298)}$	29.9	29.9

$\Delta S^\circ = 0$
$\Delta H^\circ = 0$
$\Delta C^\circ_p = 0$

log A	E	log k_T (530)	Conditions	System	Surface	References
11.1	35.5	−3.50	(530 °K)			[1] V. Toscano and W. von E. Doering, unpublished work.

Preferred: Reliable.
   log $k = 11.1 - 35.5/\theta$.

Comments: Transition state estimate of A gives log $A_{est} = 10.7$ (see section IV–1.0).

Experimental

[1] Unpublished work. "Cope" rearrangement.

Reaction: 1,5-Heptadiene

	I	II
$\Delta H^\circ_{f(298)}$	12.4	12.0
$S^\circ_{(298)}$	99.4	96.9
$C^\circ_{p(298)}$	34.0	36.6
$C^\circ_{p(500)}$	49.0	51.1

$\Delta S^\circ = -2.5$ g/mole
$\Delta H^\circ = -0.4$ kcal/mole
$\Delta C^\circ_p = 2.6$ g/mole

log A	E	log k_T (485)	Conditions	System	Surface	References
9.09	32.5	−5.55	451–523 °K 2 torr	static		[1] A. Amano and M. Uchiyama, J. Phys. Chem. **69**, 1278 (1965).

Preferred:
   log $A_{\text{est}} = 11.1$

Comments: Arrhenius parameters are certainly too low, although rate constants are reasonable. See comments on the reverse reaction and also section III–2.0.

Experimental

[1] Analysis by G.L.C. Radical-induced decomposition was not detected.

Reaction: 3-Methyl-1,5-hexadiene

	I	II
$\Delta H^\circ_{f(298)}$	12.0	12.4
$S^\circ_{(298)}$	96.9	99.4
$C^\circ_{p(298)}$	36.6	34.0
$C^\circ_{p(500)}$	51.1	49.0

$\Delta S^\circ = 2.5$ g/mole
$\Delta H^\circ = 0.4$ kcal/mole
$\Delta C^\circ_p = -2.6$ g/mole

log A	E	log k_T (485)	Conditions	System	Surface	References
9.84	32.5	−4.80	451–523 °K 2 torr	static		[1] A. Amano and M. Uchiyama, J. Phys. Chem. **69**, 1278 (1965).
10.85	*34.95					[2] H. M. Frey (private communication)* to be published.

Preferred:
   log $k = 10.85 - 34.95/\theta$.

Comments: Cope rearrangement. This reaction is probably unimolecular under the conditions studied but the Arrhenius parameters are unreasonably low. The transition state estimate of A gives log $A_{est} = 11.3$ Further evidence against the reported A-factor may be found in the analogous isomerization

whose A-factor is log $A = 11.1$.

Experimental

[1] Rate and analysis by G.L.C. The isomerization proceeded to the equilibrium state, giving an equilibrium constant for the reaction (as written) of $K_{eq} \simeq 5.6$, independent of the temperature. The absence of propylenes and butenes in the products was cited as evidence against the formation of allylic radicals in the primary act (i.e., bond fission followed by recombination).

[2] The system is well represented by,

All processes are important.
   Arrhenius parameters are:
   log $k_1 = 10.55 - 34.20/\theta$
   log $k_2 = 10.39 - 35.34/\theta$
   log $k_3 = 10.54 - 35.72/\theta$
   log $k_4 = 10.66 - 36.72/\theta$

---

*Results added to data sheet after its original preparation. Comments have been left in their original form to illustrate the degree of reliability inherent in the transition state estimates.

Reaction: 3-Vinyloxy-1-propene (vinyl allyl ether)

	I	II
$\Delta H^{\circ}_{f(298)}$	-8.7	-25.8
$S^{\circ}_{(298)}$	90.0	89.3
$C^{\circ}_{p(298)}$	26.9	28.1

$\Delta S^{\circ} = -0.7$ g/mole
$\Delta H^{\circ} = -17.1$ kcal/mole
$\Delta C^{\circ}_{p} = 1.2$ g/mole

log A	E	log k_T (455)	Conditions	System	Surface	References
11.70	30.6	-2.99	440–473 °K 150–400 torr	static	none	[1] F. W. Schuler and G. W. Murphy, J. Am. Chem. Soc. **72**, 3155 (1950).

Preferred:
    log $k = 11.70 - 30.6/\theta$.

Comments: Reliable. Transition state calculation of the A-factor gives log $A_{\text{est}} = 11.1$ (see section IV–1.0).

Experimental

[1] Analysis by U.V. absorption of the aldehyde. Reaction was first order out to 99 percent reaction. Cope rearrangement.

Reaction: 3-Isopropenoxy-1-propene (isopropenyl allyl ether)

$$CH_3-\underset{\underset{CH_2}{\|}}{C}-O-CH_2-CH=CH_2 \ (I) \longrightarrow CH_3-\overset{\overset{O}{\|}}{C}-CH_2-CH_2-CH=CH_2 \ (II)$$

	I	II
$\Delta H^\circ_{f(298)}$	-18.1	-37.0
$S^\circ_{(298)}$	95.9	98.0
$C^\circ_{p(298)}$	33.1	32.9

$\Delta S^\circ = 2.1$ g/mole
$\Delta H^\circ = -18.9$ kcal/mole
$\Delta C^\circ_p = -0.2$ g/mole

log A	E	log k_T (440)	Conditions	System	Surface	References
11.73	29.3	-2.82	416–467 °K 20–760 torr	static	none	[1] L. Stein and G. W. Murphy, J. Am. Chem. Soc. **74**, 1041 (1952).

Preferred:
    log $k = 11.73 - 29.3/\theta$.

Comments: Transition state estimate gives, log $A = 11.3$ (see section IV–1.0).

Experimental

[1] Analysis by U.V. on the ketone. Unconditioned surfaces produced rate acceleration. Cope rearrangement.

Reaction: 2-Methyl-3-vinyloxy-1-propene (2-methallyl vinyl ether)

	I	II
$\Delta H^\circ_{f(298)}$	-16.4	-32.4
$S^\circ_{(298)}$	96.4	97.4
$C^\circ_{p(298)}$	32.9	33.7

$\Delta S^\circ = \quad 1.0$ g/mole
$\Delta H^\circ = -16.0$ kcal/mole
$\Delta C^\circ_p = \quad 0.8$ g/mole

log A	E	log k_T (440)	Conditions	System	Surface	References
11.15	29.1	-3.30	423–461 °K 6–100 torr (10–15)	static	none	[1] H. M. Frey and B. M. Pope, J. Chem. Soc. **B**, 209 (1966).

Preferred:
   log $k = 11.15 - 29.1/\theta$.

Comments: Transition state estimation of A gives log $A_{est} = 11.3$ (same as vinyl allyl ether and vinyl isopropenyl allyl ether, see section IV–1.0).

Experimental

   [1] Analysis by G.L.C. It was concluded, very reasonably, that a six-centered ring complex was involved in the transition state, since a four-centered ring complex would lead to 3-methylpent-4-enal (not observed) and since the observed A-factor is quite similar to those found for allyl and isopropenyl allyl ethers. Cope rearrangement.

---

*The product of this reaction was mistakenly reported as *trans*-hex-4-enal.

Reaction: 1-Buten-3-yl vinyl ether

(I)   (II)

	I	II
$\Delta H^\circ_{f(298)}$	-18.0	-33.2
$S^\circ_{(298)}$	96.3	97.8
$C^\circ_{p(298)}$	33.0	33.4

$\Delta S^\circ = 1.5$ g/mole
$\Delta H^\circ = -15.2$ kcal/mole
$\Delta C^\circ_p = 0.4$ g/mole

Path	log A	E	log k (440)	Conditions	System	Surface	References
	11.32	27.87		423–461° K 6–100 torr	static, analysis G.L.C.	No effect (14 x s/V) in aged vessels	H. M. Frey, unpublished results

Preferred:
$\log k = 11.32 - 27.87/\theta$

Comments: Reliable. Y. Pocker, Proc. Chem. Soc., 141 (1961), has shown that the rate of loss of optical activity of active ether is nearly identical with its rate of conversion to aldehyde, thus verifying a single, irriversible intramolecular reaction path.

Experimental

[1] Analysis was by G.L.C. Product confirmation by N.M.R. and I.R.

Reaction: 1,2,6-Heptatriene

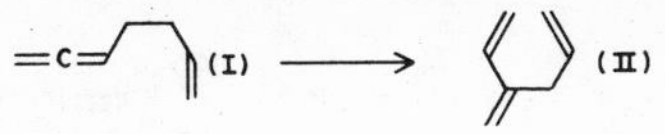

$$=c= \quad \text{(I)} \quad \longrightarrow \quad \text{(II)}$$

	I	II
$\Delta H^\circ_{f(298)}$	57.3	26.4
$S^\circ_{(298)}$	96.8	94.6
$C^\circ_{p(298)}$	32.6	34.0

$S^\circ = -2.2$ g/mole
$H^\circ = -20.9$ kcal/mole
$C^\circ_p = 1.4$ g/mole

log A	E	log k_T (470)	Conditions	System	Surface	References
9.97	28.47	−3.27	445–491 °K 0.5–20 torr	static	none	[1] H. M. Frey and D. H. Lister, J. Chem. Soc. **A**, 26 (1967).

Preferred:
   log $k = 9.97 - 28.47/\theta$.

Comments: Cope rearrangement. Reliable study, although the Arrhenius parameters are somewhat lower than those estimated by transition state methods. log $A_{\text{est}} = 10.8$ (see section IV–1.0).

Experimental

[1] Analysis was by G.L.C. Product confirmation by N.M.R. and I.R.

Reaction: *cis*-1,3,5-Hexatriene

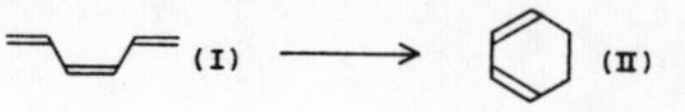

	(I)	(II)
$\Delta H^\circ_{f(298)}$	40.8	26.3
$S^\circ_{(298)}$	78.0	72.1
$C^\circ_{p(298)}$	27.3	23.4

$\Delta S^\circ = -5.9$ g/mole
$\Delta H^\circ = -14.5$ kcal/mole
$\Delta C^\circ_p = -3.9$ g/mole

log A	E	log k_T (425°)	Conditions	System	Surface	References
11.85	29.9	−3.52	390–463 °K 60–200 torr	static	none	[1] K. E. Lewis and H. Steiner, J. Chem. Soc. 3080 (1964).

Preferred:

log $k = 11.85 - 29.9/\theta$

$A_{\mathrm{est}} = 10^{11.5}$ sec^{-1} (see section IV–1.0).

Experimental

[1] Rates followed by U.V. spectroscopy. Calculated E_a using the Polanyi-Evans method agreed with the observed value. A-factor calculations based on cyclic and linear activated complexes gave the best agreement with the cyclic complex.

$A^{\ddagger}$(cyclic) $\simeq 4-8 \times 10^{11}$ sec^{-1}
$A^{\ddagger}$(linear) $= 1-4 \times 10^{13}$ sec^{-1}.

Reaction: *cis*-1,3-Hexadiene

$$\underset{\text{(I)}}{\text{≕⌇⌇}} \longrightarrow \underset{\text{(II)}}{\text{⌇⌇⌇}}$$

	I	II
$\Delta H^\circ_{f(298)}$	14.6	12.1
$S^\circ_{(298)}$	84.9	83.6
$C^\circ_{p(298)}$	28.5	28.6

$\Delta S^\circ = -1.3$ g/mole
$\Delta H^\circ = -2.5$ kcal/mole
$\Delta C^\circ_p = 0.1$ g/mole

log A	E	log k_T (500°)	Conditions	System	Surface	References
10.8	32.5	−3.42	474–518 °K 2–70 torr	static	none	[1] H. M. Frey and B. M. Pope, J. Chem. Soc. **A**, 1701 (1966).

Preferred:
   log $k = 10.8 - 32.5/\theta$.

Comments: log $A_{est} = 11.9$. The non-polar "ene" reactions seem to have A-factors about an order of magnitude lower than calculated. (See also *cis*-2-methyl penta-1,3-diene and its reverse.)

Experimental

[1] Rates were based on G.L.C. analysis. The equilibria were found to be too far on the product side to measure. This is not reflected in the thermodynamic estimates which suggest K_{eq} (500 °K) ≈ 6.5.)

Reaction: 2-Methyl-*cis*-1,3-pentadiene

	I	II
$\Delta H^\circ_{f(298)}$	11.7	11.4
$S^\circ_{(298)}$	*83.6	83.7
$C^\circ_{p(298)}$	29.1	29.5
$C^\circ_{p(500)}$	40.0	40.6

$\Delta S^\circ = 0.1$ g/mole*
$\Delta H^\circ = -0.3$ kcal/mole*
$\Delta C^\circ_p = 0.4$ g/mole

Path	log A	E	log k_T (495)	Conditions	System	Surface	References
a	11.24	32.76	−3.22	473–510 °K 2–15 mm	static	none	[1] H. M. Frey and R. J. Ellis, J. Chem Soc. 4770 (1965).

Preferred:
   log $k = 11.24 - 32.76/\theta$.

Comments: The transition state calculation of A for a concerted "ene"-six-center reaction gives log $A_{est} = 11.1$

Experimental

[1] Analysis by G.L.C. The reaction proceeds to an equilibrium state. The equilibrium constant found for the reaction as written above was $K_{eq} = 10^{-0.477+3.43/\theta}$. (A correction to the sign of the entropy change as reported has been made.)

---

*These values indicate interesting *cis-cis* methyl-methyl next to nearest neighbor interactions (i.e., an entropy enhancement of 2 g/mole and a steric repulsion of 3.4 kcal/mole in the reactant. Note that the estimated thermochemistry using group values (nearest neighbor interactions only) do not show this *cis-cis* effect. A similar (but opposite) effect is apparent in the equilibrium constant found for *cis* ⇄ *trans* methyl crotonate. This strain energy is about the same as the double bond interaction in butadiene (3.6 kcal), and this would be compatible with a non-planar configuration of the double bonds in the *cis*-diene. Such a structure would have about 2 g/mole more entropy from optical isomerism, plus a lower frequency in the (=CH⊖CH=) torsion.

Reaction: 4-Methyl-1,3-pentadiene

	I	II
$\Delta H^\circ_{f(298)}$	11.4	11.7
$S^\circ_{(298)}$	83.7	83.6
$C^\circ_{p(298)}$	29.5	29.1

$\Delta S^\circ = -0.1$ g/mole
$\Delta H^\circ = 0.3$ kcal/mole
$\Delta C^\circ_p = -0.4$ g/mole

log A	E	log k_T (495)	Conditions	System	Surface	References
11.72	36.19	−4.25	473–510 °K 2–15 torr	static	none	[1] H. M. Frey and R. J. Ellis, J. Chem. Soc. 4770 (1965).

Preferred:
   log $k = 11.72 - 36.16/\theta$.

Comments: Estimated thermodynamic properties are not in very good agreement with the kinetic observations on the equilibrium properties of the reaction. (See *cis*-2-methylpenta-1,3-diene.)

   log $A_{est} = 12.5$ (see section IV–2.0).

Experimental

[1] See *cis*-2-methylpenta-1,3-diene.

Reaction: 3,7-Dimethyl-1,6-octadiene

	I	II
$\Delta H^\circ_{f(298)}$	-17.6	-23.6
$S^\circ_{(298)}$	122.0	113.8
$C^\circ_{p(298)}$	52.2	51.7
$C^\circ_{p(700)}$	94.5	94.2

$\Delta S^\circ = -8.2$ g/mole
$\Delta H^\circ = -6.0$ kcal/mole
$\Delta C^\circ_p = -0.5$ g/mole

log A	E	log k_T (670)	Conditions	System	Surface	References
9.06	35.2	-2.42	656–682 °K	flow		[1] W. D. Huntsman and T. H. Curry, J. Am. Chem. Soc. **80**, 2252 (1958).

Preferred:
  $\log k = 9.06 - 35.2/\theta$.

Comments: Transition state estimates of the A-factor suggest that the rate constant parameters may be slightly low.
  $\log A_{est} \simeq 9.6$ (see section IV–1.0).

Experimental

[1] Analysis by I.R. and quantitative hydrogenation. The rate was unaffected by radical chain sensitizers (ethylene oxide and t-butyl peroxide) and by NO. It was suggested that the reaction proceeded through a bicyclic (five-center and six-center) transition state with (C—C) and (C⟨H⟩C) bridges. The energetics exclude a biradical mechanism. The reaction must be concerted.

Reaction: Methyl isocyanide

$$CH_3NC \text{ (I)} \longrightarrow CH_3CN \text{ (II)}$$

	I	II
$\Delta H^\circ_{f(298)}$	35.9	19.2
$S^\circ_{(298)}$	59.1	58.7
$C^\circ_{p(298)}$	12.8	12.5

$S^\circ = -0.4$ g/mole
$H^\circ = -16.7$ kcal/mole
$C^\circ_p = -0.3$ g/mole

log A	E	log k_T (500)	Conditions	System	Surface	References
13.6	38.4	−3.18	472–533 °K $10^{-2.5} - 10^5$ torr	static	none	[1] F. W. Schneider and B. S. Rabinovitch, J. Am. Chem. Soc. **84**, 4215 (1962).

Preferred:
  $\log k = 13.6 - 38.4/\theta$.

Experimental

[1] Analysis by G.L.C. Added air (~ 5 percent) and < 0.15 percent t-butyl peroxide gave no rate acceleration. Falloff behavior studied in detail. Rates began to falloff at about 1000 torr at 200 °C. The methyl-d_1 and methyl-d_3 isotope effects for the methyl isocyanide have been studied by B. S. Rabinovitch, P. W. Gilderson, and F. W. Schneider, J. Am. Chem. Soc. **87**, 158 (1965) and by F. W. Schneider and B. S. Rabinovitch, J. Am. Chem. Soc. **85**, 2365 (1963) respectively. This reaction has also been studied at high temperatures behind reflected shocks in the falloff region by A. Lifshitz, H. F. Caroll, and S. H. Bauer, J. Am. Chem. Soc. **86**, 1488 (1964).

Reaction: *p*-Tolyl isocyanide

	I	II
$\Delta H^\circ_{f(298)}$	61	44.4
$S^\circ_{(298)}$	87	87
$C^\circ_{p(298)}$	33	33

$\Delta S^\circ = \quad 0$ g/mole
$\Delta H^\circ = -16.6$ kcal/mole
$\Delta C^\circ_p = \quad 0$ g/mole

log A	E	log k_T (475)	Conditions	System	Surface	References
12.5	33.8	−3.05	453–493 °K 17–30 torr	static		[1] G. Kohlmaier and B. S. Rabinovitch, J. Phys. Chem. **63**, 1793 (1959).

Preferred:
   log $k = 13.7 - 36.8/\theta$. Rate constants are reliable.

Comments: The solution results suggest that the Arrhenius parameters reported for the gas phase isomerization may be slightly low. Solution parameters are preferred.

Experimental

[1] Analysis by I.R. Rates in solution of nujol gave $k = 10^{13.7} \times 10^{-36.8/\theta}$ sec^{-1}.

Reaction: (*l*)2,2'-Diamino-6,6'-dimethyldiphenyl

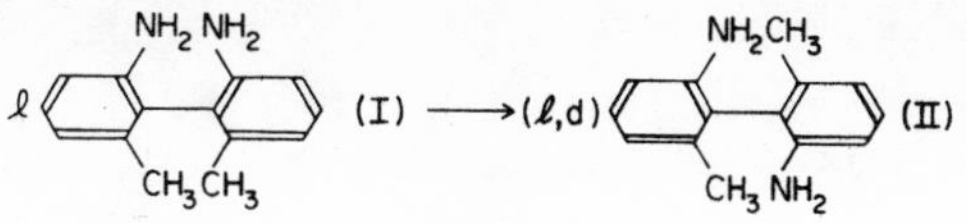

$$\Delta H^\circ_{f(298)}$$

$$S^\circ_{(298)}$$

$$C^\circ_{p(298)}$$

$\Delta S^\circ =$
$\Delta H^\circ =$
$\Delta C^\circ_p =$

log A	E	log k_T (635)	Conditions	System	Surface	References
10.37	45.1	−5.15	615–660 °K 50–150 mm Hg	static		[1] G. B. Kistiakowsky and W. R. Smith, J. Am. Chem. Soc. **58**, 1043 (1936).

Preferred:
   log $k = 11.0 - 46.9/\theta$.

Comments: The solution *A*-factor seems the more reasonable.

Experimental

[1] Rates of racemization were followed by optical rotation measurements. The racemization kinetics were also followed in solution. Activation energies were identical but the liquid phase *A*-factor was higher by a factor of about 2.3.

Reaction: *trans*-Difluorodiazine

	I	II
$\Delta H^\circ_{f(298)}$	19.4	16.4
$S^\circ_{(298)}$	(64.0)	(64.0)
$C^\circ_{p(298)}$	(13.2)	(13.2)

$\Delta S^\circ = 0$ g/mole
$\Delta H^\circ = -3.0$ kcal/mole
$\Delta C_p = 0$ g/mole

log A	E	log k_T (590)	Conditions	System	Surface	References
14.0	32.2	+2.07	570–615 °K $P \sim 1.6$ atm	S. P. Shock	None	[1] J. Binenboym, A. Burcat, A. Lifshitz, J. Shamir, J. Am. Chem. Soc. **88**, 5039 (1966).

Preferred:
  Suspect.

Comments: Although the *A*-factor is of the right order for a *cis-trans* rotation, the energy is far too low. For the process $t\text{-}N_2F_2 \longrightarrow N_2 + 2F$, $\Delta H^\circ = 19$ kcal. It is very unlikely that F atoms are not produced in the temperature range studied. This is supported by the observation that $F_2 + N_2$ was produced at higher temperatures. The chain reaction would be:

$$N_2F_2 + M \longrightarrow N_2 + 2F + M$$

$$F + t\text{-}N_2F_2 \rightleftharpoons N_2F_3 \rightleftharpoons cis\text{-}N_2F_2 + F$$

$$F + F + M \longrightarrow F_2 + M.$$

Thermochemical estimates of the Pi-bond strength in N_2F_2 range from 57 kcal to 84 kcal, depending on the choice of N-F bond strength. A value closer to 60 kcal is more likely.

Experimental

[1] Single-pulse shock tube (1/70) in argon. The authors suggested a linear transition state because of thermodynamic considerations. Alster and Burnelle have performed extended Huckel calculations for the perpendicular transition state, J. Am. Chem. Soc. **88**, 5039 (1966), and concluded that the Pi-bond in difluorodiazine could be weak and that a perpendicular transition state was possible; however, see comments.

Reaction: Nitrosomethane

$$CH_3NO \; (I) \longrightarrow CH_2{=}NOH \; (II)$$

	I	II
$\Delta H^\circ_{f(298)}$	17	0
$S^\circ_{(298)}$	63.6	64.6
$C^\circ_{p(298)}$	14.3	13

$\Delta S^\circ = \quad 1.0$ g/mole
$\Delta H^\circ = -17$ kcal/mole
$\Delta C^\circ_p = \quad -1.3$ g/mole

log A	E	log k_T (665)	Conditions	System	Surface	References
8.9	27.1	0.00	633–698 °K $P_t = 4.5$ torr	flow	[a] large effects	[1] L. Batt and B. G. Gowenlock, Trans. Faraday Soc. **56**, 682 (1960).

Preferred:
$\log k = 12.9 - 39.3/\theta$.

Comments: It seems unlikely that the conditions employed to isolate the homogeneous part of the reaction would really do so. The large negative entropy of activation (i.e., $\Delta S^\ddagger = -20$ g/mole) would not be consistent with the four-center transition state proposed. One may conclude that heterogenity was still a problem in this system.

If we accept the observed reaction rates as representative (within a factor of 2–4) of the homogeneous isomerization and estimate the A-factor by transition state methods, the preferred parameters are obtained.

Experimental

[1] Analysis made spectrophotometrically on (CH_3NO) remaining (nitrosmethane when warmed from -190 °C to -78 °C forms the *cis*-dimer exclusively.)

---

[a] Heterogeneous effects were large and the first order rate constant was divided into homogeneous and heterogeneous components. The homogeneous parameters were those obtained at the lowest (S/V) ratio and in the presence of C_6F_{12} (0.5 torr).

4. Simple Bond Fission Reactions

$$CH_4 \text{ (I)} \xrightarrow{a} CH_3 \cdot \text{ (II)} + H \cdot \text{ (III)}$$
$$\xrightarrow{b} CH_2 : \text{(IV)} + H_2 \text{ (V)}$$

	I	II	III	IV	V
$\Delta H^\circ_{f(298)}$	−17.9	34.0	52.1	88	0
$S^\circ_{(298)}$	44.5	46.5	27.4	49.0	31.2
$C^\circ_{p(298)}$	8.5	8.8	5.0	(8.1)	(7.0)
$C^\circ_{p(1000)}$	17.2	14.5	5.0		

a

$S^\circ = 29.4$ g/mole
$H^\circ = 104$ kcal/mole
$C_p^\circ = 5.3$ g/mole

Path	log A	E	log k_T (1500)	Conditions	System	Surface	References
	14.71	100.1	0.12	1200–1800 °K 1–12% CH$_4$ in Ar with total $P = 5$ atm	shock		[1] G. B. Skinner and R. A. Ruehwein, J. Phys. Chem. **63**, 1736 (1959).
	13.65	91.0	0.39	1670–2070 °K 2–10% in Ar $P_T = 4$ atm	S.P.Sh.		[2] G. I. Kozlov and V. G. Knore, Russ. J. Phys. Chem. **37**, 1128 (1963).
	14.12	93.0	0.57	1656–1965 °K 10% in Ar $P_{CH_4} = 290$ torr	S.P.Sh.		[3] V. Kevkorian, C. E. Heath, and M. Boudart, J. Phys. Chem. 64, 964 (1960).
+b	14.88	103.0	−0.13	1148–1398 °K	flow		[4] H. B. Palmer and T. J. Hirt, J. Phys. Chem. 67, 709 (1963).

Preferred:
   log $k_a = 15.3 - 104/\theta$.

Comments: One might at first expect such a small molecule to exhibit appreciable pressure falloff behavior. However, from the thermodynamics (which are well known) and the kinetic theory maximum recombination rate constant ($k_{rec} = 10^{11.5}$ l/mole-sec $= 1/4\ Z$) high pressure rate constants close to those reported are obtained. The RRK $− M_{1/2} = 16$ atm $n = 6$. Thus at least seven of the nine oscillators must be active. The initiation reaction in the methane pyrolysis is one of conjecture. There is no way of distinguishing between paths a and b, although path a would seem the more likely reaction. All rate constants reported are reasonably consistent with the rates calculated from the preferred high-pressure limiting Arrhenius parameters for

(*Continued*)

Methane (*Continued*)

path *a*. The mechanism is probably [1],

$$CH_4 \longrightarrow CH_3 \cdot + H \cdot$$
$$H \cdot + CH_4 \rightleftharpoons H_2 + CH_3 \cdot$$
$$CH_3 \cdot + CH_3 \cdot \rightleftharpoons C_2H_6$$

Ethane is unstable at high temperatures and will go on to form principally ethylene and hydrogen. From the entropy and *A*-factor one obtains $k_{rec} = 10^{11.4}$ l/mole-sec.

For earlier work on the CH_4 pyrolysis see:

L. S. Kassel, J. Am. Chem. Soc. **54,** 3949 (1932)

H. H. Storch, Ind. Eng. Chem. **26,** 56 (1934)

F. deRudder and H. Biedermann, Bull. Soc. Chim. France **47,** 704 (1930)

A. S. Gordon, J. Am. Chem. Soc. **70,** 395 (1948)

P. S. Shantorovitch and B. V. Pavlov, Zhur. Fiz. Khim. **30,** 811 (1956)

J. E. Germain and C. Vaniscotte, Bull. Soc. Chim. France, 692 (1957); 319 (1958)

Experimental

[1] Rates equated to CH_4 disappearance. Product yields of C_2H_6, C_2H_4, C_2H_2, and H_2 were determined. A chain length of 2 was inferred from the mechanism.

[2] Products analyzed were $CH_4, C_2H_6, C_2H_4, C_2H_2$, and H_2. Rates based on disappearance of CH_4 were equated to path *b*. The absence of appreciable effects of different additives (i.e., $C_2H_4, H_2, C_2H_6, C_2H_2$) was taken as evidence of very short reaction chains. The overall rate was attributed to the first step in the CH_4 decomposition, which was assumed to be an H_2 molecular elimination because of the "low" activation energy.

[3] Rates were based on the disappearance of methane. First-order rate constants were independent of methane partial pressures and total pressure at all temperatures studied. The reaction was not inhibited by H_2. Path *a* was thought to be dominant.

[4] Rates were determined by resistance changes in the carbon deposited on a carbon rod. Data of prior studies (covering a 1400 °K range) were summarized to give the parameters given above.

Reaction: Ethane

$$CH_3CH_3 \text{ (I)} \xrightarrow{a} 2CH_3. \text{ (II)}$$
$$\xrightarrow{b} C_2H_4 + H_2$$

	I	II
$\Delta H^\circ_{f(298)}$	-20.2	34.0
$S^\circ_{(298)}$	54.9	46.4
$C^\circ_{p(298)}$	12.6	8.3
$C^\circ_{p(1000)}$	29.6	14.4

Path a

$\Delta S^\circ = 37.9$ g/mole
$\Delta H^\circ = 88.2$ kcal/mole
$\Delta C^\circ_p = 4.0$ g/mole

Path	log A	E	log k_T (900)	Conditions	System	Surface	References
a	14.7	79.3	-4.56	1057–1418 °K δP (1–6% in Ar)	S. P. Shock		[1] G. B. Skinner and W. E. Ball, J. Phys. Chem. **64**, 1025 (1960).
a	17.45	91.74	-4.83	838–872 °K 61–202 torr	static		[2] C. P. Quinn, Proc. Roy. Soc. **A275**, 190 (1963).
a	16.37	88.0	-5.00				[3] R. W. Dexter and A. B. Trenwith, Proc. Chem. Soc., 392 (1964).
a	14.7	79.3	-4.56				[4] V. G. Knorre and G. I. Kozlov, Rus. J. Phys. Chem. **11**, 1427 (1964).
a	15.45	87±2	-5.68	1039–1109 °K $\delta P = 0.1$ torr $P_T = 10$ torr	flow		[5] C. H. Leigh, M. Szwarc and J. Bigeleisen, J. Am. Chem. Soc. **77**, 2193 (1955).
a	16.0	86.0	-4.88	823–893 °K 40–600 torr	static	none	[6] M. C. Lin and M. H. Back, Can. J. Chem. **44**, 2357 (1967).
							[7] H. G. Davis and K. D. Williamson, World Petr. Cong. Proc., 5th, Vol. IV, 37 New York (1959).

(Continued)

383

Ethane (*Continued*)

Preferred:

$$\log k_a = 16.75 - 89.5/\theta.$$

Comments: Preferred parameters are those calculated from the reaction enthalpy, an average heat capacity of $\Delta C_p^\circ = 2.3$ g/mole (298–858 °K) and the rate constant of [6]. The A-factor and reaction entropy set the methyl radical recombination rate constant at $k_{\mathrm{rec}} = 10^{9.9}$ l./mole-sec (850 °K). This is in fair agreement with the recombination rate of methyl radicals measured by sector techniques at lower temperatures (i.e., 300–400 °K, $k_{\mathrm{rec}} = 10^{10.3}$ l./mole-sec).

Earlier studies on the ethane pyrolysis, concerned more with the overall decomposition kinetics, are summarized in, E. W. R. Steacie, *Atomic and Free Radical Reactions*, 2d ed., Reinhold Publ. Corp., New York, N.Y. (1954).

Experimental

[1] G.L.C. analysis for CH_4, H_2, C_2H_6, C_2H_4, C_2H_2, C_3H_8, C_3H_6, and C_4H_{10}. Assumed Rice-Herzfeld mechanism and that the formation of CH_4 was a measure of path a. Rate constants were calculated from the rate of ethane pyrolysis divided by the chain length (i.e., $2 \times C_2H_4/CH_4$).

[2] Rate by initial rates of methane formation. Complete product analysis by G.L.C. An additional source of CH_4 was found and attributed to the n-butyl radical decomposition in the latter stages of reaction

$$(C_2H_4 + \dot{C}_2H_5 \cdot \longrightarrow C_4H_9 \cdot; \quad C_4H_9 \cdot \longrightarrow C_3H_6 + CH_3 \cdot). \text{ This seems unlikely.}$$

[3] Rates were obtained from CH_4 production. Assumed $E_a = 88$ kcal/mole. Observed pressure dependence at $P < 100$ torr.

[4] Used the rate constant of [2] in a Rice-Herzfeld mechanism on a computer to calculate the rate of ethane pyrolysis. Calculated rates agreed with observed rates, except at the high temperatures (where the calculated rates were high).

[5] Toluene carrier technique. C^{14} labeled ethane was used to distinguish between CH_4 produced from the toluene carrier decomposition and that arising from ethane. Amount of decomposition was less than 1 percent. Rates were independent of the ethane partial pressure.

[6] Rates were based on the formation of CH_4 in the initial stages, which was equated with the initiation reaction. Chain termination was attributed to the combination and disproportionation of ethyl radicals. Analysis for methane was made by standard gas analysis techniques. A surface dependence of the overall rate of the ethane pyrolysis was attributed to absorption of H-atoms at the surface leading to H-atom chain termination with ethyl radicals.

Reaction: *n*-Butane

$$\xrightarrow{a} 2C_2H_5\cdot \quad (II)$$

$$CH_3CH_2CH_2CH_3 \quad (I)$$

$$\xrightarrow{b} CH_3\cdot \quad (III) + C_3H_7\cdot \quad (IV)$$

	I	II		III	IV	
		$V=4.0$	$V=0$		$V=4.0$	$V=0$
$\Delta H^\circ_{f(298)}$	-30.2	25.7		34.0	20.7	
$S^\circ_{(298)}$	74.1	57.8	59.6	46.4	67.2	69.0
$C^\circ_{p(298)}$	23.3	12.1	10.9	8.3	17.6	16.4
$C^\circ_{p\,(800)}$	48.2	24.0	23.0	12.7	35.1	34.1

	$V=4.0^*$ a	$V=4.0^*$ b	
$\Delta S^\circ =$	41.5	39.5	g/mole
$\Delta H^\circ =$	81.6	84.9	kcal/mole
$\Delta C^\circ_p =$	0.9	2.6	g/mole

Path	log A	E	log k_T (748)	Conditions	System	Surface	References
$a+b$	18.58	86.3	-6.64	693–803 °K 10–150 torr	static		[1] J. H. Purnell and C. P. Quinn, Proc. Roy. Soc. **A270**, 267 (1962); Nature (L) **189**, 656 (1961); J. H. Purnell and C. P. Quinn, Can. J. Chem. **43**, 721 (1965).

Preferred:

log $k_a = 17.27 - 81.8/\theta$;

log $k_b \simeq 17.6 - 85.9/\theta$ (estimated).

Comments: The thermodynamics indicate that path b should be about a factor of 10 slower than path a. Adjustment of the rate constant parameters to the expected energy change of the reaction seems warranted considering the mechanistic complexities of this system. From the reaction entropies and the preferred parameters, one obtains, $k_{-a} = 10^{10.0+0.2}_{-0.3}$ l/mole-sec; $k_{-b} = 10^{10.5}$ l/mole-sec. The value reported for ethyl radical recombination rate from sector measurements is $k_{rec} = 10^{10.2}$ l/mole-sec.

Experimental

[1] Total product analysis by G.L.C. as a function of the extent of reaction. Rates of formation of C_2H_6, CH_4, and C_2H_4 were followed. Parameters of the above initiation steps were obtained from ethane formation using:

$$2C_2H_5\cdot \xrightarrow{t} C_4H_{10}, \; k_t = 1.57 \times 10^{10} \text{ l/mole-sec} \quad \text{and}$$

$$C_2H_5\cdot + C_4H_{10} \xrightarrow{4} C_2H_6 + n\text{Bu}\cdot, \quad k_4 = 5.9 \times 10^8 \times 10^{-15.2/\theta} \text{ l/mole-sec}.$$

Pressure dependence of the ethyl radical decomposition was demonstrated.

*See discussion preceeding bond fission reactions concerning radical entropies and rotational barriers.

Reaction: 2,2-Dimethylpropane (neopentane)

$$(CH_3)_3C\text{—}CH_3 \text{ (I)} \longrightarrow CH_3 \cdot \text{ (II)} + (CH_3)_3C \cdot \text{ (III)}$$

	I	II	III $V=4.0$	$V=0$	$V=8$
$\Delta H^\circ_{f(298)}$	-39.7	34.0	6.7		
$S^\circ_{(298)}$	73.2	46.4	*70.3	75.4	67.6
$C^\circ_{p(298)}$	29.1	8.3	22.6	18.7	21.7

$V=4$
$\Delta S^\circ = 43.5$ g/mole
$\Delta H^\circ = 80.4$ kcal/mole
$\Delta C_p = 1.8$ g/mole
$\langle \Delta \bar{C}^\circ_p = -0.3 \rangle$

log A	E	log k_T (400)	Conditions	System	Surface	References
17.4	83 ± 5	0.91	803–840 °K 80–450 torr	static		[1] J. Engel, A. Combe, M. Letort and M. Niclause, Compt. Rend. **244**, 453 (1957).
16.1	78.2	0.56	~1000–1200 °K ~0.7% in 4-atm Ar with 1% toluene	S.P. shock		[2] W. Tsang, J. Chem. Phys. **44**, 4283 (1966).

Preferred:
$\log k = 16.7 - 80.4/\theta$.

Comments: The activation energy of [2] is in reasonable agreement with the reaction thermodynamics. Recombination rate constants calculated for the various rotational barriers to the methyl groups in the t-butyl radical give: $V=4.0$, $k_{rec}=10^{9.3}$ l/mole-sec; $V=0$, $k_{rec}=10^{9.0}$ l/mole-sec; $V=8$, $k_{rec}=10^{9.8}$ l/mole-sec. Rate constants obtained by sector technique for $(CH_3 + CH_3)$ and $(tBu \cdot + tBu \cdot)$ are, respectively: 10^{10} l/mole-sec [A. Shepp, J. Chem. Phys. **24**, 939 (1956)], and $10^{9.5}$ l/mole-sec [E. Metcalfe, J. Chem. Soc. 3560 (1963)]. Assuming $k_{(CH_3 + tBu)} = 2(k_{CH_3 + CH_3} \times k_{tBu + tBu})^{1/2}$, one obtains $k_{CH_3 + tBu} = 10^{10.2}$ l/mole-sec. The recombination rate constant calculated from the dissociation reaction kinetics and the estimated thermodynamics is closest to the expected value when the t-butyl radical entropy, based on 8 kcal rotational barriers, is used. However, such a barrier is quite unreasonable.

Experimental

[1] Rates were obtained from pressure-time curves. Kinetics were deduced from the mechanism:

$$k = k_3 \left(\frac{k_1}{k_4}\right)^{1/2} = 1.5 \times 10^{13} \times 10^{\frac{-51.5}{\theta}} \quad \text{sec}^{-1}\left(\frac{cc}{moles}\right)^{1/2}.$$

---

*See section V–6.0.

(Continued

$$\text{initiation} \begin{cases} C_5H_{12} \xrightarrow{\ 1\ } C_4H_9\cdot + CH_3\cdot \\ C_4H_9\cdot + C_5H_{12} \longrightarrow C_4H_{10} + C_5H_{11}\cdot \end{cases}$$

$$\text{chain} \begin{cases} C_5H_{11}\cdot \xrightarrow{\ 2\ } C_4H_8 + CH_3\cdot \\ CH_3\cdot + C_5H_{12} \xrightarrow{\ 3\ } CH_4 + C_5H_{11}\cdot \end{cases}$$

$$\text{termination } 2CH_3\cdot \xrightarrow{\ 4\ } C_2H_6\cdot$$

[2] Comparative rate standard was 2,3-dimethylbutane. G.L.C. analysis. Products were *i*-butene and CH_4. Small amounts of C_2H_6 and propylene were also detected.

Reaction: 2,3-Dimethylbutane

$$(CH_3)_2CHCH(CH_3)_2 \quad (I) \xrightarrow[b]{a} \begin{array}{l} 2[(CH_3)_2\dot{C}H] \quad (II) \\ CH_3\dot{C}HCH(CH_3)_2 \quad (III) + CH_3\cdot \quad (IV) \end{array}$$

	I	II			III			IV
		$V=4$	$V=0^*$	$V=8$	$V=4$	$V=0^*$	$V=8$	
$\Delta H^\circ_{f(298)}$	-42.5	-17.6			5.6			34.0
$S^\circ_{(298)}$	87.4	65.4	69.0	63.8	83.9	86.5	81.3	46.5
$C^\circ_{p(298)}$	33.6	17.7	15.1	17.1	28.4	25.8	27.8	8.8
$C^\circ_{p(1000)}$	79.1	39.1	37.9	40.3	64.0	62.8	65.2	14.5

	$V=4.0$ a	$V=4.0$ b
$\Delta S^\circ =$	*43.4	*43.0 g/mole
$\Delta H^\circ =$	77.7	82.1 kcal/mole
$\Delta C^\circ_p =$	$+1.8$	3.6 g/mole

Path	log A	E	log k_T (1100)	Conditions	System	Surface	References
a	16.1	76.0	1.00	1000–1200 °K 1% in Ar, with 1% toluene	S.P.Sh.		[1] W. Tsang, J. Chem. Phys. **43**, 352 (1965).
b	16.6	81.1	0.49	(as above)			(as above)

Preferred:

$\log k_a = 16.5 - 78.0/\theta.$

$\log k_b = 17.0 - 83.1/\theta.$

Comments: The thermodynamics predict activation energies of $E_a = 78.0$ and $E_b = 83.1$ kcal/mole. Both are in reasonable agreement with the reported values. The recombination rate constants calculated from the thermodynamics and A-factors are:

$$k_{-a} = 10^{9.0 \pm 0.5} \text{ l/mole-sec} \quad \text{and} \quad k_{-b} = 10^{9.2 \pm 0.3} \text{ l/mole-sec.}$$

Experimental

[1] Comparative rate technique with cyclohexene decomposition as the standard. Analysis of products by G.L.C. Path a products: $C_3H_6 + H_2$, $C_2H_4^{**} + CH_4$.
Path b products:

---

*See section V–6.0.

**Production of C_2H_4 from the decomposition of the (CH_3CHCH_3) radical (as proposed by the author) does not seem reasonable.

Reaction: 2,2 methylbutane

$$(CH_3)_3C—CH(CH_3)_2 \quad (I) \longrightarrow (CH_3)_3C \cdot \quad (II) + (CH_3)_2CH \cdot \quad (III)$$

	I	II			III		
		$V=4$	$V=8*$	$V=0$	$V=4$	$V=8*$	$V=2$
$\Delta H^\circ_{f(298)}$	-48.6	6.8			17.6		
$S^\circ_{(298)}$	91.6	70.3	67.6	75.4	65.4	63.6	66.2
$C^\circ_{p(298)}$	39.9	22.6	21.7	18.7	17.7	17.1	17.5
$C^\circ_{p(1000)}$	92.7	51.3	52.8	49.2	39.1	40.3	38.1

$V=4$
$\Delta S^\circ = 44.1$ g/mole
$\Delta H^\circ = 73.0$ kcal/mole
$\Delta C^\circ_p = 0.4$ g/mole
$\Delta C^\circ_{p(1000)} = -2.3$ g/mole

log A	E	log k_T (1133)	Conditions	System	Surface	References
16.2	73.0	2.12	1069–1197 °K 0.01% in 4 atm Ar with 1% toluene	S.P.Sh.		[1] W. Tsang, J. Chem. Phys. **44**, 4283 (1966).

Preferred:
   $\log k = 16.05 - 72.2/\theta$.

Comments: The thermodynamics predict an activation energy of about 72 kcal/mole, which is within experimental error. Recombination rate constants obtained from the reaction entropies are $\log k_{rec}$ (l/mole-sec) $= 8.7^{+0.8}_{-0.4}$ (depending on the radical models assumed). The high barrier model seems to be the more consistent with reported parameters and the observed recombination rates. However, it is not reasonable.

Experimental

[1] The comparative rate standard was cyclohexene. Rates were based on G.L.C. analysis of products which were found to be primarily isobutene, propylene, and 2-methylbut-2-ene. Ethylene and 2,3-dimethylbut-2-ene were also detected.

---

*See section V–6.0 for a discussion of rotational barriers in free radicals.

Reaction: 2,2,3,3-Tetramethylbutane (hexamethyl ethane)

$$(CH_3)_3CC(CH_3)_3 \; (I) \longrightarrow 2[(CH_3)_3C \cdot] \; (II)$$

	I	II		
		$V=8*$	$V=4*$	$V=0*$
$\Delta H^0_{f(298)}$	-54.7	....	6.8	....
$S^0_{(298)}$	93.2	67.6	70.3	75.4
$C^0_{p(298)}$	45.9	21.7	22.6	18.7
$C^0_{p(1000)}$	106.2	52.8	51.3	49.2

	$V=8$	$V=4$	$V=0$	
$\Delta S^\circ =$	42.0	47.4	57.6	g/mole
$\Delta H^\circ =$	68.3	68.3	68.3	kcal/mole
$\Delta C^\circ_p =$	-2.5	-0.7	-8.5	g/mole

log A	E	log k_T (1052)	Conditions	System	Surface	References
16.3	68.5	2.07	985–1119 °K < 0.1% in 4 atm Ar with 1% toluene	S. P. Sh.		[1] W. Tsang, J. Chem. Phys. **44**, 4283 (1966).

Preferred:

$$\log k = 16.07 - 67.2/\theta$$
$$\log k_{\text{rec}} \; (1/\text{mole-sec}) = 8.3^{+0.9}_{-0.6}$$

Comments: The thermodynamics predict an activation energy of about 67.2 kcal/mole which is just within the limits of experimental error. The back recombination rate constant has been measured. The value reported is $k_{\text{rec}} = 10^{9.5}$ 1/mole-sec, E. L. Metcalfe, J. Chem. Soc., 3560 (1963). The kinetics of the decomposition reactions seem to support the low entropy, high rotational barrier model of the t-butyl radical. This, however, is not very reasonable.*

Experimental

[1] Comparative rate standard was cyclohexene. Rates were based on G.L.C. analysis of the products: i-butene, propylene, 2,3-dimethylbut-2-ene, benzene, methane and C_2 hydrocarbons. Isobutene represented at least 90 percent of the decomposition product. It was assumed that all chain decomposition was quenched by the toluene.

---

*See section V–6.0 for a discussion of this reaction.

Reaction: Propene (propylene)

$$CH_3CH{=}CH_2 \text{ (I)} \longrightarrow CH_2{=}CHCH_2 \cdot \text{ (II)} + H \cdot \text{ (III)}$$

	I	II	III
$\Delta H^\circ_{f(298)}$	4.8	(38.0)	52.1
$S^\circ_{(298)}$	63.7	61.4	27.4
$C^\circ_{p(298)}$	15.5	16.8	5.0
$C^\circ_{p(1000)}$	34.5	33.5	5.2

$\Delta S^\circ = 25.1$ g/mole
$\Delta H^\circ = 87.9$ kcal/mole
$\Delta C^\circ_p = 6.3$ g/mole
$\langle \Delta \bar{C}^\circ_p = 5.2 \rangle$

log A	E	log k_T (1048)	Conditions	System	Surface	References
13.40	78.0	−2.87	953–1143 °K 2–14 torr	flow	none	[1] M. Szwarc, J. Chem. Phys., **17**, 284 (1949).

Preferred:
log $k \simeq 15.3 - 89.2/\theta$. Reported parameters are unreliable. Rate constants are probably roughly reliable.

Comments: The discrepancy between the reported activation energy and the thermodynamic estimate of the energy is too large to be reconciled. Certainly the mechanistic assumptions are questionable. If the overall decomposition rate constant is scaled to the preferred activation energy, one obtains log $k_{max} = 16.6 - 89.9/\theta$. This includes the chain length and therefore gives a maximum value for the A-factor. From A and the reaction entropy, a maximum value for the recombination rate constant is obtained, k_{rec} (max) $= 10^{11.7}$ l/mole-sec. A reasonable estimate of the recombination rate constant from kinetic theory considerations is about 1/4 (spin restrictions) × 1/5 (resonance steric factor) × (collision frequency rate constant) $Z \simeq 10^{12.0}$ l/mole-sec) $\simeq 10^{10.7}$ l/mole-sec. Thus a chain length of about 10 is inferred. This is equal to the value assumed by Szwarc. Reaction is probably not at high-pressure limit.

Experimental

[1] Rate constants were calculated from the rates of $(CH_4 + H_2)$ formation. Unpyrolysed propylene was found to decompose at a slightly lower rate than prepyrolysed propylene. Prepyrolysed propylene decomposed at a constant rate. The latter was used for rate constant determinations. Products observed were CH_4, H_2, C_2H_4, and allene (C_3H_4) in ratio of $(CH_4/H_2) \simeq 2$, $(C_2H_4/CH_4) \simeq 1$, $(C_3H_4/H_2 + CH_4) \simeq 1$. Added allene had no effect on the rate; 1–4 percent diallyl accelerated the rate and changed $(CH_4/H_2) \to 1.0$.

$$CH_2{=}CHCH_3 \xrightarrow{1} CH_2{=}CHCH_2 + H \cdot$$

$$CH_2{=}CHCH_2 \cdot \xrightarrow{5} CH_2{=}C{=}CH_2 + H \cdot$$

$$CH_2{=}CHCH_3 + H \cdot \xrightarrow{2} CH_2{=}CHCH_2 \cdot + H_2$$

$$CH_2{=}CHCH_3 + H \cdot \xrightarrow{3a} C_2H_4 + CH_3 \cdot$$

$$CH_2{=}CHCH_3 + CH_3 \cdot \xrightarrow{3b} CH_2{=}CHCH_2 \cdot + CH_4$$

$$CH_2{=}CHCH_2 \cdot + H \cdot \xrightarrow{6} CH_2{=}CHCH_3$$

From the steady state relations, $k_{dec} = (k_1 k_5 k_2/k_6)^{1/2} = 1.1 \times 10^{13-72/\theta}$ sec^{-1}. k was calculated by assuming a chain length of 10 and equating $k_2 = k_6$.

391

Reaction: 1-Butene

$$CH_2{=}CHCH_2CH_3 \text{ (I)} \xrightarrow{\text{(+ M)}} CH_2{=}CHCH_2{\cdot} \text{ (II)} + CH_3{\cdot} \text{ (III)}$$

	I	II	III
$\Delta H^\circ_{f(298)}$	0	(38.0)	34.0
$S^\circ_{(298)}$	73.6	61.4	46.4
$C^\circ_{p(298)}$	20.5	16.8	8.3
$C^\circ_{p(1000)}$	47.0	33.5	14.4

$\Delta S^\circ = 34.2$ g/mole
$\Delta H^\circ = 72.0$ kcal/mole
$\Delta C^\circ_p = 4.6$ g/mole
$\langle \Delta C^\circ_p \rangle = 2.7$ g/mole

log A	E	log (945)	Conditions	System	Surface	References
13.0	61.5	−1.23	935–1051 °K 0.1–0.6 torr $P_T \simeq 15$ torr	flow	none	[1] A. H. Sehon and M. Szwarc, Proc. Roy. Soc. **A202**, 263 (1950); J. Chem. Phys. **18**, 237 (1950)
12.7!	59.1	−0.97	900–990 °K 4–21.3 torr			[2] J. A. Kerr, R. Spencer, and A. F. Trotman-Dickenson, J. Chem. Soc., 6652 (1965)

Preferred:
   Rate constants are low; parameters are unreliable.

Comments: The reported parameters apply to the pressure dependent region of decomposition [2] and are therefore unreliable. It is apparent from the reaction thermodynamics that both A and E should be considerably higher. We estimate $\log k_\infty = 16.0{-}73.3/\theta$ and $k_{rec} = 10^{9.8}$ l/mole·sec.

Experimental

   [1] Toluene carrier technique. Rates of reaction were equated to rates of CH_4 formation. Pressure dependence of the rate constants was evident at the high temperatures. Hydrogen and 1,3-butadiene were also found in the products. Ratio $(ØCH_2)_2/(CH_4{+}H_2) \simeq 0.3$ reasonably explained on basis of $ØCH_2{\cdot} + CH_2{=}CHCH_2{\cdot}$ reactions.
   [2] Aniline carrier technique. Rates were based on CH_4 formation and the usual mechanism. A strong pressure dependence of the rate constants was observed. A high-pressure activation energy of about 71.5 kcal/mole was estimated on the basis of 19 effective oscillators (analogous to methyl cyclopropane). A high-pressure rate constant of $\log k = 15.0{-}71.5/\theta$ was estimated.

Reaction: 2-Methyl-1-butene (2-methylpropene) (isobutene)

$$(CH_3)_2C\!\!=\!\!CH_2 \ (I) \longrightarrow \begin{array}{c} CH_3 \\ \diagdown \\ \cdot CH_2 \diagup \end{array}\!\!C\!\!=\!\!CH_2 \ (II) + H\cdot \ (III)$$

	I	II	III
$\Delta H^\circ_{f(298)}$	-4.0	(29.6)	52.1
$S^\circ_{(298)}$	70.2	69.0	27.4
$C^\circ_{p(298)}$	21.4	23.0	5.0
$C^\circ_{p(1000)}$	50.6	46.0	5.2

$\Delta S^\circ = 26.2$ g/mole
$\Delta H^\circ = 85.7$ kcal/mole
$\Delta C^\circ_p = 6.6$ g/mole
$\langle \Delta C^\circ_p = 3.6 \rangle_{298-1000}$

log A	E	log k_T (1006)	Conditions	System	Surface	References
13.7	76 ± 4	-2.81	930–1082 °K 1–20 torr	flow	none	[1] M. Szwarc, J. Chem. Phys. **17**, 292 (1949).

Preferred:
   Unreliable (see comments on propylene decomposition).

Comments: From the thermodynamics, we estimate $\log k_{max} = 17.0 - 88.2/\theta$; $k_{rec} \simeq 10^{12.3}$ 1/mole·sec (apparent). Using the same "real" recombination rate constant deduced in the propylene decomposition system ($k_{rec} = 10^{10.7}$ 1/mole·sec), one obtains a chain length of about 40.

Experimental

   [1] Toluene carrier technique. Rate constant parameters were deduced from the mechanism and the rate of formation of ($H_2 + CH_4$). Products of the decomposition were H_2, CH_4, and allene. The ratio $CH_4/H_2 \simeq 9$ was taken as the value of the chain length. The mechanism assumed was similar to that proposed for the propylene pyrolysis and by F. O. Rice and W. S. Haynes, J. Am. Chem. Soc. **70**, 964 (1948). The experimental first order rate constant obtained for the reaction (including the chain contribution) was $k_{(exp)} = 10^{12.7} \times 10^{-67\pm4/\theta}$ sec^{-1}.

Reaction: Toluene

$$\text{ØCH}_3 \text{ (I)} \longrightarrow \text{ØCH}_2 \cdot \text{ (II)} + \text{H} \cdot \text{atom (III)}$$

	I	II	III
$\Delta H^\circ_{f(298)}$	12.0	45.0	52.1
$S^\circ_{(298)}$	76.4	75.3	27.4
$C^\circ_{p(298)}$	24.8	25.6	5.0
$C^\circ_{p(1000)}$	62.5	60.6	5.0

$\Delta S^\circ = 26.3$ g/mole
$\Delta H^\circ = 85.1$ kcal/mole
$\Delta C^\circ_p = 5.8$ g/mole

log A	E	log k_T (1070)	Conditions	System	Surface	References
13.3	77.5	−2.50	1007–1137 °K 2–15 torr	flow	none	[1] M. Szwarc, Disc. Faraday Soc. **10**, 222 (1951); Disc. Faraday Soc. **2**, 39 (1947); Nature **160**, 403 (1947); J. Chem. Phys. **16**, 128, 637 (1948).
(See Experimental)			1133–1213 °K	flow		[2] H. Blades, A. T. Blades and E. W. R. Steacie, Can. J. Chem. **32**, 298 (1954).
(See Experimental)		−2.53	1010–1226 °K 4–10 torr	flow		[3] M. Takahasi, Bull. Chem. Soc. (Japan) **33**, 801 (1960); Ibid. **33**, 808 (1960).
14.8	85.0		913–1143 °K 6.3–22.1 torr	flow	signif- icant.	[4] S. J. Price, Can. J. Chem. **40**, 1310 (1962).

Preferred:
   log $k = 15.5 - 88.3/\theta$.

Comments: Accepting the rate constants of [4] as those appropriate to the homogeneous decomposition reaction, and scaling the parameters to fit the thermodynamic enthalpy, one obtains the preferred parameters. From the reaction entropy one then can calculate $k_{rec} = 10^{10.5}$ l/mole-sec in agreement with estimates based on kinetic theory collision frequencies. The results of Price [4] are in reasonable agreement with the thermodynamics of the reaction, where the benzyl radical heat of formation has been determined by two separate kinetic measurements to be $\Delta H^\circ_f(\text{ØCH}_2 \cdot) = 45 \pm 1$ kcal/mole (R. Walsh, D. M. Golden, and S. W. Benson, J. Am. Chem. Soc. **88**, 650 (1966); G. L. Esteban, J. A. Kerr, and A. F. Trotman-Dickenson, J. Chem. Soc., 3879 (1963)).

   One of the complications of this reaction, which makes it difficult to accept the parameters determined in any of the studies, concerns the fate of the "nonreactive" benzyl radicals. The mechanism proposed as

(Continued)

Toluene (*Continued*)

sumes complete recombination of benzyl radicals to form dibenzyl. The thermodynamics, however, clearly show that at temperatures above 1000 °K and at relatively low toluene pressures and percent reaction, the concentration of benzyl radicals in equilibrium with dibenzyl must be high.

At 1000 °K the equilibrium constant for the reaction $(\text{ØCH}_2)_2 \rightleftarrows 2\text{ØCH}_2\cdot$ equals $Keq = 10^{-1.1}$ torr. Thus for a toluene pressure of about 10 torr and a 1 percent decomposition, the ratio of $(\text{ØCH}_2\cdot/\text{ØCH}_2)_2)$ would be close to unity. Clearly, benzyl radicals cannot be "dead" in the system but must be involved in secondary reactions. The pertinent question is whether the secondary reactions of benzyl radicals contribute to the H_2 or CH_4 used to measure the bond breaking step. The answer seems to be "yes" in at least one instance. Blades and Steacie showed that styrene was an important nonvolatile product. Styrene probably results from molecular elimination of H_2 from dibenzyl. In a pyrolysis of dibenzyl in toluene, Blades and Steacie also showed that H_2 was an important product. Rate constants could, then, be in error by as much as a factor of two. Fortunately CH_4 was not found in the dibenzyl-toluene system; thus H-atoms, which could be chain propagators if they were formed from dibenzyl, were probably not present. In spite of the wealth of data for this reaction, the exact nature of the decomposition (i.e., the elementary reactions involved) has not been satisfactorily elucidated and the assignment of the overall kinetics to a particular bond-breaking reaction must also be considered somewhat suspect. Nevertheless, the agreement of the parameters of [4] with those estimated from the thermodynamics tends to support their validity.

Experimental

[1] Rate constants were based on $(H_2 + CH_4)$ yields analyzed by standard gasometric methods. Products were H_2, CH_4, and dibenzyl in the following proportions: $(H_2/CH_4) = 3/2$, $(H_2 + CH_4) = (\text{ØCH}_2)_2$. The mechanism proposed was:

$$\text{ØCH}_3 \xrightarrow{1} \text{ØCH}_2\cdot + \text{H}\cdot \qquad \text{rate determining}$$

$$\text{H}\cdot + \text{ØCH}_3 \xrightarrow{2} H_2 + \text{ØCH}_2\cdot$$

$$\text{H}\cdot + \text{ØCH}_3 \xrightarrow{3} \text{ØH} + \text{CH}_3\cdot$$

$$\text{CH}_3\cdot + \text{ØCH}_3 \xrightarrow{4} CH_4 + \text{ØCH}_2\cdot$$

$$2\text{ØCH}_2\cdot \xrightarrow{5} (\text{ØCH}_2)_2$$

[2] This study repeated the toluene pyrolysis over a broader range of conditions than those of [1]. It was found that the rate constants based on yields of $(H_2 + CH_4)$ varied with contact time, initial pressure, and surface conditioning. In addition, as much as 50 percent of the nonvolatile products were found to be styrene and dimethyldiphenyls rather than dibenzyl. Since the reaction order was not unity, and since the activation energy seemed to depend on the experimental conditions (e.g., with $t_c = 0.068$ sec, $E_{act} = 90$ kcal/mole), it was concluded that a correlation of activation energy with the bond dissociation energy could not be made.

[3] Rate constants were calculated as in [1] and [2]. Analysis was by M.S. Arrhenius parameters were shown to depend on the temperature range of study. Between (764–843 °C), $E_{act} \simeq 78$ kcal/mole and between (850–898 °C) $E_{act} \simeq 90$ kcal/mole. The conclusion was that the curvature was a result of competitive reactions rather than variable experimental conditions.

[4] Rates were determined as in [1] and [2]. The reaction was found to be strongly surface dependent at temperatures below 1050 °K. Isolation of the homogeneous reaction gave the parameters reported. Results of [3] were concluded to arise from heterogeneous effects at the lower temperatures. The best straight line through all high temperature results of [2] and [3] gave $E_{act} = 86$ kcal/mole.

Reaction: Toluene

$$\text{ØCH}_3 \quad \text{(I)} \longrightarrow \text{Ø} \cdot \text{(II)} + \text{CH}_3 \cdot \text{(III)}$$

	I	II	III
$\Delta H^\circ_{f(298)}$	12.0	80	34.0
$S^\circ_{(298)}$	76.4	69.2	46.5
$C^\circ_{p(298)}$	24.8	19.2	8.3
$C^\circ_{p(1000)}$	62.5	47.0	14.4

$\Delta S^\circ = 41.3$ g/mole
$\Delta H^\circ = 102.0$ kcal/mole
$\Delta C_p^\circ = 2.7$ g/mole

log A	E	log k_T (1223)	Conditions	System	Surface	References
14.53	80.0	0.23	1073–1373 °K	flow	none	[1] L. A. Errede and F. De Maria, J. Phys. Chem. **66**, 2664 (1964).

Preferred:
   Not reliable.

Comments: This reaction is thermodynamically unsound. If a reasonable recombination rate is assumed, $k_{rec} \geq 10^{9.6}$ l/mole-sec, one obtains an estimate of the reaction of interest: $k \geq 10^{15.5} \times 10^{-102/\theta}$ sec^{-1}. This is almost three orders of magnitude slower than the reported rate.

Experimental

   [1] Rate constant parameters were deduced from the rate of benzene formation in the p-xylene decomposition. It was assumed that the mechanism for benzene formation from toluene was the same as the mechanism of toluene formation from xylene. The parameters were not definitely attributed to the above reaction, although it was considered the most likely initiation (and rate determining) process.

Reaction: Ethylbenzene

$$\text{ØCH}_2\text{CH}_3 \text{ (I)} \longrightarrow \text{ØCH}_2 \cdot \text{(II)} + \text{CH}_3 \cdot \text{(III)}$$

	I	II	III
$\Delta H^\circ_{f(298)}$	7.2	45.0	34.0
$S^\circ_{(298)}$	86.2	75.3	46.4
$C^\circ_{p(298)}$	30.9	25.6	8.3
$C^\circ_{p(1000)}$	74.8	60.6	14.4

$\Delta S^\circ = 35.5$ g/mole
$\Delta H^\circ = 71.8$ kcal/mole
$\Delta C^\circ_p = 3.0$ g/mole

log A	E	log k_T (938)	Conditions	System	Surface	References
13.0	63.2	−1.73	888–1018 °K 0.1–0.35 torr	flow		[1] M. Szwarc, J. Chem. Phys. **17**, 431 (1949).
14.6	70.1	−1.74	876–1000 °K	flow	none	[2] G. L. Esteban, J. A. Kerr, and A. F. Trotman-Dickenson, J. Chem. Soc., 3873 (1963).

Preferred:
   log $k = 15.3 - 73.0/\theta$.

Comments: From the thermodynamics and $\overline{\Delta C^\circ_p} = 1.9$, the estimated activation energy is 73.0 kcal, which is probably within experimental error. The heat of formation of the benzyl radical used above is therefore supported. The methyl-benzyl radical recombination constant is calculated to be $k_{\text{rec}} = 10^{9.0}$ l/mole-sec.

Experimental

   The rate constants of both studies were calculated on the basis of the rate of CH_4 formation. Standard gas analysis techniques were employed.

   [1] Toluene carrier technique. Basic mechanism assumed: $\text{ØCH}_2\text{CH}_3 \xrightarrow{1} \text{ØCH}_2 \cdot + \text{CH}_3 \cdot$; $\text{CH}_3 \cdot + \text{ØCH}_3 \xrightarrow{2} \text{CH}_4 + \text{ØCH}_2 \cdot$; $2\text{ØCH}_2 \cdot \xrightarrow{3} (\text{ØCH}_2)_2$. Products observed: $(CH_4/(\text{ØCH}_2)_2) \simeq 1$ with a gas composition of 2 percent C_2, 15–25 percent $(H_2 + CH_4)$. Most of the H_2 formed was attributed to a heterogeneous decomposition: $\text{ØCH}_2\text{CH}_3 \longrightarrow \text{ØCH}=\text{CH}_2 + H_2$.

   [2] Aniline carrier technique employed. Basic mechanism: $\text{ØCH}_2\text{CH}_3 \longrightarrow \text{ØCH}_2 \cdot + \text{CH}_3 \cdot$; $\text{CH}_3 \cdot + \text{ØNH}_2 \longrightarrow \text{CH}_4 + \text{ØNH}$; $\text{ØNH} \longrightarrow$ polymer. Main products were CH_4, H_2, and C_2H_4 roughly produced in the ratio of 20/10/1, respectively. Benzene was a minor product.

   The origin of the H_2 in both studies has not been satisfactorily explained, but could well arise from a molecular elimination from $(\text{ØCH}_2)_2$ or $(\text{ØNH}_2)_2$ (see comments on toluene).

Reaction: *n*-Propylbenzene

$$\text{ØCH}_2\text{CH}_2\text{CH}_3 \text{ (I)} \longrightarrow \text{ØCH}_2 \cdot \text{ (II)} + \text{C}_2\text{H}_5 \cdot \text{ (III)}$$

	I	II	III ($V = 4.5^*$)
$\Delta H^\circ_{f(298)}$	2.3	45.0	25.7
$S^\circ_{(298)}$	95.6	75.3	57.8
$C^\circ_{p(298)}$	36.4	25.6	12.1
$C^\circ_{p(1000)}$	87.1	60.6	27.2

$\Delta S^\circ = 37.5$ g/mole
$\Delta H^\circ = 68.4$ kcal/mole
$\Delta C^\circ_p = 1.3$ g/mole

log A	E	log k_T (934)	Conditions	System	Surface	References
12.5	57.5	−0.96	883–1033 °K 0.3–1.5 torr	flow	none	[1] C. H. Leigh and M. Szwarc, J. Chem. Phys. **20,** 403 (1952).
14.9	68.6	−1.15	860–1008 °K	flow	none	[2] G. L. Esteban, J. A. Kerr, and A. F. Trotman-Dickenson, J. Chem. Soc. 3873 (1963).

Preferred:
   log $k = 14.9$–$68.6/\theta$.

Comments: From the thermodynamics, $E = 69.0$ kcal/mole in good agreement with [2]. This gives a recombination rate constant of $k_{\text{rec}} = 10^{8.7}$ l/mole-sec.

Experimental

[1] Rate constants were based on C_2 hydrocarbon formation (i.e. $[C_2H_4 + C_2H_6]$). Analysis was by standard gasometric techniques. Products observed were: C_2H_4, H_2, CH_4, $(\text{ØCH}_2)_2$ and minor amounts of C_2H_6 in the approximate ratios:

$$(\text{H}_2 + \text{CH}_4)/\text{C}_2\text{H}_4 \simeq 0.85; \ (\text{H}_2/\text{CH}_4) \simeq 3/2; \ \frac{(\text{C}_2\text{H}_4)}{\text{C}_2\text{H}_4 + \text{C}_2\text{H}_6} \simeq 0.9.$$

Decomposition of the ethyl radical relative to trapping with toluene was the preferred reaction mode. First-order rate constants were independent of t_c, P_T, and δP reactant.

[2] Aniline carrier technique. Rate constants were based on C_2H_6 and C_2H_4 analyzed by G.L.C. Mechanism:

$$\text{ØC}_3\text{H}_7 \xrightarrow{1} \text{ØCH}_2 \cdot + \text{C}_2\text{H}_5 \cdot; \ \text{C}_2\text{H}_5 \cdot \xrightarrow{2} \text{C}_2\text{H}_4 + \text{H} \cdot;$$

$$\text{C}_2\text{H}_5 \cdot + \text{ØNH}_2 \xrightarrow{3} \text{C}_2\text{H}_6 + \text{ØNH}; \ \text{H} \cdot + \text{ØNH}_2 \xrightarrow{4} \text{H}_2 + \text{ØNH}.$$

Main products were; C_2H_4, H_2, C_2H_6 and CH_4. Methane production was attributed to the reaction:

$$\text{ØC}_3\text{H}_7 \longrightarrow \text{ØC}_2\text{H}_5 \cdot + \text{CH}_3.$$

*(See discussion on rotational barriers in radicals preceding bond breaking reactions.)

Reaction: *n*-Butylbenzene

$$\text{Ø(CH}_2)_3\text{CH}_3 \text{ (I)} \xrightarrow{a} \text{ØCH}_2 \cdot \text{(II)} + \text{C}_3\text{H}_7 \cdot \text{(III)}$$
$$\xrightarrow{b} \text{ØCH}_2\text{CH}_2 \cdot \text{(IV)} + \text{C}_2\text{H}_5 \cdot \text{(V)}$$

	I	II	III $(V=4.0)$	IV $(V=4.0)$	V $(V=4.5^*)$
$\Delta H^\circ_{f(298)}$	-2.9	45.0	20.7	52.6	25.7
$S^\circ_{(298)}$	105.0	75.3	67.2	89.2	57.8
$C^\circ_{p(298)}$	41.9	25.6	17.6	30.7	12.1
$C^\circ_{p(1000)}$	99.4	60.6	39.5	72.3	27.2

	a	b
$\Delta S^\circ =$	37.5	42.0 g/mole
$\Delta H^\circ =$	68.6	81.2 kcal/mole
$\Delta C^\circ_p =$	1.3	0.9 g/mole

Path	log A	E	log k_T (936)	Conditions	System	Surface	References
a	14.5	65.0	-0.69	879–947 °K 0.2–1 torr	flow	none	[1] C. H. Leigh and M. Szwarc, J. Chem. Phys. **20,** 407 (1952).
a	14.5	67.1	-1.18	863–1008 °K	flow	——————	[2] G. L. Esteban, J. A. Kerr, and A. F. Trotman-Dickenson, J. Chem. Soc., 3873 (1963).

Preferred:
   $\log k_a = 14.5 - 67.1/\theta$.

Comments: Thermodynamics give $\Delta H^\circ_T = E_a = 69.2$ kcal/mole. From the entropy one obtains, $k_{-a} = 10^{8.7}$ l/mole-sec. If the recombination rate constant, k_{-b} is assumed to be a factor of 5 larger than k_{-a} (i.e., no resonance tightening in the transition state), then path (b) reaction thermodynamics give a rate constant for decomposition of about: $k_b = 10^{16.8} \times 10^{-81.5/\theta}$ sec^{-1}. This suggests about 10 percent decomposition via path (b), see [2].

Experimental

[1] Toluene carrier technique. Rates of the reaction were based on the C_2H_4 formation. Complete decomposition of the *n*-propyl radical (i.e., $C_3H_7 \longrightarrow CH_3 \cdot + C_2H_4$) was reasonably assumed. The main products were C_2H_4, CH_4, and $(ØCH_2)_2$. Ratios of products suggested side reactions: $(CH_4 + H_2)/C_2H_4 \simeq 0.7$; $(H_2/CH_4 + H_2) \simeq 0.2$; $(ØCH_2)_2/C_2H_4 = 0.4$. The usual mechanism (see ethyl benzene) was assumed.

[2] Aniline carrier technique. Rate constants were based on CH_4 formation. Overall decomposition rates were based on C_2H_4 formation. Accuracy was not sufficient to determine parameters of path b, which was thought to be competitive. Mechanism:

$$\text{ØC}_4\text{H}_9 \xrightarrow{1} \text{ØCH}_2 \cdot + \text{C}_3\text{H}_7 \cdot \qquad \text{C}_3\text{H}_7 \cdot \xrightarrow{2} \text{CH}_3 \cdot + \text{C}_2\text{H}_4$$

(Continued)

---

*See discussion on rotational barriers in radical preceding bond fission reactions.

n-Butylbenzene *(Continued)*

$$CH_3 \cdot + \emptyset NH_2 \xrightarrow{3} CH_4 + \emptyset NH \qquad \emptyset C_4H_9 \xrightarrow{4} \emptyset C_2H_4 \cdot + C_2H_5 \cdot$$

$$C_2H_5 \cdot \xrightarrow{5} H \cdot + C_2H_4.$$

Principal products were: CH_4, H_2, and C_2H_4. Yields of C_2H_6, C_3H_8, and C_3H_6 were less than 1 percent of the gaseous products.

Reaction: Isopropylbenzene (cymene)

	I	II ($V=4^*$)	III
$\Delta H^\circ_{f(298)}$	0.9	(36.6)	34.0
$S^\circ_{(298)}$	92.9	84.1	46.4
$C^\circ_{p(298)}$	36.3	31.6	8.3
$C^\circ_{p(1000)}$	87.3	73.5	14.4

$\Delta S^\circ = 37.6$ g/mole
$\Delta H^\circ = (69.7)$ kcal/mole
$\Delta C^\circ_p = 3.6$ g/mole $\langle \Delta \bar{C}^\circ_p = 2.0 \rangle_{298-900}$

log A	E	log k_T (940)	Conditions	System	Surface	References
13.3	61	-0.88	865–935 °K 0.9–1.2 torr	flow		[1] C. H. Leigh and M. Szwarc, J. Chem. Phys. **20**, 844 (1952).
14.3	66.0	-1.04	892–989 °K (7 torr total)	flow		[2] J. A. Kerr, A. F. Trotman-Dickenson, and M. Wolter, J. Chem. Soc. 3584 (1964).

Preferred:
log $k = 15.45 - 71.0/\theta$.

Comments: The heat of formation of the radical in parenthesis corresponds to a resonance energy of 13.5 kcal/mole (as in the benzyl radical). The thermodynamics then predict an activation energy of $E \simeq 71.0$ kcal/mole, which is within experimental error of [2]. The higher (thermodynamic) value gives a more reasonable recombination rate constant ($k_{rec} = 10^{8.6}$ l/mole-sec) and is therefore preferred.

Experimental

[1] Rates were based on the rate of CH_4 produced. (See comments on *p*-isopropyl toluene.) The *A*-factor ($10^{13.3}$) was assumed.
[2] Rates were based on the CH_4 production.

---

*See discussion on rotational barriers in radicals preceding bond fission reactions.

Reaction: *t*-Butylbenzene

	I	II ($V=4$)	III
$\Delta H^\circ_{f(298)}$	-5.3	(26.2)	34
$S^\circ_{(298)}$	95.0	89.6	46.5
$C^\circ_{p(298)}$	42.3	36.6	8.5
$C^\circ_{p(1000)}$	100	85.3	14.4

$\Delta S^\circ = 41.1$ g/mole
$\Delta H^\circ = 65.5$ kcal/mole
$\Delta C^\circ_p = 2.8$ g/mole

log A	E	log k_T (*900*)	Conditions	System	Surface	References
13.48	59.5	-0.97	865–935 °K 0.9–1.2 torr	flow		[1] C. H. Leigh and M. Szwarc, J. Chem. Phys **20,** 844 (1952).

Preferred:
   $\log k = 15.2 - 66.6/\theta$.

Comments: The *A*-factor assumed by the authors is in error. The preferred parameters were obtained b scaling the reported parameters to the indicated reaction enthalpy, assuming a benzyl resonance energ of 13.5 kcal/mole for the product radical. Using the reaction entropy* one obtains: $k_{rec} = 10^{7.8}$ l/mole-sec.

Experimental

[1] Analysis and rates were based on CH_4 formation. (See comments on *p*-isopropyl toluene.) The *A*-factor reporte was assumed (by analogy) to be the same as that for ethylbenzene corrected for the different reaction path degeneracies

---

*See discussion on rotational barriers in radicals preceding bond fission reactions.

Reaction: *p*-Isopropyltoluene (*p*-cymene)

	I	II($V=4$)	$CH_3\cdot$
$\Delta H^\circ_{f(298)}$	-7.0	(28.7)	34.0
$S^\circ_{(298)}$	101.3	92.5*	46.4
$C^\circ_{p(298)}$	41.9	37.2	8.3
$C^\circ_{p(1000)}$	99.2	85.4	14.4

$\Delta S^\circ = 37.6$ g/mole
$\Delta H^\circ = 69.7$ kcal/mole
$\Delta C^\circ_p = 3.6$ g/mole

log A	E	log k_T (900)	Conditions	System	Surface	References
13.3	60	-1.27	865–935 °K 0.9–1.2 torr	flow		[1] C. H. Leigh and M. Szwarc, J. Chem. Phys. **20**, 844 (1952).

Preferred:
   $\log k = 16.0 - 71.0/\theta$.

Comments: Reported parameters are undoubtedly too low since the *A*-factor assumed was in error. The preferred values were obtained by scaling to the indicated reaction enthalpy. The latter is based on an assigned resonance energy in the product radical of 13.5 kcal/mole. From the reaction entropy (see discussion on rotational barriers in radicals), one can calculate $k_{rec} = 10^{9.1}$ l/mole-sec.

Experimental

[1] Rate constants were based on 5/7 the rate of CH_4 reaction. This factor accounted for the CH_4 produced ultimately by the reaction $H\cdot + \emptyset CH_3 \longrightarrow CH_3\cdot + \emptyset H$, which was important under similar conditions in the toluene pyrolysis system. Reported Arrhenius parameters were calculated from the rate constants and were based on an *A*-factor assumed to be $2 \times A$ (ethylbenzene). (The factor of 2 corrects for the difference in reaction path degeneracies of the two reactions.) Reasonable agreement between the calculated Arrhenius line and the experimental data was demonstrated.

---

*See discussion on rotational barriers in radicals preceding bond fission reactions.

Reaction: Dibenzyl (1,2-diphenylethane)

$$\text{ØCH}_2\text{—CH}_2\text{Ø(I)} \longrightarrow 2[\text{ØCH}_2 \cdot] \text{ (II)}$$

	I	II
$\Delta H^\circ_{f(298)}$	34.4	45.0
$S^\circ_{(298)}$	114.5	75.3
$C^\circ_{p(298)}$	50.0	25.6
$C^\circ_{p(1000)}$	119.9	60.6

$\Delta S^\circ = 36.1$ g/mole
$\Delta H^\circ = 55.6$ kcal/mole
$\Delta C^\circ_p = 1.2$ g/mole

log A	E	log k_T (975)	Conditions	System	Surface	References
9.3	48.0	-1.46	903–1047 °K .01–.4 torr	flow	< 5%	[1] C. Horrex and S. E. Mil Disc. Faraday Soc. 1(187 (1951).

Preferred:
   Not reliable.

Comments: Kinetic results are badly scattered and show sizable dependence on initial pressures and co tact times. In addition, the reported rates of reaction are at least two orders of magnitude lower than the reasonably estimated from the thermodynamics and back reaction rate constant. The reason for this d crepancy probably arises from the dibenzyl $\rightleftharpoons$ benzyl equilibrium which should be rapidly achieved. T observed decomposition kinetics would therefore not apply to the bond-breaking step, but rather to t secondary free radical chain processes following and including the initial equilibrium. By assuming a reco bination A-factor of $10^{8.1 \pm 0.5}$ 1/mole-sec, an estimate of the decompositon kinetics can be made from t thermodynamics. $k_{est} \simeq 10^{14.4 \pm 0.5 - 56.8/\theta}$ sec^{-1}.

Experimental

   [1] Analysis was by ordinary chemical techniques and by V.P. and U.V. Products were complex. Main produc styrene, toluene, benzene, and stilbene; minor products: CH_4, H_2. The overall stoichiometry employed in obtaini the rate constants was, $3\text{ØCH}_2\text{CH}_2\text{Ø} \longrightarrow 2\text{ØCH}_3 + \text{ØH} + \text{ØCH}=\text{CH}_2 + \text{ØCH}=\text{CHØ}$. The rate of toluene forr tion (taken as 55 percent of the weight of the liquid products) was equated to the rate of benzyl radical formation.

	I	II	III	IV	V
$\Delta H^\circ_{f(298)}$	4.8	72.2	34.0	37.8	52.1
$S^\circ_{(298)}$	84.0	78.9	46.4	83.0	27.4
$C^\circ_{p(298)}$	31.3	23.4	8.5	31.0	5.0

	a	b
$S^\circ =$	41.3	26.4 g/mole
$H^\circ =$	101.4	85.1 kcal/mole
$C^\circ_p =$	0.6	4.7 g/mole

Path	long A	E	log k_T (1000)	Conditions	System	Surface	References
	12.3	67.0	−2.32	917–978 °K	flow		[1] J. G. Burr and J. D. Strong, J. Am. Chem. Soc., **86**, 5065 (1964).
	13.7	74.8	−2.64	1003–1110 °K	flow		[2] M. Szwarc, J. Chem. Phys., **16**, 128 (1948); Nature **160**, 403 (1947).

referred:
Not reliable.

omments: Both sets of Arrhenius parameters are quite incompatible thermodynamically with the processes dicated. The parameters should be very similar to those of the corresponding toluene reaction. Adjusting om the toluene parameters for differences in symmetry and for ortho substituent group effects one prects for these reactions: log $k_a = 15.8 - 102/\theta$; log $k_b = 15.8 - 88.3/\theta$.

Reaction *a* is therefore much too slow at reaction temperatures to be important. Since the reported tes are faster than those predicted (by factors of 4 to 10), some chain decomposition seems likely in both stems.

Experimental

[1] Hydrogen and deuterium carriers used on normal and methyl d_6 xylenes. Products were CH_4 and $\emptyset CH_3$. Proosed path (*a*) as the primary split in xylene to explain the relatively low rate of H–D exchange in the methyl groups of e recovered xylene. H-atom displacement of CH_3 in xylene was ruled out. However, see S. W. Benson and R. Shaw, Chem. Phys. **47**, 4052 (1967); J. Am. Chem. Soc. **89**, 5351 (1967), for a detailed treatment of the mechanism.

[2] Principal products were CH_4 and H_2 in a 1/1 ratio. C_2 hydrocarbons represented 10 percent of the gaseous oducts. Large yields of H_2 were taken as evidence for the (C–H) bond rupture in the primary process. Analogous oduct ratios on the xylene and toluene systems were given as evidence for similar reaction mechanisms.

Reaction: *m*-Xylene

	I	II	III
$\Delta H^\circ_{f(298)}$	4.2	37.2	52.1
$S^\circ_{(298)}$	84.8	83.7	27.4
$C^\circ_{p(298)}$	30.2	30.6	5.0

$\Delta S^\circ = 26.3$ g/mole
$\Delta H^\circ = 85.1$ kcal/mole
$\Delta C^\circ_p = 5.4$ g/mole

log A	E	log k_T (1077)	Conditions	System	Surface	References
13.6	77.1	(−2.05)	1013–1140 °K	flow	none	[1] M. Szwarc, J. Chem. Phys., **16,** 128 (1948)

Preferred:
   Not reliable.

Comments: Rate constants are probably close to correct. By comparison with the toluene reaction, one would predict, log $k_{est} = 15.8 - 88.3/\theta$.

Experimental

   [1] The (H_2/CH_4) ratios were identical to those found in the toluene pyrolysis, namely about 3/2. See comments on *o*-xylene.

Reaction: *p*-Xylene

	I	II	III	IV	V
$\Delta H^\circ_{f(298)}$	4.8	37.2	52.1	72.2	34.0
$S^\circ_{(298)}$	84.0	83.7	27.4	77.5	46.5
$C^\circ_{p(298)}$	31.3	29.3	5.0	24.7	8.5

	a	b	
$\Delta S^\circ =$	27.1	40	g/mole
$\Delta H^\circ =$	84.5	101.4	kcal/mole
$\Delta C^\circ_p =$	3.0	1.9	g/mole

Path	log A	E	log k_T	Conditions	System	Surface	References
a	13.7	76.2	−5.67	1018–1123 °K	flow		[1] M. Szwarc, J. Chem. Phys. **16**, 128 (1948).
a	13.97	76	−5.35	1073–1373 °K ~ 0.2 mm Hg	flow		[2] L. A. Errede and F. DeMaria, J. Phys. Chem. **66**, 2664 (1962).
b	12.97	72˙	−5.33	(as above)			(as above)
b	12.3	67	−4.73	917–978 °K	flow		[3] J. G. Burr and J. D. Strong, J. Am. Chem. Soc. **86**, 5065 (1964).
a	14.43	79.5	−5.78	795–920 °K	flow		[4] J. R. Schaefgen, J. Polymer Sci. **15**, 203 (1955).
b	14.67	81.8	−6.12				

Preferred:
Rate constants for path *a* are probably reliable. Parameters are low. Path *b* rate constants are unreliable.

Comments: Estimate:
log $k_a = 15.8 - 88.3/\theta$
log $k_b = 15.8 - 102/\theta$.
(See comments on *o*- and *m*-xylenes.)

Experimental

[1] The (H_2/CH_4) ratios were about 6.5/3.5, slightly higher than those obtained in the toluene pyrolysis. Rate constants were calculated on the basis of the ($CH_4 + H_2$) produced.

[2] Path *a* parameters were determined on the basis of *p*-xylyl equivalents (defined as all products of the reaction other than toluene and benzene). Path *b* parameters were obtained on the basis of the toluene and benzene production where it was assumed that toluene produced benzene by the same mechanism as xylene decomposed to toluene.

[3] See [1] for *o*-xylene.

[4] Rate constants for path *a* were based on the rate of H_2 formation, and those of path *b* were based on the CH_4 formation. Analysis by M.S. Qualitative product identification by I.R. Rate constants of path *b* varied with contact time and pressure.

Reaction: α — Methylnaphthalene (α = ortho)

β — Methylnaphthalene (β = meta)

	I	II	III	IV	V
$\Delta H^\circ_{f(298)}$	-29.0	-29.0	4.0	4.0	52.1
$S^\circ_{(298)}$	81.7	81.7	80.6	80.6	27.4
$C^\circ_{p(298)}$					5.0

Path a

$\Delta S^\circ = 26.3$ g/mole
$\Delta H^\circ = 85.1$ kcal/mole
$\Delta C^\circ_p =$

Path	log A	E	log k_T	Conditions	System	Surface	References
a	13.2	73.5		none given	(flow)		[1] M. Szwarc and A. Shaw, unpublished, quoted by Szwarc, Chem. revs. **47**, 75 (1950).
b	13.2	73.5					

Preferred:
$\log k_a = 15.5 - 84.3/\theta$
$\log k_b = 15.5 - 84.3/\theta$.

Comments: The rate constants are probably reliable, but the parameters are certainly low. One would expect the A-factor to be the same as that for toluene, and adjustment to that value gives the preferred parameters.

Experimental

See [2] for *o*-xylene.

Reaction: Para, ortho, and meta fluorotoluenes

$$\text{para } CH_3\text{ØF (I)} \xrightarrow{\ a\ } \text{para·}CH_2\text{ØF (II)} + H \cdot \text{(III)}$$

$$\text{ortho } CH_3\text{ØF} \xrightarrow{\ b\ } \text{ortho · } CH_2\text{ØF} + H \cdot$$

$$\text{meta } CH_3\text{ØF} \xrightarrow{\ c\ } \text{meta · } CH_2\text{ØF} + H \cdot$$

	I	II	III
$\Delta H^\circ_{f(298)}$	-34.3	-1.3	52.1
$S^\circ_{(298)}$	80.8	79.7	27.4
$C^\circ_{p(298)}$	27.7	28.1	5.0
$C^\circ_{p(1000)}$	64.2	62.3	5.0

$\Delta S^\circ = 26.3$ g/mole
$\Delta H^\circ = 85.1$ kcal/mole
$\Delta C^\circ_p = 5.4$ g/mole

Path	log A	E	log k_T (1080)	Conditions	System	Surface	References
a	13.3	78	-2.49	(~ 1080 °K) (~ 1108 °K)	flow		[1] M. Szwarc and J. S. Roberts, J. Chem. Phys. **16**, 609 (1948).
b	13.3	78	-2.49	as above			
c	13.3	78	-2.49	as above			

Preferred:
Rate constants probably reliable. Parameters are low.
$\log k = 15.5 - 88.8/\theta$.

Comments: Errors inherent in the toluene results have been introduced here. Scaling the reported parameters to the "corrected" toluene A-factor gives the preferred values above.

Experimental

[1] Analysis procedures and interpretation were identical to those employed in the toluene system. The observed rates were within 20 percent of the toluene rates at 1080 and at 1108 °K. Activation energies were calculated assuming an A-factor equivalent to that of the toluene decomposition.

Reactants: α-Picoline
β-Picoline
γ-Picoline

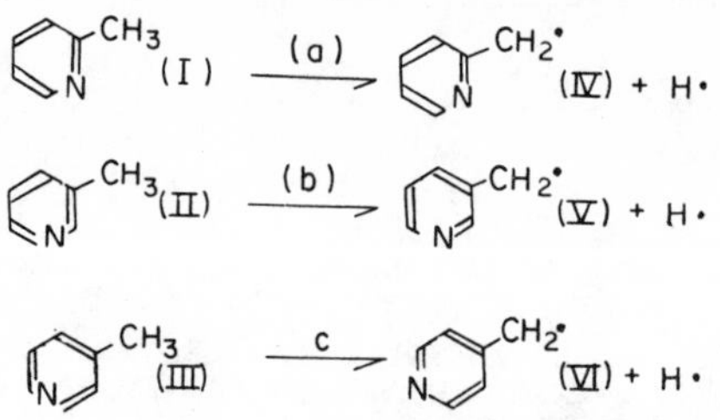

	I	II	III	IV	V	VI	H·
$\Delta H^\circ_{f(298)}$	23.6	25.3	25.3	54.6	55.6	56.6	52.1
$S^\circ_{(298)}$	77.8	77.8	76.4	76.7	76.7	75.3	27.4
$C^\circ_{p(298)}$	24.1	23.9	24.0	24.6	24.6	24.6	5.0

a
$\Delta S^\circ = 26.3$ g/mole
$\Delta H^\circ = 83.1$ kcal/mole
$\Delta C^\circ_p = 5.5$ g/mole

Path	log A	E	log k_T (1054)	Conditions	System	Surface	References
a	13.3	75.5	−2.36	~1058 °K	flow		[1] J. S. Roberts and M. Szwarc, J. Chem Phys., **16**, 981 (1948).
b	13.3	76.5	−2.56	~1054 °K	flow		
c	13.3	77.5	−2.77	~1056 °K	flow		

Preferred:
Rate constants probably reliable but parameters are low. Adjustment to the preferred values for toluene gives:

α-picoline: log $k = 15.5 - 86.2/\theta$;
β-picoline: log $k = 15.5 - 87.2/\theta$;
γ-picoline: log $k = 15.5 - 88.2/\theta$.

Experimental

[1] Procedures, analysis, and interpretation were identical to those for toluene [1]. The same A-factor as the toluene decomposition was assumed and the activation energy was calculated from the observed rate constants.

$$\text{ØCH}_2\text{COOH (I)} \xrightarrow{\;a\;} \text{ØCH}_2 \cdot \text{(II)} + \cdot \text{COOH (III)}$$
$$\xrightarrow{\;b\;} \text{ØCH} = \text{CO} + \text{H}_2\text{O}$$

	I	II	III
$\Delta H^\circ_{f(298)}$	-75.8	45.0	(-53.3)
$S^\circ_{(298)}$	97.3	75.3	60.7
$C^\circ_{p(298)}$	34.3	25.6	10.3
$C^\circ_{p(1000)}$	76.9	60.4	16.8

$^\circ = 38.7$ g/mole
$^\circ = 67.5$ kcal/mole
$^\circ_p = 1.6$ g/mole $\langle \overline{\Delta C^\circ_p} \approx 1.0 \rangle$

Path	log A	E	log k_T (928)	Conditions	System	Surface	References
	12.9	55.0	-0.06	860–995 °K 4.7–12.8 torr	flow	< 5%	[1] M. H. Back and S. H. Sehon, Can. J. Chem. **38**, 1261 (1960).
	14.3	66	-1.26				[2] J. W. Taylor and M. Szwarc, M. Sci. Thesis (J. W. Taylor), Univ. of Manchester (1951).

eferred:

$\log k_a = 14.3 - 68.1/\theta.$

mments: The observed A-factors imply recombination rate constants of about $10^{6.4}$ l/mole-sec and $10^{7.8}$ nole-sec ([1, 2] respectively). A reasonable guess would be about $10^{8.6 \pm 0.5}$ l/mole-sec (i.e., a mean be- een the k_{rec} obtained for ($C_3H_7 \cdot + \text{ØCH}_2 \cdot$) and ($CH_3 \cdot + \text{ØCHCH}_3$). The preferred parameters give ΔH°_f COOH) $= -53.3$ and $DH^\circ (\text{H} - \text{COOH}) = 87.3$ kcal/mole.

Experimental

[1] Toluene carrier technique. Products of the reaction were mainly CO_2 and dibenzil with smaller yields of CO. and CH₄ were formed in amounts between 20 and 60 percent of the CO_2. Phenylketone was also detected by hy- olysis and titration as the acid. Path (a) parameters were calculated from the rate of ($CO + CO_2$) production. Rate nstants were independent of tc, P_T and $\delta P_{reactant}$.

Rate constants of path b (not sufficiently accurate for an Arrhenius analysis) were obtained from the total acid e of decomposition less the ($CO + CO_2$) production rate. The standard toluene carrier mechanism was assumed. me indication of oxalic acid as a product under certain conditions was noted. Formic acid was not observed.

Reaction: Diphenylethanoic acid (diphenylacetic acid)

$$\text{Ø}_2\text{CHCOOH (I)} \longrightarrow \text{Ø}_2\text{CH} \cdot \text{(II)} + \cdot \text{COOH (III)}$$

	I	II	III
$\Delta H^\circ_{f\,(298)}$	-52.5	(59.3)	$[-53.3]$
$S^\circ_{(298)}$	123.7	100.2	60.7
$C^\circ_{p\,(298)}$	52.8	44.5	10.3
$C^\circ_{p\,(1000)}$	122.3	107.3	16.8

$\Delta S^\circ = 37.2$ g/mole
$\Delta H^\circ = 58.5$ kcal/mole
$\Delta C^\circ_p = 2.0$ g/mole

log A	E	log k_T (848)	Conditions	System	Surface	References
12.9	52	-0.50	788–909 °K	flow	(partly hetero-geneous ~ 11%)	[1] M. H. Back and A. H. Sehon, Can. J. Chem. **38**, 1271 (1960).

Preferred:
Suspect (see comments).

Comments: The partial heterogeneous nature of the secondary reactions could easily produce sizable error in the Arrhenius parameters. The very low A-factor reported implies an unreasonably low back reaction recombination rate of $k_r \leq 10^{6.2}$ l/mole-sec. Assuming that the rates observed do represent within a factor of 2 or 3 the reaction of interest, and taking a recombination rate of $k_r \simeq 10^{8.1}$ l/mole-sec, one obtains more reasonable parameters. log $k = 14.8 - 59.4/\theta$, ΔH°_f (Ø$_2$CH) $= 59.2 \pm 3$ kcal/mole. Resonance energy 22.8 kcal/mole.

Experimental

[1] Toluene carrier technique. Rates were based on CO and CO$_2$ production. Products observed were CO$_2$, CO, H$_2$ and CH$_4$. Rate constants were apparently independent of tc, P_T, and $\delta P_{\text{reactant}}$. Production of CO was increased the packed vessel, therefore, a heterogeneous decomposition of $\cdot$ COOH was suggested.

Reaction: Peracetic acid

$$CH_3COOOH\ (I) \longrightarrow CH_3COO \cdot\ (II) + \cdot OH\ (III)$$

	I	II	III
$\Delta H^\circ_{f(298)}$	-80.9	-49.7	8.0
$S^\circ_{(298)}$	80.4	67.4	43.9
$C^\circ_{p(298)}$	20.0	13.9	7.1

$\Delta S^\circ = 30.9$ g/mole
$\Delta H^\circ = 39.2$ kcal/mole
$\Delta C^\circ_p = 1.0$ g/mole

log A	E	log k_T (516)	Conditions	System	Surface	References
14.0	32 ± 2	$+0.46$	400–633 °K 1.6–22.7 torr	flow	(appreciable)	[1] C. Schmidt and A. H. Sehon, Can. J. Chem. **41**, 1819 (1963).

Preferred:
 Not reliable.

Comments: It seems likely that the homogeneous decomposition was never effectively isolated from the heterogeneous effects. The thermodynamics predict a considerably higher activation energy and though the heats of formation of the various species are somewhat uncertain, it is unlikely that they could be in error by the amount required by the reported kinetic parameters.

Experimental

 [1] Toluene carrier technique. Rates were calculated from the amount of decomposed peracetic acid. Stoichiometry was: $\Delta(P) \simeq CO_2 + CH_3COOH$. It was necessary to make appreciable adjustments on observed k's in order to isolate the homogeneous from the heterogeneous reactions. Main products were CO_2, CH_3COOH, C_2H_6, H_2CO, O_2, traces of CO, and $(\emptyset CH_2)_2$. The rate constant parameters were obtained by assuming $A = 10^{14.0}$ sec^{-1}. Large scatter in the rate constants prohibited a more exact treatment.

413

Reaction: Dimethyl ether

$$CH_3OCH_3 \; (I) \longrightarrow CH_3O \cdot \; (II) + CH_3 \cdot \; (III)$$

	I	II	III
$\Delta H^{\circ}_{f(298)}$	-43.7	3.9	34.0
$S^{\circ}_{(298)}$	63.7	54.6	46.4
$C^{\circ}_{p(298)}$	15.6	8.4	8.3
$C^{\circ}_{p(1000)}$	34.2	18.6	14.4

$\Delta S^{\circ} = 37.3$ g/mole
$\Delta H^{\circ} = 81.6$ kcal/mole
$\Delta C^{\circ}_p = 1.1$ g/mole
$< \Delta C^{\circ}_p > \simeq 0.3$ g/mole

log A	E	log k_T (785)	Conditions	System	Surface	References
18.1	81.0	-4.46	750–820 °K 35–400 torr			[1] S. W. Benson and D. V. Jain, J. Chem. Phys. 3 1008 (1959).
17.5	81.0	-5.06	(as above)			[2] K. H. Anderson and S. V Benson, J. Chem. Phy **39,** 1677 (1963).

Preferred:
   $\log k = 16.0 - 81.0/\theta$.

Comments: Rate constants are probably somewhat too high. The thermodynamics are consistent with reported activation energy. The preferred A-factor and reaction thermodynamics predict a recombination constant of $k_{rec} = 10^{9.9}$ l/mole-sec. The reported A-factors could easily be in error.

Experimental

[1] Observed order dependence ($n = \frac{3}{2}$). Deduced initiation kinetics from analysis of a complex mechanism..
[2] Slight revisions in reaction mechanism of [1] lead to the revised A-factor.

NOTES: McKenney and Laidler, Can. J. Chem. **41,** 1984 (1963) and McKenney, B. W. Wojciechowski, and K. J. Laidler, Can Chem. **41,** 2009 (1963) suggest that the above reaction is in its pressure-dependent region. F. O. Rice and W. R. Johnston, J. Am. Che Soc. **56,** 214 (1934), by the Paneth technique, estimate $E \simeq 81.1$ kcal/mole.

Reaction: Diethyl ether

$$C_2H_5OC_2H_5 \text{ (I)} \xrightarrow{\quad a \quad} C_2H_5 \cdot \text{(II)} + C_2H_5O \cdot \text{(III)}$$
$$\xrightarrow{\quad b \quad} C_2H_4 + C_2H_5OH$$

	I	II	III
$\Delta H^\circ_{f(298)}$	-60.7	25.7	-4.6
$S^\circ_{(298)}$	84.7	57.8	65.3
$C^\circ_{p(298)}$	25.7	12.1	14.0
$C^\circ_{p(1000)}$	58.9	27.2	31.3

$\Delta S^\circ = 38.4$ g/mole
$\Delta H^\circ = 81.8$ kcal/mole
$\Delta C^\circ_p = 0.4$ g/mole

Path	log A	E	log k_T (863)	Conditions	System	Surface	References
b	18.0	84	-3.28	833–913 °K 10–360 torr	static		[1] K. J. Laidler and D. J. McKenney, Proc. Roy. Soc. **278A**, 517 (1964).
a	14.0	78	-5.76	833–893 °K 15–320 torr	static		[2] K. J. Laidler and D. J. McKenney, Proc. Roy. Soc. **278A**, 505 (1964).

Preferred:
    Reaction a—rate constants probably reliable.
    Reaction b—not reliable.

Comments: By transition state considerations, reaction a should have a larger, more positive entropy of activation than reaction b. Since the opposite has been reported, one must be suspicious of the mechanism assumed and the validity of the conclusions. A fairly reliable estimate for the parameters of reaction a can be made from the thermodynamics by assuming a recombination rate constant of $k_{rec} = 10^{9.7 \pm 1.0}$ l/mole-sec. One then obtains $\log k_a = 16.3 - 81.8/\theta$.

Experimental

    [1] Inhibited reaction with NO. Complex mechanism was proposed from which the rate constant was derived.
    [2] Uninhibited reaction. Interpreted order change from 1.0 (low pressures) to (3/2) (high pressures) to two terms in the rate expression (i.e., a molecular path and a free radical path). The observed kinetics parameters were fit by using those reported above for the initiation reaction.

Reaction: Propanone (acetone)

$$CH_3COCH_3 \text{ (I)} \longrightarrow CH_3\cdot \text{ (II)} + CH_3\dot{C}O \text{ (III)}$$

	I	II	III
$\Delta H^\circ_{f(298)}$	-51.7	34.0	-5.4
$S^\circ_{(298)}$	70.5	46.5	64.5
$C^\circ_{p(298)}$	17.9	8.3	12.7
$C^\circ_{p(1000)}$	39.2	14.4	23.8

$\Delta S^\circ = 40.5$ g/mole
$\Delta H^\circ = 80.3$ kcal/mole
$\Delta C^\circ_p = 3.1$ g/mole
$< \Delta C^\circ_p \simeq 1.1 >_{298-1050}$

log A	E	log k_T (1050)	Conditions	System	Surface	References
14.38	72.0	-0.61	993–1101 °K 0.07–0.26 torr	flow		[1] M. Szwarc and J. W. Taylor, J. Chem. Phys. **23**, 2310 (1955).
14.15	70.9	-0.61	990–1110 °K 1% in toluene at 13 torr			[2] D. Clark and H. O. Pritchard, J. Chem. Soc. 2136 (1956).

Preferred:
   log $k = 16.26$–$81.0/\theta$.

Comments: The reported parameters must be low because the thermodynamics of the reaction are well established. A pressure falloff could be responsible, although some chain decomposition (evidenced by the formation of ketene in appreciable yields) seems the more likely explanation. The rate constant parameters have been scaled to fit the reaction enthalpy. From ΔS° and A, one obtains a recombination rate constant of $10^{9.1}$ l/mole-sec.

Experimental

[1] Toluene carrier technique. It was assumed that all acetyl radicals decomposed to CO and the rate constants were calculated on the basis of (CO) production. From 10 to 15 percent ketene was also detected. First-order rate constants were found to increase slightly with increasing total pressure. Rate constants were independent of t_c, percent conversion, and δP of acetone.

[2] Toluene carrier techniques. Rate constants were based on (CO) yields (see acetophenone [1]).

Reaction: Acetophenone

$$CH_3C\varnothing \quad (I) \longrightarrow CH_3 \cdot (II) + \varnothing - \overset{\displaystyle O}{\overset{\displaystyle \parallel}{C}}. \quad (III)$$

	I	II	III
$\Delta H^\circ_{f(298)}$	-22.0	34	[21.0]
$S^\circ_{(298)}$	87.0	46.4	79.5
$C^\circ_{p(298)}$	32.2	8.3	26.0
$C^\circ_{p(1000)}$	72.5	14.4	57.6

$\Delta S^\circ = 38.9$ g/mole
$\Delta H^\circ = 77.0$ kcal/mole
$\Delta C^\circ_p = 2.1$ g/mole
$\langle \Delta C^\circ_p \simeq 0.8 \rangle_{298-1000}$

log A	E	log k_T (1045)	Conditions	System	Surface	References
15.71	77.6	-0.52	980–1110 °K 1% reactant in 13 ± 1 mm of toluene	flow		[1] D. Clark and H. O. Pritchard, J. Chem. Soc., 2136 (1956).

Preferred:
   $\log k = 15.7 - 77.6/\theta$.

Comments: The reported parameters give $\Delta H^\circ_f (\varnothing \dot{C}O) = 21.0$ kcal/mole (see benzil). Recombination rate constant of $k_{rec} \simeq 10^{8.9}$ 1/mole-sec can be estimated from the reaction entropy and A-factor. New values of $\Delta H^\circ_f (\varnothing \dot{C} O) = 29 \pm 1$ kcal/mole cast some doubt on E_{obs}.

Experimental

[1] Toluene carrier technique. Rate constants were obtained from the rates of carbon monoxide production. Analysis of CO was made be oxidation to CO_2 with I_2O_5. A multiple critical oscillator theory (see section V–5.0) was invoked to explain the high-frequency factor for the reaction.

The following sequence of reactions was assumed: $CH_3CO\varnothing \longrightarrow CH_3 \cdot + \varnothing \dot{C}O; \quad \varnothing \dot{C}O \longrightarrow \varnothing \cdot + CO$.

Reaction: 1-Phenyl-2-propanone (benzyl methyl ketone)

$$\underset{\displaystyle}{\text{Ø}CH_2\overset{\displaystyle O}{\overset{\|}{C}}CH_3} \text{ (I)} \longrightarrow \text{Ø}CH_2 \cdot \text{(II)} + CH_3CO \text{ (III)}$$

	I	II	III
$\Delta H^\circ_{f(298)}$	-25.8	45.0	-5.4
$S^\circ_{(298)}$	101.9	75.3	64.5
$C^\circ_{p(298)}$	36.8	25.6	12.7
$C^\circ_{p(1000)}$	84.3	60.6	23.8

$\Delta S^\circ = 37.9$ g/mole
$\Delta H^\circ = 65.4$ kcal/mole
$\Delta C^\circ_p = 1.5$ g/mole

log A	E	log k_T (900)	Conditions	System	Surface	References
16.0	68.2	-0.56	$[\bar{T} \simeq 900\ °K]$	flow		[1] J. W. Taylor, Ph. D. Thesis, Univ. of Manchester (1953).

Preferred:
  $\log k = 15.3 - 65.9/\theta$.

Comments: The thermodynamics suggest that the reported parameters may be somewhat high. The preferred A-factor and reaction entropy give a reasonable recombination rate constant, $k_{\text{rec}} = 10^{8.7}$ l/mole-sec.

Experimental

[1] Toluene carrier technique.

Reaction: Benzophenone

$$
\underset{\text{ØCØ}}{\overset{\overset{\displaystyle O}{\|}}{}} \quad (I) \longrightarrow Ø \cdot (II) + \underset{\text{ØC}\cdot}{\overset{\overset{\displaystyle O}{\|}}{}} (III)
$$

	I	II	III
$\Delta H^\circ_{f(298)}$	12.5	80.0	[21.0] or [29]
$S^\circ_{(298)}$	104.2	69.2	79.5
$C^\circ_{p(298)}$	46.2	19.2	26.0
$C^\circ_{p(1000)}$	106	47.0	57.6

$\Delta S^\circ = 44.5$ g/mole
$\Delta H^\circ = 88.5$ kcal/mole
$\Delta C^\circ_p = -1.0$ g/mole
$\langle \Delta C^\circ_p \simeq -1.27 \rangle_{298-1100}$

log A	E	log k_T (1112)	Conditions	System	Surface	References
16.2	87.5	−0.99	1075–1150 °K 1% reactant in 13 torr or toluene	flow	none	[1] D. Clark and H. O. Pritchard, J. Chem. Soc., 2136 (1956).

Preferred:
   log $k = 16.2 - 87.5/\theta$ or $16.2 - 95/\theta$.

Comments: The activation energy has been used to obtain $\Delta H^\circ_f (\text{ØCO}) = 21.0$ kcal/mole (see benzil). This may be too low. The reaction entropy along with A gives $k_{rec} \simeq 10^{8.8}$ l/mole-sec.

Experimental

[1] See acetophenone.

Reaction: 1,3-Diphenyl-1,2-propanone (dibenzilketone)

$$\underset{\text{(I)}}{\varnothing CH_2\overset{\displaystyle O}{\overset{\|}{C}}CH_2\varnothing} \longrightarrow \underset{\text{(II)}}{\varnothing CH_2\overset{\displaystyle O}{\overset{\|}{C}}\cdot} + \cdot CH_2\varnothing \text{ (III)}$$

	I	II	III
$\Delta H^\circ_{f(298)}$	2.5	[22.5]	45.0
$S^\circ_{(298)}$	130	95.6	75.3
$C^\circ_{p(298)}$	54.4	31.9	25.6
$C^\circ_{p(1000)}$	129.9	69.0	60.6

$\Delta S^\circ = 40.9$ g/mole
$\Delta H^\circ = 65.0$ kcal/mole
$\Delta C^\circ_p = 3.1$ g/mole
$\langle \Delta C^\circ_p \simeq 1.7 \rangle_{298-860}$

log A	E	log k_T (860)	Conditions	System	Surface	References
17.25	71.8	−1.00	810–910 °K 1% reactant in toluene (13 torr)	flow	none	[1] D. Clark and H. O. Pritchard, J. Chem. Soc. 2136 (1956).

Preferred:
   log $k = 16.13 - 67.5/\theta$. Rate constants are probably reliable.

Comments: The heat of formation ΔH°_f ($\varnothing CH_2\dot{C}O$) has been estimated from the acetyl radical heat of formation (-5.4 kcal/mole) and group additivities. On the basis of the thermodynamics, the reported parameters seem too high. Adjusting A and E to the reaction enthalpy gives a reasonable value for the back reaction rate constant, $k_{rec} = 10^{8.7\pm1}$ l/mole-sec.

Experimental

[1] See acetophenone.

Reaction: 1,2-Diphenyl-1,2-ethanedione (benzil)

$$\underset{\substack{\| \\ \text{O}}}{\text{ØC}} \underset{\substack{\| \\ \text{O}}}{\text{—— CØ}} \text{(I)} \text{—— ØCO (II)} + \text{ØCO}$$

	I	II
$\Delta H^\circ_{f(298)}$	-21.8	[22.3]
$S^\circ_{(298)}$	116.2	79.5
$C^\circ_{p(298)}$	51.6	26.0

$\Delta S^\circ = 42.8$ g/mole
$\Delta H^\circ = 66.4$ kcal/mole
$\Delta C^\circ_p = 0.4$ g/mole

log A	E	log k_T (860)	Conditions	System	Surface	References
16.3	66.4	-0.57	$[\bar{T} \simeq 860\ °\text{K}]$	flow		[1] Jacquiss, Ph.D. Thesis, University of Manchester (1953).

Preferred:
   $\log k = 16.3 - 66.4/\theta.$

Comments: The kinetics give $\Delta H^\circ_f(\text{Ø}\dot{\text{C}}\text{O}) = 22.4$ kcal/mole. This should be compared to the value obtained from the acetophone and benzophenone decompositions of 21.0 kcal/mole respectively. A recombination rate constant of about $k_{\text{rec}} \simeq 10^{8.8}$ l/mole-sec is obtained from the reaction entropy and reported A-factor. Recent data give $\Delta H^\circ_f(\text{Ø}\dot{\text{C}}\text{O}) = 29$ kcal/mole, which would give $E \simeq 78$ kcal/mole.

Reaction: 1,1,1-Trifluoro-2-propanone (trifluoroacetone)

$$CF_3COCH_3 \ (I) \xrightarrow[\ \ b\ \ ]{\ \ a\ \ } \begin{array}{l} CF_3\cdot \ (II) + CH_3CO\cdot \ (III) \\ CH_3\cdot \ (IV) + CF_3CO\cdot \ (V) \end{array}$$

	I	II	III	IV	V
$\Delta H^\circ_{f(298)}$	−200.2	−112.5	−5.4	34	
$S^\circ_{(298)}$	83.9	62.4	64.5	46.4	
$C^\circ_{p(298)}$	24.5	12.2	12.7	8.3	

a

$\Delta S^\circ = 43.0$ g/mole
$\Delta H^\circ = 82.3$ kcal/mole
$\Delta C^\circ_p = 0.4$ g/mole

Path	log A	E	log k_T (1023)	Conditions	System	Surface	References
a or b	13.48	67.8	−1.01	970–1075 °K 1% in 13 torr of toluene.	flow	————	[1] D. Clark and H. O. Pritchard, J. Chem. Soc., 2136 (1956).

Preferred:

log $k_a = 16.6 - 81.9/\theta$. Rate constants probably reliable.

Comments: Arrhenius parameters are certainly low. The situation is similar to that of acetone where the activation energy obtained from the toluene carrier technique is 10 kcal/mole less than the bond dissociation energy in that molecule. Although the bond dissociation energy ($D(CH_3CO—CF_3)$) is not known, it is unlikely to be much less than that for path *b*. The preferred parameters have been obtained by assuming the mean rate constant reported to be roughly valid, and setting the recombination rate constant equal to that calculated for acetone, (i.e., $k_{rec} \simeq 10^{9.1}$ l/mole-sec).

Experimental

[1] Toluene carrier technique. Rates were based on the CO formation. The path of the decomposition (*a* or *b* above) was not ascertained. (See acetophenone.)

Reaction: α,α,α-Trifluoroacetophenone

$$\underset{\parallel}{\overset{\displaystyle O}{CF_3C\varnothing}} \text{ (I)} \longrightarrow CF_3 \cdot \text{ (II)} + \varnothing\dot{C}O \text{ (III)}$$

	I	II	III
$\Delta H^\circ_{f(298)}$	(-169.5)	-112.5	21.0 *or* 29
$S^\circ_{(298)}$	101	62.4	79.5
$C^\circ_{p(298)}$	39.2	12.2	26.0
$C^\circ_{p(800)}$	75.5		52.3

$\Delta S^\circ = 40.9$ g/mole
$\Delta H^\circ = 78.0$ kcal/mole (or 86)
$\Delta C^\circ_p = -1.0$ g/mole

log A	E	log k_T (817)	Conditions	System	Surface	References
15.25	73.8	-4.49	787–847 °K 1% reactant in 13 torr of toluene	flow	none	[1] D. Clark and H. O. Pritchard, J. Chem. Soc., 2136 (1956).

Preferred:
    $\log k = 15.25 - 73.8/\theta$.

Comments: All heats of formation are uncertain to at least ± 2 kcal/mole. The discrepancy between the observed activation energy and the estimated ΔH° reaction is within these limits. From A and ΔS° one obtains $k_{rec} \simeq 10^{8.4}$ 1/mole= sec.

Experimental

[1] See acetophenone.

Reaction: 2,3-Butanedione (biacetyl)

$$CH_3CO\text{---}COCH_3 \ (I) \longrightarrow 2CH_3\dot{C}O \ (II)$$

	I	II
$\Delta H^\circ_{f(298)}$	-78.0	-5.4
$S^\circ_{(298)}$	85.8	64.5
$C^\circ_{p(298)}$	23.6	12.7
$C^\circ_{p(800)}$	44.0	21.4

$\Delta S^\circ = 43.2$ g/mole
$\Delta H^\circ = 67.2$ kcal/mole
$\Delta C^\circ_p = 1.8$ g/mole
$\langle \Delta C^\circ_p \simeq 0.8 \rangle$

$\log A$	E	$\log k_T$ (662)	Conditions	System	Surface	References
15.94	63.2	-4.92	626–698 °K ~ 200 torr	static	$< 10\%$	[1] (a) F. O. Rice and W. D. Walters, J. Chem. Phys. **7**, 1015 (1939). (b) W. D. Walters, J. Am. Chem. Soc. **62**, 880 (1940).
15.7	66	-6.09				[2] J. W. Taylor, Ph. D. Thesis, Univ. of Manchester (1953).

Preferred:
   $\log k = 16.2 - 67.5/\theta$.

Comments: Kinetics [2] and thermodynamics are fairly consistent. From the reaction entropy and the reported A-factor one obtains $k_{rec} = 10^{8.5}$ l/mole-sec.

Experimental

[1] Rates were obtained from initial ΔP data [1a], and from the analysis of undecomposed biacetyl [1b]. Biacetyl was converted to dimethylglyoxime and precipitated as nickel dimethylglyoxime. Products were CO, CH_4, and $CH_2\!\!=\!\!C\!\!=\!\!O$. Rates were first order in the intial stages only. A free radical chain process was assumed since reaction rates were lower in the presence of propylene. The observed parameters were indentified with a Rice-Herzfeld chain mechanism.

[2] Toluene carrier technique.

Reaction: Benzylethanoate (benzyl acetate)

$$CH_3COO\text{—}CH_2\emptyset \ (I) \longrightarrow CH_3CO_2\cdot \ (II) + \emptyset CH_2\cdot \ (III)$$

	I	II	III
$\Delta H^\circ_{f(298)}$	-72.2	-49.7	45.0
$S^\circ_{(298)}$	109.3	67.4	75.3
$\Delta C^\circ_{p(298)}$	38.5	13.9	25.2

$\Delta S^\circ = 33.4$ g/mole
$\Delta H^\circ = 67.5$ kcal/mole
$C_p^\circ = 0.6$ g/mole

$\log A$	E	$\log k_T$ (800)	Conditions	System	Surface	References
14.5	67	-3.81		flow		[1] J. W. Taylor (with M. Szwarc), M. Sci. Thesis, Univ. of Manchester (1951); M. Szwarc and J. Watson Taylor, J. Chem. Phys. **21**, 1746 (1953).

Preferred:
   Reliable. $\log k = 14.5 - 67/\theta$.

Comments: From A and the reaction entropy one obtains $k_{rec} = 10^{9.0}$ l/mole-sec.

Experimental
   [1] Toluene carrier technique. Products were principally CO_2 and CH_4, on whose rates of formation the reported parameters were based. CO and $\emptyset CH{=}O$ were also observed and attributed to a concerted elimination reaction of the benzyl acetate. However, some induced radical decomposition forming these products is more likely (see benzyl benzoate and as follows):

CO formation:

$$R\cdot + CH_3CO_2CH_2\emptyset \longrightarrow RH + CH_3CO_2\dot{C}H\emptyset$$

$$CH_3CO_2\dot{C}H\emptyset \longrightarrow CH_3\dot{C}O + \emptyset CH{=}O$$

$$CH_3\dot{C}O + (M) \longrightarrow CH_3\cdot + CO + (M).$$

Reaction: Benzylbenzoate

$$\text{ØCOOCH}_2\text{Ø (I)} \longrightarrow \text{ØCO}_2 \cdot \text{(II)} + \text{ØCH}_2 \cdot \text{(III)}$$

	I	II	III
$\Delta H^\circ_{f(298)}$	-43.1	(-21.7)	45.0
$S^\circ_{(298)}$	128	87.9	75.3
$C^\circ_{p(298)}$	53	28.9	25.6

$\Delta S^\circ = 35.2$ g/mole
$\Delta H^\circ = 66.4$ kcal/mole
$\Delta C^\circ_p = 1.5$ g/mole

$\log A$	E	$\log k_T$ (950)	Conditions	System	Surface	References
15.3	69	-0.58	900–1000 °K	flow		[1] M. Szwarc and J. Watson Taylor, J. Chem. Phys. **21**, 1746 (1953).

Preferred:
   $\log k = 14.8 - 66.8/\theta$.

Comments: The heat of formation of $(\text{ØCO}_2^{\cdot})$ has been estimated from the heat of formation of $(\text{CH}_3\text{CO}_2 \cdot)$ with additivity relations. Reported parameters seem slightly high. From A and the reaction entropy, one obtains, $k_{rec} = 10^{8.9}$ l/mole-sec.

Experimental

[1] Toluene carrier technique. Rates obtained from CO_2 production. Rate constants were independent of tc, P_T and δP reactant. Liquid chromatographic analysis showed that $[(CO_2) = (\text{ØCH}_2)_2 = \Delta(\text{reactant})]$. CH_4 and H_2 (with yields ≈ 25 percent of CO_2) were attributed to the decompostion of dibenzyl. Carbon monoxide and benzaldehyde (both minor products) were thought to arise as follows:

$$\text{Ø} \cdot + \text{ØCO}_2\text{CH}_2\text{O} \longrightarrow \text{ØH} + \text{ØCO}_2\overset{.}{\text{C}}\text{HØ}$$

$$\text{ØCO}_2\overset{.}{\text{C}}\text{HØ} \longrightarrow \text{Ø}\overset{.}{\text{C}}\text{O} + \text{ØCHO}$$

$$\text{Ø}\overset{.}{\text{C}}\text{O} \longrightarrow \text{Ø} \cdot + \text{CO}$$

426

Reaction: Dimethylperoxide

$$CH_3OOCH_3 \text{ (I)} \longrightarrow 2CH_3O\cdot \text{ (II)}$$

	I	II
$\Delta H^\circ_{f(298)}$	-29.4	[3.9]
$S^\circ_{(298)}$	74.6	54.6
$C^\circ_{p(298)}$	17.6	8.4
$C^\circ_{,p(500)}$	24.4	11.7

$\Delta S^\circ = 34.6$ g/mole
$\Delta H^\circ = 37.2$ kcal/mole
$\Delta C^\circ_p = -0.8$ g/mole

log A	E	log k_T (440)	Conditions	System	Surface	References
15.61	36.9	-2.74	427–452 °K	static		[1] Y. Takezaki and C. Takeuchi, J. Chem. Phys. **22**, 1527 (1954).
15.2	35.3	-2.35	393–435 °K 3–30 torr	static		[2] P. L. Hanst and J. G. Calvert, J. Phys. Chem. **63**, 104 (1959).

Preferred:
   $\log k = 15.6 - 36.9/\theta$.

Comments: $k_{rec} \simeq 10^{9.9}$ l/mole-sec, calculated from the reaction entropy and the preferred A-factor.

Experimental

[1] Decomposition was performed in excess methanol. The only major products were CH_3OH and CO. Extensive correlations of stoichiometry and products with the mechanism were made. Rates followed by ΔP. Analysis for H_2CO and ethylene glycol were made by titrating with I_2 and HIO_4 respectively.

[2] Rates were followed by time sampling and I.R. analysis on both the products and the residual peroxide. Stoichimetry: 2 Peroxide $\longrightarrow 3ROH + CO$. The only important products were CH_3OH and CO. Addition of NO led to the formation of methyl nitrite as the only product.

Reaction: Diethyl peroxide

$$C_2H_5OOC_2H_5 \ (I) \longrightarrow 2C_2H_5O\cdot \ (II)$$

	I	II
$\Delta H^\circ_{f(298)}$	-47.0	$[-4.9]$
$S^\circ_{(298)}$	93.4	65.9
$C^\circ_{p(298)}$	29.2	14.2
$C^\circ_{p(500)}$	42.8	20.9

$\Delta S^\circ \ = 38.4$ g/mole
$\Delta H^\circ \ = 37.2$ kcal/mole
$\Delta C^\circ_p \ = -0.8$ g/mole

$\langle \overline{\Delta C^\circ_p} = -0.9 \rangle$ g/mole

log A	E	log k_T (435)	Conditions	System	Surface	References
14.7	31.5	-1.13	413–457 °K 2–29 torr	static	none	[1] E. J. Harris and A. C. Edgerton, Proc. Roy. Soc. (L) **A168,** 1 (1938).
13.2	31.7	-2.73	479–518 °K	flow		[2] R. E. Rebbert and K. J. Laidler, J. Chem. Phys. **20,** 574 (1952).
12.04	29.9	-2.99				[3] K. Moriya, Rev. Phys. Chem. (Japan), Shinkichi Horiba 143 (1946).
14.2	34.1	-2.94	(recalculated)			[4] P. L. Hanst and J. G. Calvert, J. Phys. Chem. **63,** 104 (1959).
	37.3			flow in excess NO	none	[5] J. Thynne (personal communication).

Preferred:
   log $k = 15.6 - 37.3/\theta$.

Comments: From additivity and ΔH°_f $(CH_3O\cdot) = 3.9$ kcal/mole, one obtains ΔH°_f $(C_2H_5O\cdot) = -4.6$ kcal/mole in good agreement with the kinetics. From the reaction entropy and the A-factor, $k_{rec} = 10^{8.9}$ l/mole-sec.

Experimental

   [1] Rates by pressure change. $(P_f/P_o) \sim 2.17 \pm 0.03$.. Products observed were H_2CO, CH_3CHO, C_2H_5OH, CO, H_2, CH_4, and C_2H_6 with good mass balances. A mechanism was not proposed.
   [2] Toulene flow system. Main products were C_2H_6 and H_2CO; minor products were $(\emptyset CH_2)_2$ and CH_4. Rates were calculated from the rate of change of $(C_2H_6 + \frac{1}{2}CH_4)$ determined gasometrically. Total decomposition of $C_2H_5O \longrightarrow CH_3 + CH_2O$ was observed.
   [4] The combined results of [1], [2], and [3] when plotted together in the Arrhenius form gave the reported values.

Reaction: di-*n*-Propyl peroxide

$$nC_3H_7OOnC_3H_7 \text{ (I)} \longrightarrow 2[n\text{-}C_3H_7O\cdot] \text{ (II)}$$

	I	II
$\Delta H^\circ_{f(298)}$	-56.9	-9.7
$S^\circ_{(298)}$	112.2	75.3
$C^\circ_{p(298)}$	40.2	19.0
$C^\circ_{p(500)}$	59.3	29.2

$\Delta S^\circ = 38.4$ g/mole
$\Delta H^\circ = 37.5$ kcal/mole
$\Delta C^\circ_p = -2.2$ g/mole
$\langle \overline{\Delta C^\circ_p} \simeq -1.5 \rangle$ g/mole

log A	E	log k_T (434)	Conditions	System	Surface	References
15.3	36.5	-3.08	420–448 °K 0.4–2.6	static	none	[1] E. J. Harris, Proc. Roy. Soc. (L) **A173**, 126 (1939).

Preferred:
   log $k = 15.6 - 37.2/\theta$.

Comments: The reaction kinetics give $[\Delta H^\circ_f (C_3H_7O\cdot) = -10.0$ kcal/mole]. $k_{rec} = 10^{8.9}$ l/mole-sec is obtained from A and the reaction entropy.

Experimental

[1] Rates were followed by pressure measurements with $P_f/P_o \simeq 2.5$. Products identified were C_3H_7OH, C_2H_5CHO, CH_2O, C_4H_{10}, CO, and H_2. No mechanism was proposed.

Reaction: di-*t*-Butyl peroxide

$$(CH_3)_3COOC(CH_3)_3 \ (I) \longrightarrow 2[(CH_3)_3CO\cdot] \ (II)$$

$\Delta H^\circ_{f(298)}$	-80.5	$[-21.5]$
$S^\circ_{(298)}$	112.1	76.5
$C^\circ_{p(298)}$	52.5	25.7
$C^\circ_{p(500)}$	79.5	38.5

$\Delta S^\circ = 40.9$ g/mole
$\Delta H^\circ = 37.5$ kcal/mole
$\Delta C^\circ_p = -1.1$ g/mole
$\langle \overline{\Delta C^\circ_p} = -1.5 \rangle$ g/mole

log A	E	log k_T (423)	Conditions	System	Surface	References
16.51	39.1	-3.70	413–433 °K 50–380 torr	static	none	[1] J. H. Raley, F. F. Rust, and W. E. Vaughan, J. Am. Chem. Soc. **70**, 88 (1948).
14.74	36.0 ± 1	-3.86	(a) 393–553 °K 10–112 torr	static		[2] J. Murawski, J. S. Roberts, and
[13.3	34.0]	-4.27	(b) 724–832 °K 0.03–3.5 torr	flow	none	M. Szwarc, J. Chem. Phys. **19**, 698 (1951); M. Szwarc and J. S. Roberts, J. Chem. Phys. **18**, 561 (1950).
16.4	38.7	-3.60				[3] A. R. Blake and K. O. Kutschke, Can. J. Chem. **37**, 1462 (1959).
15.6	37.4	-3.73	403–443 °K 27–130 torr			[4] L. Batt and S. W. Benson, J. Chem. Phys. **36**, 895 (1962).
15 ± 1	38 ± 2	-4.64	402–427 °K $\sim$ 20 torr			[5] R. K. Burton and D. H. Volman, J. Chem. Phys. **20**, 25 (1952).
15.85	38	-3.79	553–623 °K $P_T \simeq 5$–13 torr	flow		[6] F. P. Lossing and A. W. Tickner, J. Chem. Phys. **20**, 907 (1952).

Preferred:
   $\log k = 15.6 - 37.4/\theta$.

Comments: From the entropy one obtains $k_{rec} = 10^{8.3}$ l/mole·sec. Additivity relations give $\Delta H^\circ_f(t\mathrm{BuO}\cdot) = -21.3$ kcal/mole.

(Continued)

Experimental

[1] Rates were followed manometrically using stoichiometry of $1 \mapsto 3$. Analysis by M. S. Products were CH_3COCH_3, H_4, C_2H_6 and $CH_3COC_2H_5$.

[2] Pyrolysis in static and flow systems was performed in the presence of toluene. Rate constants were calculated two ways and agreed within 20 percent. Parameters obtained assuming that all benzyl radicals produced by methyl-H-abstraction dimerized are in brackets. Other parameters were obtained by assuming all benzyl radicals terminated with methyl radicals.

[3] Rate constants were based on the rate of $CH_4 + C_3H_6$ formation.

[4] Rates by pressure change. Total analysis of products by G.L.C. gave a stoichiometry of $1 \rightarrow 3$. The authors demonstrated that temperature gradients resulting from the reaction exothermicity could lead to appreciable error in the Arrhenius parameters.

[5] Analysis by M.S. of quenched reaction mixture.

[6] Analysis by M.S. The carrier gas was He.

Reaction: Diethyanoyl peroxide (diacetyl peroxide)

$$CH_3\overset{\overset{O}{\|}}{C}OO\overset{\overset{O}{\|}}{C}CH_3 \text{ (I)} \longrightarrow 2[(CH_3COO \cdot)] \text{ (II)}$$

	I	II
$\Delta H^\circ_{f(298)}$	-129.2	(-49.7)
$S^\circ_{(298)}$	101.4	67.4
$C^\circ_{p(298)}$	31.6	13.9
$C^\circ_{p(500)}$	42	19.7

$\Delta S^\circ = 33.4$ g/mole
$\Delta H^\circ = 29.8$ kcal/mole
$\Delta C^\circ_p = -3.8$ g/mole
$\langle \overline{\Delta C^\circ_p} = -3.5 \rangle_{298-410}$

log A	E	log k_T (413)	Conditions	System	Surface	References
14.25	29.5	-1.37	363–463 °K 0.03–0.156 torr	flow		[1] A. Rembaum and M. Szwarc, J. Am. Chem. Soc. **76**, 5975 (1954).

Preferred:
    $\log k = 14.25 - 29.5/\theta$.

Comments: The reaction entropy and observed A-factor give $k_{rec} = 10^{8.7}$ 1/mole-sec. The heat of formation of the acetoxy radical gives $DH^\circ(CH_3CO_2-H) = 106$ kcal/mole.

Experimental

[1] Toluene and benzene carriers employed. Standard gas analysis for CO_2, C_2H_6, and CH_4 confirmed the stoichiometry: $\left(\dfrac{CO_2}{C_2H_6 + CH_4}\right) = 2$. This is consistent with

$$(CH_3COO)_2 \longrightarrow 2CO_2 + C_2H_6; \quad (CH_3COO)_2 + \emptyset CH_3 \longrightarrow 2CO_2 + CH_4 + \tfrac{1}{2}(\emptyset CH_2)_2 \cdot$$

Rate constants were independent of P_T, $\delta P_{reactant}$, and t_c.

Reaction: Dipropanoyl peroxide (dipropionyl peroxide)

$$\underset{\substack{\| \\ O}}{C_2H_5C}\underset{\substack{\| \\ O}}{OOC}C_2H_5 \ (I) \longrightarrow 2[C_2H_5CO_2 \cdot] \ (II)$$

	I	II
$\Delta H^\circ_{f(298)}$	-139.8	$[-55.0]$
$S^\circ_{(298)}$	119.4	76.4
$C^\circ_{p(298)}$	45.0	20.6
$C^\circ_{p(500)}$	57.6	27.5

$\Delta S^\circ = 33.4$ g/mole
$\Delta H^\circ = 29.8$ kcal/mole
$\Delta C^\circ_p = -3.8$ g/mole

log A	E	log k_T (418)	Conditions	System	Surface	References
14.4	30.0	-1.27	373–464 °K 7.6–20.6 torr	flow	————	[1] A. Rembaum and M. Szwarc, J. Chem. Phys. **23,** 909 (1955).

Preferred:
   log $k = 14.4 - 30.0/\theta$.

Comments: A recombination rate constant of $k_{rec} = 10^{8.8}$ l/mole-sec is obtained from the reaction entropy and the observed A-factor.

Experimental

[1] Toluene and benzene carriers were employed. Rates were equated to $\frac{1}{2}$ the rate of formation of CO_2. Other products: C_2H_4 (8 percent), C_2H_6 (8.6 percent), n-C_4H_{10} (80.9 percent). First-order rate constants were independent of t_c, T, and $\delta P_{reactant}$.

Reaction: Dibutanoyl peroxide (dibutyrl peroxide)

$$CH_3CH_2CH_2\overset{\overset{O}{\|}}{C}O{-}O\overset{\overset{O}{\|}}{C}\bar{C}_3H_7-n \text{ (I)} \rightarrow 2[CH_3(CH_2)_2CO_2\cdot] \text{ (II)}$$

	I	II
$\Delta H^\circ_{f(298)}$	-152.0	$[-61.1]$
$S^\circ_{(298)}$	137.4	85.4
$C^\circ_{p(298)}$	58.4	27.3

$\Delta S^\circ = 33.4$ g/mole
$\Delta H^\circ = 29.8$ kcal/mole
$\Delta C^\circ_p = -3.8$ g/mole
$\langle \Delta C^\circ_p = -3.5 \rangle_{298-T}$ g/mole

log A	E	log k_T (411)	Conditions	System	Surface	References
14.28	29.6	-1.46	370–452 °K	flow		[1] A. Rembaum and M. Szwarc, J. Chem. Phys. **23**, 909 (1955).

Preferred:
log $k = 14.3 - 29.6/\theta$.* Rate constant is reliable.

Comments: A recombination rate constant of $10^{8.7}$ l/mole-sec is obtained from the reaction entropy and th observed A-factor.

Experimental

[1] Benzene and toluene carrier gases were employed. Stoichiometry of 1 peroxide $\longrightarrow 2CO_2$ was confirmed ar the decomposition rate was obtained from the CO_2 formation rate. Rate constants were independent of t_c, P_T, ar $\delta P_{reactant}$.

---

*The isobutyl peroxide decomposition has been studied in solution of isooctane, J. Smid and M. Szwarc, J. Chem. Phys. **29**, 4: (1958). Rate constants were consistent with log $k = 14.45 - 27.3/\theta$.

Reaction: Methyl hydroperoxide

$$CH_3OOH\ (I) \xrightarrow{(M)} CH_3O\ (II) + OH\ (III)$$

		I	II	III
$\Delta H^\circ_{f(298)}$		-32.0	(3.9)	8.0
$S^\circ_{(298)}$		65.8	54.6	43.9
$C^\circ_{p(298)}$		14.7	8.4	7.1

$\Delta S^\circ = 32.7$ g/mole
$\Delta H^\circ = 43.9$ kcal/mole
$\Delta C^\circ_p = 0.8$ g/mole

$\log A$	E	$\log k_T$ (608)	Conditions	System	Surface	References
11 ± 2	32 ± 5	(-0.5)	565–651 °K 22–49 torr	flow	(see below)	[1] A. D. Kirk, Can. J. Chem. **43**, 2236 (1965).

Preferred:
   $\log k = 14.9 - 43.0/\theta$. Rate constants may be slightly low.

Comments: The rate constants in the middle of the range are reasonable, but (as the author was aware) the thermodynamics coupled with a normal recombination rate ($k_{rec} \simeq 10^{9.6}$ l/mole-sec) predict considerably higher Arrhenius parameters.
   Higher values have, in fact, been observed in solution and are preferred.

Experimental

   [1] Toluene carrier technique was employed. Rates were obtained from the iodimetric titration of the remaining hydroperoxide and the ratio of $(\emptyset CH_2)_2/(CH_3O_2)$. Products analysed by G.L.C.: major product, $(\emptyset CH_2)_2$; minor products, CH_4, CO, O_2, and C_2H_6. Heterogeneous decomposition in the low-temperature range was indicated since the ratio of $(\emptyset CH_2)_2/\Delta(CH_3OOH)$ varied from 0.05–0.80 from 290–380 °C.

Reaction: Ethyl hydroperoxide

$$C_2H_5OOH \text{ (I)} \longrightarrow C_2H_5O\cdot \text{ (II)} + \cdot OH \text{ (III)}$$

	I	II	III
$\Delta H^\circ_{f(298)}$	-40.5	-4.9	8.0
$S^\circ_{(298)}$	76.3	65.9	43.9
$C^\circ_{p(298)}$	19.7	14.0	7.1

$\Delta S^\circ = 33.5$ g/mole
$\Delta H^\circ = 43.6$ kcal/mole
$\Delta C^\circ_p = 1.4$ g/mole

log A	E	log k_T (605)	Conditions	System	Surface	References
13.4	37.7	-0.22	553–653 °K	flow	(considerable)	[1] A. D. Kirk and J. H. Knox, Trans. Faraday Soc. **56,** 1296 (1960); A. D. Kirk and J. H. Knox, Proc. Chem. Soc., 384 (1959).

Preferred:
    log $k = 15.35 - 43.0/\theta$. Rate constants are probably reliable.

Comments: It is unlikely that the cross recombination is unimportant in this system. The thermodynamics indicate that the Arrhenius parameters are low. Assuming that the rate constants are valid, one obtains the preferred values and $k_{rec} = 10^{9.7}$ l/mole-sec.

Experimental

[1] Benzene carrier technique. Rate constants were calculated on the basis of the amount of diphenyl produced and the amount of peroxide decomposed, assuming further that all hydroxyl radicals formed abstracted H from benzene and that all methyl radicals combined to form ethane. Decomposition of the peroxide also occurred heterogeneously. Since the biphenyl yields were essentially invariant to the (S/V) ratios, they were used as a measure of the homogeneous bond fission reaction.

Mechanism:

$$ROOH \xrightarrow{1} RO\cdot + \cdot OH$$
$$\cdot OH + \varnothing H \xrightarrow{2} H_2O + \varnothing\cdot$$
$$RO\cdot \xrightarrow{3} CH_3\cdot + R_1COR_2$$
$$CH_3\cdot + CH_3\cdot \xrightarrow{4} C_2H_6$$
$$\varnothing\cdot + \varnothing\cdot \xrightarrow{5} \varnothing_2.$$

Reaction: Isopropyl hydroperoxide

$$(CH_3)_2CHOOH \ (I) \longrightarrow (CH_3)_2CHO\cdot \ (II) + \cdot OH \ (III)$$

	I	II	III
$\Delta H^\circ_{f(298)}$	-47.4	(-12.4)	8.0
$S^\circ_{(298)}$	82.6	72.2	43.9
$C^\circ_{p(298)}$	25.7	20.0	7.1

$\Delta S^\circ = 33.5$ g/mole
$\Delta H^\circ = 43.0$ kcal/mole
$\Delta C^\circ_p = 1.4$ g/mole

log A	E	log k_T (603)	Conditions	System	Surface	References
15.2	40.0	0.70	553–653 °K	flow	(appreciable)	[1] A. D. Kirk and J. H. Knox, Trans. Faraday Soc. **56**, 1296 (1960);
*14.5	40.7	-0.25				*A. D. Kirk and J. H. Knox, Proc. Chem. Soc., 384 (1959).

Preferred:
Estimate log $k = 15.5 - 43.0/\theta$.

Comments: The kinetics [1]* and thermodynamics agree within experimental error. A recombination rate constant of $k_{rec} = 10^{9.9}$ l/mole-sec is obtained from the reaction entropy and preferred A-factor.

Experimental

[1] Benzene carrier technique was employed.

---

*See comments on ethyl hydroperoxide.

Reaction: *t*-Butyl hydroperoxide

$$(CH_3)_3COOH \text{ (I)} \longrightarrow (CH_3)_3CO\cdot \text{ (II)} + \cdot OH \text{ (III)}$$

	I	II	III
$\Delta H^\circ_{f(298)}$	-56.5	-21.3	8.0
$S^\circ_{(298)}$	86.4	76.5	43.9
$C^\circ_{p(298)}$	31.4	25.7	7.1

$\Delta S^\circ = 34.0$ g/mole
$\Delta H^\circ = 43.2$ kcal/mole
$\Delta C^\circ_p = 1.4$ g/mole

log A	E	log k_T (*603*)	Conditions	System	Surface	References
13.7	37.8	0.00	553–653 °K	flow	(appreciable)	[1] A. D. Kirk and J. H. Knox, Trans. Faraday Soc. **56**, 1296 (1960); A. D. Kirk and J. H. Knox, Proc. Chem. Soc. 384 (1959).

Preferred:
  log $k = 15.6 - 43.0/\theta$.

Comments: Rate constant parameters have been scaled to give agreement with the ΔH°_f. This is consistent with a recombination rate constant of $k_{rec} = 10^{9.9}$ l/mole-sec. The preferred value is also consistent with the rates found in dilute, non-polar solvents, R. R. Hiatt and K. C. Irwin, J. Org. Chem. **33**, 1436 (1968).

Experimental

[1] Benzene carrier technique. See comments on ethyl hydroperoxide.

Reaction: Hydrazine

$$NH_2-NH_2 \text{ (I)} \longrightarrow 2[NH_2\cdot] \text{ (II)}$$

	I	II
$\Delta H^\circ_{f(298)}$	22.8	**(46.0)
$S^\circ_{(298)}$	56.9	48.2
$C^\circ_{p(298)}$	12.2	8.1
$C^\circ_{p(1000)}$	23.0	10.0

$\Delta S^\circ = 39.5$ g/mole
$\Delta H^\circ = (69.2)$ kcal/mole
$\Delta C^\circ_p = 4.0$ g/mole
$\Delta C^\circ_p = -3.0$ g/mole

log A	E	log k_T (980)	Conditions	System	Surfaces	References
12.6	60	−0:78	903–1053 °K $\delta P \simeq 0.05–.78$ $P_T = 5–15$ mm Hg	flow	none* (90% hetero-geneous)	[1] M. Szwarc, J. Chem. Phys. **17**, 505 (1949); Proc. Roy. Soc. **A198**, 267 (1949).
11.7	54.4	−0.43	887–1034 °K 6.7–28.5 mm Hg	flow	none	[2] J. A. Kerr, R. C. Sekhar, and A. F. Trotman-Dickenson, J. Chem. Soc. 3217 (1963); J. A. Kerr, A. F. Trotman-Dickenson and M. Wolter, J. Chem. Soc. 3584 (1964).
13.0	54.0	+0.96	970–1120 °K 2–9 atm 1% in Ar	S.P.Sh.		[3] E. T. McHale, B. E. Knox, and H. P. Palmer, Tenth Symposium International on Combustion, Butterworths Publication, London, 1965, p. 341.

Preferred:
Suspect. log $k = 16.5-70.8/\theta$**. Reference [3] rate scaled.

Comments: This reaction is certainly in its second-order region for all studies reported. Pressure dependence for the reaction has been demonstrated by several workers in addition to those referenced here (see M. Gilbert, Comb. & Flames **2**, 149 (1958); R. W. Diesen, J. Chem. Phys. **39**, 2121 (1963)).

The best heat of formation for $(NH_2\cdot)$ consistent with the kinetics of all of the hydrazine and amine decompositions, assuming that the rate constant parameters reported are correct, is $\Delta H^\circ_f (NH_2\cdot) = 41.0$

(Continued)

---

*A decomposition into N_2 and H_2 was also observed which was strongly affected by the (S/V)ratio.
**Preferred parameters for this reaction (and the other similar studies) have been calculated on the basis of assumed recombination rate constants. (The analysis is discussed in detail in section V–8.0).

Hydrazine *(Continued)*

kcal/mole. However, the recombination rate constants calculated for these reactions from the reported A-factors and estimated reaction entropies are anomolously low and very difficult to believe. In addition, the bond (N—H) dissociation energy in ammonia, using 41.0 kcal/mole for the NH_2 heat of formation is the same as the first (C—H) bond energy in methane (i.e., 104 kcal/mole), which does not make too much sense.

It seems very likely that the usual problem with the toluene carrier technique (i.e., "low" activation energies, probably due to a combination of induced decomposition and surface catalysis), is showing up in this and the other hydrazine and amine studies. If such is the case, the activation energies and A-factors for all studies should be higher.

Experimental

[1] Toluene carrier technique. Rates were based on dibenzyl formation.

[2] Toluene carrier technique . Heterogeneous decomposition observed and corrections made to the rate. Reaction rates were strongly pressure dependent indicating that the reaction was well into its falloff region. The parameters reported are for $P_T \simeq 14.5$ mm Hg.

[3] There was no internal standard employed in the S.P.Sh. tube experiments. The ratio of $(NH_3/N_2) \simeq 2.15$ and indicates some chain reaction. Parameters reported were estimates for the high-pressure region reaction.

Reaction: Methylhydrazine

$$CH_3NHNH_2 \text{ (I)} \longrightarrow CH_3NH \cdot \text{(II)} + \cdot NH_2 \text{ (III)}$$

	I	II	III
$\Delta H^\circ_{f(298)}$	22.2	(41.7)	(46.0)
$S^\circ_{(298)}$	66.9	58.2	48.2
$C^\circ_{p(298)}$	17.1	11.6	8.1
$C^\circ_{p(1000)}$	34.6	24.2	10.0

$\Delta S^\circ = 39.5$ g/mole
$\Delta H^\circ = (65.5)$ kcal/mole
$\Delta C^\circ_p = 2.6$ g/mole
$\Delta C^\circ_p = -0.4$ g/mole

log A	E	log k_T (805)	Conditions	System	Surface	References
13.19	51.9	−0.90	746–862 °K $\delta P = 0.2$–1.2 mm Hg $P_T \simeq 10$–15 mm Hg	flow	none	[1] J. A. Kerr, R. C. Sekhar, and A. F. Trotman-Dickenson, J. Chem. Soc. 3217 (1963).

Preferred:
   log $k = 16.7 - 64.8/\theta$.

Comments: Arrhenius parameters are suspect. Rate constants are probably reliable, although pressure falloff may have been important. (See hydrazine decomposition and section V–8.0.)

Experimental

[1] Toluene carrier technique. Rates were based on the production of ammonia. A heterogeneous decomposition into CH_4, H_2, and N_2 was also observed. Homogeneous products were CH_4, H_2, NH_3, and $(\emptyset CH_2)_2$.

Reaction: 1,1-Dimethylhydrazine

$$(CH_3)_2NNH_2 \ (I) \longrightarrow (CH_3)_2N \cdot \ (II) + \cdot NH_2 \ (III)$$

	I	II	III
$\Delta H^\circ_{f(298)}$	20.4	(37.4)	(46.0)
$S^\circ_{(298)}$	71.8	65.4	48.4
$C^\circ_{p(298)}$	23.5	16.1	8.1
$C^\circ_{p(1000)}$	47.8	35.1	10.1

$\Delta S^\circ = \ \ 42.0$ g/mole
$\Delta H^\circ = \ \ 63.0$ kcal/mole
$\Delta C^\circ_p = \ \ \ \ 0.7$ g/mole
$\Delta C^\circ_p = -2.6$ g/mole

log A	E	log k_T (770)	Conditions	System	Surface	References
13.2	49.6	−0.88	709–831 °K $P_T = 10$–15 mm Hg	flow	none	[1] J. A. Kerr, R. C. Sekhar and A. F. Trotman-Dickenson, J. Chem. Soc. 3217 (1963).

Preferred:
Suspect. Estimate, log $k = 16.9 - 62.7/\theta$ (see below).

Comments: Arrhenius parameters are low. Rate constants are probably reliable. (See hydrazine decomposition and section V–8.0.)

Experimental

[1] Toulene carrier technique. Rates were based on ammonia formation. Dimethylamine was not observed as a product. This implies that the $(CH_3)_2N \cdot$ did not abstract hydrogen from toluene.

Reaction: Benzylamine (phenylaminomethane)

$$\text{ØCH}_2\text{—NH}_2 \text{ (I)} \longrightarrow \text{ØCH}_2 \cdot \text{ (II)} + \cdot \text{NH}_2 \text{ (III)}$$

	I	II	III
$\Delta H^\circ_{f(298)}$	21.0	45.0	(46.0)
$S^\circ_{(298)}$	87.6	75.3	48.2
$C^\circ_{p(298)}$	30.1	25.6	8.1
$C^\circ_{p(1000)}$	70.1	60.6	10.0

$\Delta S^\circ = 35.9$ g/mole
$\Delta H^\circ = 70.0$ kcal/mole
$\Delta C^\circ_p = 3.6$ g/mole
$\Delta C^\circ_p = 0.5$ g/mole

log A	E	log k_T (945)	Conditions	System	Surface	References
12.8	59	−0.85	923–1073 $P_T = 7$–15 mm Hg	flow	none	[1] M. Szwarc, J. Chem. Phys. **17**, 505 (1949); Proc. Roy. Soc. **A198**, 285 (1949).
13.0	59.8	−0.83	829–1061 °K	flow		[2] J. A. Kerr, R. C. Sekhar, and A. F. Trotman-Dickenson, J. Chem. Soc. 3217 (1963).

Preferred:
   log $k = 15.3$–69.8/θ.

Comments: Reported parameters are suspect. (See discussion on the hydrazine decomposition and section V–8.0.)

Experimental

[1] Toluene carrier technique. $\Delta(\text{NH}_3) = (\text{ØCH}_2)_2$. Rate was based on the ammonia production.
[2] Toluene carrier technique. Rates were based on ammonia formation. Product identifications by G.L.C.

Reaction: N-Methylbenzylamine

$$\text{ØCH}_2\text{NHCH}_3 \text{ (I)} \longrightarrow \text{ØCH}_2\cdot \text{ (II)} + \cdot\text{NHCH}_3 \text{ (III)}$$

	I	II	III
$\Delta H^\circ_{f(298)}$	21.5	45.0	(41.7)
$S^\circ_{(298)}$	94.8	75.3	58.2
$C^\circ_{p(298)}$	34.8	25.2	11.6
$C^\circ_{p(1000)}$	83.4	60.6	24.2

$\Delta S^\circ = 38.7$ g/mole
$\Delta H^\circ = (65.2)$ kcal/mole
$\Delta C^\circ_p = 2.0$ g/mole
$\Delta C^\circ_p = 1.4$ g/mole

log A	E	log k_T (875)	Conditions	System	Surface	References
12.86	57.7	−1.55	819–936 °K $P_T \simeq 15$ mm Hg.	flow		[1] J. A. Kerr, R. C. Sekhar, and A. F. Trotman-Dickenson, J. Chem. Soc. 3217 (1963).

Preferred:
    log $k = 15.7 - 69.0/\theta$.

Comments: Rate constants are probably reliable. The Arrhenius parameters are suspect. (See discussion on the hydrazine decomposition and also section V–8.0.)

Experimental

[1] Toluene carrier technique. Rates based on formation of (CH_3NH_2).

Reaction: Phenylhydrazine

$$\text{ØNHNH}_2 \text{ (I)} \longrightarrow \text{ØNH} \text{ (II)} + \cdot\text{NH}_2 \text{ (III)}$$

	I	II	III
$\Delta H^\circ_{f(298)}$	50.3	(55.0)	(46.0)
$S^\circ_{(298)}$	87.0	76.3	48.2
$C^\circ_{p(298)}$	30.9	25.2	8.1
$C^\circ_{p(800)}$	63.1	51.2	9.3

$\Delta S^\circ = 37.5$ g/mole
$\Delta H^\circ = 50.7$ kcal/mole
$\Delta C^\circ_p = 2.4$ g/mole
$\Delta C^\circ_p = -2.6$ g/mole

log A	E	log k_T (655)	Conditions	System	Surface	References
11.8	40.0	−1.55	600–712 °K	flow		[1] J. A. Kerr, Margaret Walter, and A. F. Trotman-Dickenson, J. Chem. Soc. 3584 (1964).

Preferred:
   $\log k = 15.5 - 51.1/\theta$.

Comments: Arrhenius parameters are highly suspect. Rate constants are probably reliable. (See discussion on the hydrazine decomposition, section V–8.0.)

Experimental

[1] Aniline carrier technique. Rate constants based on ammonia formation. (See methylaniline for the mechanism.)

Reaction: N-Methylaniline

$$\text{ØNHCH}_3 \text{ (I)} \longrightarrow \text{Ø}\dot{\text{N}}\text{H (II)} + \dot{\text{C}}\text{H}_3 \text{ (III)}$$

	I	II	III
$\Delta H^\circ_{f(298)}$	20.7	(55.0)	34.0
$S^\circ_{(298)}$	86.2	76.3	46.4
$C^\circ_{p(298)}$	30.9	25.5	8.3
$C^\circ_{p(1000)}$	74.5	56.8	14.4

$\Delta S^\circ = 36.5$ g/mole
$\Delta H^\circ = (68.3)$ kcal/mole
$\Delta C^\circ_p = 2.9$ g/mole
$\Delta C^\circ_p = -3.3$ g/mole

log A	E	log k_T (880)	Conditions	System	Surface	References
13.4	60.0	-1.50	812–949 °K $P_T = 7$–12.2 mm Hg	flow	none	[1] G. L. Estelban, J. A. Kerr and A. F. Trotman-Dickenson, J. Chem. Soc. 3879 (1963)

Preferred:
   log $k = 15.3$–$67.7/\theta$.

Comments: Arrhenius parameters are suspect. The rate constants are probably reliable. (See discussio
on the hydrazine decomposition and section V–8.0.)

Experimental

[1] Aniline carrier technique. Rate constants were based on the methane formation. Mechanism proposed:

$$\text{ØNH–CH}_3 \longrightarrow \text{ØNH}\cdot + \text{CH}_3\cdot$$
$$\text{CH}_3\cdot + \text{ØNH}_2 \longrightarrow \text{CH}_4 + \text{Ø}\dot{\text{N}}\text{H}$$
$$2\text{Ø}\dot{\text{N}}\text{H} \longrightarrow (\text{ØNH}_2)_2.$$

Reaction: NN-Dimethylaniline

$$\text{Ø N(CH}_3)_2 \text{ (I)} \longrightarrow \text{Ø\.{N}CH}_3 \text{ (II)} + \text{CH}_3 \cdot \text{ (III)}$$

	I	II	III
$\Delta H^\circ_{f(298)}$	*(22.7)	[53.5]	34.0
$S^\circ_{(298)}$	92.0	84.1	46.4
$C^\circ_{p(298)}$	36.2	31.1	8.3
$C^\circ_{p(1000)}$	85.0	70.3	14.4

$\Delta S^\circ = \ \ 37.4$ g/mole
$\Delta H^\circ = $ *(65.1) kcal/mole
$\Delta C^\circ_p = \ \ \ 0.9$ g/mole
$\Delta C^\circ_p = -0.3$ g/mole

log A	E	log k_T (870)	Conditions	System	Surface	References
12.9	57.0	−1.10	825–954 °K $P_T=6$–12 mm Hg	flow		[1] J. A. Kerr, Margaret Walter, and A. F. Trotman-Dickenson, J. Chem. Soc. 3584 (1964)

Preferred:
  log $k = 15.0 - 65.2/\theta$.

Comments: Arrhenius parameters are suspect. Rate constants are probably reliable. (See hydrazine decomposition and section V−8.0.)

Experimental

[1] Aniline carrier technique. Rate constants were based on the CH_4 formation (see methylaniline).

---

*The group values in the aryl amines do not look right. A better value for the reactant heat of formation is probably ΔH°_f (ØN(CH$_3$)$_2$) $=18.8$ kcal/mole. This would give ΔH°_f (Ø\.{N}CH$_3$) $\simeq 49.6$ kcal/mole.

Reaction: Azomethane

$$CH_3N{=}NCH_3 \text{ (I)} \longrightarrow CH_3\cdot \text{ (II)} + \cdot N{=}NCH_3 \text{ (III)}$$

	I	II	III
$\Delta H^\circ_{f(298)}$	43.8	34.0	*[50.9]
$S^\circ_{(298)}$	71.0	46.4	65.0
$C^\circ_{p(298)}$	20.1	8.3	13.6
$C^\circ_{p(800)}$	35.9	12.7	23.0

$\Delta S^\circ = 39.6$ g/mole
$\Delta H^\circ = (52.5)^*$ kcal/mole
$\Delta C^\circ_p = 1.9$ g/mole
$\Delta C^\circ_p = -0.9$ g/mole
$\langle \Delta C^\circ_p \simeq 0.5 \rangle$

log A	E	log k_T (575)	Conditions	System	Surface	References
16.5	52.5	−3.45	552–600 °K 36–435 mm Hg	static	none	[1] H. C. Ramsperger, J. Am. Chem. Soc. **49**, 912 (1927).
14.2	46	−3.28	663–723 °K ($P_T \simeq 15$ mm Hg)	flow		[2] M. Page, H.O. Pritchard, and A. F. Trotman-Dickenson, J. Chem. Soc., 3878 (1953).
15.7	51.2	−3.76	502–594 °K 0.2–800 mm Hg (130–170 mm propylene)	static		[3] C. Steel and A. F. Trotman-Dickenson, J. Chem. Soc., 975 (1959).
(16.5)	(53.3)	−3.76		shock		[4] G. Chiltz, C. F. Aten, Jr., and S. H. Bauer, J. Phys. Chem. **66**, 1426 (1962).
17.3	55.4	−3.76	523–573 °K 164 mm Hg			[5] W. Forst and O. K. Rice, Can. J. Chem. **41**, 562 (1963).
14.5	49.4	−4.28	1.06 mm Hg (pressure dependence)			
15.9	50.2	−2.70	563–583 °K 1.2–120 mm Hg (100)	static		[6] O. K. Rice and D. V. Sickman, J. Chem. Phys. **4**, 242 (1936).

(Continued)

See sections V–7.0 and V–4.1–c.

(*590*)

16.5	52.5	−2.95	563–613 °K (100–140 mm Hg)	static	[7] H. A. Taylor and F. P. Jahn, J. Chem. Phys. **7**, 470 (1939).

Preferred:

$\log k = 16.5 - 52.5/\theta$;

$k_{rec} = 10^{9.4}$ l/mole-sec.

Experimental

[1] Rates were obtained from pressure-time measurements. Products were found to be principally C_2H_6 and N_2 with small yields of CH_4, C_2H_4, and H_2 also obtained.

[2] Toluene carrier technique. Rates based on N_2 formation.

[3] Rate by N_2 Production. High-pressure reaction indicated the presence of short chains. Propylene increased the rate at low pressures (due to pressure dependence of rate constant), but inhibited the reaction at high pressures by stopping chains.

[4] Rates based on N_2 formation. Points scattered, but fell in the middle of the extrapolated Arrhenius plots of [3] and [5].

[5] Rates obtained from N_2 formation. Inhibition by NO, ethylene, and propylene indicated the importance of short chains in the pure azomethane decomposition. Pressure dependence of the rate constant below 20 mm Hg was also demonstrated.

[6] Rate constants were obtained from the pressure-time curves with an assumed stoichiometry of 1–2. Reported parameters are the extrapolated values for P since the reaction was found to be in the falloff over the entire pressure range.

[7] Rates were followed manometrically with $P_f/P_o = 2.15$.

Reaction: Hexafluoroazomethane (perfluoroazomethane)

$$CF_3N{=}NCF_3 \text{ (I)} \begin{array}{c} \xrightarrow{\;a\;} CF_3 \cdot \text{(III)} + CF_3N{=}N \cdot \text{(IV)} \\ \xrightarrow{\;b\;} N_2 \text{ (II)} + 2CF_3 \cdot \end{array}$$

	I	II	III	IV
$\Delta H^\circ_{f(298)}$	[−245.6]	0	−112.5	[−77.1]
$S^\circ_{(298)}$	95.2	45.8	62.4	77.1
$C^\circ_{p(298)}$	33.1	7.0	12.2	20.1

a

$\Delta S^\circ = 44.3$ g/mole
$\Delta H^\circ = 56.0$ kcal/mole
$\Delta C^\circ_p = -0.8$ g/mole

Path	log A	E	log k_T (605)	Conditions	System	Surface	References
a	16.2	55.2	−3.74	572–634 °K 0.3–73 mm Hg (63 mm Hg)	static	none	[1] E. Leventhal, C. R. Simonds, and C. Steel, Can. J. Chem. **40**, 930 (1962).
b	13.9	48.5	−3.62	690–769 °K 1% of $P_T = 13$ mm Hg	flow		[2] D. Clark and H. O. Pritchard, J. Chem. Soc. 2136 (1956).

Preferred:
    log $k_a = 16.2-55.2/\theta$.

Comments: In view of the large uncertainties associated with the estimated thermodynamics, the agreement with the observed kinetics is quite satisfactory. Clearly path a is the principal reaction pathway. $k_{rec} = 10^{8.6}$ l/mole-sec.

Experimental

[1] Rate by N_2 formation. The rate constants were found to be pressure dependent below 60 mm Hg. The only non-condensable product formed was N_2; the $CF_3 \cdot$ evidently added to the reactant.

[2] Toluene carrier technique. Rates were based on the N_2 formation. The low Arrhenius parameters of [2] may in part be attributed to the pressure dependence of the decomposition below 60 mm Hg.

Reaction: Azoethane

$$C_2H_5N{=}NC_2H_5 \ (I) \longrightarrow C_2H_5 \cdot (II) + \cdot N{=}NC_2H_5 \ (III)$$

	I	II	III
$\Delta H^\circ_{f(298)}$	32.2	25.7	(56.5)*
$S^\circ_{(298)}$	90.0	57.8	73.7
$C^\circ_{p(298)}$	31.4	12.1	19.5
$C^\circ_{p(500)}$	44.7	17.7	26.1

$\Delta S^\circ = 41.5$ g/mole
$\Delta H^\circ = 50.0^*$ kcal/mole
$\Delta C^\circ_p = 0.2$ g/mole
$\Delta C^\circ_p = -0.9$ g/mole

log A	E	log k_T (575)	Conditions	System	Surface	References
16.0	51.2	−3.46	551–600 °K 0.3–708 mm Hg	flow		[1] H. C. Ramsperger, J. Am. Chem. Soc. **49,** 912 (1927).
15.7	48.5	−2.73	533–583 °K	static		[2] W. D. Clark, Ph. D. thesis, University of Oregon (1958).

Preferred:
  log $k = 16.3 - 50.0/\theta$.

Comments: $k_{rec} = 10^{9.0}$ l/mole-sec using the preferred A-factor and reaction entropy. (See section V–7.0 and azomethane.)

Experimental

[1] Rates were obtained from pressure measurements.
[2] Mass spectrometric study particularly concerned with the pressure falloff of the rate constants.

*See section V–7.0.

Reaction: Azobutane

$$C_4H_9N{=}NC_4H_9 \text{ (I)} \longrightarrow C_4H_9N{=}N \cdot \text{(II)} + n\text{-}C_4H_9 \cdot \text{(III)}$$

	I	II	III
$\Delta H^\circ_{f(298)}$	12.4	46.6*	15.7
$S^\circ_{(298)}$	127.6	92.5	76.6
$C^\circ_{p(298)}$	53.4	30.5	23.1

$\Delta S^\circ = \quad 41.5$ g/mole
$\Delta H^\circ = {}^*(49.9)$ kcal/mole
$\Delta C^\circ_p = \quad 0.2$ g/mole

log A	E	log k_T (565)	Conditions	System	Surface	References
17.71	53.2	−2.87	473–673 °K 0.9% in He	flow		[1] A. U. Blackham and N. L. Eatough, J. Am. Chem. Soc. **84**, 2922 (1962).

Preferred:
    log $k = 16.5 - 50.0/\theta$.

Comments: From the preferred A-factor and reaction entropy one obtains $k_{rec} = 10^{9.2 {+0.2 \atop -0.3}}$ l/mole-sec.

Experimental

[1] Both He and H_2 carriers were employed. (E_{act} in He are reported here.) Rates were based on N_2 formation. Analysis of the gaseous products was made by G.L.C. Products in decreasing order of importance were C_2H_4, C_4H_{10}, C_3H_8, C_2H_6, and CH_4.

---

*See section V–7.0.

Reaction: 1,1′-Azoisobutane

$$CH_3CH(CH_3)CH_2N{=}NCH_2CHCH(CH_3)_2 \text{ (I)} \longrightarrow (CH_3)_2CHCH_2N{=}N \cdot \text{ (II)} + (CH_3)_2CH\dot{C}H_2 \text{ (III)}$$

	I	II	III
$\Delta H^\circ_{f(298)}$	9.8	45.3*	13.7
$S^\circ_{(298)}$	122.2	89.8	73.9
$C^\circ_{p(298)}$	52.8	30.2	22.9

$\Delta S^\circ = $ 41.5 g/mole
$\Delta H^\circ = $ *(49.2) kcal/mole
$\Delta C^\circ_p = $ 0.3 g/mole

log A	E	log k_T (575)	Conditions	System	Surface	References
16.23	49.0	−2.39	473–673 °K 1–4% in He	flow	none	[1] A. U. Blackham and N. L. Eatough, J. Am. Chem. Soc. **84**, 2922 (1962).

Preferred:
   log $k = 16.23 - 49.0/\theta$.

Comments: This is consistent with a recombination rate constant of $k_{rec} = 10^{9.0^{+0.2}_{-0.3}}$ l/mole-sec (i.e., using reaction entropy and reported A-factor).

Experimental

   [1] Helium carrier. Rates were based on N_2 formation. Products analyzed by G.L.C. (in decreasing order of importance) were C_3H_6, N_2, C_2H_6, CH_4, i-C_4H_{10}, i-C_4H_8, and C_3H_8.

---

*See section V–7.0.

Reaction: Azoisopropane

$$(CH_3)_2CHN{=\!=}NCH(CH_3)_2 \ (I) \longrightarrow (CH_3)_2CH \cdot (II) + \cdot N{=\!=}NCH(CH_3)_2 \ (III)$$

	I	II	III
		$(V=4.0)$	
$\Delta H^\circ_{f(298)}$	21.0	17.6	(50.9)*
$S^\circ_{(298)}$	103.3	65.4	80.4
$C^\circ_{p(298)}$	41.9	17.7	24.7

$\Delta S^\circ = \ 42.5$ g/mole
$\Delta H^\circ = \ ^*47.5$ kcal/mole
$\Delta C^\circ_p = \ \ 0.5$ g/mole

log A	E	log k_T (545)	Conditions	System	Surface	References
13.75	40.9	−2.66	523–563 °K 0.25–46 mm Hg	static	none	[1] H. C. Ramsperger, Proc. Nat. Acad. Sci. 1: 849 (1927); J. Am. Chem Soc. **50**, 714 (1928).

Preferred:
$\log k = 16.4 - 47.5/\theta.$

Comments: From the preferred A-factor and reaction entropy, one obtains $k_{rec} = 10^{8.5\pm0.3}$ l/mole-sec (see sections V–4.1–c and V–7.0).

Experimental

[1] Rates were obtained from pressure measurements. Slight falloff in the rate constants was observed at the lower pressures. Reaction products were believed to be principally n-hexane and N_2 with smaller amounts of propylene and propane.

---

*See section V–7.0.

$$CH_3CH_2CH(CH_3)N=Nsec\text{-}butyl\ (I) \longrightarrow CH_3CH_2CH(CH_3)N=N\cdot (II) + CH_3CH_2\dot{C}HCH_3\ (III)$$

	I	II	III
$\Delta H^\circ_{f(298)}$	12.6	*46.7	12.6
$S^\circ_{(298)}$	122.1	89.8	76.2
$C^\circ_{p(298)}$	52.7	30.2	23.2

$\Delta S^\circ = 43.9$ g/mole
$\Delta H^\circ = *(46.7)$ kcal/mole
$\Delta C^\circ_p = 0.5$ g/mole

log A	E	log k_T (580)	Conditions	System	Surface	References
17.28	48.4	−0.96	539–618 °K (4.1% in He)	flow		[1] A. U. Blackham and N. L. Eatough, J. Am. Chem. Soc. **84**, 2922 (1962).

Preferred:
    $\log k = 16.6 - 46.7/\theta$.

Comments: From the reaction entropy and the preferred A-factor one obtains $k_{rec} \simeq 10^{8.4}$ l/mole-sec.

Experimental

[1] Rates based on N_2 formation. Products by G.L.C. analysis were found to be (in decreasing order of importance) C_3H_6, N_2, $n\text{-}C_4H_{10}$, C_2H_6, $1\text{-}C_4H_8$, $2\text{-}C_4H_8$, and CH_4.

---

*See section V–7.0.

Reaction: Methyl isopropyl diimide

$$CH_3N{=}NCH(CH_3)_2 \text{ (I)} \xrightarrow[b]{a} CH_3 \cdot \text{(IV)} + \cdot N{=}NCH(CH_3)_2 \text{ (V)}$$
$$\xrightarrow{b} CH_3N{=}N \cdot \text{(II)} + \cdot CH(CH_3)_2 \text{ (III)}$$

	I	II	III	IV	V
$\Delta H^\circ_{f(298)}$	32.2	(62.3)*	17.6	34.0	(50.7)*
$S^\circ_{(298)}$	88.6	64.2	65.4	46.4	80.4
$C^\circ_{p(298)}$	31.1	14.0	17.7	8.3	24.7

	a	b
$\Delta S^\circ =$	38.2	41.0 g/mole
$\Delta H^\circ =$	*(52.5)	*(47.7) kcal/mole
$\Delta C^\circ_p =$	1.9	0.6 g/mole

Path	log A	E	log k_T (575)	Conditions	System	Surface	References
b	15.45	47.5	−2.72	543–605 °K (0.1–90 mm Hg)	static		[1] H. C. Ramsperger, J. A. Chem. Soc. **51**, 2134 (1929); reviewed by L. S. Kassel, *Kinetics of Homogeneous Gas Reactions*, Chemical Catalog Co., Inc., New York (1932).

Preferred:
Suspect. The rate constant looks too low. We feel parameters should be like azoisopropane and prefe. log $k = 16.4$–$47.5/\theta$.

Comments: Path b is favored by almost 5 kcal/mole in E and about 3 g/mole in the activation entropy. Reaction a should therefore not compete.

Experimental

[1] Rates were followed manometrically. Falloff was observed over the entire pressure range and $k\infty$ values were obtained by extrapolation of plots of $1/k$ versus $1/p$.

---

*See section V–7.0.

Reaction: 2,2'-Azoisobutane

$$(CH_3)_3CN{=}NtBu \; (I) \longrightarrow tBuN{=}N \cdot (II) + (CH_3)_3C \cdot (III)$$

	I	II	III $(V=4.0)$
$\Delta H^\circ_{f(298)}$	7.4	$(44.1)^*$	6.8
$S^\circ_{(298)}$	109.3	83.4	70.3
$C^\circ_{p(298)}$	53.9	30.8	22.6

$\Delta S^\circ = \;\; 44.4$ g/mole
$\Delta H^\circ = *(43.5)$ kcal/mole
$\Delta C^\circ_p = \; -0.5$ g/mole

$\log A$	E	$\log k_T$ (575)	Conditions	System	Surface	References
16.34	42.8	+0.07	453–493 °K 22 mm Hg	static	none	[1] J. B. Levy and B. K. W. Copeland, J. Am. Chem. Soc. **82**, 5314 (1960).
17.15	43.0	+0.81	473–673 °K 1–4% in He	flow		[2] A. U. Blackham and N. L. Eatough, J. Am. Chem. Soc. **84**, 2922 (1962).

Preferred:
   $\log k = 17.15 - 43.5/\theta$.

Comments: There is an appreciable discrepancy between the rates of the studies. We prefer the most recent values. From the A-factor and the reaction entropy, one obtains $k_{rec} \simeq 10^{8.9}$ l/mole-sec.

Experimental

[1] Rates were obtained manometrically. M.S. analysis showed that N_2 and $i\text{-}C_4H_{10}$ were the main products (i.e., $\simeq 90$ percent). The effect of NO and isobutene on the reaction was investigated.

[2] Rates were based on N_2 production. Products by G.L.C. analysis (in decreasing order of importance) were N_2, $i\text{-}C_4H_8$, and $i\text{-}C_4H_{10}$.

---

*See section V–7.0.

Reaction: Azotoluene

$$\text{ØCH}_2\text{N}\!=\!\text{NCH}_2\text{Ø} \text{ (I)} \longrightarrow \text{ØCH}_2\overset{|}{\text{N}}\!=\!\text{N}\cdot \text{ (II)} + \cdot\text{CH}_2\text{Ø} \text{ (III)}$$

	I	II	III
$\Delta H^\circ_{f(298)}$	98.0	90.4	45.0
$S^\circ_{(298)}$	129.6	94.7	75.3
$C^\circ_{p(298)}$	56.7	32.2	25.6

$\Delta S^\circ = 40.4$ g/mole
$\Delta H^\circ = 37.4$ kcal/mole
$\Delta C^\circ_p = 1.1$ g/mole

log A	E	log k_T (485)	Conditions	System	Surface	References
14.1	35.0	−1.67	455–511 °K 2.5–11 mm Hg	static	none	[1] G. Williams and A. S. C. Lawrence, Proc. Roy. Soc. (L) **A156,** 455 (1936).

Preferred:
  log $k = 15.3-37.6/\theta$; $k_{\text{rec}} = 10^{7.7}$ l/mole-sec.

Comments: Heats of formation have been obtained from additivity values and are based on azomethane and the $(\text{CH}_3\text{N}\!=\!\text{N}\cdot)$ radical. Scaled parameters look reasonable and are therefore preferred; however, uncertainties do exist in the estimates (see V–7.0).

Experimental

[1] Rates were followed manometrically. The formation of N_2 and dibenzyl was not quantitative $(P_f/P_o) = 1.77$. Products were not analyzed.

Reaction: Tetramethyltetrazine

$$(CH_3)_2NN\!\!=\!\!NN(CH_3)_2 \text{ (I)} \xrightarrow{\ \ a\ \ } 2[(CH_3)_2N\cdot]\text{ (II)} + N_2 \text{ (IV)}$$
$$\xrightarrow{\ \ b\ \ } (CH_3)_2NN\!\!=\!\!N\cdot \text{ (III)} + \cdot N(CH_3)_2$$

	I	II	III	IV
$\Delta H^\circ_{f(298)}$	(72.3)	(37.4)	[ ]	0
$S^\circ_{(298)}$	103.2	65.4	(77.0)	45.8
$C^\circ_{p(298)}$	39.9	16.1	24.3	7.0

	a	b	
$\Delta S^\circ =$	73.4	39.2	g/mole
$\Delta H^\circ =$	(2.5)	( )	kcal/mole
$\Delta C^\circ_p =$	-0.7	0.5	g/mole

Path	log A	E	log k_T (450)	Conditions	System	Surface	References
*	11.4	31.9±3	-4.10	399–421 °K	static		[1] J. S. Watson and A. J. Waring, Can. J. Chem. **38**, 298 (1960).
*	14.4	36.1	-3.13	466–539 °K 6–12 mm Hg	flow	none	[2] B. G. Gowenlock and P. P. Jones, Can. J. Chem. **41**, 1911 (1963); Chem. and Industry, 557 (1960).

Preferred:
  log $k_b = 14.4 - 36.1/\theta$.

Comments: The A-factor seems low by about a factor of 10, since from the observed A-factor and reaction entropy one obtains $k_{rec} \simeq 10^{7.4}$ l/mole-sec.

Experimental

[1] Rates were based on N_2 formation.
[2] SF_6-CO_2 and NO-CO_2 carriers were employed. Rates were based on the amount of N_2 produced and upon G.L.C. analysis of the liquid products. Principal products were N_2 and tetramethylhydrazine (in the SF_6-CO_2 carrier) and dimethylnitrosoamine (in the NO-CO_2 carrier).

---

*Multiple bond rupture, path a, is not likely and path b is preferred. (See section V-7.0.)

Reaction: Tetraethyltetrazine

$$(C_2H_5)_2NN{=}NN(C_2H_5)_2 \ (I) \longrightarrow (C_2H_5)_2N\cdot (II) + \cdot N{=}NN(C_2H_5)_2 \ (III)$$

	I	II	III
$\Delta H^\circ_{f(298)}$	49.1	(24.2)	[ ]
$S^\circ_{(298)}$	141	84.2	96.0
$C^\circ_{p(298)}$	62	27.1	35.3

$\Delta S^\circ = 39.2$ g/mole
$\Delta H^\circ =$
$\Delta C^\circ_p = 0.4$ g/mole

log A	E	log k_T (490)	Conditions	System	Surface	References
13.7	33.0	−1.02	471–508 °K 9–29 mm Hg	flow	none	[1] B. G. Gowenlock, P. P. Jones, and D. R. Snelling, Can. J. Chem. **41**, 1911 (1963).

Preferred:
log $k = 14.4 - 34.5/\theta$ (see below).

Comments: Tetramethyltetrazine should have a higher activation energy than tetraethyltetrazine by about gauche repulsions (i.e., ~ 1.6 kcal/mole); therefore the two studies are in fair internal agreement. The A-factor of both reactions, however, seems low.

Experimental

[1] Rates were based on N_2 formation. G.L.C., M.S., and spectroscopic analysis on the products were employed Products included diethylamine, diethylmethylamine, ethylithlideneamine, tetraethylhydrazine and 1,3,5-triethyl hexahydro-s-triazene.

Reaction: Propanonitrile (ethyl cyanide)

$$C_2H_5CN\ (I) \begin{cases} \xrightarrow{\ a\ } CH_3\cdot(II) + \cdot CH_2CN\ (III) \\ \xrightarrow{\ b\ } H_2 + CH_2{=}CHCN \\ \xrightarrow{\ c\ } HCN + C_2H_4 \end{cases}$$

	I	II	III
$\Delta H^\circ_{f(298)}$	12.7	34.0	[51.1]
$S^\circ_{(298)}$	68.4	46.5	58.5
$C^\circ_{p(298)}$	17.3	8.8	10.4
$C^\circ_{p(1000)}$	36.1	14.4	20.7

$\Delta S^\circ \quad = 36.6$ g/mole
$\Delta H^\circ \quad = 72.4$ kcal/mole
$\Delta C^\circ_p \quad = \quad 1.9$ g/mole
$\Delta C^\circ_{p(1000)} = -1.0$ g/mole

Path	log A	E	log k_T	Conditions	System	Surface	References
a	14.1	72.7		958–1038 °K 6.5–15.8 mm Hg	flow	none	[1] M. Hunt, J. A. Kerr, and A. F. Trotman-Dickenson, J. Chem. Soc. 5074 (1965)

See molecular eliminations for discussion of paths b and c.)

Preferred:
tentative, log $k_a = 14.1 - 72.7/\theta$.

Comments: The kinetics give a resonance energy of about 12.5 kcal/mole for ($\cdot CH_2CN$) and a recombination rate constant of $k_{rec} = 10^{7.9}$ l/mole·sec. The latter seems low and may be indicative of a pressure falloff. A calculation of the $M_{1/2}$ (the middle of the pressure falloff region) with $n = 16$ and an assumed $A_\infty = 10^{15.3}$ sec^{-1} gives $M_{1/2} \simeq 5$ mm Hg.

Note that if $\cdot CH_2CN$ resonance is of the order of 10 kcal, then $\varnothing\dot{N}H + EtCN \longrightarrow \varnothing NH_2 + CH_3\dot{C}HCN$ is close to thermoneutral. Free radical chain decomposition of ethylcyanide would then be likely.

Experimental

[1] Aniline carrier technique. *Path a:* Rates were based on the methane formation. *Path b:* Rates were based on the H_2 production. *Path c:* Rates were based on the C_2H_4 formation. Analysis was performed by standard gasometric techniques and checked by G.L.C. The mechanism assumed was,

$$C_2H_5CN \longrightarrow CH_3\cdot + \cdot CH_2CN$$

$$CH_3\cdot + \varnothing NH_2 \longrightarrow CH_4 + \varnothing\dot{N}H$$

$$2\varnothing\dot{N}H \longrightarrow (\varnothing NH)_2 \text{ or polymer}$$
$$C_2H_5CN \longrightarrow H_2 + CH_2{=}CHCN$$

$$C_2H_5CN \longrightarrow C_2H_4 + HCN$$

Reaction: 2,2-Dimethylpropanonitrile (*t*-butyl cyanide)

$$t\text{-BuCN (I)} \longrightarrow CH_3 \cdot (II) + (CH_3)_2\dot{C}CN \text{ (III)}$$

	I	II	III
$\Delta H^\circ_{f(298)}$	−2.0	34.0	[33.8]
$S^\circ_{(298)}$	76.6	46.5	74.0
$C^\circ_{p(298)}$	28.2	8.8	21.3
$C^\circ_{p(1000)}$	60.0	14.4	44.6

$\Delta S^\circ \quad = 43.9$ g/mole
$\Delta H^\circ \quad = 69.8$ kcal/mole
$\Delta C^\circ_p \quad = 1.9$ g/mole
$\Delta C^\circ_{p(1000)} = -1.0$ g/mole

log A	E	log k_T (900)	Conditions	System	Surface	References
15.16	70.2	−1.89	875–925 °K 8.6–12.0 mm Hg	flow	none	[1] M. Hunt, J. A. Kerr and A. F. Trotman-Dickenson, J. Chem. Soc. 5074 (1965).

Preferred:
log $k = 15.16 - 70.2/\theta$.

Comments: If the kinetics are taken as correct, the heat of formation of the radical in brackets is obtained. This is consistent with a resonance energy of 10.6 kcal/mole. From the reaction entropy a recombination rate constant of $k_{rec} = 10^{7.4}$ l/mole-sec is obtained.

Experimental

[1] Aniline carrier technique. Rates were based on CH_4 formation. Appreciable yields of H_2 were tentatively ascribed to the decomposition of the cyano radical,

$$(CH_3)_2\dot{C}CN \longrightarrow CH_2 = C \overset{CN}{\underset{CH_3}{\diagup\diagdown}} + H\cdot$$

Otherwise the mechanism assumed was the usual free radical non-chain path to products (see ethanonitrile).

Reaction: 2-Methyl-2-phenylpropanonitrile (cumyl cyanide)

	I	II	III
$\Delta H^\circ_{f(298)}$	28.5	[54.4]	34.0
$S^\circ_{(298)}$	99.9	91.0	46.5
$C^\circ_{p(298)}$	43.1	35.0	8.8
$C^\circ_{p(1000)}$	93.8	78.6	14.4

ΔS° $= 37.6$ g/mole
ΔH° $= 59.9$ kcal/mole
ΔC°_p $= 0.7$ g/mole
$\Delta C^\circ_{p(1000)} = -0.8$ g/mole

log A	E	log k_T (845)	Conditions	System	Surface	References
12.3	54.1	−1.69	794–897 °K 5.3–13.7 mm Hg	flow	none	[1] M. Hunt, J. A. Kerr and A. F. Trotman-Dickenson, J. Chem. Soc. 5074 (1965).

Preferred:
log $k = 13.8 - 59.9/\theta$.

Comments: Preferred parameters are based on the reaction entropy and a recombination rate constant of $k_{rec} \cong 10^{7.4}$ l/mole-sec (i.e., this is the recombination rate constant found for the reverse of the t-butyl benzene reaction). The heat of formation of the cyano radical in brackets is then calculated and suggests a total resonance energy of 22.1 kcal/mole. This is close to the sum of the benzyl and cyano resonance energies (i.e., $\simeq 13.5 + 10.6 = 24.1$ kcal/mole).

Experimental

[1] Aniline carrier technique. Rates were based on CH_4 production. Since the A-factor was relatively low, the authors suggested that the CH_4 formation could arise from a four-center molecular elimination reaction rather than the bond-breaking process indicated above.* Appreciable yields of hydrogen were again observed whose origin could not be determined.

---

*The proposed molecular elimination of methane is not considered here to be reasonable; it would involve pentavalent carbon in the transition state.

Reaction: Nitritomethane (methyl nitrite)

$$CH_3ONO \ (I) \longrightarrow CH_3O \cdot \ (II) + NO \ (III)$$

	I	II	III
$\Delta H^\circ_{f(298)}$	-15.6	3.9	21.6
$S^\circ_{(298)}$	72.3	54.6	50.3
$C^\circ_{p(298)}$	15.4	8.4	7.1

$\Delta S^\circ = 32.6$ g/mole
$\Delta H^\circ = 41.1$ kcal/mole
$\Delta C^\circ_p = 0.1$ g/mole

log A	E	log k_T (485)	Conditions	System	Surface	References
13.2	36.4	-3.20	463–513 °K 5.2⟶51.4 mm Hg	static	< 5%	[1] E. W. R. Steacie and G. T. Shaw, Proc. Roy. Soc. **A146**, 388 (1934).
13.1	36.1	-3.17	483–513 °K 0.05–50 mm Hg	static		[2] E. W. R. Steacie and D. S Calder, J. Chem. Phys. **4**, 96 (1936).
*(13.0)	(36.6)	-3.49	453–513 °K	static	(none)	[3] L. Phillips, J. Chem. Soc. 3082 (1961).

Preferred:
   $\log k = 15.6 - 41.1/\theta$
   $\log k_{\exp} = 13.0 - 36.6/\theta.$**

Comments: The mechanism for nitrite (and nitrate) decompositions currently accepted, G. Baker and R Shaw, J. Chem. Soc., 6965 (1965), relates the experimental first-order rate constant to the initial (N—O split and to the recombination and disproportionation reactions of the alkoxy radical with NO (and NO_2) The mechanism proposed for nitrite:

$$RONO \underset{2}{\overset{1}{\rightleftharpoons}} RO \cdot + NO$$
$$RO \cdot + NO \overset{3}{\longrightarrow} HNO + R_{-H}O$$
$$2HNO \overset{4}{\longrightarrow} H_2O + N_2O$$
$$2RO \cdot \overset{5}{\longrightarrow} ROH + R_{-H}O$$

Steady state relations give, $k_{\exp} = \dfrac{k_1 k_3}{k_2 + k_3}$. Other studies (see Baker and Shaw for references) have obtained disproportionation to combination ratios $\left(\dfrac{k_3}{k_2}\right)$ for NO with $CH_3O \cdot (0.5)$, with $C_2H_5O \cdot (0.3)$, and with $i\text{PrO} \cdot (0.15)$. Therefore rate constants for the decompositions obtained by pressure measurement should be higher than those reported by about factors of 3–10. Although the activation energies for reaction

(Continued

---

*Originally reported as $\log A = 12.2$, $E = 34.3$.
**A very plausible explanation for the "lower than predicted" experimental parameters in this and other nitrite and nitrate decompositions is that some direct molecular elimination may also be taking place via a four-center transition state to $CH_2O + HNO$.

Nitritomethane *(Continued)*

2 and 3 are certainly low, they are not necessarily zero. The discrepancy in rates between disproportionation and recombination could arise from differences in activation energies as well as from differences in A-factors. Comparison of the observed activation energies to the reaction thermodynamics suggests that activation energy differences of $E_2 - E_3 \simeq 0\text{--}2$ kcal/mole are possible.

Rate constant analysis*: From the mechanism, $k_1 = k_{exp}\left(\dfrac{k_2 + k_3}{k_3}\right)$. We have assumed that $E_2 - E_3 = 0$.

Therefore, $A_1 = A_{exp} \times \left(\dfrac{k_2 + k_3}{k_3}\right)$. Since $E_1 = \Delta H_T^\circ$, the preferred parameters have been obtained by scaling the "corrected" reported values to the reaction enthalpy. Thus for methylnitrite ($k_{obs} = 10^{13.0 - 36.6/\theta}$):

$$A_{1(exp)} = 10^{13.0} \times 3 = 10^{13.48}.$$

$$E_1 = 41.1 \text{ kcal/mole},$$

therefore
$$A_{1(corrected)} = 10^{15.6} \text{ sec}^{-1}.$$

From this follow the rate constants and preferred parameters given above. From A and the reaction entropy one obtains $k_{-1(rec)} = 10^{9.8}$ l/mole-sec.

Experimental

[1] Rate by ΔP. Qualitative identification of CH_2O and CH_3OH as products.

[2] Rate by ΔP. Most of the study was performed in an apparent falloff region.

[3] Analysis was by I.R. of the total product mixture. M.S. and Chem. were also made. Rate constants calculated from the pressure change and those calculated from methylnitrite disappearance were in good agreement. The mechanism proposed was:

$$MeONO \underset{2}{\overset{1}{\rightleftharpoons}} MeO\cdot + NO$$

$$MeO\cdot + NO \xrightarrow{3} CH_2O + HNO$$

$$2HNO \xrightarrow{4} H_2O + N_2O$$

$$2MeO\cdot \xrightarrow{5} CH_2O + MeOH$$

The observed rate constant then was equated to, $k_{obs} = \left(\dfrac{k_1 k_3}{k_2 + k_3}\right)$.

***NOTE added in proof: *Preferred* Arrhenius parameters on the data sheets for the higher alkyl nitrites and nitrates are slightly low, as they were originally estimated on the basis of different free radical heats of formation. On the other hand, the thermodynamics given on the data sheets represent our "best" thermochemical estimates at this time. Activation energies should therefore be higher by about 1 kcal/mole, and A- factors for dissociation and recombination should be higher by about 0.5 log units.

Reaction: Nitritoethane (ethyl nitrite)

$$C_2H_5ONO \text{ (I)} \longrightarrow C_2H_5O \cdot \text{ (II)} + NO \text{ (II)}$$

	I	II	III
$\Delta H^\circ_{f(298)}$	-24.5	-4.9	21.6
$S^\circ_{(298)}$	80.6	65.9	50.3
$C^\circ_{p(298)}$	(20.4)	14.0	7.1

$\Delta S^\circ = 35.6$ g/mole
$\Delta H^\circ = 41.2$ kcal/mole
$\Delta C^\circ_p = 0.7$ g/mole

log A	E	log k_T (455)	Conditions	System	Surface	References
14.1	37.7	-4.01	484–505 °K 10–210 mm Hg	static	none	[1] E. W. R. Steacie and G. T. Shaw, J. Chem. Phys. **2**, 345 (1934).
13.8	37.5	-4.21	434–474 °K 10–50 mm Hg	static	none	[2] J. B. Levy, J. Am. Chem. Soc. **78**, 1780 (1956).

Preferred:
   log $k = 16.07 - 40.5/\theta$; $k_{rec} = 10^{9.8}$ l/mole·sec
   log $k_{exp} = 14.1 - 37.7/\theta$ (see methyl nitrite).

Experimental

[1] Rates determined from pressure changes.
[2] Rates followed by I.R. analysis for disappearance of C_2H_5ONO and appearance of CH_3CHO and N_2O. Observed that the rate of reaction in excess NO was equal to the initial rates for the pure nitrite decomposition. Mechanism proposed was:

$$C_2H_5ONO \underset{-1}{\overset{1}{\rightleftharpoons}} C_2H_5O \cdot + NO$$

$$C_2H_5O \cdot + NO \overset{2}{\longrightarrow} HNO + CH_3CHO$$

$$2HNO \overset{3}{\longrightarrow} N_2O + H_2O$$

$$C_2H_5O \cdot + HNO \overset{4}{\longrightarrow} C_2H_5OH + NO$$

where $k_{obs} = \dfrac{k_1 k_2}{k_{-1}}$.

466

ction: 1-Nitritopropane (*n*-propyl nitrite)

$$n\text{-}C_3H_7ONO \ (I) \longrightarrow n\text{-}C_3H_7O \cdot (II) + NO \ (III)$$

	I	II	III
$\Delta H^\circ_{f(298)}$	(−29.5)	−9.7	21.6
$S^\circ_{(298)}$	90.0	75.3	50.3
$C^\circ_{p(298)}$	25.9	19.5	7.1

= 35.6 g/mole
= 41.4 kcal/mole
= 0.7 g/mole

g A	E	log k_T (465)	Conditions	System	Surface	References
14.4	37.7	−3.32	443–483 °K 60–170 mm Hg	static	none	[1] E. W. R. Steacie and G. T. Shaw, J. Chem. Phys. **3**, 344 (1935).

erred:
$\log k = 16.2 - 40.2/\theta$; $k_{rec} = 10^{10.1}$ l/mole-sec
$\log k_{exp} = 14.4 - 37.7/\theta$

ments: See methyl nitrite for a discussion of the mechanism and the method of rate constant evaluation
d here.

Experimental

[1] Identified overall kinetic rate to that of the initiation step. Rates were followed manometrically.

Reaction: 2-Nitritopropane (isopropyl nitrite)

$$(CH_3)_2CHONO \ (I) \longrightarrow (CH_3)_2CHO \cdot (II) + NO \ (III)$$

	I	II	III
$\Delta H^\circ_{f(298)}$	-32.3	-12.4	21.6
$S^\circ_{(298)}$	86.9	74.4	50.3
$C^\circ_{p(298)}$	26.4	20.0	7.1

$\Delta S^\circ = 37.8$ g/mole
$\Delta H^\circ = 41.5$ kcal/mole
$\Delta C^\circ_p = \ 0.7$ g/mole

log A	E	log k_T (465)	Conditions	System	Surface	References
14.1	37.0	-3.30	443–483 °K 100–227 mm Hg	static	none	[1] E. W. R. Steacie and G. T. Shaw, Proc. R Soc **A151**, 685 (193 E. W. R. Steacie and S. Katz, J. Chem. Phys. **5**, 125 (1937).

Preferred:
   log $k = 16.5 - 40.2/\theta$; $k_{rec} = 10^{9.9}$ l/mole-sec
   log $k_{exp} = 14.1 - 37.0/\theta$ (see methyl nitrite).

Comments: For references to the mechanism of the reaction and the method of the rate constant evalua used here, see methyl nitrite.

Experimental

[1] Rates were followed manometrically.

ction: 1-Nitritobutane (*n*-butyl nitrite)

$$n\text{-}C_4H_9ONO \ (I) \longrightarrow n\text{-}C_4H_9O \cdot \ (II) + NO \ (III)$$

	I	II	III
$\Delta H^\circ_{f(298)}$	-34.5	-14.7	21.6
$S^\circ_{(298)}$	99.8	84.3	50.3
$C^\circ_{p(298)}$	31.4	25.0	7.1

= 35.6 g/mole
= 41.4 kcal/mole
= 0.7 g/mole

g A	E	log k_T (465)	Conditions	System	Surface	References
14.48	37.0	-2.92	443–485 °K 50–400 mm Hg	static	none	[1] E. W. R. Steacie and W. McF. Smith, J. Chem. Phys. **4**, 504 (1936).

erred:
log $k = 16.3 - 40.5/\theta$; $k_{rec} = 10^{10.1}$ l/mole-sec
log $k_{exp} = 14.48 - 37.0/\theta$ (see methyl nitrite).

ments: See methyl nitrite for a discussion of the mechanism and of the method of rate constant evaluation
d here.

Experimental

[1] Rates were followed manometrically. The system was complicated by the formation of polymeric products.

469

Reaction: Nitratomethane (methyl nitrate)

$$CH_3ONO_2 \text{ (I)} \longrightarrow C\dot{H}_3O \cdot \text{ (II)} + NO_2 \text{ (III)}$$

	I	II	III
$\Delta H^\circ_{f(298)}$	-28.6	3.9	8.1
$S^\circ_{(298)}$	75.3	54.6	57.5
$C^\circ_{p(298)}$	18.3	8.4	8.7

$\Delta S^\circ = 36.8$ g/mole
$\Delta H^\circ = 40.6$ kcal/mole
$\Delta C^\circ_p = -1.2$ g/mole

log A	E	log k_T (500)	Conditions	System	Surface	References
14.4	39.5	-2.86	483–513 °K 5–15 mm Hg	static	none	[1] A. Appin, J. Chariton, and O. Todes, Acta Physiochim., U.S.S. **5**, 655 (1936).

Preferred:

log $k = 15.5 - 39.8/\theta$; $k_{rec} = 10^{9.6}$ l/mole-sec.

For $CH_3O + NO_2$, $\dfrac{k_{disp}}{k_{rec}} \approx 0.1$ (G. Baker and R. Shaw, J. Chem. Soc. 6965 (1965)).

log $k_{exp} = 14.4 - 39.5/\theta$ (see methyl nitrite).

Comments: It is quite possible that some direct five-center molecular elimination to $CH_2O + HONO$ occurs here. (See methyl nitrite for a discussion of the mechanism and method of rate constant evaluati͏

Experimental

[1] Rates were followed manometrically. Reaction products, CH_2O, CH_3OH, and NO_2, were qualitatively identifi͏

Reaction: Nitratoethane (ethyl nitrate)

$$C_2H_5ONO_2 \, (I) \longrightarrow C_2H_5O \cdot (II) + NO_2 \, (III)$$

	I	II	III
$\Delta H^\circ_{f(298)}$	-36.7	-4.9	8.1
$S^\circ_{(298)}$	85.1	65.9	57.5
$C^\circ_{p(298)}$	(23.3)	14.0	8.7

$\Delta S^\circ = 38.3$ g/mole
$\Delta H^\circ = 39.9$ kcal/mole
$\Delta C^\circ_p = -0.6$ g/mole

log A	E	log k_T (455)	Conditions	System	Surface	References
15.8	39.9	-3.36	453–488 °K 30–50 mm Hg	static	none	[1] G. K. Adams and C. E. K. Bawn, Trans. Faraday Soc. **45**, 494 (1949).
13.86	36.0	-3.43				[2] L. Phillips, Nature **165**, 564 (1950).
16.0	39.3	-2.88	434–474 °K	static		[3] J. B. Levy, J. Am. Chem. Soc. **76**, 3254 (1954); 3790 (1954).
16.9	41.2	-2.89				
14.74	38.0	-3.51	448–482 °K 30–100 mm Hg	static		[4] F. H. Pollard, H. S. B. Marshall, and A. E. Pedler, Trans. Faraday Soc. **52**, 59 (1956).

Preferred:
log $k_1 = 16.5 - 39.4/\theta$; $k_{rec} = 10^{9.8}$ l/mole-sec.

For $C_2H_5O + NO_2$, $\dfrac{k_{disp}}{k_{rec}} = 0.46$ (G. Baker and R. Shaw, J. Chem. Soc., 6965 (1965)).

log $k_{exp} = 16.0 - 39.3/\theta$.

Comments: Agreement between the predicted and experimental kinetics tends to support exclusive initiation via the (RO—NO$_2$) bond rupture. (See methyl nitrite for a discussion of the mechanism.)

Experimental

[1] Rates were followed by pressure changes. Products identified were CH_3CHO, CO, and CO_2.

[3] Analysis by I.R. and visible absorption spectroscopy. Followed product buildup and reactant disappearance as a function of time. Found that the discrepancies between [1] and [2] resulted from calculating rate constants from different regions of the pressure-time curves. Also found that the mechanism of the decomposition was more complex than originally assumed.

[4] Rates were followed spectrophotometrically (in the UV on NO$_2$) and by pressure changes. Identified initial rates of reaction to the above bond-breaking reactions.

Reaction: 1,2-Dinitratoethane (ethylene glycol dinitrate) $\xrightarrow{\ a\ }$

1,3-Dinitratopropane (trimethylene glycol dinitrate) $\xrightarrow{\ b\ }$

1,2-Dinitratopropane (propylene glycol dinitrate) $\xrightarrow{\ c\ }$ } (product analyses were not made)

Nitroglycerine $\xrightarrow{\ d\ }$

Trimethylol-nitromethane trinitrite $\xrightarrow{\ e\ }$

$$\Delta H^\circ_{f(298)}$$

$$S^\circ_{(298)}$$

$$C^\circ_{p(298)}$$

$\Delta S^\circ =$
$\Delta H^\circ =$
$\Delta C^\circ_p =$

Path	$\log A$	E	$\log k_T$	Conditions*	System	Surface	References
a	15.9	39	$-7.14(370)$	358–378 °K	static		[1] L. Phillips, Nature **160,** 753 (1947).
b	15.2	38.1	$-7.30(370)$	358–383 °K			
c	15.2	37.4	$-7.20(365)$	353–373 °K			
d	17.1	40.3	$-7.03(365)$	348–378 °K			
e	15.3	36.4	$-6.80(360)$	348–368 °K			

Preferred:
    Reasonable as reported.

Comments: The similarity in the Arrhenius parameters to those of the methyl and ethyl nitrate decompositions indicates, similar reaction mechanisms. The high A-factors suggest exclusive initial (RO—NO₂) bond rupture.

Experimental

[1] Rate constants are those for the overall decomposition and were obtained from the pressure-time curves. Identification of the Arrhenius parameters with those of the initial (RO—NO₂) bond split was considered likely.

---

*No other conditions were specified.

Reaction: Nitromethane

$$CH_3NO_2 \; (I) \xrightarrow{\;1\;} CH_3\cdot \; (II) + NO_2 \; (III)$$

	I	II	III
$\Delta H^\circ_{f(298)}$	-17.9	34.0	8.1
$S^\circ_{(298)}$	65.8	46.1	57.3
$C^\circ_{p(298)}$	16.8	8.8	8.7

$\Delta S^\circ = 37.6$ g/mole
$\Delta H^\circ = 60.0$ kcal/mole
$\Delta C^\circ_p = 0.7$ g/mole

log A	E	log k_T (1000)	Conditions	System	Surface	References
14.6	53.6	+2.88	653–703 °K 200–400 mm Hg	static	none	[1] T. L. Cottrell, T. E. Graham, and T. J. Reid, Trans. Faraday Soc. **47**, 584 (1951).
13.6	50.6	+2.54	693–753 °K $\delta P_0 \simeq 0.06$–0.18 mm Hg	flow	none	[2] L. J. Hildebrand, Jr., and M. L. Kilpatrick, J. Chem. Phys. **19**, 381 (1951).
13.43	50.0	+2.50	as above	flow	none	[3] ibid.; J. Chem. Phys. **21**, 525 (1953).
11.4	42.8	+2.04	~ 660 °K	static	————	[4] C. Frejacques, Comp. Rend. **231**, 1061 (1950).
15.1	57	+2.64	700–1300 °K	Sh.T-study of ignition delay in O_2 + CH_3NO_2	none	[5] A. A. Borisov, S. M. Kogarko, and G. I. Skachkov, Kinetika i Kataliz. **7**, 589 (1966).
13.73	49.2	+2.98	585–613 °K 40 atm	static	————	[6] A. Makovky and T. B. Gruenwald, Trans. Faraday Soc. **55**, 952 (1959).
16.6	61±3	+3.27	553–593 °K 25–200 torr	static	none in early stages	[7] H. A. Taylor and V. V. Vesselovsky, J. Phys. Chem. **39**, 1095 (1935).

Preferred:
   log $k = 15.6 - 59.0/0.$*

(Continued)

---

*Calculated from the kinetics of the back reaction (see [4] above) and from the reaction thermochemistry.

Nitromethane (*Continued*)

Experimental

[1] Parameters were obtained from the initial rates of the pressure-time curves. Products found were NO, CO, CH_4, N_2O, H_2O, and CO_2. Product ratios were temperature independent. A fairly complex mechanism was proposed. They assumed no chain on the basis of lack of inhibition by NO. This is not a valid criterion.

[2] Rates were obtained from polarographic analysis of the undecomposed nitromethane. High initial yields of H_2CO were taken as an indication of some intramolecular reaction.

[3] Procedures as in [2]. Reproducible kinetics were obtained only after passing wet N_2 carrier through the reaction chamber prior to each run.

[4] The kinetics of the back reaction have been measured by L. Phillips and R. Shaw, Tenth Int. Symp. on Comb., 453 (1964) (Williams and Williams, Balt., Md.). They found $k_{-1} = 10^{9.2}$ l/mole-sec. This has since been confirmed by V. YaShtern, Chemical Kinetics and Chain Reactions, 286 (see p. 313), (1966), U.S.S.R. Academy of Sciences, Moscow. From these numbers and the thermochemistry, we obtain: $k_1 = 10^{15.6 - 59.0/\theta}$.

[5] A composite plot of all of the data from 600 to 1200 °K was used to obtain the Arrhenius parameters.

[6] Main products were NO, HCN, CO_2, H_2CO, and H_2O. Effects of additives (NO, NO_2, O_2, $(CH_3CO_2)_2$) were investigated. HCN yields increased with initial pressures but were inhibited by O_2. Induced free radical chain decomposition was invoked to rationalize the "low" Arrhenius parameters.

[7] Parameters obtained from one-fourth-lives. Below 400 °C these showed small inverse pressure dependence. They proposed split into $CH_3NO + O$, which has $\Delta H = 91$ kcal and thus impossibly slow. He, N_2, NO, CO_2 had no effect on t-ΔP curves. O_2 changed ΔP_∞ slightly and reduced $t_{1/4}$ slightly. $\Delta P_\infty/p_0 \sim 1.3$ in absence of O_2. Surface increases reduced $\Delta P_\infty/P_0$ to 0.92.

$$C_2H_5NO_2 \text{ (I)} \longrightarrow C_2H_5 \cdot \text{(II)} + NO_2 \text{ (I)}$$

	I	II	III
$\Delta H^\circ_{f(298)}$	-23.9	25.7	8.1
$S^\circ_{(298)}$	75.3	57.8	57.5
$C^\circ_{p(298)}$	20.0	12.1	8.7

$^\circ = 40.0$ g/mole
$^\circ = 57.7$ kcal/mole
$^\circ_p = 0.8$ g/mole

og A	E	log k_T (785)	Conditions	System	Surface	References
17.6	60.6 ± 5	$+0.72$	763–808 °K	flow		[1] K. A. Wilde, J. Phys. Chem. **61**, 385 (1957).

eferred:
    Unreliable.

mments: G. N. Spokes and S. W. Benson, using a very low-pressure–high-temperature pyrolysis technique, ve shown that the initiation steps in the pyrolysis of 1 and 2-nitro-propanes are molecular elimination of NO₂. Rate constants in the 800 to 1100 °K range coupled with the low-temperature data in the 600 to) °K range gave Arrhenius parameters which were in good agreement with the low-temperature molecular mination mechanism. Thus the mechanistic change proposed cannot be supported.

The reaction at all temperatures appears to be $C_2H_5NO_2 \longrightarrow C_2H_4 + HNO_2$; presumably a five-center mination; with $\log k = 11.75 - 43/\theta$.

Experimental

[1] Rates were based on G.L.C. analysis of the nitroethane remaining. Reaction products were HNO₂ and C₂H₄. increase in the slope of the Arrhenius equation at high temperatures led to postulation of the above initiation (R—NO₂) d rupture process.

Reaction: Nitrotrichloromethane

$$CCl_3NO_2 \; (I) \xrightarrow{a} CCl_3 \cdot (II) + \cdot NO_2 \; (III)$$
$$\xrightarrow{b} COCl_2 + NOCl$$

	I	II	III
$\Delta H^\circ_{f(298)}$	( )	18.5	8.1
$S^\circ_{(298)}$	86.2	72	57.5
$C^\circ_{p(298)}$	25.5	14.7	8.7

$\Delta S^\circ = 43.3$ g/mole
$\Delta H^\circ =$
$\Delta C^\circ_p = -0.1$ g/mole

log A	E	log k_T (425)	Conditions	System	Surface	References
15.69	37.7	−3.70	411–443 °K 60–200 mm Hg	static	none	[1] E. W. R. Steacie and W. McF. Smith, J. Chem. Phys. **6**, 145 (1938); Can. J. Re **B16**, 222 (1938).

Preferred:

Suspect as unimolecular reactions.

Comments: From the complexity of the reaction products one would not expect the reported paramet to be related simply to the bond fission reaction.

Experimental

[1] Rates were followed manometrically. The reaction products were phosgene (COCl₂, NO, NOCl, and Cl₂. The N and Cl₂ were presumably formed from the secondary decomposition of NOCl, although the amounts of NO and Cl₂ w found to be in excess of those expected from the NOCl decomposition alone.

Tetranitromethane

$$C(NO_2)_4 \longrightarrow \cdot C(NO_2)_3 + NO_2$$

$$\Delta H^\circ_{f(298)}$$

$$S^\circ_{(298)}$$

$$C^\circ_{p(298)}$$

$S^\circ =$
$H^\circ =$
$C_p =$

log A	E	log k_T	Conditions	System	Surface	References
17.53	40.88		443–506 °K $\delta P = 1.09$ torr $P_T = 1$ atm (He)	Stirred flow reactor		[1] J. M. Sullivan and A. E. Axworthy, J. Phys. Chem. **70,** 3366 (1966).

Preferred:

Reasonable.
log $k = 17.53 - 40.88/\theta$.

Comments: The A-factor is in the region expected for such a decomposition (see neopentane).

Experimental

[1] Analysis by G.L.C. On reactant. Products identified by M.S. and I.R. were NO_2, NO, N_2O, and CO_2. Mass balances were not obtained. The rate determining step was assumed to be the above bond fission. Subsequent fast, non-chain, reactions of the primary fission products were postulated.

Reaction: Ethanaldoxime (acetaldoxime)

$$CH_3CH\!\!=\!\!NOH \text{ (I)} \longrightarrow CH_3CH\!\!=\!\!N\cdot \text{ (II)} + \cdot OH \text{ (III)}$$

	I	II	III
$\Delta H^\circ_{f(298)}$	-7.3	[33.1]	8.0
$S^\circ_{(298)}$	72.4	64.6	43.9
$C^\circ_{p(298)}$	18.8	13.1	7.1

$\Delta S^\circ = 36.1$ g/mole
$\Delta H^\circ = 48.4$ kcal/mole
$\Delta C^\circ_p = 1.4$ g/mole

log A	E	log k_T (660)	Conditions	System	Surface	References
12.83	47	-2.73	603–713 °K	static	~8%	[1] G. L. Pratt and J. H. Purnell, Trans. Faraday Soc. **58**, 692 (196

Comments: Very careful study; however, the reaction is extremely complex and the interpretation ne‹ verification. The A-factor looks low by about a factor of 10. If correct, the acetaldimene radical hea‹ formation is $\Delta H^\circ_f(CH_3CH\!\!=\!\!N.) \approx 33.1$ kcal/mole. The similarity in activation energies of the acetaldoxi‹ decomposition and of the nitric and nitrous acid decompositions (i.e., 47, 49, and 47 kcal/mole respectiv‹ is probably more than fortuitous.

Experimental

[1] Rates were followed manometrically and by G.L.C. Complete mass balances were made on the follow‹ products: N_2, CO, CH_4, CO_2, N_2O, C_2H_4, C_2H_6, C_3H_6, C_3H_8, HCN, CH_3CHO, and CH_3CN. An initial slow rate (ind‹ tion period) was followed by a fast reaction. The slow reaction kinetics were tentatively equated to the above dissociat‹ (rate determining) on the basis of the thermochemistry. The mechanisms proposed were very complex. The fast react‹ was inhibited by propylene and sensitized by NO and O_2 in amounts greater than 1 percent. A four-center molec‹ elimination directly to CH_3CN and H_2O was also considered possible. On the basis of the molecular product yiel‹ this accounted for less than 25 percent of the total oxime decomposition. No reasonable mechanism could be propo‹ for the formation of CO_2, N_2, CH_3NO_2, CH_3CHO, and CO.

Reaction: Dimeric nitrosomethane

$$\underset{O}{\overset{CH_3}{N}}\!\!-\!\!\underset{CH_3}{\overset{O}{N}} \quad (I) \longrightarrow 2CH_3NO \ (II)$$

	I	II
$\Delta H^\circ_{f(298)}$	( )	17
$S^\circ_{(298)}$	79	63.5
$C^\circ_{p(298)}$	24.2	13.3

$\Delta S^\circ = 48$ g/mole
$\Delta H^\circ =$
$\Delta C^\circ_p = 2.4$ g/mole

log A	E	log k_T (390)	Conditions	System	Surface	References
13.4	23	+0.51	374–404 °K $\delta P = 10^{-3} - 10^{-4}$ mm Hg $P_T \sim 4$–8 mm Hg	flow		[1] L. Batt, B. G. Gowenlock, and J. Trotman, J. Chem. Soc. 2222 (1960).

Preferred:
Reasonable. log $k = 13.4 - 23/\theta$.

Comments: Parameters should be slightly higher if the pressure falloff is real. The activation energy reported is in good agreement with solution studies which yield $E_a = 20.9$ to 24.0 kcal/mole for a variety of dimers. (Anderson and Hammick, J. Chem. Soc. 30 (1935); Bamberger and Seligman, Ber. **36,** 685 (1903); Hammick and Lister, J. Chem. Soc. 489 (1937)).

Experimental

[1] Nitrogen carrier. Analyses were made spectrophotometrically on the *cis* dimer. Monomeric nitrosoalkanes at liquid N₂ temperatures form *cis* dimers exclusively when warmed to −78 °C. Increasing the total pressure (with N₂) increased the reaction rates by about 35 percent although perfluorocyclohexane had no accelerating effect.

Reaction: Dimeric 2-methyl-1-nitrosopropane (dimeric nitrosoisobutane)

$$(CH_3)_2CHCH_2 \begin{array}{c} \quad \quad O \\ N-N \\ O \quad \quad iBu \end{array} \quad (I) \longrightarrow 2[iBuNO] \quad (II)$$

	I	II
$\Delta H^\circ_{f(298)}$	( )	( )
$S^\circ_{(298)}$	111	79.6
$C^\circ_{p(298)}$	45.3	24.5

$\Delta S^\circ = 48.2$ g/mole
$\Delta H^\circ =$
$\Delta C^\circ_p = 3.7$ g/mole

log A	E	log k_T (390)	Conditions	System	Surface	References
14.4	25.6	+0.05	374–402 °K $\delta P \simeq 10^{-3}-10^{-4}$ torr $P_T \simeq 4$–8 torr	flow		[1] L. Batt, B. G. Gowenlock, and J. Trotman, J. Chem. Soc. 2222 (1960).

Preferred:
    Reasonable. log $k = 14.4-25.6/\theta$.

Experimental

[1] See dimeric nitrosomethane.

Reaction: Diazomethane

$$CH_2{=}N{=}N \text{ (I)} \longrightarrow CH_2: \text{ (II)} + N_2 \text{ (III)}$$

	I	II	III
$\Delta H^\circ_{f(298)}$	(71)	(90)	0
$S^\circ_{(298)}$	58.1	43.3	45.8
$C^\circ_{p(298)}$	12.6	7.5	7.0

$\Delta S^\circ = 31$ g/mole
$\Delta H^\circ = 19$ kcal/mole
$\Delta C^\circ_p = 1.9$ g/mole

log A	E	log k_T (610)	Conditions	System	Surface	References
13.0	35	+0.46	498–723 °K 25 mm Hg	static	< 10%	[1] D. W. Setzer amd B. S. Rabinovitch, Can. J. Chem. **40**, 1425 (1962).
11.9	31.75	+0.52	603–773 °K	flow		[2] P. S. Shantarovich, Doklady Akad. Nauk, S.S.S.R. **116**, 255 (1957).
12.95	32	+1.48	566–666 $\delta P = 4$–95.5 mm Hg $P_{H_2} = 151$–716 mm Hg $\delta P = 0.4$–2 mm Hg flow $P_{H_2} = 100$–400 mm Hg	static		[3] W. J. Dunning and C. C. McCain, J. Chem. Soc. (B) 68 (1966).

Preferred:
  log $k = 13.0 - 35/\theta$.

Comments: From the thermodynamics one can calculate a rate constant for methylene addition to nitrogen of log $k_{(1/\text{mole-sec})} = 8.3 - 17.2/\theta$.

Experimental

[1] Analysis by G.L.C. The experimental rate constants, given by $k_{25 \text{ mm Hg}} = 1.2 \times 10^{12} \times 10^{-34/\theta}$, were shown to be in the pressure falloff region. Parameters reported above were the estimated P_∞ values.

[3] Analysis by M.S. Decompositions performed in the presence of H_2 and Ar.

Reaction: Azidomethane (methyl azide)

$$CH_3N_3 \ (I) \longrightarrow CH_3\ddot{N} \ (II) + N_2 \ (III)$$

	I	II	III
$\Delta H^\circ_{f(298)}$	(66)	[106.2]	0
$S^\circ_{(298)}$	66.6	53.4	45.8
$C^\circ_{p(298)}$	15.9	8.5	7.0

$\Delta S^\circ = 32.6$ g/mole
$\Delta H^\circ = [40.2]$ kcal/mole
$\Delta C^\circ_p = -0.4$ g/mole

log A	E	log k_T (495)	Conditions	System	Surface	References
15.48	43.5	−3.73	473–513 °K 0.8–466 mm Hg (> 100 mm Hg)	static	none	[1] J. A. Leermakers, J. Am. Chem. Soc. **55**, 3098 (1933).

Preferred:
  Suspect.

Comments: The reaction complexities are apparent from the products formed. H-atom induced decomposition of the reactant is suggested by the presence of HN_3. Identification of the observed kinetics with the initiation step above is questionable.

Experimental

[1] Rates were followed manometrically ($P_f/P_o = 1.66$). Products were HN_3, N_2, NH_3, C_2H_6, C_2H_4 and hexamethylene tetraamine (($CH_2)_6N_4$). Other modes of scission were proposed on the basis of the products; however, the major decomposition path (i.e., ~ 75 percent) was believed to be the above. Rate constants exhibited pressure falloff below 100 mm Hg.

Reaction: Azidoethane (ethyl azide)

$$C_2H_5N_3 \text{ (I)} \longrightarrow C_2H_5N: \text{(II)} + N_2 \text{ (III)}$$

	I	II	III
$\Delta H^\circ_{f(298)}$	(59.4)	[99.6]	0
$S^\circ_{(298)}$	76	62.8	45.8
$C^\circ_{p(298)}$	21.4	14.0	7.0

$\Delta S^\circ = 32.6$ g/mole
$\Delta H^\circ = 40.2$ kcal/mole
$\Delta C^\circ_p = -0.4$ g/mole

log A	E	log k_T (495)	Conditions	System	Surface	References
14.3	39.74	-3.25	473–513 °K 0.8–195 mm Hg	static	< 10%	[1] J. A. Leermakers, J. Am. Chem. Soc. **55**, 2719 (1933).

Preferred:
  Suspect.

Comments: Obviously complex reaction; very likely with induced decomposition. (See methylazide.)

Experimental

[1] Rates were followed manometrically. Products formed were N_2, C_2H_4, C_4H_{10}, $CH_3CH{=}NH$, and HN_3. A falloff in the rate constants was observed at pressures around 60 mm Hg.

Reaction: Methanethiol (methyl mercaptan)

$$CH_3SH \ (I) \longrightarrow CH_3 \cdot \ (II) + HS \cdot \ (III)$$

	I	II	III
$\Delta H^\circ_{f(298)}$	-5.5	34.0	(35.5)
$S^\circ_{(298)}$	59.9	46.5	46.7
$C^\circ_{p(298)}$	12.1	8.8	7.1
$C^\circ_{p(1000)}$	21.4	14.4	7.3

$\Delta S^\circ \quad = 33.3$ g/mole
$\Delta H^\circ \quad = 75.0$ kcal/mole
$\Delta C^\circ_p \quad = 3.8$ g/mole
$\Delta C^\circ_{p(1000)} = 0.3$ g/mole

log A	E	log k_T (1055)	Conditions	System	Surface	References
13.48	*67±2	−0.40	1005–1102 °K $\delta P \sim 0.5$ mm Hg $P_T \simeq 12$ mm Hg		none	[1] A. H. Sehon and B. deB. Darwent, J. Am. Chem. Soc. **76**, 4806 (1954).

Preferred:
   $\log k = 15.5 - 76.6/\theta$. Rate constants are probably low.

Comments: From A and the reaction entropy one obtains $k_{rec} = 10^{9.6}$ l/mole-sec. Even this value for recombination seems low. RRK estimates indicate that the reaction could well be in its falloff region (i.e., RRK $-M_{1/2} = 3$ atm, for $n \simeq 7$). The heat of formation of (HS·) used comes from recent mass-spectrometric studies on sulfides.
   (See J. A. Kerr, Chem. Rev. **66**, 465 (1966).)

Experimental

   [1] Toluene carrier technique. Rates were calculated on the basis of the H_2S formed, which was analyzed by iodometric titration in acid solution. The products were CH_4, H_2S, H_2, and $(ØCH_2)_2$. The ratio of dibenzl to H_2S varied irregularly and at the higher temperatures appreciable decomposition of toluene also occurred. The experimental results are therefore somewhat suspect.

---

*The activation energy was calculated assuming $A = 3 \times 10^{13}$ sec^{-1}, which is equivalent to a recombination rate constant of about 10^8 l/mole-sec. This is certainly too low.

Reaction: Ethanethiol (ethyl mercaptan)

$$C_2H_5SH \ (I) \xrightarrow{\ a\ } C_2H_5 \cdot (II) + HS \cdot (III)$$
$$\xrightarrow{\ b\ } C_2H_4 \ (IV) + H_2S \ (V)$$

	I	II	III	IV	V
$\Delta H^\circ_{f(298)}$	-11.0	25.7	(35.5)	12.5	-4.8
$S^\circ_{(298)}$	70.4	57.8	46.7	52.5	49.2
$C^\circ_{p(298)}$	17.2	11.9	7.1	10.4	8.1

a

$\Delta S^\circ = 34.1$ g/mole
$\Delta H^\circ = 71.0$ kcal/mole
$\Delta C^\circ_p = 1.8$ g/mole

Path	log A	E	log k_T	Conditions	System	Surface	References
a	13.48	63 ± 1		785–938 °K $\delta P \sim 0.7$ mm Hg $P_T \sim 12$ mm Hg	flow		[1] A. H. Sehon and B. deB. Darwent, J. Am. Chem. Soc. **76**, 4806 (1954).
b	13.0	51.5 ± 3.5		(as above)		see experimental	[1]

Preferred:
   log $k_a = 15.8 - 72.2/\theta$. Rate constants in the middle of the range are probably reliable.

Comments: See molecular eliminations for path *b* evaluation. The frequency factor assumed for path *a* is undoubtedly low. Scaling to the calculated activation energy obtained from the suggested reaction enthalpy gives the preferred values. One also obtains a reasonable recombination rate constant of $k_{-a} = 10^{10.2}$ l/mole-sec.

Experimental

[1] Toluene carrier technique. (For the mechanism assumed see benzyl mercaptan.)
   Path *b* predominated at the lower temperatures since below 787°K no dibenzyl was formed and the products were exclusively C_2H_4 and H_2S. At the higher temperatures, H_2S and C_2H_4 were the major products, but H_2, CH_4, and dibenzyl were also formed. Rate constants of path *a* were equated to the production of $(H_2 + CH_4)$, and those of path *b* were obtained from $[H_2S - (H_2 + CH_4)]$. The molecular reaction appeared to be somewhat surface dependent at the lower temperatures. Rate constant parameters were deduced by assuming the frequency factors reported and calculating the activation energies from the rate constants.

485

Reaction: Phenyl methanethiol (benzyl mercaptan)

	I	II	III
$\Delta H^\circ_{f(298)}$	21.9	45.0	(35.5)
$S^\circ_{(298)}$	90.8	75.3	46.7
$C^\circ_{p(298)}$	29.9	25.6	7.1
$C^\circ_{p(298)}$	66.7	60.6	7.3

ΔS° = 31.2 g/mole
ΔH° = 58.6 kcal/mole
ΔC°_p = 2.8 g/mole
$\Delta C^\circ_{p(1000)}$ = 1.2 g/mole

$\log A$	E	$\log k_T$ (890)	Conditions	System	Surface	References
13.48	53	+0.46	760–1020 °K 0.065–1.47 mm Hg	flow	none	[1] A. H. Sehon and B. deB. Darwent, J. Am. Chem. Soc. **76**, 4806 (1954).

Preferred:
   $\log k = 15.1 - 59.7/\theta$. Rate constants in the middle of the temperature range are probably reliable.

Comments: Parameters are probably low, typical of the toluene carrier technique results. From the preferred A-factor and the reaction entropy one obtains $k_{rec} = 10^{9.7}$ l/mole-sec. This is just about the mean of the recombination rate constants for H and CH_3 with $\emptyset CH_2 \cdot$ radicals—i.e., $10^{10.5}$ l/mole-sec and $10^{9.0}$ l/mole-sec, respectively.

Experimental

[1] Toluene carrier technique. Rates were based on the H_2S production which was analyzed by iodometric titration in acid solution. Products of the reaction were principally H_2S and dibenzl with minor amounts of CH_4, H_2, and stilbene. The mechanism assumed was.

$$\emptyset CH_2SH \longrightarrow \emptyset CH_2 \cdot + SH \cdot$$

$$HS \cdot + \emptyset CH_3 \longrightarrow H_2S + \emptyset CH_2 \cdot$$

$$2\emptyset CH_2 \cdot \longrightarrow (\emptyset CH_2)_2$$

Reaction: Thioanisole (phenylmethyl sulfide)

$$\text{ØSCH}_3 \ (I) \longrightarrow \text{ØS} \cdot (II) + \text{CH}_3 \cdot (III)$$

	I	II	III
$\Delta H^\circ_{f(298)}$	23.5	[49.5]	34.0
$S^\circ_{(298)}$	87.7	76.5	46.4
$C^\circ_{p(298)}$	30.0	23.7	8.5

$\Delta S^\circ = 35.2$ g/mole
$\Delta H^\circ = 60.0$ kcal/mole
$\Delta C^\circ_p = 2.2$ g/mole

log A	E	log k_T (900)	Conditions	System	Surface	References
14.48	60.0	−0.09	823–979 °K	flow		[1] M. H. Back and A. H. Sehon, Can. J. Chem. **38**, 1076 (1960).

Preferred:
Reasonable. log $k = 14.48 - 60.0/\theta$.

Comments: This gives, from A and the reaction entropy, $k_{rec} = 10^{8.7}$ l/mole-sec (assuming $\overline{\Delta C^\circ_p} = 0$). The reported parameters, however, could be low since the ØS · radical would be expected to have a stability similar to ØCH$_2$ · and therefore participate in radical termination processes. One would expect that the rate of methane formation would be a better measure of the reaction rate.

Experimental

[1] Toluene carrier technique. Mercaptan product (ØSH) was analyzed by potentiometric titration with AgNO$_3$. Noncondensable products were analyzed by combustion over CuO at 300 °C. Major products were ØSH, CH$_4$, and (ØCH$_2$)$_2$ with smaller yields of H$_2$. Neither C$_2$H$_6$ nor CH$_3$SH were detected. Rate constants were calculated from rate of formation of thiophenol. The usual mechanism was assumed (see benzyl mercaptan).

Reaction: Methyl benzyl sulfide

$$\text{ØCH}_2\text{SCH}_3 \ (I) \longrightarrow \text{ØCH}_2 \cdot (II) + \text{CH}_3\text{S} \cdot (III)$$

	I	II	III
$\Delta H^\circ_{f(298)}$	19.0	45.0	[28.0]
$S^\circ_{(298)}$	99.5	75.3	57.2
$C^\circ_{p(298)}$	35.5	25.6	9.6
$C^\circ_{p(1000)}$	80.3	60.6	19.4

$\Delta S^\circ \quad = \ 33.0$ g/mole
$\Delta H^\circ \quad = \ 54.0$ kcal/mole
$\Delta C^\circ_p \quad = -0.3$ g/mole
$\Delta C^\circ_{p(1000)} = -0.3$ g/mole

log A	E	log k_T (830)	Conditions	System	Surface	References
13.48	51.5±2	−0.08	818–844 °K 0.1–1.3 mm Hg	flow	none	[1] E. H. Braye, A. H. Sehon, and B. de B. Darwent, J. Am. Chem. Soc. **77**, 5282 (1955).

Preferred:
log $k = 14.1 - 53.8/\theta$. Rate constants are probably reliable in the middle of the temperature range.

Comments: The preferred parameters have been obtained from fitting the A-factor to the reaction entropy and with an assumed recombination rate constant of $k_{\text{rec}} = 10^{8.8}$ l/mole-sec (i.e., an average of the recombination rate constants of $(\text{CH}_3 + \text{ØCH}_2 \cdot)$ and $(\text{C}_2\text{H}_5 \cdot + \text{ØCH}_2 \cdot)$). The heat of formation obtained for $(\text{CH}_3\text{S} \cdot)$ is that given in brackets. From an analysis of all available thermal data, Kerr suggests $\Delta H^\circ_f (\text{CH}_3\text{S} \cdot) = 30$ kcal/mole [J. A. Kerr, Chem. Revs. **66**, 465 (1077)]. This value would give an even higher activation energy than the one preferred here, which is quite likely.

Experimental

[1] Toluene carrier technique. (For the mechanism assumed, see benzyl mercaptan.) Products of the decomposition were principally CH_3SH and $(\text{ØCH}_2)_2$, with less than 17 percent H_2S and minor amounts of H_2 and CH_4. The origin of H_2S as a product was uncertain although it was thought to arise from the $\text{CH}_3\text{S}.$ radical. Rate constants were calculated from the $(\text{CH}_3\text{SH} + \text{H}_2\text{S})$ yields analyzed by standard chemical methods.

Reaction: Methanylsulfonylphenylmethane (benzyl methyl sulfone)

$$CH_3SO_2CH_2\emptyset \text{ (I)} \longrightarrow \emptyset CH_2 \cdot \text{(II)} + CH_3SO_2 \cdot \text{(III)}$$

	I	II	III
$\Delta H^\circ_{f(298)}$	-68.0	45.0	$[-63.3]$
$S^\circ_{(298)}$	104	75.3	65.6
$C^\circ_{p(298)}$	41.1	25.6	16.6
$C^\circ_{p(800)}$	84.7	54.4	28.4

$\Delta S^\circ \quad = 36.9$ g/mole
$\Delta H^\circ \quad = 49.7$ kcal/mole
$\Delta C^\circ_p \quad = 1.1$ g/mole
$\Delta C^\circ_{p(800)} = -1.9$ g/mole

log A	E	log k_T (705)	Conditions	System	Surface	References
14.52	51.25	-1.37	660–750 °K 0.34 → 0.44 mm Hg	flow	none	[1] W. K. Busfield and K. J. Ivin, Trans. Faraday Soc. **57**, 1044 (1961).

Preferred:
   log $k = 14.52 - 51.25/\theta$. (However, see dimethylsulfone.)

Comments: The kinetics are in reasonably good agreement with the thermodynamics which confirms the heat of formation of the benzyl radical and the benzyl resonance energy. A recombination rate constant of $k_{rec} = 10^{8.2}$ l/mole-sec is obtained from the reaction entropy and reported A-factor.

Experimental

[1] Toluene carrier technique. Rates were based on the iodometric titration of SO_2 produced in the subsequent decomposition of the methyl sulfonyl radical ($CH_3\dot{S}O_2 \longrightarrow CH_3 \cdot + SO_2$).

Reaction: Methanesulfonylmethane (dimethyl sulfone)

$$CH_3SO_2CH_3 \text{ (I)} \longrightarrow CH_3SO_2 \cdot \text{(II)} + CH_3 \cdot \text{(III)}$$

	I	II	III
$\Delta H^\circ_{f(298)}$	-89.9	$[-63.3]$	34
$S^\circ_{(298)}$	72.6	65.6	46.4
$C^\circ_{p(298)}$	22.3	16.6	8.3
$C^\circ_{p(800)}$	43.4	28.4	12.7

$\Delta S^\circ = 39.4$ g/mole
$\Delta H^\circ = 60.6$ kcal/mole
$\Delta C^\circ_p = 2.6$ g/mole
$\Delta C^\circ_{p(800)} = -2.3$ g/mole

log A	E	log k_T (850)	Conditions	System	Surface	References
14.33	60.6	-1.25	783–913 °K 0.2–0.7 mm Hg	flow	none	[1] W. K. Busfield and K. J. Ivin, Trans. Faraday Soc. **57**, 1044 (1961).

Preferred:
  log $k = 14.3 - 60.6/\theta$. However, see below.

Comments: From the kinetics the heat of formation of radical ($CH_3SO_2 \cdot$) in brackets is obtained. One also can calculate $k_{rec} = 10^{7.8}$ l/mole-sec. The three sulfone pyrolysis by these workers are mutually consistent. That is, the heats of formation of benzyl and allyl radicals calculated from the heat of formation of ($CH_3\dot{S}O_2$) obtained from the methyl sulfone pyrolysis are in reasonably good agreement with other determinations. However, because of the general systematic trends toward low Arrhenius parameters in the toluene carrier systems, and because of the relatively low value for the calculated recombination rate constant, the heat of formation of ($CH_3\dot{S}O_2$) should not be considered to be known with certainty. In fact, intuitively, one would be tempted to place the recombination rate constant closer to that of ($CH_3 \cdot + t$Bu$\cdot$) or about $10^{9.3}$ l/mole-sec. This would raise the heat of formation of ($CH_3SO_2 \cdot$) to about $\Delta H^\circ_f(CH_3\dot{S}O_2) \approx -58.0$ kcal/mole.

Experimental

Toluene carrier technique.
[1] Rates were based on the production of SO_2, which was determined by iodometric titration. Other products were CH_4, $CH_3CH_2\text{Ø}$, $(\text{Ø}CH_2)_2$, and small amounts of C_2H_6 (CH_4/SO_2) ratios varied randomly between 1.24 and 1.46. The fraction of $CH_3 \cdot$ radicals forming CH_4 changed from 25 percent (370 °C) up to 70 percent (600 °C). Analyses of ethylbenzene and dibenzyl were made by I.R. (qualitative) and by G.L.C. (semi quantitative). The mechanism assumed was,

$$CH_3SO_2CH_3 \longrightarrow CH_3SO_2 \cdot + CH_3 \cdot$$
$$CH_3SO_2 \cdot \longrightarrow CH_3 \cdot + SO_2$$
$$CH_3 \cdot + \text{Ø}CH_3 \longrightarrow CH_4 + \text{Ø}CH_2 \cdot$$
$$CH_3 \cdot + \text{Ø}CH_2 \cdot \longrightarrow \text{Ø}CH_2CH_3$$
$$2\text{Ø}CH_2 \cdot \longrightarrow (\text{Ø}CH_2)_2.$$

Reaction: 3-Methanesulfonyl-1-propene (allyl methyl sulfone)

$$CH_2{=}CHCH_2SO_2CH_3 \ (I) \longrightarrow CH_2{=}CHCH_2 \cdot \ (II) + CH_3SO_2 \cdot \ (III)$$

	I	II	III
$\Delta H^\circ_{f(298)}$	-73.5	38.0	$[-63.3]$
$S^\circ_{(298)}$	91.1	61.4	65.6
$C^\circ_{p(298)}$	30.5	16.8	16.6
$C^\circ_{p(800)}$	59.3	29.6	28.4

$\Delta S^\circ = 35.9$ g/mole
$\Delta H^\circ = 48.2$ kcal/mole
$\Delta C^\circ_p = 2.9$ g/mole
$\Delta C^\circ_{p(800)} = -1.3$ g/mole

$\log A$	E	$\log k_T$ (685)	Conditions	System	Surface	References
14.1	47.7	-1.12	633–733 °K 0.26–1.65 mm Hg	flow	none	[1] W. K. Busfield and K. J. Ivin, Trans. Faraday Soc. **57**, 1044 (1961).

Preferred:
$\log k = 14.1 - 47.7/\theta$. Tentatively acceptable; however, see comments on dimethyl sulfone.

Comments: With a $\overline{\Delta C^\circ_p} \simeq 1.0$ g/mole, the thermodynamics predict an activation energy of 48.6 kcal/mole. The discrepancy is within experimental error. A recombination rate constant of $k_{rec} \simeq 10^{7.8}$ l/mole-sec is obtained from the entropy and reported A-factor.

Experimental

[1] Toluene carrier technique. Rates were based on the iodometric titration of SO_2. In addition to the expected products, small amounts of diallyl and 1-butene were observed. The general reaction mechanism therefore was extended to include.

$$2CH_2{=}CHCH_2 \cdot \longrightarrow (CH_2{=}CHCH_2)_2$$

$$CH_3 \cdot + CH_2{=}CHCH_2 \cdot \longrightarrow CH_2{=}CHCH_2CH_3.$$

An expected termination product, 4-phenyl-1-butene, was not detected.

Reaction: Perfluoroethane

$$C_2F_6 \ (I) \longrightarrow 2CF_3 \cdot (II)$$

	I	II
$\Delta H^\circ_{f(298)}$	−316.8	(−112.5)
$S^\circ_{(298)}$	79.4	62.4
$C^\circ_{p(298)}$	25.4	12.2
$C^\circ_{p(1500)}$	41.4	19.1

$\Delta S^\circ \quad = 45.4$ g/mole
$\Delta H^\circ \quad = 91.8$ kcal/mole
$\Delta C^\circ_p , \quad = -1.0$ g/mole
$\Delta C^\circ_{p(1500)} = -3.2$ g/mole

log A	E	log k_T (1450)	Conditions	System	Surface	References
17.63	94.4±4	+3.40	1300–1600 °K Ar/H$_2$/C$_2$F$_6$ ~ (7500/17.4/1)	S.P. shock		[1] E. Tschouikow-Roux, J. Chem. Phys. **43**, 2251 (1965); J. Phys. Chem. **69**, 1075 (1965).

Preferred:
log $k = 17.27 - 92/\theta$.

Comments: Initiation kinetics were deduced from the reaction mechanism and depend on the activation energy of CF$_3$ + H$_2$. The author used the experimental E of this reaction. However, the reaction was measured at 500 °K and should be corrected to ~ 1450 °K. When the heat capacity correction is applied, $E_{\text{dissociation}} \simeq 92$ kcal/mole. The kinetics agree with the thermodynamics within the error limits noted. From the entropy and the reported A-factor, one obtains $k_{\text{rec}} = 10^{10.5}$ l/mole-sec. (observed $k_{\text{rec}} = 10^{10.36}$ l/mole-sec − P. B. Ayscough, J. Chem. Phys. **24**, 944 (1956).) The heat of formation of CF$_3 \cdot$ has been determined by Whittle, using competitive bromination techniques − Trans. Faraday Soc. **61**, 1182 (1965).

Experimental

[1] Analysis by G.L.C. Products were HCF$_3$ and C$_2$F$_4$. The reaction scheme proposed was quite complex, and included the following steps to explain the products:

$$C_2F_6 \longrightarrow 2CF_3 \cdot$$
$$CF_3 \cdot + H_2 \longrightarrow CF_3H + H \cdot$$
$$H \cdot + C_2F_6 \longrightarrow C_2F_5 \cdot + HF$$
$$C_2F_5 \cdot + H_2 \longrightarrow C_2F_5H + H \cdot$$
$$C_2F_5H \longrightarrow C_2F_4 + HF$$

$$CF_3H \xrightarrow{(M)} CF_2 : + HF$$
$$CF_2 : + CF_3H \longrightarrow (C_2F_5H)^* \longrightarrow C_2F_4 + HF.$$

Reaction: Perfluoropropene

$$CF_3CF{=}CF_2 \ (I) \longrightarrow C_2F_4 \ (II) + CF_2{:} \ (III)$$

	I	II	III
$\Delta H^{\circ}_{f(298)}$	(-269.0)	-155.6	-39.7
$S^{\circ}_{(298)}$	90.0	71.6	59.6
$C^{\circ}_{p(298)}$	26.4	18.4	9.1

$\Delta S^{\circ} = {}_1 41.2$ g/mole
$\Delta H^{\circ} = (73.7)$ kcal/mole
$\Delta C^{\circ}_p = 1.1$ g/mole

$\log A$	E	$\log k_T$ (885)	Conditions	System	Surface	References
13.0	≤ 75	-5.52	$823{-}948 \ ^{\circ}K$	static		[1] B. Atkinson and V. Atkinson, J. Chem. Soc., 2086 (1957).

Preferred:
Very questionable reaction.

Comments: Perhaps a more reasonable mechanism also consistent with the kinetics is

$$CF_3CF{=}CF_2 \rightleftharpoons \triangle_{F_6}; \ \triangle_{F_6} \longrightarrow C_2F_4 + CF_2{:}$$

Experimental

[1] Continuous reactant-product time curves were obtained by I.R. analysis. The mechanism assumed fit a 3/2 order production of perfluoroisobutene and was consistent with an apparent induction period in the total pressure curve.
Mechanism proposed:

$$CF_3CF{=}CF_2 \longrightarrow C_2F_4 + CF_2{:}$$

$$C_2F_4 + CF_2{:} \longrightarrow CF_3CF{=}CF_2$$

$$CF_2{:} + CF_3CF{=}CF_2 \longrightarrow (CF_3)_2C{=}CF_2$$

$$C_2F_4 + CF_3CF{=}CF_2 \longrightarrow (CF_3)_2C{=}CF_2 + CF_2{:}$$

Reaction: Perfluoro-2-methyl-1-propene (perfluoroisobutene)

$$(CF_3)_2C{=}CF_2 \text{ (I)} \longrightarrow CF_3 \cdot \text{ (II)} + CF_3\overset{|}{C}{=}CF_2 \text{ (III)}$$

	I	II	III
$\Delta H^\circ_{f(298)}$	(-380.0)	-112.5	$[-176.0]$
$S^\circ_{(298)}$	104.4	62.4	86.6
$C^\circ_{p(298)}$	34.4	12.2	23.4

$\Delta S^\circ = 44.6$ g/mole
$\Delta H^\circ = 91.5$ kcal/mole
$\Delta C^\circ_p = 1.2$ g/mole

log A	E	log k_T (1000)	Conditions	System	Surface	References
14.04	82.7	-4.04	973–1023 °K	static		[1] B. Atkinson and V. Atkinson, J. Chem. Soc., 2086 (1957).

Preferred:
   Suspect.

Comments: Arrhenius parameters are certainly low for this reaction. Also, the kinetic interpretation is complex enough to entail grave uncertainties. However, if the rate constant is accepted along with a reasonable recombination rate of $k_{rec} \simeq 10^{9.0}$ l/mole-sec, one obtains log $k = 15.9{-}91.4/\theta$ and $\Delta H^\circ_f(CF_3C\cdot{=}CF_2) = -176.0$ kcal/mole.

Experimental

[1] Products were perfluoroethane and polymer. Rates of reaction were followed by IR analyses and were shown to be first order. The mechanism proposed was

$$(CF_3)_2C{=}CF_2 \longrightarrow CF_3 \cdot + CF_3CF{=}CF.$$
$$CF_3 \cdot + (CF_3)_2C{=}CF_2 \longrightarrow C_2F_6 + CF_3CF{=}CF.$$
$$CF_3[CF{=}CF]_n + CF_3[CF{=}CF]_m \longrightarrow CF_3[CF{=}CF]_{n+m} + CF_3 \cdot$$
$$CF[CF{=}CF]_p + CF_3[CF{=}CF]_q \longrightarrow CF_3[CF{=}CF]_{p+q}CF_3 \cdot$$

The parameters reported were considered minimum values for the initial split.

Reaction: Bromomethane (methyl bromide)

$$CH_3Br \ (I) \longrightarrow CH_3 \cdot (II) + Br \cdot (III)$$

	I	II	III
$\Delta H^\circ_{f(298)}$	-9.3	34.0	26.7
$S^\circ_{(298)}$	58.3	46.5	41.8
$C^\circ_{p(298)}$	10.3	8.4	5.0
$C^\circ_{p(1000)}$	17.5	14.5	5.0

$S^\circ \quad = 30.0$ g/mole
$H^\circ \quad = 70.0$ kcal/mole
$C^\circ_p \quad = \ 3.1$ g/mole
$C^\circ_{p(1000)} = 2.0$ g/mole

log A	E	log k_T (1030)	Conditions	System	Surface	References
13.3	67.5	-1.02	977–1080 °K $\delta P_o \simeq 0.7$ mm Hg $P_T \sim 5$–20 mm Hg	flow	$< 5\%$	[1] A. H. Sehon and M. Szwarc, Proc. Roy. Soc. (L) **A209**, 110 (1951).

Preferred:
  log $k_{(minimum)} = 14.2 - 71.7/\theta$ (see below). Rate constants are probably low.

Comments: An RRK calculation with all possible oscillators active (i.e., $\sim n = 9$) indicates that for the reaction conditions reported, the CH_3Br decomposition is probably well into the pressure falloff region RRK-$M_{1/2} \simeq 20$ mm Hg). The parameters reported, then, are certainly low as the thermodynamics would suggest. If a minimum high-pressure rate constant of twice those reported is used and the parameters are scaled to agree with ΔH°_r, fairly reasonable Arrhenius values are obtained.

  The A-factor must be at least $\left(\dfrac{ekT}{h}\right)$, and $\Delta S^\ddagger \simeq 2$–4 g/mole seems quite possible for a transition state in which the (H—C—Br) bending modes have been loosened. The preferred parameters give a minimum recombination rate constant of

$$k_{rec \ (minimum)} \simeq 10^{8.8} \text{ l/mole-sec,}$$

which is still about a factor of 10 lower than one would expect.

Experimental

[1] Toluene carrier technique. Rates were calculated on the basis of the HBr formation. Ratios of $\dfrac{(\text{ØCH}_2)_2}{(\text{HBr})}$ were always less than unity and varied with temperature. The HBr rates of production increased with increasing δP_o and P_T. The usual Arrhenius plots were therefore considered unreliable and the rate constant parameters were obtained from the rate constants and *an assumed A-factor*. Mechanism proposed:

$$CH_3Br \longrightarrow CH_3 \cdot + Br \cdot$$

$$R + \text{ØCH}_3 \longrightarrow RH + \text{ØCH}_2 \cdot$$

$$2\text{ØCH}_2 \cdot \longrightarrow (\text{ØCH}_2)_2$$

Reaction: Dibromomethane (methylene dibromide)

$$CH_2Br_2 \text{ (I)} \longrightarrow CH_2Br \cdot \text{(II)} + Br \cdot \text{(III)}$$

	I	II	III
$\Delta H^\circ_{f(298)}$	( )	( )	26.7
$S^\circ_{(298)}$	70.6	60.0	41.8
$C^\circ_{p(298)}$	13.1	8.6	5.0

$\Delta S^\circ = 31.2$ g/mole
$\Delta H^\circ = ($ $)$ kcal/mole
$\Delta C^\circ_p = 0.5$ g/mole

log A	E	log k_T (970)	Conditions	System	Surface	References
13.3	62.5	−0.78	921–1021 °K $\delta P_o \sim 0.5$ mm Hg $P_T \sim 5$–20 mm Hg	flow	none	[1] A. H. Sehon and M. Szwarc, Proc. Roy. So‹ (L) **A209,** 110 (1951).

Preferred:
log $k_{min} = 14.0 - 65.6/\theta$.

Comments: Arrhenius parameters are low. Reaction is probably in the pressure falloff region. (See commen‹ on chlorobromomethane.)

Experimental

[1] Toluene carrier technique.

Reaction: Tetrabromomethane (carbon tetrabromide)

$$CBr_4 \text{ (I)} \longrightarrow CBr_3 \cdot \text{ (II)} + Br \cdot \text{ (III)}$$

	I	II	III
$\Delta H^\circ_{f(298)}$	38.0	(63.7 ± 4)	26.7
$S^\circ_{(298)}$	85.4	80.8	41.8
$C^\circ_{p(298)}$	21.8	16.1	5.0

$\Delta S^\circ = 37.2$ g/mole
$\Delta H^\circ = (52.4)$ kcal/mole
$\Delta C_p^\circ = -0.7$ g/mole

log A	E	log k_T (740)	Conditions	System	Surface	References
13.3	49.0	-1.17	687–792 °K $\delta P_o \simeq 0.5$ mm Hg $P_T \sim 5$–20 mm Hg	flow	~32%	[1] A. H. Sehon and M. Szwarc, Proc. Roy. Soc. (L) **A209**, 110 (1951).

Preferred:
   log $k_{\text{minimum}} = 14.3 - 52.4/\theta$. Rate constants may be low.

Comments: Arrhenius parameters are low. Reaction is probably in the pressure falloff region. (See comments on CH_3Br.)

Experimental

[1] Toluene carrier technique.

Reaction: Chlorobromomethane

$$CH_2ClBr \ (I) \longrightarrow \cdot CH_2Cl \ (II) + Br \cdot \ (III)$$

	I	II	III
$\Delta H^\circ_{f(298)}$	−9.0	[25.3]	26.7
$S^\circ_{(298)}$	68.6	57.0	41.8
$C^\circ_{p(298)}$	12.3	8.4	5.0

$\Delta S^\circ = 30.2$ g/mole
$\Delta H^\circ = 61 \pm 4$ kcal/mole
$\Delta C^\circ_p = 1.1$ g/mole

log A	E	log k_T (755)	Conditions	System	Surface	References
13.3	61.0	−0.66	909–1000 °K $\delta P_o \sim 0.5$ mm Hg $P_T = 5$–20 mm Hg	(flow)	none	[1] A. H. Sehon and M. Szwarc, Proc. Roy. Soc. (L) **A209,** 110 (1951).

Preferred:
    log $k_{\min} = 13.7 - 62.8/\theta$.

Comments: Arrhenius parameters are low. Reaction is probably in the pressure falloff region. (See comment on CH_3Br.)

Experimental

[1] Toluene carrier technique. Rates (based on HBr formation) were slightly total pressure dependent. A-factor was assumed. The mechanism proposed was the same as that for CH_3Br.

Reaction: Dichlorobromomethane

$$CHCl_2Br \text{ (I)} \longrightarrow CHCl_2 \cdot \text{(II)} + Br \cdot \text{(III)}$$

	I	II	III
$\Delta H^\circ_{f(298)}$	( )	( )	26.7
$S^\circ_{(298)}$	75.4	65.6	41.8
$C^\circ_{p(298)}$	16.1	11.3	5.0

$\Delta S^\circ = 32$ g/mole
$\Delta H^\circ = ($) kcal/mole
$\Delta C^\circ_p = 0.2$ g/mole

log A	E	log k_T (845)	Conditions	System	Surface	References
13.3	53.5	−0.54	800–891 °K $\delta P_o \simeq 0.5$ mm Hg $P_T \sim 5-20$ mm Hg	flow	~8%	[1] A. H. Sehon and M. Szwarc, Proc. Roy. Soc. (L) **A209**, 110 (1951)

Preferred:
    log $k_{min} = 13.7 - 55.0/\theta$.

Comments: Arrhenius parameters are low. Reaction is probably in the pressure falloff region. (See comments on CH_3Br.)

Experimental

[1] Toluene carrier technique.

Reaction: Trichlorobromomethane

$$CCl_3Br \text{ (I)} \longrightarrow CCl_3 \cdot \text{(II)} + Br \cdot \text{(III)}$$

	I	II	III
$\Delta H^\circ_{f(298)}$	-9.4	18.5	26.7
$S^\circ_{(298)}$	79.9	72	41.8
$C^\circ_{p(298)}$	20.5	14.7	5.0

$\Delta S^\circ = 33.9$ g/mole
$\Delta H^\circ = 54.6$ kcal/mole
$\Delta C^\circ_p = -0.8$ g/mole

log A	E	log k_T (770)	Conditions	System	Surface	References
13.3	50 ± 2	-0.89	718–827 °K $\delta P^\circ \simeq 0.5$ mm Hg $P_T \simeq 5$–20 mm Hg	flow	~ 11%	[1] A. H. Sehon and M. Szwarc Proc. Roy. Soc. **A209,** 110 (1951); J. Chem. Phys. **18,** 1685 (1950)

Preferred:

   log $k_{(minimum)} = 14.3 - 53.7/\theta$; log $k_{rec\,(minimum)} = 10^{9.5}$ l/mole-sec.

Comments: Reaction is in the pressure falloff region.

Experimental

[1] Toluene carrier technique. Kinetics were followed by the rate of HBr formation. The above rate constant parameters have been corrected for the heterogeneous contribution to the rate of reaction. Rate constants were total pressure dependent (i.e., a factor of 4 increase in total pressure increased the rate constants by about 20 percent at the lower temperatures and nearly 60 percent at the higher temperatures).

Reaction: Trifluorobromomethane

$$CF_3Br\ (I) \longrightarrow CF_3 \cdot (II) + Br \cdot (III)$$

	I	II	III
$\Delta H^\circ_{f(298)}$	-152.4	-112.5	26.7
$S^\circ_{(298)}$	71.2	58.8	41.8
$C^\circ_{p(298)}$	16.6	11.2	5.0

$\Delta S^\circ = 29.4$ g/mole
$\Delta H^\circ = 66.6$ kcal/mole
$\Delta C^\circ_p = -0.4$ g/mole

log A	E	log k_T (1055)	Conditions	System	Surface	References
13.3	64.5	-0.06	1021–1090 °K $\delta P \simeq 0.5$ mm Hg $P_T \sim 5$–20 mm Hg	flow	$< 5\%$	[1] A. H. Sehon and M. Szwarc, Proc. Roy. Soc. (L) **A209**, 110 (1951).

Preferred:

log $k_{minimum} = 13.7 - 66.3/\theta$; $k_{rec\ (minimum)} = 10^{9.0}$ l/mole-sec.

Comments: Arrhenius parameters are low. Reaction is probably in the pressure falloff region. (See comments on CH_3Br.)

Experimental

[1] Toluene carrier technique.

Reaction: Tribromomethane

$$CHBr_3 \ (I) \longrightarrow CHBr_2 \cdot (II) + Br \cdot (III)$$

$$\Delta H^\circ_{f(298)}$$

$$S^\circ_{(298)}$$

$$C^\circ_{p(298)}$$

$\Delta S^\circ =$
$\Delta H^\circ =$
$\Delta C^\circ_p =$

log A	E	log k_T (840)	Conditions	System	Surface	References
13.3	55.5	-1.14	786–899 °K $\delta P = 0.5$ torr $P_T = 5$–20 torr	flow	$\sim 12\%$	[1] A. H. Sehon and M. Szwarc, Proc. Roy. Soc. (L) **A209,** 110 (1951).

Preferred:
  log $k_{minimum} = 14.2 - 59.0/\theta$.
  Reported parameters are probably low.

Experimental

[1] Toluene carrier technique. (See comments on CH_3Br.)

Reaction: Bromobenzene

$$\text{ØBr (I)} \longrightarrow \text{Ø} \cdot \text{(II)} + \text{Br} \cdot \text{(III)}$$

	I	II	III
$\Delta H^\circ_{f(298)}$	25.8	80.0	26.7
$S^\circ_{(298)}$	77.9	67.9	41.8
$C^\circ_{p(298)}$	22.7	18.5	5.0

$\Delta S^\circ = 31.8$ g/mole
$\Delta H^\circ = 80.9$ kcal/mole
$\Delta C^\circ_p = 0.8$ g/mole

log A	E	log k_T (1085)	Conditions	System	Surface	References
13.3	70.9	−0.98	1030–1143 °K $\delta P_o \simeq 0.12$–1.24 mm Hg $P_T \simeq 15$ mm Hg	flow		[1] D. Williams and M. Szwarc, J. Chem. Phys. **20,** 1171 (1952).
13.3	70.9	−0.98	1023–1143 °K $\delta P_o \simeq 0.13$–0.78 mm Hg $P_T \simeq 12$–15 mm Hg	flow		[2] M. Ladacki and M. Szwarc, Proc. Roy. Soc. (L) **A219,** 341 (1953).

Preferred:
   $\log k = 15.3 - 80.9/\theta$.

Comments: The thermodynamics indicate that the reported parameters are low. If one assumes that the observed rate constants are roughly representative of the decomposition rate and adjusts the Arrhenius parameters to the reaction enthalpy, one obtains the preferred values. These are consistent with $k_{rec} = 10^{10.4}$ l/mole-sec.

Experimental

[1] Toluene carrier technique. Rates were based on HBr formation.

Reaction: Substituted bromobenzenes

$$(X\text{---}\emptyset\text{Br})\longrightarrow X\text{---}\emptyset\cdot + \text{Br}\cdot$$

$$\Delta H^\circ_{f(298)}$$

$$S^\circ_{(298)}$$

$$C^\circ_{p(298)}$$

$\Delta S^\circ =$
$\Delta H^\circ =$
$\Delta C^\circ_p =$

X	$\log A$	E	$\log k_T$	Conditions	System	Surface	References
p-F	13.3	70.4	$-1.01(1075)$	1053–1098 °K	flow		[1] M. Szwarc and D. Williams, Proc. Roy. Soc. (L) **A219**, 353 (1953).
p-Cl	13.3	70.3	$-0.93(1080)$	1044–1119 °K			
m-Cl	13.3	69.9	$-0.90(1070)$	1033–1107 °K			
o-Cl	13.3	69.7	$-0.81(1080)$	1043–1113 °K			
p-Br	13.6	70.6	$-0.69(1080)$	1047–1113 °K			
o-Br	13.6	69.1	$-0.45(1075)$	1041–1111 °K			
p-CH$_3$	13.3	70.7	$-1.08(1075)$	1046–1100 °K			
m-CH$_3$	13.3	70.7	$-1.14(1070)$	1044–1098 °K			
o-CH$_3$	13.3	70.1	$-1.02(1070)$	1043–1096 °K			
p-$\emptyset$	13.3	70.7	$-1.14(1070)$	1036–1100 °K			
m-$\emptyset$	13.3	70.1	$-0.82(1085)$	1047–1119 °K			
o-$\emptyset$	13.3	68.2	$-0.70(1065)$	1031–1103 °K			
p-CN	13.3	70.6	$-1.06(1075)$	1042–1109 °K			
m-CN	13.3	70.1	$-1.09(1065)$	1042–1090 °K			
o-CN	13.3	70.3	$-0.99(1075)$	1048–1098 °K			
p-OH	13.3	67.0	$-0.45(1065)$	1035–1093 °K			
o-OH	13.3	67.1	$-1.01(1025)$	1005–1043 °K			

Preferred:
Reported Arrhenius parameters are suspect (see bromobenzene).

Comments: The assumption regarding the A-factors of these reactions (see below) would seem to be reasonable except for compounds with ortho substituents where the thermodynamic and kinetic properties should reflect the interraction of neighboring groups. The kinetic parameters reported for the substituted bromobenzenes should have the same reliability as those for the parent compound (i.e., bromobenzene). It would appear that they are all low, although the rate constants should be nearly correct in the middle of the temperature range.

Experimental

[1] Toluene carrier technique. Partial pressures of the individual compounds were not varied appreciably from about 0.2 mm Hg. Rates were based on HBr formation. A-factors were assumed to be the same as that observed for bromobenzene.

Reaction: 3-Bromopyridene (*a*)

2-Bromopyridene (*b*)

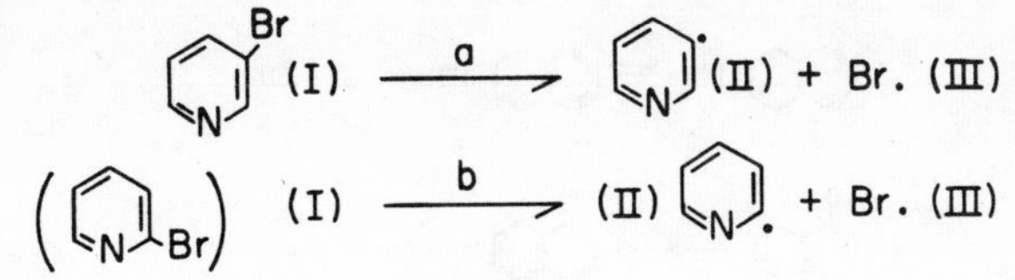

	I	II	III
$\Delta H^{\circ}_{f(298)}$	[39.5]	( )	26.7
$S^{\circ}_{(298)}$	81.3	69.1	46.1
$C^{\circ}_{p(298)}$	21.6	17.4	5.0

a

$\Delta S^{\circ} = 33.9$ g/mole
$\Delta H^{\circ} =$
$\Delta C^{\circ}_{p} = 0.8$ g/mole

Path	log A	E	log k_T (1200)	Conditions	System	Surface	References
a	13.3	75.9	−0.53	1179–1220 °K $\delta P_o \simeq 0.5$ mm Hg	flow		[1] M. Szwarc and D. Williams, Proc. Roy. Soc. **A219**, 353 (1953).
			(1085)				
b	13.3	71.5	−1.10	1054–1115 °K $\delta P_o \simeq 0.25$ mm Hg			

Preferred:

The Arrhenius parameters are undoubtedly low (see bromobenzene). However, the rate constants around $\bar{T}$ should be reasonably reliable.

Experimental

[1] Toluene carrier technique. Rates were based on HBr formation. An *A*-factor equal to that of bromobenzene was assumed.

Reaction: 2-Bromonaphthalene (β-bromonaphthalene) (*a*)

1-Bromonaphthalene (α-bromonaphthalene) (*b*)

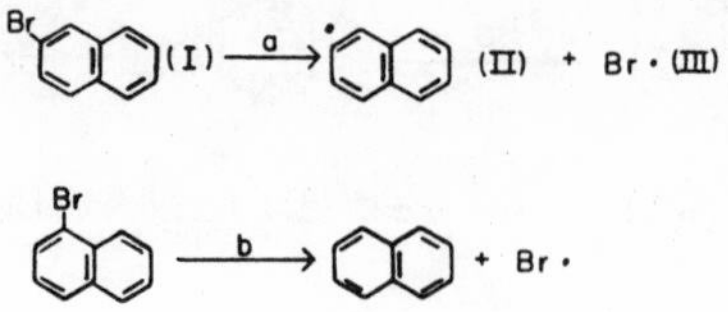

	I	II	III
$\Delta H^{\circ}_{f(298)}$			26.7
$S^{\circ}_{(298)}$			46.1
$C^{\circ}_{p(298)}$			5.0

$\Delta S^{\circ} =$
$\Delta H^{\circ} =$
$\Delta C^{\circ}_{p} =$

Path	log A	E	log k_T (*1075*)	Conditions	System	Surface	References
a	13.2	70.0	−1.03	1022–1133 °K	flow	none	[1] M. Ladaki and M. Szwarc, Proc Roy. Soc. (L) **A219**, 341 (1953); J. Chem. Phys. **20**, 1814 (1952).
b	13.5	70.9	−0.92	1014–1133 °K $\delta P \simeq 0.3$ torr $P_T \simeq 10$–15 torr			

Preferred:

These reactions, as noted by the authors, should be very similar to bromobenzene. Since slightly higher parameters are more reasonable for bromobenzene, the above should also probably be scaled correspondingly upward. Rate constants for decomposition are probably reliable around T_m.

Experimental

[1] Toluene carrier technique. δP were varied over a factor of 3 to 5 with no effect on the rates. Rates based on HBr formation. Some difficulties in obtaining the absolute value of the frequency factors was noted, although activation energies were considered reliable.

Reaction: 9-Bromophenanthrene (*a*)

9-Bromoanthracene   (*b*)

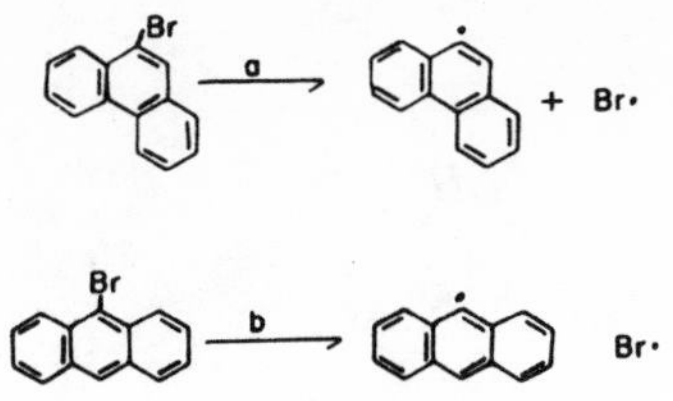

$$\Delta H^\circ_{f(298)}$$

$$S^\circ_{(298)}$$

$$C^\circ_{p(298)}$$

$\Delta S^\circ =$
$\Delta H^\circ =$
$\Delta C^\circ_p =$

Path	log A	E	log k_T (*1065*)	Conditions	System	Surface	References
a	13.0	67.7	−0.90	1002–1125 °K	flow	none	[1] M. Ladaki and M. Szwarc, Proc. Roy. Soc. (L) **A219**, 341 (1953); J. Chem. Phys. **20**, 1814 (1952).
			(*1015*)				
b	13.2	65.6	−0.93	964–1062 °K $\delta P \simeq 0.3$ torr $P_T \simeq 10$–15 torr			

Preferred:

   These reactions, as noted by the authors, should be very similar to bromobenzene. Since slightly higher parameters are more reasonable for bromobenzene, the above should also be scaled correspondingly upward. Rate constants for decomposition are probably realiable.

Experimental

   [1] Toluene carrier technique. δP were varied over a factor of 3 to 5 with no effect on the rates. Rates based on HBr formation. Some difficulties in obtaining the absolute value of the frequency factors was noted, although activation engeries were considered reliable.

Reaction: 2-Bromothiophene

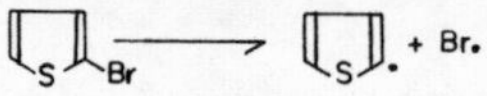

$$\Delta H^{\circ}_{f(298)}$$

$$S^{\circ}_{(298)}$$

$$C^{\circ}_{p(298)}$$

$\Delta S^{\circ} =$
$\Delta H^{\circ} =$
$\Delta C^{\circ}_p =$

log A	E	log k_T (1055)	Conditions	System	Surface	References
13.3	68.5	−0.89	1028–1082 °K $\delta P_o \simeq 0.5$ mm Hg			[1] M. Szwarc and D. Williams, Proc. Roy. Soc. **A219**, 353 (1953).

Preferred:

The Arrhenius parameters are undoubtedly low (see bromobenzene). Rate constants around $\bar{T}$ are probably reliable.

Experimental

[1] Toluene carrier technique. Rates were based on HBr formation. An A-factor equal to that of bromobenzene was assumed.

Reaction: 3-Bromo-1-propene (allylbromide)

$$CH_2\!\!=\!\!CHCH_2Br \;(I) \longrightarrow CH_2\!\!=\!\!CHCH_2\!\cdot \;(II) + Br\cdot \;(III)$$

	I	II	III
$\Delta H^\circ_{f(298)}$	10.9	40.6	26.7
$S^\circ_{(298)}$	75.8	61.4	41.8
$C^\circ_{p(298)}$	18.7	14.4	5.0

$\Delta S^\circ = 27.4$ g/mole
$\Delta H^\circ = 56.4$ kcal/mole
$\Delta C^\circ_p = 0.7$ g/mole

log A	E	log k_T (800)	Conditions	System	Surface	References
12.7	47.5 ± 2	−0.28	732–865 °K	flow	< 5%	[1] M. Szwarc, B. N. Ghosh, and A. H. Sehon, J. Chem. Phys. **18**, 1142 (1950); M. Szwarc and B. N. Ghosh, J. Chem. Phys. **17**, 744 (1949).
12.3	45.5	−0.13	593–653 °K	static	< 1%	[2] A. Maccoll, J. Chem. Phys. **17**, 1350 (1949).

Preferred:
Unreliable. We favor: $\log k = 14.3 - 56.4/\theta$.

Comments: The reaction rates of both studies are faster (by about a factor of 10–100) than is reasonable on the basis of the thermodynamics and a reasonable recombination rate constant. Chain decomposition of the allylbromide is therefore indicated. This is supported by the poor mass balances in the system and the deficiencies of termination product yields relative to HBr yields.

A very reasonable chain process for HBr formation exists in this system:

$$R\cdot + CH_2\!\!=\!\!CHCH_2Br \longrightarrow RCH_2CHCH_2Br$$
$$RCH_2CHCH_2Br \longrightarrow RCH_2CH\!\!=\!\!CH_2 + Br\cdot$$

where $R\cdot = \text{\O}CH_2\cdot$ or $CH_2\!\!=\!\!CHCH_2$.

Since HBr is a better radical trap than toluene (by at least a factor of 10^2) most of the propylene formed probably came from the reaction:

$$CH_2\!\!=\!\!CHCH_2\cdot + HBr \longrightarrow CH_2\!\!=\!\!CHCH_3 + Br.$$

It is also quite likely that all the allyl radicals formed were trapped as propylene, and that the propylene would have been the better measure of the rate of the (C—Br) dissociation. With regard to study [2], the observed first-order kinetics were equated to the initiation step of a complex free radical mechanism which could not be given in any detail. It was assumed that no chain decomposition occurred since addition

(Continued)

509

of propylene did not appreciably alter the reaction rate. However, if the chain process suggested were operative, no inhibition would be expected and this assumption regarding chains would then be unjustified

Experimental

[1] Toluene carrier technique. Rates were based on HBr formation. The (dibenzyl/HBr) ratios varied from ~ 0.2 (766 °K) to ~ 0.4 (865 °K). Large amounts of propylene were observed but very little allene (< 1 percent propylene). Propylene yields, however, were considerably smaller (~ 20 percent) than those of HBr. The usual mechanism was assumed with the addition of the two termination reactions: 2 allyl· ⟶ diallyl; allyl + ØCH₂· ⟶ products.

[2] Rates were followed manometrically and by HBr formation. Rate constants were deduced from an assumed free radical mechanism. Products identified were isopropyl bromide, benzene, and 1-bromopropene.

Reaction: Bromophenylmethane (benzyl bromide)

$$\text{ØCH}_2\text{Br(I)} \longrightarrow \text{ØCH}_2 \cdot \text{(II)} + \text{Br} \cdot \text{(III)}$$

	I	II	III
$\Delta H^\circ_{f(298)}$	16.0	45.0	26.7
$S^\circ_{(298)}$	88.4	75.3	41.8
$C^\circ_{p(298)}$	28.2	25.6	5.0
$C^\circ_{p(1000)}$	(64.5)	60.6	5.0

$\Delta S^\circ = 28.7$ g/mole
$\Delta H^\circ = 55.7$ kcal/mole
$\Delta C^\circ_p = 2.4$ g/mole
$\Delta C^\circ_p = 1.1$ g/mole

log A	E	log k_T (820)	Conditions	System	Surface	References
13.0	50.5	-0.46	768–872 °K $\delta P = 0.01\text{--}2.3$ mm Hg $P_T \approx 8.7\text{--}15.2$ mm Hg	flow	none	[1] M. Szwarc, B. N. Ghosh, and A. H. Sehon, J. Chem. Phys. **18**, 1142 (1950).

Preferred:
    log $k = 14.6 - 56.7/\theta$.

Comments: The reaction enthalpy has been well established; thus the reported parameters are low. Assuming valid rate constants and scaling to the reaction enthalpy gives the preferred values. These are consistent with a recombination rate constant of $k_{\text{rec}} = 10^{9.9}$ l/mole-sec.

Experimental

[1] Toluene carrier technique. Rates were based on the rate of formation of HBr. The mechanism proposed was:

$$\text{ØCH}_2\text{Br} \longrightarrow \text{ØCH}_2 \cdot + \text{Br} \cdot$$

$$\text{Br} \cdot + \text{ØCH}_3 \longrightarrow \text{HBr} + \text{ØCH}_2 \cdot$$

$$2\text{ØCH}_2 \cdot \longrightarrow (\text{ØCH}_2)_2$$

$(\text{HBr}/(\text{ØCH}_2)_2)$ ratios were unity within experimental error; $(\text{H}_2/\text{CH}_4) \approx 3/2$, as found in the toluene pyrolysis. The latter is indicative of secondary reactions.

Reaction: Substituted bromophenylmethanes (substituted benzylbromides)

$$(X—\text{ØCH}_2\text{Br}) \text{ (I)} \longrightarrow X—\text{ØCH}_2 \cdot \text{(II)} + \text{Br} \cdot \text{(III)}$$

$$\Delta H^\circ_{f(298)}$$

$$S^\circ_{(298)}$$

$$C^\circ_{p(298)}$$

$\Delta S^\circ =$
$\Delta H^\circ =$
$\Delta C^\circ_p =$

X	log A	E	log k_T	Conditions	System	Surface	References
o-chloro	13.0	49.6	−0.22 (720)	788–848 °K	flow		[1] C. H. Leigh, A. H.
m-Cl	13.0	50.4	−0.68 (805)	780–829 °K			Sehon, and M.
p-Cl	13.0	50.1	−0.52 (810)	789–830 °K			Szwarc, Proc. Roy.
m-Br	13.3	50.2	−0.59 (790)	771–809 °K			Soc. (L) **A209**, 97
p-Br	13.3	50.2	−0.42 (800)	774–825 °K			(1951).
o-CH₃	13.0	48.5	−0.51 (785)	753–814 °K			
m-CH₃	13.0	50.5	−0.80 (800)	781–820 °K			
p-CH₃	13.0	49.1	−0.59 (790)	750–833 °K			
m-NO₂	13.0	48.4	−0.39 (790)	753–825 °K			
p-NO₂	13.0	49.4	−0.58 (795)	762–826 °K			
m-CN	13.0	49.1	−0.59 (790)	753–825 °K			
p-CN	13.0	49.8	−0.95 (780)	729–831 °K			

Preferred:

The above parameters should all be scaled up a factor of 40 in A and about 6.0 kcal/mole in E (see bromotoluene). Rate constants are probably reliable around $\overline{T}$.

Experimental

[1] Toluene carrier technique. Rates were found to be independent of the substituted benzylbromide and toluene pressures. Arrhenius parameters were obtained from the rate constants using the assumption that all A-factors should be the same as that for the benzyl bromide decomposition.

Reaction: *p*-Bromomethyltoluene (*p*-xylyl bromide) (*a*)

ω,ω′-dibromo *para*-xylene (*b*)

	I	II	III
$\Delta H^\circ_{f(298)}$	[6.8]	37.2	26.7
$S^\circ_{(298)}$	98.2	83.7	46.1
$C^\circ_{p(298)}$	34.7	29.3	5.0

a
$\Delta S^\circ = 31.6$ g/mole
$\Delta H^\circ = 57.1$ kcal/mole
$\Delta C^\circ_p = -0.4$ g/mole

Path	log A	E	log k_T (780)	Conditions	System	Surface	References
a	13.0	50.5	−1.15	748–814 °K $\delta P \simeq 0.05$–1.0 mm Hg			[1] M. Levy, M. Szwarc and J. Throssell, J. Chem. Phys. **22**, 1904 (1954).
			(775)				
b	13.3	50.5	−0.94	748–802 °K $\delta P \simeq 0.05$ mm Hg			(as above).

Preferred:
The parameters should be similar to those of benzylbromide:
log $k_a = 14.6$–56.6/θ.
log $k_b = 14.9$–56.6/θ.

Comments: The authors appear to have discounted their rate constants at the lower temperature. If all the data are used, an activation energy of 54.5 kcal/mole is obtained.

Experimental

[1] Toluene carrier technique. Rates were based on HBr formation.

Reaction: Benzoyl bromide

$$\text{ØCOBr (I)} \longrightarrow \text{ØĊO (II)} + \text{Br. (III)}$$

	I	II	III
$\Delta H^\circ_{f(298)}$	-12.3	$[21.0]$	26.7
$S^\circ_{(298)}$	94.3	79.5	46.1
$C^\circ_{p(298)}$	31.3	26.0	5.0
$C^\circ_{p(1000)}$	(63.9)	57.6	5.0

$\Delta S^\circ = 31.3$ g/mole
$\Delta H^\circ = 60.0$ kcal/mole
$\Delta C^\circ_p = -0.3$ g/mole
$\langle \Delta C^\circ_p \rangle = (-1.3)$ g/mole

log A	E	log k_T (880)	Conditions	System	Surface	References
13.7	57.0	-0.46	814–946 °K $\Delta P = 0.1$–2.45 mm Hg $P_T = 5$–16 mm Hg	flow	none	[1] M. Ladaki, C. H. Leigh, and M. Szwarc, Proc. Roy. Soc. **A214**, 273 (1952).

Preferred:
   log $k = 14.3 - 59.7/\theta$ (see below).

Comments: Parameters have been adjusted to the estimated reaction enthalpy. The recombination rate constant calculated from the A-factor and reaction entropy is then quite reasonable. $k_{rec} = 10^{9.5}$ l/mole-sec.

Experimental

[1] Toluene carrier technique. Rate by (CO) production. $\Delta(\text{CO}) = \Delta(\text{HBr})$.

Reaction: Chlorophenylmethane (benzyl chloride)

$$\text{ØCH}_2\text{Cl (I)} \longrightarrow \text{ØCH}_2 \cdot \text{(II)} + \text{Cl} \cdot \text{(III)}$$

	I	II	III
$\Delta H^\circ_{f(298)}$	(7.0)	45.0	29.0
$S^\circ_{(298)}$	85.4	75.3	39.5
$C^\circ_{p(298)}$	28.8	25.2	5.2

$\Delta S^\circ = 29.4$ g/mole
$\Delta H^\circ = 67.0$ kcal/mole
$\Delta C^\circ_p = 1.6$ g/mole

log A	E	log k_T (990)	Conditions	System	Surface	References
14.83	68.0	−0.18	922–1020 °K $\delta P \simeq 0.12$–0.66 mm Hg	flow	~ 10%	[1] M. Szwarc and J. W. Taylor, J. Chem. Phys. **22**, 270 (1954).

Preferred:
    Reliable. log $k = 14.8 - 68.0/\theta$.
    From A and the reaction entropy one obtains: $k_{rec} = 10^{9.6}$ l/mole-sec.

Experimental

[1] Toluene carrier technique. Rates based on HCl formation. $\Delta(\text{HCl}) = \Delta(\text{ØCH}_2)_2$ as required by the usual mechanism (see benzyl bromide).

Reaction: Benzoyl chloride

$$\text{ØCOCl (I)} \longrightarrow \text{ØĊO (II)} + \text{Cl}\cdot \text{(III)}$$

	I	II	III
$\Delta H^\circ_{f(298)}$	(−26.8)	(21.0)	29.0
$S^\circ_{(298)}$	90.4	79.5	39.5
$C^\circ_{p(298)}$	30.3	26.0	5.2

$\Delta S^\circ = 28.6$ g/mole
$\Delta H^\circ = 76.8$ kcal/mole
$\Delta C^\circ_p = 0.9$ g/mole

log A	E	log k_T (1025)	Conditions	System	Surface	References
15.38	73.6	−0.32	971–1080 °K $\delta P \simeq 0.03$–0.28 mm Hg $P_T \simeq 6.7$–21 mm Hg	flow	~6%	[1] M. Szwarc and J. W. Taylor, J. Chem. Phys. **22**, 270 (1954).

Preferred:
   log $k = 15.38 - 73.6/\theta$.

Comments: Although the observed activation energy is in only fair agreement with the estimated thermodynamics, the difference is not outside the error limits. From A and the reaction entropy, one obtains, $k_{rec} \simeq 10^{10.9}$ l/mole-sec (which seems slightly high).

Experimental

[1] Toluene carrier technique. Rates were based on CO formation. Mass balances were good.

$$\Delta(\text{ØCOCl}) = \Delta(\text{HCl}) = \Delta(\text{CO}).$$

Reaction: Iodoethane (ethyl iodide)

$$C_2H_5I \text{ (I)} \longrightarrow C_2H_5 \cdot \text{(II)} + I \cdot \text{(III)}$$

	I	II	III
$\Delta H^\circ_{f(298)}$	-2.2	25.7	25.5
$S^\circ_{(298)}$	70.7	57.8	43.2
$C^\circ_{p(298)}$	15.4	12.1	5.0
$C^\circ_{p(800)}$	32.0	24.0	5.0

$\Delta S^\circ = 30.3$ g/mole
$\Delta H^\circ = 53.4$ kcal/mole
$\Delta C^\circ_p = 1.7$ g/mole
$\Delta C^\circ_p = -3.0$ g/mole

log A	E	log k_T (740)	Conditions	System	Surface	References
13.65	50.0	(-1.11)	704–774 °K $\delta P = 0.6$–0.4 mm Hg $P_T \simeq 2$–18 mm Hg	flow	none	[1] Joe-Hyun Yang and D. C. Conway, J. Chem. Phys. **43**, 1296 (1965).

Preferred:
  $\log k = 14.6 - 53.2/\theta$ (based on the reaction enthalpy).

Comments: This gives a back reaction rate constant of: $k_b = 10^{9.8}$ l/mole-sec. An RRK calculation of the pressure falloff region with $s = 16$ gives an $M_{1/2} \simeq 10$ mm Hg. Therefore some pressure falloff in the reaction rates under the above conditions is possible.

Experimental

[1] Toluene carrier technique. Rates were determined from scintillation counter measurements of the C^{14} content in ethane (ethyl iodide was C^{14} labeled). Hydrogen halide elimination was competitive (see HI elimination reactions).

Reaction: Dimethylmercury

$$CH_3HgCH_3 \text{ (I)} \xrightarrow{\;a\;} CH_3Hg \cdot \text{(II)} + CH_3 \cdot \text{(III)}$$
$$\xrightarrow{\;b\;} 2CH_3 \cdot + \cdot Hg \cdot \text{(IV)}$$

		I	II	III	IV
	$\Delta H^\circ_{f(298)}$	22.4	(46)	34.1	14.7
	$S^\circ_{(298)}$	74.0	63.3	46.5	41.8
a	$C^\circ_{p(298)}$	(15.7)	(9.7)	8.8	5.0

$\Delta S^\circ = 35.8$ g/mole
$\Delta H^\circ = 57.7$ kcal/mole
$\Delta C^\circ_p = 2.8$ g/mole

log A	E	log k_T (645)	Conditions	System	Surface	References
15.02	58	−4.63	588–704 °K 10–575 mm Hg	static	(*)	(1) A. S. Kallend and J. H. Purnell, Trans. Faraday Soc. **60**, 103 (1964); ibid. **60**, 93 (1964).
14.8	53.7	−3.40	693–800 °K $P_T \simeq 3.6$–260 mm Hg	flow		(2) M. Krech and S. J. Price, Can. J. Chem. **41**, 224 (1963).
15.7	57.9	−3.92	555–621 °K 59–72 mm Hg	static		(3) M. E. Russell and R. B. Bernstein, J. Chem. Phys. **30**, 607 (1959).
13.1	50.1	−3.88	738–881 °K (16 mm Hg)	flow		(4) S. J. W. Price and A. F. Trotman-Dickenson, Trans. Faraday Soc. **53**, 939 (1957).
14.3	51.3	−3.08	567–606 °K 70–80 mm Hg	static	<2%	(5) C. M. Laurie and L. H. Long, Trans. Faraday Soc. **51**, 665 (1955).
(16.9)	57.0	−2.42	579–615 °K 10–70 mm Hg	static		(6) L. M. Yeddanapalli, R. Srinivason, and V. J. Paul, J. Sci. Industr. Res. **13B**, 232 (1954).
13.5	51.5	−3.95	762–825 °K (10 mm Hg)	flow	<10%	(7) B. G. Gowenlock, J. C. Polanyi, and E. Warhurst, Proc. Roy. Soc. **A218**, 269 (1953).

Preferred:
    log $k = 15.0 - 58/\theta$.

Comments: $D_1 + D_2 = 57.3 \pm 4$ (Mortimer, Pritchard, and Skinner, Trans. Faraday Soc. **48**, 220 (1952)). $D_1 + D_2 = 57.1 \pm 2$ (Carson, Carson, and Wilmhurst, Nature **170**, 320 (1952)). However, more recent thermo-
(Continued)

Dimethylmercury *(Continued)*

dynamic data give $D_1 + D_2 = \Delta H_b^\circ = 62.5$ kcal/mole. Clearly path b is not compatible with any observed activation energies.

Experimental

[1] Rates obtained from G.L.C. product analysis. Products were CH_4, C_2H_6, C_3H_8, C_2H_4, C_3H_6, and Hg+ polymer. Mechanism proposed was consistent with product studies and explained many of the earlier noted experimental anomalies. Decomposition was shown to be in the falloff region at the P and T of many of the earlier studies.

[2] Benzene carrier employed. Rates were based on carbon balance of the products which were analyzed by G.L.C. Believed high-pressure rates were achieved at $P > 100$ mm Hg and that the rate parameters reported pertained to this region. At $P = 16$ mm Hg, $\log k = 13.6 - 51.0/\theta$.

[3] M.S. analysis on all products. Found rate constants under maximum inhibition of free radical chains with cyclopentene to be pressure dependent in the regions of study. Reported parameters are those obtained from the usual extrapolation to P_∞.

[4] Analysis by G.L.C. on hydrocarbon products. Toluene carrier technique.

[5] Rate based on CH_4 and C_2H_6 formation.

[6] Rates were based on gaseous product analysis (Blacet Leighton micro gas analysis). The kinetics were shown to follow more appropriately a 3/2 order rather than a 1 order mechanism. The reported activation energy was deduced from the mechanism (as was the A-factor for this monograph). (Polymer formed and disappeared in presence of H_2.)

[7] Rates based on gas analysis (CH_4, C_2H_6, and C_2H_4). Pressure dependence of the rate constants was observed. Toluene in N_2 and CO_2 carriers was used. The A-factor of $10^{13.5}$ was assumed.

---

* Surface decomposition was shown to occur, altering both the rate and the product distribution.

Reaction: Diethylmercury

$$C_2H_5HgC_2H_5 \ (I) \longrightarrow C_2H_5 \cdot \ (II) + \cdot HgC_2H_5 \ (III)$$

	I	II	III
$\Delta H^\circ_{f(298)}$	15.9	25.7	[36.7]
$S^\circ_{(298)}$	93.8	57.8	73
$C^\circ_{p(298)}$	(26.7)	12.1	(15.2)

$\Delta S^\circ = 37.0$ g/mole
$\Delta H^\circ = 46.5$ kcal/mole
$\Delta C^\circ_p = 0.6$ g/mole

log A	E	log k_T (620)	Conditions	System	Surface	References
14.1	41.5	−0.53	593–643 °K 4 (10 mm Hg)	flow		[1] B. G. Gowenlock, J. C. Polanyi, and E. Warhurst, Proc. Roy. Soc. **A218,** 269 (1953).
14.1	42.5±2	−0.88	593–690 °K (10 mm Hg)	flow		[2] H. V. Carter, E. I. Chapell, and E. Warhurst, J. Chem. Soc., 106 (1956).

Preferred:
   Parameters are too low. We prefer log $k = 15.5 - 46.5/\theta$.

Comments: Pressure dependence of the rate constants [1] indicates that the reaction could well be in its fall-off region. Free radical chain decomposition is also quite possible. Arrhenius parameters are clearly low (i.e., compare to dimethyl mercury, di-*n*-propyl mercury, etc., with $A > 10^{15.0}$ sec^{-1}). $D_1 + D_2 = 50.2$ kcal/mole.

Experimental

   [1] N_2, CO_2, and H_2 carriers with added toluene. Rates were based on the yields of gaseous products (C_4H_{10}, C_2H_6, and C_2H_4) and checked reasonably well with the Hg produced. Rate constants were dependent on the total pressure.
   [2] N_2 carrier with and without added toluene. Rates were based on the hydrocarbon product yields and from the yields of Hg. Ratios (C_2H_6/C_2H_4) = 1 and C_4/C_2 = 4 were essentially temperature independent.

Reaction: di-*n*-Propylmercury

$$C_3H_7HgC_3H_7 \text{ (I)} \longrightarrow C_3H_7 \cdot \text{ (II)} + \cdot HgC_3H_7 \text{ (III)}$$

	I	II	III
$\Delta H^\circ_{f(298)}$	4.2	20.7	[30.6]
$S^\circ_{(298)}$	112.6	67.2	82.5
$C^\circ_{p(298)}$	(37.7)	17.6	(20.7)

$\Delta S^\circ = 37.1$ g/mole
$\Delta H^\circ = 47.1$ kcal/mole
$\Delta C^\circ_p = 0.6$ g/mole

log A	E	log k_T (640)	Conditions	System	Surface	References
15.5	47.1	−0.59	605–677 °K (4.4 mm Hg)	flow	none	[1] H. T. J. Chilton and B. G. Gowenlock, Trans. Faraday Soc. **50**, 824 (1954).

Preferred:
Reliable. log $k = 15.5 - 47.1/\theta$
$D_1 + D_2 = 50.2$ kcal/mole.

Experimental

[1] N_2 and NO carriers employed. Rates were based on Hg formation. The rate constants were observed to be total pressure dependent. Products in the N_2 carrier system were C_2, C_3, and C_6 hydrocarbons.

Reaction: di-*n*-Butyl mercury

$$n\text{C}_4\text{H}_9\text{Hg}n\text{C}_4\text{H}_9(\text{I}) \longrightarrow n|\text{C}_4\text{H}_9 \cdot (\text{II}) + \cdot \text{Hg}n\text{C}_4\text{H}_9 (\text{III})$$

	I	II	III
$\Delta H^\circ_{f(298)}$	-5.8	15.7	[26.3]
$S^\circ_{(298)}$	131.4	76.6	92.0
$C^\circ_{p(298)}$	(48.7)	23.1	(26.2)

$\Delta S^\circ = 37.2$ g/mole
$\Delta H^\circ = 47.8$ kcal/mole
$\Delta C^\circ_p = 0.6$ g/mole

log A	E	log k_T (*650*)	Conditions	System	Surface	References
15.8	47.8 ± 2	-0.27	617–686 °K	flow	none	[1] B. H. M. Billinge and B. G. Gowenlock, Trans. Faraday Soc. **59**, 690, (1963).

Preferred:
   Reliable.
   log $k = 15.8 - 47.8/\theta$.

Experimental

[1] CO_2, SF_6, N_2, and NO carriers employed. Rates were based on Hg formation.

Reaction: Diisopropylmercury

$$(CH_3)_2CHHgiPr(I) \xrightarrow{\quad a \quad} 2(iPr\cdot) + Hg\,(III)$$
$$\xrightarrow{\quad b \quad} iPr\cdot\,(II) + \cdot HgiPr\,(IV)$$

	I	II	III	IV
$\Delta H^\circ_{f(298)}$	8.7	17.6	14.5	[31.8]
$S^\circ_{(298)}$	107.5	65.4	41.8	79.7
$C^\circ_{p(298)}$	37.3	17.7	5.0	(20.5)

b

$\Delta S^\circ = 37.6$ g/mole
$\Delta H^\circ = 40.7$ kcal/mole
$\Delta C^\circ_p = 0.9$ g/mole

Path	log A	E	log k_T (475)	Conditions	System	Surface	References
a	16.2	40.4	-2.39	502–714 °K (7.4 mm Hg)	flow	none	[1] H. T. J. Chilton and B. G. Gowenlock, Trans. Faraday Soc. **49**, 1451 (1953).
a	16.4	40.7	-2.33	513–573 °K 4.6–12 mm Hg	flow	none	[2] B. H. M. Billinge and B. G. Gowenlock, Trans. Faraday Soc. **59**, 690 (1963), Proc. Chem. Soc., 24 (1962).
b	11.0	27 ± 5	-1.43	443–503 °K			

Preferred:
   log $k_b = 16.4 - 40.7/\theta$.

Comments: Although $D_1 + D_2 = \Delta H^\circ_a = 41.0$, the simultaneous bond rupture is not considered here to be probable. Identification of the observed kinetics with path b is preferred.

Experimental

[1] N_2 and NO carriers. Rates were based on Hg formation. Sensitivity to total pressure was observed.

[2] NO, SF_6, CO_2, and N_2 used as carrier gases. Rates were pressure independent in the ranges studied. Rates were based on G.L.C. analysis of the gaseous products. Path b and a were suggested to be examples of single and multiple critical oscillator reactions.

Reaction: Divinylmercury

$$CH_2=CHHgCH=CH_2 \text{ (I)} \longrightarrow CH_2=CH \cdot \text{(II)} + \cdot HgCH=CH_2 \text{ (III)}$$

	I	II	III
$\Delta H^\circ_{f(298)}$	( )	69	( )
$S^\circ_{(298)}$	88.6	56.6	(70.4)
$C^\circ_{p(298)}$	( )	9.7	( )

$\Delta S^\circ = 38.4$ g/mole
$\Delta H^\circ =$ kcal/mole
$\Delta C^\circ_p =$ g/mole

log A	E	log k_T (845)	Conditions	System	Surface	References
11.94	48.3	−0.55	775–915 °K 16–24 mm Hg	flow	none	[1] A. F. Trotman-Dickenson, J. Chem. Soc. 2580 (1961).

Preferred:

Parameters are not reliable. We favor $\log k \simeq 16-64/\theta$. Rate constants are probably reliable around $\bar{T}$ of study.

Comments: Since the entropy of activation is certainly positive for this reaction, the reported parameters are clearly too low. The reported A-factor implies an entropy of activation of $\Delta S^\ddagger = -8.3$ g/mole, which is not possible for the bond fission reaction.

Experimental

[1] Toluene carrier technique. Rates based on Hg production were concordant with measurements of ethylene, acetylene, and 1,3-butadiene formed at the lower temperatures. At the higher temperatures faster rates were calculated on the basis of the Hg production. Heterogeneous polymerization of some of the gaseous products was considered the likely cause of this discrepancy. $\text{ØCH}_2 \cdot$ radicals can initiate a displacement chain in the system.

Reaction: Diphenylmercury

$$\text{ØHgØ (I)} \xrightarrow{a} 2\text{Ø}\cdot + \text{Hg}\cdot \text{(III)}$$
$$\xrightarrow{b} \text{Ø}\cdot \text{(II)} + \cdot\text{HgØ (IV)}$$

	I	II	III	IV
$\Delta H^\circ_{f(298)}$	(88.0)	80.0	14.5	([76])
$S^\circ_{(298)}$	(114.0)	69.2	41.8	(84)
$C^\circ_{p(298)}$	( )	19.2	5.0	( )

	b	a	
$\Delta S^\circ =$	39.2		g/mole
$\Delta H^\circ =$	68	86.5	kcal/mole
$\Delta C^\circ_p =$			

log A	E	log k_T (930)	Conditions	System	Surface	References
16.0	68±4	+0.02	896–960 °K (10± mm Hg)	flow	none	[1] H. V. Carter, E. I. Chappell, and E. Warhurst, J. Chem. Soc. 106 (1956).

Preferred:

log $k_b = 16.0 - 68/\theta$.

Comments: We prefer to identify the observed kinetic parameters with path b since $D_1 + D_2 \simeq 86.5$ kcal/mole and since the high entropy of activation for path b is consistent with A observed.

Experimental

[1] N_2 carrier with added toluene. Rates were based on yields of Hg· (by weight). Path a was considered the most likely primary split.

Reaction: Phenylmercuric chloride

$$\varnothing HgCl \ (I) \quad \begin{array}{c} \xrightarrow{\ a\ } \varnothing \cdot \ (II) + \cdot \ HgCl \ (III) \\[4pt] \xrightarrow{\ b\ } \varnothing \cdot + Hg \ (IV) + Cl \cdot \ (V) \\[4pt] \xrightarrow{\ c\ } \varnothing Hg \cdot \ (VI) + Cl \cdot \end{array}$$

	I	II	III	IV	V	VI
$\Delta H^\circ_{f(298)}$	25 ± 5	80 ± 2	19	14.7	29	[76]
$S^\circ_{(298)}$	92	69	62	41.8	39.5	84
$C^\circ_{p(298)}$		19		5.0	5.2	

	a	b	c	
$\Delta S^\circ =$	39	58.3	31.5	g/mole
$\Delta H^\circ =$	74	98.7	80	kcal/mole
$\Delta C^\circ_p =$				

Path	log A	E	log k_T (1015)	Conditions	System	Surface	References
a	13.0	59 ± 3	$+0.30$	975–1055 °K (10 mm Hg)	flow	none	[1] H. V. Carter, E. I. Chappell, and E. Warhurst, J. Chem Soc. 106 (1956).

Preferred:

Parameters are suspect.

log $k_a = 15.6 - 71/\theta$. Rate constants are probably reliable around $\bar{T}$ of study.

Comments: The observed activation energy is well below any reasonable estimate which can be made for path a. Paths b and c are prohibitively endothermic. If a recombination rate constant of about $k_{-a} = 10^{9.0}$ l/mole-sec is assumed, one obtains from the reaction entropy, $A_a = 10^{15.6}$ sec^{-1}. Adjusting the reported parameters to this value gives a more reasonable rate constant expression in terms of the thermodynamics.

Experimental

[1] N_2 carrier with added toluene. Rates were based on the yields of Hg and Hg_2Cl_2. The latter product was analyzed by reaction with hot KI solution. (KI + $HgX_2 \longrightarrow$ Hg + $HgX_4^=$) Changes in substrate concentration and time of contact did not affect the rate constants. Path a was preferred.

Reaction: Phenylmercuric bromide

$$\text{ØHgBr (I)} \xrightarrow{a} \text{Ø} \cdot \text{(II)} + \cdot\text{HgBr (III)}$$
$$\xrightarrow{b} \text{Ø} \cdot + \text{Hg} \cdot \text{(IV)} + \text{Br} \cdot \text{(V)}$$

	I	II	III	IV	V
$\Delta H^{\circ}_{f(298)}$	(33 ± 5)	80 ± 2	23	14.7	26.7
$S^{\circ}_{(298)}$	95	69	65	41.8	41.8
$C^{\circ}_{p(298)}$		19		5.0	5.0

	a	b
$\Delta S^{\circ} =$	39	57.6 g/mole
$\Delta H^{\circ} =$	70	88.4 kcal/mole
$\Delta C^{\circ}_p =$		

Path	log A	E	log k_T (975)	Conditions	System	Surface	References
a	14.3	63 ± 2	$+0.18$	943–1010 °K	flow	none	[1] H. V. Carter, E. I. Chappell, and E. Warhurst, J. Chem. Soc., 106 (1956).

Preferred:

From the thermodynamics, the parameters seem low. We favor
log $k_a = 15.6 - 68.8/\theta$.

Experimental

[1] N_2 carrier with added toluene. Rates were based on yields of Hg and Hg_2Br_2 (see ØHgCl).

Reaction: Phenylmercuric iodide

$$\text{ØHgI (I)} \xrightarrow[\quad\;]{\;a\;} \text{Ø} \cdot \text{(II)} + \text{Hg (III)} + \text{I} \cdot \text{(IV)}$$
$$\xrightarrow[\quad\;]{\;b\;} \text{Ø} \cdot + \text{HgI} \cdot \text{(V)}$$
$$\xrightarrow[\quad\;]{\;c\;} \text{ØHg} \cdot \text{(VI)} + \text{I} \cdot$$

	I	II	III	IV	V	VI
$\Delta H^\circ_{f(298)}$	43 ± 5	80 ± 2	14.5	25.5	33	76 ± 5
$S^\circ_{(298)}$	97	69	41.8	43.2	67	84
$C^\circ_{p(298)}$		19	5.0	5.0		

	a	b	c	
$\Delta S^\circ =$	57	39	30.2	g/mole
$\Delta H^\circ =$	77	70	58.5	kcal/mole
$\Delta C^\circ_p =$				

Path	log A	E	log k_T (885)	Conditions	System	Surface	References
a	15.7	63 ± 2	$+0.14$	848–924 °K $P_T \simeq 8.5 \pm 0.5$ mm Hg	flow		(1) M. Cowperthwaite and E. Warhurst, J. Chem. Soc., 2429 (1958)

Preferred:

Suspect. log $k_{b+c} = 15.7 - 63/\theta$ (see below).

Comments: The parameters look reasonable, although they are not in agreement with the estimated thermodynamics. One can estimate that $A_b = 10^{15.7}$ sec^{-1} (as observed) and $A_c = 10^{14.0}$ sec^{-1}. Thus, in view of the reaction enthalpies of paths b and c, along with their possible errors, both b and c look like possible competitive processes. Path a is prohibitively endothermic.

Experimental

(1) N_2 carrier with added toluene. Rates were based on undecomposed ØHgI. Products were Hg, Hg_2I_2, and hydrocarbons. Path a was favored.

Reaction: Dimethylcadmium

$$CH_3CdCH_3 \text{ (I)} \begin{array}{c} \xrightarrow{\quad a \quad} CH_3 \cdot \text{ (II)} + CH_3Cd \cdot \text{ (III)} \\ \xrightarrow{\quad b \quad} 2CH_3 + Cd \cdot \text{ (IV)} \end{array}$$

	I	II	III	IV
$\Delta H^\circ_{f(298)}$	25.2	34.0	[45.6]	26.8
$S^\circ_{(298)}$	72.5	46.5	62	40.1
$C^\circ_{p(298)}$		8.8		5

a

$\Delta S^\circ = 36.0$ g/mole
$\Delta H^\circ = [54.4]$
$\Delta C^\circ_p =$

Path	log A	E	log k_T (770)	Conditions	System	Surface	References
a	13.4	48.8	-0.45	743–800 °K 16.3–162 mm Hg	flow	none	[1] M. Krech and S. J. Price, Can. J. Chem. **43**, 1929 (1965)
a	11.9	45.8	-1.10	742–844 °K 4.4–25 mm Hg (18 mm)	flow		[2] S. J. W. Price and A. F. Trotman-Dickenson, Trans. Faraday Soc. **53**, 939 (1957)
a	(13.0)	43.5	$+0.65$	531 °K (20 mm Hg)	static	(*)	[3] C. M. Laurie and R. H. Long, Trans. Faraday Soc. **53**, 1431 (1957)

Preferred:
   Parameters are suspect.
   Estimate: $\log k = 15.0 - 54.4/\theta$.

Comments: Although the authors of [1] claim to have reached the high-pressure region, the "close-to-normal" A-factor reported is still probably 1 to 2 orders of magnitude too low. ($D_1 + D_2 = 69.6$ kcal/mole.)

Experimental

   [1] Benzene carrier technique. Rates were based on hydrocarbon (CH_4, C_2H_6, C_2H_4, C_3H_8) product analysis (G.L.C.). The reaction was pressure dependent below 80 mm Hg. Subsequent decomposition of ($CH_3Cd\cdot$) was fast.
   [2] Toluene carrier technique. Rates were based on CH_4 and ethane yields, and were found to be strongly pressure dependent.
   [3] A large heterogeneous contribution was observed. The A-factor was assumed and rates were based on both Cd and $CH_4 + C_2H_6$ produced.

---

* The homogeneous reaction was isolated by extrapolating the rates to zero (S/V) ratios.

Reaction: Dimethylzinc

$$(CH_3)_2Zn \text{ (I)} \longrightarrow \cdot ZnCH_3 \text{ (III)} + CH_3 \cdot \text{ (II)}$$

	I	II	III	Zn
$\Delta H^\circ_{f(298)}$	(13.0)	34.0	( )	31.2
$S^\circ_{(298)}$	74	46.5	63	38.5
$C^\circ_{p(298)}$	( )	8.8	( )	

$\Delta S^\circ = 35.5$ g/mole
$\Delta H^\circ =$
$\Delta C^\circ_p =$

log A	E	log k_T (920)	Conditions	System	Surface	References
11.25	47.2	+0.04	843–1000 °K (16 mm Hg)	flow	none	[1] S. J. W. Price and A. F. Trotman-Dickenson, Trans. Faraday Soc. **53**, 1208 (1957).

Preferred:
    Unreliable.

Comments: Not representative of the high-pressure rate constant. The low A-factor reported is indicative of free radical chain processes and/or of a unimolecular reaction well into its fall-off region. The "high" pressure" A-factor should be similar to that of mercury dimethyl (i.e., $\log A = 15.0$).

Experimental

[1] Toluene carrier technique. Gaseous product was principally CH_4, with smaller amounts of C_2H_6, H_2, and C_2H. also observed. Toluene decomposition was corrected for from the H_2 yields. Decomposition was believed to occur in two steps:

$$Zn(CH_3)_2 \xrightarrow{\;1\;} \cdot ZnCH_3 + CH_3$$

$$\cdot ZnCH_3 \xrightarrow{\;2\;} Zn + CH_3 \text{ (see free radical reactions)}.$$

The second step was much slower than the first at all temperatures. Rate constants were obtained by employing the method of consecutive reaction rates at intermediate temperatures, while at the higher temperatures the kinetics were interpreted in terms of the second step only (i.e., instantaneous decomposition of the reactant was assumed). All processes were found to be "markedly" pressure dependent. Parameters reported for the second step were $\log k_2(\text{sec}^{-1}) = 6.8 - 35/\theta$ (16 mm Hg).

Reaction: Trimethylarsine

$$(CH_3)_3As\ (I) \longrightarrow CH_3 \cdot (II) + (CH_3)_2As \cdot (III)$$

	I	II	III	As
$\Delta H^\circ_{f(298)}$	3.7	34.0	( )	( )
$S^\circ_{(298)}$	85.1	46.5	( )	( )
$C^\circ_{p(298)}$	27.5	8.8	( )	( )

$\Delta S^\circ =$
$\Delta H^\circ =$
$\Delta C^\circ_p =$

log A	E	log k_T (705)	Conditions	System	Surface	References
12.8	54.6	−4.13	683–723 °K 55–193 mm Hg (100 mm Hg)	static	none	[1] P. B. Ayscough and H. J. Eméleus, J. Chem. Soc., 3381 (1954).

Preferred:
   Unreliable.

Comments: The very large methane yields indicate that extensive H-abstraction from the parent alkyl occured (i.e., chain decomposition), thus it is unlikely that the reported parameters can be associated with the initial bond rupture. The same conclusion concerning this reaction has been reached by Price and Trotman-Dickenson by analogy with the kinetic complexities of the trimethyl antimony reaction (see $(CH_3)_3Sb$).

Experimental

[1] Rates were based on pressure changes in the initial stages of reaction $(P_f/P_o) \simeq 2.0$. M.S. product analysis CH_4 (90 percent), C_2H_6 (4 percent), C_2H_4, C_3H_6, and H_2) was stoichiometric in the initial stages. (No primary split was suggested).

Reaction: *tris*-(Trifluoromethyl)arsine

$$(CF_3)_3As\ (I) \longrightarrow CF_3 \cdot (II) + (CF_3)_2As \cdot (III)$$

	I	II	III	As
$\Delta H^\circ_{f(298)}$	( )	-112.5	( )	( )
$S^\circ_{(298)}$	( )	62.4	( )	( )
$C^\circ_{p(298)}$	( )	12.2	( )	( )

$\Delta S^\circ =$

$\Delta H^\circ =$

$\Delta C^\circ_p =$

log A	E	log k_T (655)	Conditions	System	Surface	References
15.4	57.4	-3.75	623–683 °K 51–194 mm Hg	static	< 5%	[1] P. B. Ayscough and H. J. Emeléus, J. Chem. Soc., 3381 (1954)

Preferred:

log $k = 15.4 - 57.4/\theta$.

Comments: Although subsequent reactions of products with the silica surface are evident, the reported parameters are quite reasonable.

Experimental

[1] Rates were obtained from initial pressure changes. The reaction corresponded roughly to As(CF₃)₃ ⟶ A + 3/2 C_2F_6 although up to 10 percent C_3F_8 and C_4F_{10} were also formed. Identification and analysis was by I.R. SiF and CO_2 were also observed. The ratio of $(SiF_4 + CO_2)$/fluorocarbon was strongly dependent on the nature of the surface varying between 10 and 30 percent.

Reaction: Trimethylbismuth

$$(CH_3)_3Bi \text{ (I)} \underset{b}{\overset{a}{\longrightarrow}} \begin{array}{l} CH_3 \cdot \text{(II)} + \cdot Bi(CH_3)_2 \text{ (III)} \\ 3CH_3 + Bi \end{array}$$

	I	II	III	Bi
$\Delta H^\circ_{f(298)}$	-29.2	34.0	$[-19.2]$	49.5
$S^\circ_{(298)}$	85	46.5	75.3	44.7
$C^\circ_{p(298)}$	28	8.8		5

a

$\Delta S^\circ = 36.8$ g/mole
$\Delta H^\circ = [44]$ kcal/mole
$\Delta C^\circ_p =$

Path	log A	E	log k_T (740)	Conditions	System	Surface	References
a	14.0	44.0	$+1.01$	619–857 °K $P_T - 16$ mm Hg	flow	none	[1] S. J. W. Price and A. F. Trotman-Dickenson, Trans. Faraday Soc. **54**, 1630 (1958)

Preferred:
   Suspect. However, see below.

Comments: In terms of the entropy of activation, the A-factor looks low by about an order of magnitude. However, there is considerable uncertainty in all the thermodynamic values and the reported parameters are not unreasonable.

Experimental

[1] Toluene carrier technique. Rates were based on yields of ethane and methane. (Very small yields of H_2 and C_2H_4 also obtained were considered unimportant.) Reaction rates were shown to be independent of the contact time, the metal alkyl concentration, the S/V ratio, and the total pressure above 10 mm Hg. Total decomposition to free metal and methyls occurred; thus subsequent decompositions of the metal alkyl radicals were fast relative to the initial bond rupture.

Reaction: Trimethylgallium

$$(CH_3)_3Ga\ (I) \longrightarrow CH_3 \cdot (II) + \cdot Ga(CH_3)_2\ (III)$$

	I	II	III	Ga
$\Delta H^\circ_{f(298)}$	-6.7	34.0	$[18.8]$	66
$S^\circ_{(298)}$	83.6	46.5	(75)	40.4
$C^\circ_{p(298)}$	25.9	8.8		5

$\Delta S^\circ = 37.9$ g/mole
$\Delta H^\circ = 59.5$ kcal/mole
$\Delta C^\circ_p =$

log A	E	log k_T (840)	Conditions	System	Surface	References
15.54	59.5	$+0.06$	686–983 °K 6.1–31.1 mm Hg	flow	$< 10\%$	[1] M. G. Jacko and S. J. W. Price, Can. J. Chem. **41**, 1560 (1963).

Preferred:
  log $k_1 = 15.54 - 59.5/\theta$.
  $D_1 + D_2 + D_3 = 174.7$ kcal/mole

Comments: The Arrhenius parameters are reasonable in terms of both reaction entropy and reaction enthalp

Experimental

[1] Toluene carrier technique. Rates were obtained from CH_4, C_2H_6, and C_2H_4 product yields (G.L.C. analysis Decomposition appeared to proceed principally in two steps with the second step much slower than the first.

$$(CH_3)_3Ga \xrightarrow{\ 1\ } (CH_3)_2Ga \cdot + CH_3 \cdot$$
$$(CH_3)_2Ga \cdot \xrightarrow{\ 2\ } (CH_3Ga) + CH_3 \cdot$$

High-temperature decomposition was assumed to be controlled entirely by reaction 2 (see free radical reaction), a the method of consecutive reactions was used at lower temperatures to obtain the parameters of reaction 1 (see al dimethyl zinc).

Rate constants declined markedly for (toluene/reactant) ratios less than 45 indicating a tendency for chain d composition. Rate constant (k_1) was slightly total pressure dependent, while k_2 was strongly pressure dependent. Bo constants were highly sensitive to the nature of the surface in the reaction zone. Analysis of a black polymer forme gave an empirical formula $(GaCH_3)n$.

Reaction: Trimethylindium

$$\text{In } (CH_3)_3 \ (\text{I}) \longrightarrow CH_3 \cdot (\text{II}) + \cdot \text{In } (CH_3)_2 \ (\text{III})$$

	I	II	III	In
$\Delta H^\circ_{f(298)}$	( )	34.0	( )	58.2
$S^\circ_{(298)}$	83.8	46.5	(75)	41.5
$C^\circ_{p(298)}$	27.8	8.8	( )	5

$\Delta S^\circ =$
$\Delta H^\circ =$
$\Delta C^\circ_p =$

log A	E	log k_T (665)	Conditions	System	Surface	References
15.7	47.2	+0.18	550–781 °K $P_T \simeq 6$–33.5 mm Hg (13 mm Hg)	flow	< 15%	[1] M. G. Jacko and S. J. W. Price, Can. J. Chem. **42**, 1198 (1965).

Preferred:

log $k_1 = 15.7 - 47.2/\theta$.
Parameters are reasonable.

Experimental

[1] Toluene carrier technique. Rates based on G.L.C. analysis of hydrocarbon products (CH_4, C_2H_6, C_2H_4, C_3H_6, $C_2H_5\emptyset$, and $(\emptyset CH_2)_2$). Decomposition occurred in three steps, the second being very fast and the third very slow.

$$\text{In } (CH_3)_3 \xrightarrow{\ 1\ } \cdot \text{In } (CH_3)_2 + CH_3 \cdot$$

$$\cdot \text{In } (CH_3)_2 \xrightarrow{\ 2\ } : \text{In } (CH_3) + CH_3 \cdot$$

$$: \text{In } (CH_3) \xrightarrow{\ 3\ } \overset{\cdot}{\text{In}} + CH_3 \cdot$$

Kinetics of step 3 were studied at high temperatures where steps 1 and 2 were essentially instantaneous (see free radical reactions). At lower temperatures a white polymer of composition $(In(CH_3))n$ was formed. Rate constant k_1 was slightly total pressure dependent, while k_3 was strongly total pressure dependent. k_1 and k_3 both declined rapidly for (toluene/alkyl) ratios of less than 150.

Reaction: Trimethylantimony

$$(CH_3)_3Sb \ (I) \xrightarrow[\;b\;]{\;a\;} \begin{array}{l} CH_3 \cdot \ (II) + (CH_3)_2Sb \cdot \ (III) \\ 3CH_3 \cdot + Sb \end{array}$$

	I	II	III	Sb
$\Delta H^\circ_{f(298)}$	6.4	34.0	[29.4]	62 ± 7
$S^\circ_{(298)}$	85	46.5	75.3	43.1
$C^\circ_{p(298)}$		8.8		5

a
$\Delta S^\circ = 36.8$ g/mole
$\Delta H^\circ = [57]$ kcal/mole
$\Delta C^\circ_p =$

Path	log A	E	log k_T (*840*)	Conditions	System	Surface	References
a	15.2	57.0	$+0.37$	748–937 °K (16.5 mm Hg)	flow	none	[1] S. J. W. Price and A. F. Trotman-Dickenson, Trans. Faraday Soc. **54**, 1630 (1958).

Preferred:

Suspect. However, see below.

Comments: In view of the obvious complexities of this system, little confidence can be placed in the reported Arrhenius parameters. However, the *A*-factor is about right for the reaction entropy and the activation energy is not unreasonable.

$$D_1 + D_2 + D_3 = 157.6 \text{ kcal/mole}; \ \bar{D} = 52.5 \text{ kcal/mole}.$$

Experimental

[1] Toluene carrier technique. The reaction was shown to be homogeneous, but otherwise quite complex. Yields of CH_4 and C_2H_6 were always far below the amount expected on the basis of the metal alkyl decomposed. Polymer formation was large and attributed to a polymer of the type $(SbMe)_n$. First-order rate constants based on the amount of metal produced, or on the amount of gaseous products produced, were both total pressure dependent. Parameters reported are those based on the rate of metal production and were attributed to the initial split.

Reaction: Trimethylthallium

$$(CH_3)_3Tl \ (I) \longrightarrow CH_3 \cdot \ (II) + \cdot Tl(CH_3)_2 \ (III)$$

	I	II	III	Th
$\Delta H^\circ_{f(298)}$		34.0		44.5
$S^\circ_{(298)}$	85	46.5		43.2
$C^\circ_{p(298)}$		8.8		

$\Delta S^\circ =$
$\Delta H^\circ =$
$\Delta C^\circ_p =$

$\log A$	E	$\log k_T$ (525)	Conditions	System	Surface	References
10.8	27.4	-0.61	458–591 °K $P_T = 5.6$–33.0 mm Hg	flow	(*)	[1] M. G. Jacko and S. J. W. Price, Can. J. Chem. **43**, 1961 (1965).

Preferred:
  Unreliable.

Comments: The excessively low A-factor is not reasonable, and suggests that the homogeneous reaction has not been effectively isolated.

Experimental

[1] Toluene carrier technique. Rates based on G.L.C. product analysis for CH_4, C_2H_6, C_2H_4, and $C_2H_5\emptyset$ and (or) by direct Tl analysis. The latter indicates that decomposition of the thallium alkyl radicals follow rapidly the initial bond rupture.

---

*Extensive heterogeneities were found. Even after consistent pretreatment of the reaction vessels with hot 50 percent HF, reaction rates for initial bond rupture were estimated to be 27 percent heterogeneous at the higher temperature and 13 percent at the lower. A slight total pressure effect was also observed.

Reaction: Germane

$$\text{GeH}_4 \text{ (I)} \xrightarrow{a} \text{GeH}_2 + \text{H}_2 \text{ (III)}$$
$$\xrightarrow{b} \text{GeH}_3 + \text{H} \text{ (II)}$$

	I	II	III
$\Delta H^\circ_{f(298)}$	( )	( )	0
$S^\circ_{(298)}$	51.2	( )	31.2
$C^\circ_{p(298)}$	( )	( )	7.0

$\Delta S^\circ =$
$\Delta H^\circ =$
$\Delta C^\circ_p =$

Path	log A	E	log k_T (575)	Conditions	System	Surface	References
$b(?)$	15.3	51.4	−4.23	551–608 °K 2–40 mm Hg	static		[1] Kinzi Tamaru, M. Boudart, and H. Taylor, J. Phys. (1955); P. J. Fensham, K Tamaru, M. Boudart, an H. Taylor, J. Phys. Cher **59**, 806 (1955).

Preferred:
   Observed kinetics are reasonable; however, see below.

Comments: The parameters of H-abstraction by H-atoms from germane are not known; however $H + D_2$ has a 9 kcal/mole activation energy. If, as seems reasonable, H-abstraction from GeH_4 has a much lower activation energy, the absence of HD in the D_2–GeH_4 experiments is expected. Large amounts of HD in the GeH_4–GeD_4 pyrolysis, on the other hand, with little or no isotopic mixing in the germanes, strongly suggests a free radical chain process. We favor path b and identify the reported parameters with a chain process.

Experimental

   [1] Rates followed manometrically. Complex system. A zero-order surface reaction took place on deposited germanium concurrently with the homogeneous reaction. Stoichiometry $(1 \rightarrow 2)$ was assumed. Eventual products of the decomposition were Ge and H_2; no $(GeH_2)_n$ polymer was observed. The surface reaction was catalyzed by O_2. GeH_4 pyrolyzed in D_2 gave no HD. Mixtures of GeH_4 and GeD_4 gave appreciable HD production. Since no HD was formed in the presence of D_2, the authors concluded that the initiation step was path a.

eaction: **Tetraethyl germane**

$$Ge(C_2H_5)_4\ (I) \xrightarrow{a} Ge + 4C_2H_5\cdot$$
$$\xrightarrow{b} \cdot Ge(C_2H_5)_3\ (II) + C_2H_5\cdot\ (III)$$

	I	II	III	Ge
$\Delta H^\circ_{f(298)}$	(−35.0)	( )	25.7	78.4
$S^\circ_{(298)}$	129.6	(113)	57.8	40.1
$C^\circ_{p(298)}$	54.0	( )	12.1	5

$S^\circ = 41.2$ g/mole
$H^\circ =$
$C^\circ_p =$

log A	E	log k_T (710)	Conditions	System	Surface	References
14.23	51.0	−1.47	693–723 °K 17–465 mm Hg	static	< 5%	[1] R. L. Geddes and E. Mack, J. Am. Chem. Soc. **52,** 4372 (1930)

referred:
Unreliable.

omments: The mechanism of this reaction is undoubtedly complex (see $Pb(C_2H_5)_4$). Free radical chain rocesses must be important. An identification of the reported parameters with an initial split is not possible.

Experimental

[1] Rates were followed manometrically. Gaseous products were similar to those of the *n*-butane pyrolysis being 0 to 70 percent ethane and ethylene. First-order rate constants fell off appreciably below 70 mm Hg but were unaffected y the addition of inert gases.

Reaction: Tetracarbonyl nickel (*o*) (nickel carbonyl)

$$Ni(CO)_4 \text{ (I)} \longrightarrow \cdot Ni(CO)_3 \text{ (II)} + CO \text{ (III)}$$

	I	II	III	Ni
$\Delta H^\circ_{f(298)}$	-145.1	( )	-26.4	102.8
$S^\circ_{(298)}$	( )	( )	47.3	43.5
$C^\circ_{p(298)}$	( )	( )	7.0	

$\Delta S^\circ =$
$\Delta H^\circ =$
$\Delta C^\circ_p =$

log A	E	log k_T (330)	Conditions	System	Surface	References
9.5	19.1	-3.15	308–353 °K 15–80 mm Hg	static	(*)	[1] R. K. Chan and R. McIntosh, Can. J. Chem. **40**, 845 (1962).

Preferred:
    Unreliable.

Comments: This reaction is obviously complex with appreciable surface catalysis. The abnormally low *A*-factor is untenable in terms of transition state theory.

Experimental

[1] Rates were based on pressure measurements. The homogeneous mechanism of Bawn (Trans. Faraday Soc. **31**, 440 (1935) was used.

$$Ni(CO)_4 \xrightarrow{\ 1\ } Ni(CO)_3 + CO$$

$$Ni(CO)_3 \xrightarrow{\ 2\ } Ni + 3CO$$

$$CO + Ni(CO)_3 \xrightarrow{\ 3\ } Ni(CO)_4$$

---

*A large heterogeneous component to the rate was observed and the overall kinetics were separated into homogeneous and heterogeneous parts. The heterogeneous part was assumed to be proportional to adsorbed Ni(CO)₄ which competes for adsorption sites with CO.

Reaction: Tetraethyl lead

$$(C_2H_5)_4Pb \text{ (I)} \longrightarrow C_2H_5 \cdot \text{(II)} + \cdot Pb(C_2H_5)_3 \text{ (III)}$$

	I	II	III	Pb
$\Delta H^\circ_{f(298)}$	23.0	25.7	( )	46.8
$S^\circ_{(298)}$	( )	57.8		41.9
$C^\circ_{p(298)}$		12.1	( )	5

$\Delta S^\circ =$
$\Delta H^\circ =$
$\Delta C_p^\circ =$

log A	E	log k_T (525)	Conditions	System	Surface	References
12.6	37.0	−2.80	506–548 °K 2–13 mm Hg	static	< 5%	[1] G. L. Pratt and J. H. Purnell, Trans. Faraday Soc. **60**, 519 (1964).
12.1	36.9	−3.26	518–548 °K 13–52 mm Hg	static	< 5%	[2] J. A. Leermakers, J. Am. Chem. Soc. **55**, 4508 (1933).

Preferred:
Suspect.

Comments: $D_1 + D_2 + D_3 + D_4 = 126.6$ kcal/mole; $\bar{D} = 31.7$ kcal/mole.

Reference [1] represents one of the most careful studies made on any metal alkyl reaction. However, the complexities of the reaction are apparent and a negative activation entropy is not reasonable. Free radical chain decomposition is apparently responsible for the low parameters.

Experimental

[1] G.L.C. analysis of all products. Approximately 17 products were observed, although the major products (identified also as the only initial products) were n-C_4H_{10}, C_2H_4, C_2H_6, and H_2. Rates were obtained from initial rates of product formation. Product ratios were shown to vary with percent reaction and a chain decomposition (length ∼ 4.6) was evident. Product yield versus time curves for the four major products were constructed and individual reaction orders for their formation were obtained.

[2] Rates were based on pressure measurements.

Reaction: Silane

$$SiH_4 \text{ (I)} \xrightarrow{\ a\ } SiH_2\text{: (II)} + H_2 \text{ (III)}$$
$$\xrightarrow{\ b\ } SiH_3\cdot + H\cdot$$

	I	II	III
$\Delta H^\circ_{f(298)}$	8.2	( )	0
$S^\circ_{(298)}$	49.0	( )	31.2
$C^\circ_{p(298)}$	10.3	( )	7

$\Delta S^\circ =$
$\Delta H^\circ =$
$\Delta C_p^\circ =$

$\log A$	E	$\log k_T$ (675)	Conditions	System	Surface	References
15.2	55.9	-2.90	646–703 °K 35–230 torr	static	none	[1] J. H. Purnell and R. Walsh, Proc. Roy. Soc. **A293**, 543 (1966).

Preferred:

Overall kinetics are reliable; however, identification of the parameters with any initial step is questionable.

Comments: Electron impact studies have placed $\Delta H^\circ(SiH_3\!-\!H)$ at about 94 ± 3 kcal/mole while the average $E(Si\!-\!H)$ in silane is 78 kcal/mole. The authors correctly showed that the observed activation energy is too low for mechanism B (path b) if electron impact numbers are used and can only barely be reconciled with the average bond energies. They therefore tentatively attributed the kinetics to mechanism A. However, the copyrolysis of SiH_4 and SiD_4, Ring, et al. (private communication) have shown that $H_2/HD/D_2 = 4/3/1$ the early stages of pyrolysis where H,D exchange in the silanes was negligible. This is consistent with a free radical formation of hydrogen involving H-atoms and cannot be reconciled with the silene mechanism. The mechanism of the SiH_4 decomposition, and particularly the initiation reaction, is therefore still unknown, but we favor path b initiation.

Experimental

[1] Rates were determined by complete G.L.C. analysis of the products. Principal products were Si_2H_6 and H Si_3H_8 was a minor product and a solid polymer of formula $(SiH_2)_n$ which decomposed eventually to Si, and H_2 was al formed. The reaction order in silane for the initial stages of reaction (0–2 percent) was 1.5 and was attributed to a pressure falloff in the above initiation reaction. Additions of the inert gas (SF_6) accelerated reaction rates but did not affect the order of the reaction relative to SiH_4. Latter stages of reaction (10–20 percent) were shown to be kinetically complex involving principally the decomposition of polymer and Si_2H_6 which rapidly reached steady state. Rates were first order in silane and agreed with earlier studies by Stockland and Hodgness et al. (references cited by Purnell and Walsh

$$\log k_{\text{later stages}} \simeq 13.2 - 51.2/\theta.$$

The two mechanisms considered were:

A.
$SiH_4 \longrightarrow SiH_2 + H_2$ slow
$SiH_2 + SiH_4 \rightleftharpoons Si_2H_6$ fast
$SiH_2 + Si_2H_6 \rightleftharpoons Si_3H_8$

B.
$SiH_4 \longrightarrow H + SiH_3$
$H + SiH_4 \rightleftharpoons H_2 + SiH_3$
$SiH_3 + SiH_4 \rightleftharpoons Si_2H_6 + H$
$2SiH_3 \longrightarrow Si_2H_6$

542

Reaction: Tetramethylsilane (silicon tetramethyl)

$$Si(CH_3)_4 \; (I) \xrightarrow{\;a\;} \cdot Si(CH_3)_3 \; (II) + CH_3 \cdot \; (III)$$
$$\xrightarrow{\;b\;} Si + 4CH_3 \cdot$$

	I	II	III	Si
$\Delta H^\circ_{f(298)}$	-76.0	$[-31.2]$	34.0	108
$S_{(298)}$	85.5	82	46.5	40.1
$C^\circ_{p(298)}$	33.5	$(\quad)$	8.3	5

$\Delta S^\circ = 43$ g/mole
$\Delta H^\circ = [78.8]$ kcal/mole
$\Delta C^\circ_p = (\quad)$ g/mole

$\log A$	E	$\log k_T$ (965)	Conditions	System	Surface	References
15.1	78.8	-2.75	933–933 °K 4–438 mm Hg	static	none	[1] D. F. Helm and E. Mack, J. Am. Chem. Soc. **59**, 60 (1937)
						[2] T. V. Sathyamurthy, S. Swaminathan, and L. M. Yeddanapalli, J. Ind. Chem. Soc. **27**, 509 (1950), C.A.–6469a (1951)

Preferred:
   $\log k_a = 15.1 - 78.8/\theta$.

Comments: This reaction must be a chain reaction with path a as the initiation reaction. Although the reaction must be quite complex, the parameters reported look fairly reasonable for path a.

Experimental

[1] Rates were followed by pressure changes. Products were silicon, carbon, and hydrocarbons similar to those found in the ethane decomposition. First-order constants were obtained for initial pressures greater than 100 mm Hg; higher orders ($\sim$ 3/2) were observed for lower initial pressures $(P_\infty/P_o) \simeq 2.95$–3.01.

[2] Re-analyses of rate data [1]. Free radical mechanism proposed. First-order kinetics was predicted at pressures above 149 torr.

Reaction: Tetraethylsilane (silicon tetraethyl)

$$Si(C_2H_5)_4 \ (I) \xrightarrow{\ a\ } \cdot Si(C_2H_5)_3 \ (II) + C_2H_5 \cdot (III)$$
$$\xrightarrow{\ b\ } Si + 4C_2H_5 \cdot$$

	I	II	III	Si
$\Delta H^\circ_{f(298)}$	( )	( )	25.7	108
$S^\circ_{(298)}$	123	110.2	57.8	40.1
$C^\circ_{p(298)}$	55.5		12.1	5

$$\Delta S^\circ \overset{a}{=} 45 \text{ g/mole}$$
$$\Delta H^\circ =$$
$$\Delta C^\circ_p =$$

log A	E	log k_T	Conditions	System	Surface	References
15.8	50.5		793–873 °K 20–200 mm Hg	static	none	[1] C. E. Waring, Trans. Faraday Soc. **36**, 1142 (1940)

Preferred:
  Unreliable.

Comments: At the reaction temperatures, extensive chain decomposition must take place, mainly promoted by H-atom reactions with the reactant. No identification of the parameters reported with an initial decomposition is possible.

Experimental

[1] Rates were obtained on the basis of initial pressure increases. The ratio (P_f/P_o) varied with P_o. Products were ethylene, CH_4, H_2, and Si. Addition of small quantities of NO did not appreciably affect the initial reaction rates, although inhibition in later stages was observed. Heterogeneous decomposition was appreciable in clean reaction cells but unimportant in the initial stages for Si-coated cells.

Reaction: Tetra-n-propylsilane (silicon tetra n-propyl)

$$Si(nC_3H_7)_4 \text{ (I)} \xrightarrow{a} Si(C_3H_7)_3 \text{ (II)} + nC_3H_7 \cdot \text{ (III)}$$
$$\xrightarrow{b} Si + 4[nC_3H_7]$$

	I	II	III	Si·
$\Delta H^\circ_{f(298)}$	( )	( )	20.7	108
$S^\circ_{(298)}$	160.6	138.4	67.2	40.1
$C^\circ_{p(298)}$	77.5	( )	17.6	5

$\Delta S^\circ = (45.0)$ g/mole
$\Delta H^\circ =$ kcal/mole
$\Delta C^\circ_p =$ g/mole

log A	E	log k_T	Conditions	System	Surface	References
14.14	46.0	(−2.11)	793–843 °K 20–160 mm Hg	static	none (when conditioned)	[1] C. E. Waring, Trans. Faraday Soc. **36**, 1142 (1940).

Preferred:
    Unreliable.

Comments: Must be a chain reaction.

Experimental

[1] Products were C_3H_6, C_2H_4, CH_4, H_2, and Si. See comments on $Si(C_2H_5)_4$.

Reaction: Hexamethyldisilane

$$(CH_3)_3Si\!-\!Si(CH_3)_3 \;\; (I) \longrightarrow 2(CH_3)_3Si \cdot (II)$$

	I	II
$\Delta H^\circ_{f(298)}$	( )	(-3.12)
$S^\circ_{(298)}$	(99)	(73)
$C^\circ_{p(298)}$	(50)	(27)

$\Delta S^\circ = 47.0$ g/mole
$\Delta H^\circ =$
$\Delta C^\circ_p = 4.0$ g/mole

log A	E	log k_T (980)	Conditions	System	Surface	References
12.2 ± 1	49.5 ± 6	$+1.16$	$940–1020\ °K$ $P_T \simeq 10^{-3}-10^{-5}$ torr	flow	none	[1] J. A. Connor, R. N. Haszeldine, G. J. Leigh, and R. D. Sedgwick, J. Chem. Soc. A, 768 (1967).
	58 ± 4		$923–983\ °K$ $\delta P \simeq 0.1–1$ torr $\dfrac{P_{\text{toluene}}}{\delta P} \simeq 20–170$	flow		[2] J. A. Connor, G. Finney, G. J. Leigh, R. N. Haszeldine, P. J. Robinson, R. D. Sedgwick, and R. F. Simmons, Chem. Comm., 178 (1966).

Preferred:
Parameters seem low. We estimate, log $k = 16.0 - 62.0/\theta$; however, see below.

Comments: Although there are large uncertainties in the thermodynamics, the entropy of activation for this system must be sizable. Certainly a negative activation entropy is quite impossible. The rate constants of [1] are undoubtedly pressure dependent and do not represent the reaction in its first order region. Unfortunately, no rate constants were given in [2], although the activation energy looks more reasonable. The bond dissociation energies of silicon-silicon bonds are still very much in doubt.

Experimental

[1] Straight flow technique. Analysis by M.S. directly on the products leaving the reaction zone. Similar parameters were obtained with and without toluene. Products in the presence of toluene were bibenzyl, triethylsilane and traces of other alkyl-silanes, methane and hydrogen.
[2] Toluene carrier technique. Products were those of [1].

Reaction: Tetramethyltin

$$\mathrm{Sn(CH_3)_4 \ (I)} \quad \overset{a}{\xrightarrow{\hspace{1cm}}} \cdot \mathrm{Sn(CH_3)_3 \ (II) + CH_3 \cdot \ (III)}$$
$$\overset{b}{\xrightarrow{\hspace{1cm}}} \mathrm{Sn + 4[CH_3 \cdot]}$$

	I	II	III	Sn
$\Delta H^\circ_{f(298)}$	(-4.2)	( )	34.0	72.0
$S^\circ_{(298)}$	(86)	(83)	46.7	40.2
$C^\circ_{p(298)}$	( )	( )	8.3	5

$\Delta S^\circ =$
$\Delta H^\circ =$
$\Delta C^\circ_p =$

log A	E	log k_T (740)	Conditions	System	Surface	References
21.92	82.4	-2.42	713–766 °K 5–185 mm Hg	static	$< 5\%^*$	[1] C. E. Waring and W. S. Horton, J. Am. Chem. Soc. **67,** 540 (1945).

Preferred:
Unreliable.

Comments: The reaction is far too complex to be studied by simple manometric methods. It is unlikely that the reported parameters have any relevance to the initial bond breaking reactions *a*. Reaction *b* is obviously not possible.

Experimental

[1] Rates were followed manometrically. Gaseous products were CH_4(80–90 percent), C_2H_4, H_2, and higher olefins. Initial reaction rates were used to obtain the rate constants. NO catalyzed the decomposition.

---

*In clean reaction vessels the decomposition was predominantly heterogeneous.

Reaction: Dichlorodimethylstannane (dimethyl tin dichloride)

$$(CH_3)_2SnCl_2 \; (I) \begin{array}{c} \xrightarrow{\;a\;} CH_3\cdot \; (II) + CH_3\dot{S}nCl_2 \; (III) \\ \xrightarrow{\;b\;} 2CH_3\cdot \pm SnCl_2 \end{array}$$

	I	II	III	Sn
$\Delta H^\circ_{f(298)}$	-69.4	34.0	$([-47.3])$	72
$S^\circ_{p(298)}$	95.8	46.5	$(\quad)$	40.2
$C^\circ_{p(298)}$	28.5	8.8	$(\quad)$	5

$\Delta S^\circ =$
$\Delta H^\circ =$
$\Delta C^\circ_p =$

log A	E	log k_T (895)	Conditions	System	Surface	References
13.5	56.1	-0.20	827–961 °K 16.1 mm Hg	flow	none	[1] S. J. W. Price and A. F. Trotman-Dickenson, Trans. Faraday Soc. **54**, 1630 (1958).

Preferred:

Suspect.

Comments: The total pressure dependence on the reaction rates indicates pressure falloff behavior and/or mechanistic complexities.

Experimental

[1] Toluene carrier technique. Rates were based on yields of CH_4 and C_2H_6.

Mechanism:
$$(CH_3)_2SnCl \longrightarrow CH_3\dot{S}nCl_2 + CH_3\cdot$$
$$CH_3\dot{S}nCl_2 \longrightarrow CH_3\cdot + SnCl_2$$
$$CH_3\cdot + CH_3\emptyset \longrightarrow CH_4 + \cdot CH_2\emptyset$$
$$2CH_3\cdot \longrightarrow C_2H_6$$
$$2\emptyset CH_2\cdot \longrightarrow (\emptyset CH_2)_2$$

Rate constants were shown to be independent of the contact time and of the pressure of the metal alkyl, but slightly dependent on the total pressure. Under conditions of total decomposition, $\Delta(CH_3)_2SnCl_2 = \Delta C_2H_6 + \frac{1}{2}\Delta CH_4$. Tin (II) chloride yields were not reported.

Reaction: Diborane

$$B_2H_6 \text{ (I)} \xrightarrow{\quad a \quad} BH_2 : \text{(II)} + BH_4 \text{ (III)}$$
$$\xrightarrow{\quad b \quad} BH_3 + BH_3 \text{ (IV)}$$

	I	II	III	IV
$\Delta H^\circ_{f(298)}$	9.8 ± 4	48 ± 15	( )	22.4 ± 2
$S^\circ_{(298)}$	55.7	43.0	( )	44.9
$C^\circ_{p(298)}$	13.9	8.1	( )	8.6

b

$\Delta S^\circ = 34.1$ g/mole
$\Delta H^\circ = 35.0$ kcal/mole
$\Delta C^\circ_p = 3.3$ g/mole

Path	$\log A$	E	$\log k_T$ (455)	Conditions	System	Surface	References
a	18.0	44	-3.13	(see comments)			[1] T. P. Fehlner, J. Am. Chem. Soc. **87**, 4200 (1965)
b		35 ± 3		(see comments)			[2] M. E. Garabedian and S. W. Benson, J. Am. Chem. Soc. **86**, 176 (1964)

Preferred:
   $\log k_b = 13.0 - 35/\theta$.

Comments: The activation energy of [2] has been confirmed by the kinetics and thermochemistry of the (BH_3PH_3) decomposition.

Experimental

[1] Reinterpretation of existing kinetic data. Arrhenius constants deduced from the overall kinetics and assumed parameters of the chain reactions. Mechanism proposed was a complex chain.

[Prior studies: J. K. Bragg, L. V. McCarty, and F. J. Norton, J. Am. Chem. Soc. **73**, 2134 (1951); K. Borer, A. B. Littlewood, and C. S. Phillips, J. Inorg. Nucl. Chem. **15**, 316 (1960); R. P. Pease and R. N. Pease, J. Am. Chem. Soc. **73**, 2132 (1951); R. E. Enrioni and R. Schaeffer, J. Inorg. Nucl. Chem. **18**, 103 (1961); S. H. Bauer, J. Am. Chem. Soc. **78**, 5775 (1956).]

Thermodynamics of B_2H_6 and BH_3 are from A. Shepp and S. H. Bauer, J. Am. Chem. Soc. **76**, 265 (1954).

[2] Reinterpretation of the existing data on this reaction and on the BH_3CO decomposition.

Reaction: Borine carbonyl

$$BH_3CO \text{ (I)} \longrightarrow BH_3 \text{ (II)} + CO \text{ (III)}$$

	I	II	III
$\Delta H^\circ_{f(298)}$	( )	22.4	−26.4
$S^\circ_{(298)}$	( )	44.9	47.3
$C^\circ_{p(298)}$	( )	8.6	7.0

$\Delta S^\circ =$
$\Delta H^\circ =$
$\Delta C^\circ_p =$

log A	E	log k_T (425)	Conditions	System	Surface	References
14.42	23.7	+2.23	(see Experimental)			[1] M. E. Garabedian and S. W. Benson, J. Am. Chem. Soc. **86**, 176 (1964)
14 ± 0.5	23.3	+2.01	388–462 °K 0.9–22 × 10⁻³ mm Hg	flow		[2] T. P. Fehlner and W. S. Koski, J. Am. Chem. Soc. **87**, 409 (1965)
k_{90} 11.7 torr	19.6		267–305 °K $P_T \sim 90$ torr	static		[3] J. Grotewald, E. A. Lissi, and A. E. Villa, J. Chem. Soc. **A**, 1038 (1966)
k_∞ 13.4	21.4					

Preferred:

$\log k = 14.4 - 23.7/\theta$.

Experimental

[1] Based on a reanalysis of the data of A. B. Burg, J. Am. Chem. Soc. **74**, 3482 (1952), J. Am. Chem. Soc. **59**, 780 (1937), and of Y. C. Fu and G. R. Hill, J. Am. Chem. Soc. **84**, 353 (1962).

[2] Analysis by M.S.

[3] Triethylamine was added to scavenge all BH_3 so that the initial fission kinetics could be studied. Rates were followed by CO analysis (chromatography on molecular sieves). Mechanism:

$$(M) + BH_3CO \rightarrow BH_3 + CO + (M)$$
$$BH_3 + Et_3N \rightarrow Et_3N : BH_3$$
$$BH_3CO + Et_3N \rightarrow \text{complex}$$

The $P_{1/2}$ was found to be about 90 torr from a study of total pressure effect on the reaction rate.

Reaction: Trifluorophosphine borane

$$BH_3PF_3 \ (I) \longrightarrow BH_3 \ (II) + \ : PF_3 \ (III)$$

	I	II	III
$\Delta H^\circ_{f(298)}$	(-221.5)	22 ± 2	-220 ± 4
$S^\circ_{(298)}$	$(73\ 3)$	44.9	65.2
$C^\circ_{p(298)}$	$(\quad)$	8.6	14.0

$\Delta S^\circ = 36.8$ g/mole
$\Delta H^\circ = 23.5$ kcal/mole
$\Delta C^\circ_p =$

log A	E	log k_T (300)	Conditions	System	Surface	References
13.94	23.45	-3.14	273–328 °K (10–28 torr, 170–308 torr)	static		[1] A. B. Burg and Yuan-Chin Fu, J. Am. Chem. Soc. **88**, 1147 (1966).

Preferred:
   Reliable.   log $k = 13.94 - 23.45/\theta$.

Experimental

[1] Rates were based on the formation of PF_3 which was followed by I.R. analysis. The equilibrium

$$2BH_3PF_3 \rightleftharpoons B_2H_6 + 2PF_3$$

was also studied,

$$\log K_{(atm)} = 8.67 - 11.87/\theta.$$

The mechanism proposed was:

$$BH_3PF_3 \underset{2}{\overset{1}{\rightleftharpoons}} BH_3 + \ : PF_3$$

$$BH_3 + BH_3PF_3 \underset{4}{\overset{3}{\rightleftharpoons}} B_2H_6 + PF_3 \ .$$

From the kinetics, $\log (k_1 k_3 / k_2) = 15.84 - 29.3/\theta$, and from the thermodynamics (with equilibria in units of moles/l),

$$B_2H_6 \underset{6}{\overset{5}{\rightleftharpoons}} 2BH_3, \ \Delta G^\circ_{(kcal/mole)} = 35.0 - T(0.0342).$$

Thus the activation energy for diborane decomposition was set at 35 ± 1 kcal/mole assuming $E_6 = 0$. In addition,

$$\log k_1/k_2 = 8.06 - 23.45/\theta$$

$$\log \frac{k_1 k_3}{k_2 k_4} = 8.67 - 11.88/\theta$$

$$\log k_5/k_6 = 7.47 - 35.0/\theta.$$

(Continued)

Trifluorophosphine borane *(Continued)*

The decomposition kinetics of $BH_3 \cdot CF_3PF_2$ and $BH_3 \cdot (CF_3)_2PF$ were also studied and found to conform to mechanisms similar to that for $PF_3 \cdot BH_3 \cdot$

$$(BH_3 \cdot CF_3PF_2) \ \log \left(\frac{k_1 k_3}{k_2}\right) = 11.02 - 24.47/\theta$$

$$(BH_3 \cdot (CF_3)_2PF) \ \log \left(\frac{k_1 k_3}{k_2}\right) = 11.70 - 21.54/\theta.$$

Reaction: Dinitrogen oxide (nitrous oxide)

$$N_2O \text{ (I)} \longrightarrow N_2 \text{ (II)} + O \text{ (III)}$$

	I	II	III
$\Delta H^\circ_{f(298)}$	19.5	0	59.2
$S^\circ_{(298)}$	52.6	45.8	38.5
$C^\circ_{p(298)}$	9.3	7.0	5.2

$\Delta S^\circ = 31.7$ g/mole
$\Delta H^\circ = 39.7$ kcal/mole
$\Delta C^\circ_p = 2.9$ g/mole

log A	E	log k_T (720)	Conditions	System	Surface	References
12.38	65.0	−3.06	840–999 °K 0.25–40 atm	static		[1] E. Hunter, Proc. Roy. Soc. (L) **A144**, 386 (1934).
11.7	60.6	−2.70	(reanalysis of all existing data) (40 atm)			[2] H. S. Johnston, J. Chem. Phys. **19**, 663 (1951).

Preferred:
  Not reliable.

Comments: The very low Arrhenius A-factor supports Johnston's analysis [2], as a second-order pressure dependent unimolecular reaction.

Experimental

[1] Rates followed by pressure change. Above 30 atm, the rate constants were essentially pressure independent. Mechanism:

$$N_2O \longrightarrow N_2 + O; \ 2O + M \longrightarrow O_2$$

$$O + N_2O \longrightarrow O_2 + N_2 \text{ (only in initial stages)}.$$

[2] Corrected all existing rate constants for the heterogeneous reaction at low pressures. Showed that even at 40 atm, the rate constants were still increasing with increasing pressure; therefore, the reaction was probably not in its high-pressure region.

For earlier references to this reaction see H. J. Schumacher, *Chemische Gasreaktionen*, Photo-Lithoprint Reproduction, Edwards Brothers, Inc., Lithoprinters, Ann Arbor, Michigan, 1943, p. 131.

Reaction: Dinitrogen tetroxide

$$N_2O_4 \ (I) \longrightarrow 2NO_2 \ (II)$$

	I	II
$\Delta H^\circ_{f(298)}$	2.3	8.1
$S^\circ_{(298)}$	72.7	57.5
$C^\circ_{p(298)}$	18.9	8.7

$\Delta S^\circ = 42.3$ g/mole
$\Delta H^\circ = 13.9$ kcal/mole
$\Delta C^\circ_p = -1.5$ g/mole

log A	E	log k_T (275)	Conditions	System	Surface	References
16.0	13.1	+5.59	253–301 °K $P_T \simeq 0.5$–7 atm 1% N_2O_4 in N_2 or CO	shock		[1] T. Carrington and N. Davidson, J. Phys. Chem. **57**, 418 (1953).

Preferred:

$\log k = 16.0 - 13.1/\theta$; $A_{\text{rec}} \simeq 10^{8.2}$ l/mole-sec.

Experimental

[1] Rates were followed spectrophotometrically. For earlier references see H. J. Schumacher, *Chemische Gasreaktionen*, Photo-Lithoprint Reproduction, Edwards Brothers, Inc., Lithoprinters, Ann Arbor, Mich., 1943. *A*-factor was estimated by extrapolation of data to infinite pressure.

Reaction: Dinitrogen pentoxide

$$N_2O_5 \ (I) \longrightarrow NO_2 \ (II) + NO_3 \ (III)$$

	I	II	III
$\Delta H^\circ_{f(298)}$	2.7	8.1	17.0
$S^\circ_{(298)}$	82.8	57.5	60.4
$C^\circ_{p(298)}$	23.0	8.7	11.2

$\Delta S^\circ = 35.1$ g/mole
$\Delta H^\circ = 22.4$ kcal/mole
$\Delta C^\circ_p = -3.1$ g/mole

$\log A$	E	$\log k_T$ (275)	Conditions	System	Surface	References
12.78	19	-2.32	264–283 °K 88–133 mm Hg	static		[1] A. R. Amell and F. Daniels J. Am. Chem. Soc. **74**, 6209 (1952).
13.1	20	-2.80	293–303 °K	static	(none)	[2] I. C. Hisatsune, Bryce Crawford, Jr., and R. A. Ogg, Jr., J. Am. Chem. Soc. **79**, 4648 (1957).
14.78	21	-1.91				[3] S. W. Benson, Foundation of Chemical Kinetics, McGraw-Hill Book Co., Inc., New York, 1960, p. 408.

Preferred:

$\log k = 14.78 - 21.0/\theta$; $k_{rec} = 10^{8.6}$ l/mole·sec.

Experimental

[1] Decomposed N_2O_5 in labeled $N^{15}O_2$. The rate of exchange was followed by M.S. analysis of the N_2O_5.

[2] Analysis by fast scanning I.R.

[3] Rate constants were calculated from the data of R. L. Mills and H. S. Johnston, J. Am. Chem. Soc. **73**, 938 (1951). Also see [3] for extensive referencing of the kinetics of this reaction.

The equilibrium constant has been measured as $K_c = 10^{4.97-20.1/\theta}$ mole/l.

Reaction: Nitryl chloride

$$NO_2Cl \ (I) \longrightarrow NO_2 \ (II) + Cl \ (III)$$

	I	II	III
$\Delta H^\circ_{f(298)}$	(2.9)	8.1	29.0
$S^\circ_{(298)}$	(65)	57.5	39.5
$C^\circ_{p(298)}$	(12.7)	8.7	5.2

$\Delta S^\circ = 32$ g/mole
$\Delta H^\circ = 34.2$ kcal/mole
$\Delta C^\circ_p = 1.2$ g/mole

log A	E	log k_T (390)	Conditions	System	Surface	References
12.36	27.0	−2.77	373–403 °K 103–5900 torr 11.4–430 torr	static		[1] H. J. Schumacher and G. Sprenger, Z. Anorg. Allg. Chem. **182**, 139 (1929)
(See below)						[2] H. F. Cordes and H. S. Johnston, J. Am. Chem. Soc. **76**, 4264 (1954)

Preferred:
 log $k_\infty = 15.0 - 33/\theta$.
 log $k_{rec} \simeq 9.5$. Rate constants [1] are probably reliable.

Experimental

[1] Rates were followed by pressure change. Reaction products were NO_2 and Cl_2. Rate constants were pressure dependent. k_∞ values were obtained from ($1/k$ versus $1/p$) plot extrapolations.

Mechanism: $NO_2Cl \rightleftharpoons NO_2Cl$
$Cl + NO_2Cl \rightleftharpoons Cl_2 + NO_2$
$Cl_2 + M \rightleftharpoons 2Cl + M$

Chain length is 2.

[2] The reaction was shown to be in the second order region with first order rate constants of any single run being total pressure dependent. Inert gas effects and relative collision efficiencies were studied.

Reaction: Nitroxyl fluoride (fluorine nitrate)

$$NO_3F \; (I) \text{------} NO_3 \; (II) + F \; (III)$$

	I	II	III
$\Delta H^\circ_{f(298)}$	2.5	17.1	18.3
$S^\circ_{(298)}$	70.0	59.4	37.9
$C^\circ_{p(298)}$	15.6	12.0	5.4

$\Delta S^\circ = 27.3$ g/mole
$\Delta H^\circ = 32.9$ kcal/mole
$\Delta C^\circ_p = 1.8$ g/mole

log A	E	log k_T (385)	Conditions	System	Surface	References
15.39	32.3	−2.95	363–403 °K 0.6–400 mm Hg			[1] L. Viscido, J. E. Sicre, and H. J. Schumacher, Zeit. für Physik. Chemie, **N.F. 33**, 206 (1962)
13.76	29.7	−3.11	353–379 °K 2–211 mm Hg		< 1%	[2] W. E. Skeins and G. H. Cady, J. Am. Chem. Soc. **80**, 5640 (1958)

Preferred:
   log $k = 15.39 - 32.3/\theta$.

Comments: The A-factor and reaction entropy give a recombination rate which is close to collision frequencies, $k_{rec} = 10^{10.9}$ l/mole-sec.

Experimental

[1] Rates were followed manometrically. Products were O_2 and NO_2F in stoichiometric amounts. ($NO_3F \to NO_2F + 1/2O_2$) Identification by I.R. Falloff was observed, and at 373 °K the $P_{1/2} \simeq 32$ mm Hg. The mechanism proposed was:

$$NO_3F \longrightarrow NO_3 + F$$
$$2NO_3 \longrightarrow 2NO_2 + O_2$$
$$NO_2 + F + M \longrightarrow NO_2F + M$$

[2] Rates were followed by pressure changes. Products were identified by I.R., M.S., and gas density as O_2 and NO_2F. Falloff observed at $P < 50$ mm Hg. The mechanism above was favored.

Reaction: Chlorine nitrate (nitroxyl chloride)

$$NO_3Cl \ (I) \longrightarrow NO_2 \ (II) + ClO \ (III)$$

	I	II	III
$\Delta H^\circ_{f(298)}$	( )	8.1	24.2
$S^\circ_{(298)}$	( )	57.5	54.1
$C^\circ_{p(298)}$	( )	8.7	7.5

$\Delta S^\circ =$
$\Delta H^\circ =$
$\Delta C^\circ_p =$

log A	E	log k_T (385)	Conditions	System	Surface	References
14.2	30	−2.84	363–403 °K 8–200 mm Hg	static		[1] L. F. R. Cafferata, J. E. Sicre, and H. J. Schumacher, Zeit für Physik. Chemie. **N.F. 29,** 188 (1961).

Preferred:
   log $k = 14.2 - 30/\theta$.

Experimental

[1] The reaction was followed manometrically. The stoichiometry was found to be $NO_3Cl \longrightarrow NO_2 + 1/2\,Cl_2 + 1/2\,O_2$. Rate constants were pressure dependent.

The mechanism proposed was:

$$NO_3Cl \underset{2}{\overset{1}{\rightleftharpoons}} NO_2 + OCl$$

$$ClO \overset{wall\ 3}{\rightleftharpoons} 1/2\ Cl_2 + 1/2\ O_2$$

$$ClO + NO_3Cl \overset{4^*}{\rightleftharpoons} NO_2 + O_2 + Cl_2$$

---

*Reaction 4 was not meant to represent an elementary process.

Reaction: Difluorine dioxide

$$F_2O_2 \text{ (I)} \xrightarrow[b]{a} \begin{array}{l} 2FO\cdot \text{ (II)} \\ FO_2^{\cdot} + F \end{array}$$

	I	II
$\Delta H^\circ_{f(298)}$	18 ± 5	(27)
$S^\circ_{(298)}$		
$C^\circ_{p(298)}$		

$\Delta S^\circ =$
$\Delta H^\circ =$
$\Delta C^\circ_p =$

log A	E	log k_T (230)	Conditions	System	Surface	References
12.77	17.3	-3.67	213–248 °K 2.5–500 mm Hg	static		[1] H. J. Schumacher and P. Frisch, Z. Physik. Chem. **B37**, 1 (1937).

Preferred:
Unreliable as a unimolecular reaction (see below).

Comments: Kinetic parameters are reliable; however, the proposed mechanism is not very reasonable. The kinetic data are beautifully first order over 3 half-lives, which implies that the reactant collision efficiency ($\alpha_{F_2O_2}$) for activation is just twice the sum of the product collision efficiencies. However, the authors give ($\alpha_{O_2} + \alpha_{F_2} = 1.5\ \alpha_{F_2O_2}$. The proposed split (path a) is also not favored by the reaction enthalpy. Thus we have,

$$\Delta H^\circ_f(F_2O) = 5.9 \text{ kcal/mole}$$

$$F_2O \xrightarrow{1} 2F\cdot + O \qquad \Delta H^\circ_1 \approx 91 \text{ kcal/mole}$$

If $\qquad DH^\circ(FO\!-\!F) \simeq 40 \pm 3 \text{ kcal/mole}$

then $\qquad DH^\circ(F\!-\!O) \simeq 51 \pm 3 \text{ kcal/mole}$

and $\qquad \Delta H^\circ_f(\cdot OF) \simeq 27 \text{ kcal/mole}$

Note also that,

$$F_2O_2 \xrightarrow{2} 2F + O_2 \qquad \Delta H^\circ_2 \simeq 20 \text{ kcal/mole}$$

In view of the above thermodynamics, a more reasonable interpretation of the reaction is as follows:

$$M + F_2O_2 \rightleftharpoons F + FO_2\cdot + M$$

$$M + FO_2\cdot \longrightarrow F + O_2 + M$$

(Continued)

Difluorine dioxide *(Continued)*

$$F + F_2O_2 \longrightarrow F_2 + FO_2$$

$$F \cdot \xrightarrow{\text{wall}} 1/2 \ F_2$$

$$2F \cdot + M \rightleftharpoons F_2 + M$$

Path *b* seems the more likely initiation step, and it should be pressure dependent.

Experimental

[1] Rates were followed by pressure change. Products were F_2 and O_2. The reaction was in the falloff region under experimental conditions and k_∞ values were obtained from $1/k$ versus $1/p$ plot extrapolations. P_∞ was estimated at around 10^3 mm Hg. Path *a* was proposed as the rate-determining initiation step.

The proposed mechanism was:

$$F_2O_2 \longrightarrow 2FO \cdot$$
$$2FO \cdot \longrightarrow F_2 + O_2 \cdot$$

Reaction: Chloryl fluoride

$$FClO_2 \longrightarrow FClO + O$$

$\Delta H^\circ_{f(298)}$

$S^\circ_{(298)}$

$C^\circ_{p(298)}$

$\Delta S^\circ =$
$\Delta H^\circ =$
$\Delta C_p^\circ =$

log A	E	log k_T (595)	Conditions	System	Surface	References
13.36	45.0	−3.17	573–613 °K 5–450 mm Hg	static		[1] M. J. Heras, P. J. Aymonino, and H. J. Schumacher, Zeit für Physik. Chemie, **N.F. 22,** 161 (1959).

Preferred:
Probably reliable. log $k = 13.36 - 45.0/\theta$.

Experimental

[1] Rates were followed by pressure change. Products were FCl and O_2. Reaction of FCl with the glass walls also produced Cl_2 and SiF_4.

The mechanism proposed was:

$$FClO_2 \longrightarrow FClO + O$$
$$O + FClO_2 \longrightarrow FClO + O_2$$
$$2FClO \longrightarrow 2FCl + O_2$$
$$FClO \xrightarrow{\text{wall}} FCl + 1/2\ O_2.$$

Reaction: Perchloryl fluoride

$$FClO_3 \text{ (I)} \longrightarrow FClO_2 \text{ (II)} + O \text{ (III)}$$

	I	II	III
$\Delta H^\circ_{f(298)}$	-5.1	( )	59.2
$S^\circ_{(298)}$	66.7	(63)	38.5
$C^\circ_{p(298)}$	15.5	(7.2)	5.2

$\Delta S^\circ =$
$\Delta H^\circ =$
$\Delta C^\circ_p =$

$\log A$	E	$\log k_T$ (755)	Conditions	System	Surface	References
13.59	58.4	-3.32	738–768 °K	static	none	[1] R. Gatti, J. E. Sicre, and H. J. Schumacher, Zeit. für Physik. Chemie., **N.F. 23,** 164 (1960).

Preferred: Probably reliable. $\log k = 13.59-58.4/\theta$.

Experimental

[1] The rate of reaction was followed manometrically. The products were FCl and O_2. The reaction mechanism proposed was:

$$FClO_3 \xrightarrow{\text{slow}} O + FClO_2$$
$$O + FClO_3 \longrightarrow FClO_2 + O_2$$
$$FClO_2 \longrightarrow FCl + O_2$$

Reaction: Dichlorine heptoxide

$$Cl_2O_7 \text{ (I)} \longrightarrow ClO_3 \text{ (II)} + ClO_4 \text{ (III)}$$

	I	II	III
$\Delta H^\circ_{f(298)}$	(65.0)	37	( )
$S^\circ_{(298)}$	( )	61.3	( )
$C^\circ_{p(298)}$	( )	12.1	( )

$\Delta S^\circ =$
$\Delta H^\circ =$
$\Delta C^\circ_p =$

log A	E	log k_T (385)	Conditions	System	Surface	References
15.72	33.5	−3.80	373–393 °K 1–80 mm Hg total $P \sim 400$ mm Hg	static	none	[1] E. Coloccia, R. V. Figini, and H. J. Schumacher, Angew. Chem. **68**, 492 (1956).

Preferred:
Reasonable. log $k = 15.72 - 33.5/\theta$.

Comments: With $n_{max} = 20$, an RRK $- M_{1/2} \simeq 76$ mm Hg is calculated. Thus falloff would be predicted near the pressure range observed.

Experimental

[1] Rates were followed manometrically. Products were Cl_2 and O_2. Evidence for ClO_2 as an intermediate was obtained by pyrolysis in fluorine in which $FClO_2$ was obtained as a product. Falloff of the reaction rate was observed at pressures below 10 mm Hg. At 1 mm Hg the reaction rate constant was $1/2\ k_\infty$. This may be a chemical effect, not a genuine pressure effect.

Reaction: Perchloric acid

$$HOClO_3 \text{ (I)} \longrightarrow HO \cdot \text{(II)} + \cdot ClO_3 \text{ (III)}$$

	I	II	III
$\Delta H^\circ_{f(298)}$	4 ± 4	9.4	37
$S^\circ_{(298)}$	69	43.9	61.3
$C^\circ_{p(298)}$	17.6	7.2	12.1

$\Delta S^\circ = 36.2$ g/mole
$\Delta H^\circ = 42.4 \pm 4$ kcal/mole
$\Delta C^\circ_p = 1.7$ g/mole

log A	E	log k_T	Conditions	System	Surface	References
13.8	45.1		623–712 °K	flow	< 5%	[1] J. B. Levy, J. Phys. Chem. **66**, 1092 (1962).

Preferred:
  Reasonable. log $k = 13.8 - 45.1/\theta$.

Comments: The energetics are consistent with the thermodynamics, however, a rate constant for recombination of about, $k_{rec} = 10^{7.7}$ l/mole-sec is calculated from A and ΔS° which seems low.

Experimental

[1] N_2 carrier was employed. Products were H_2O, O_2, and Cl_2. Analysis was for chloride by the Volhard and iodometric methods. The mechanism proposed was:

$$HOClO_3 \xrightarrow{\ 1\ } HO \cdot + ClO_3 \cdot$$

$$HO + HOClO_3 \xrightarrow{\ 2\ } H_2O + ClO_4 \cdot$$

$$ClO_4 \cdot \xrightarrow{\ 3\ } 1/2 Cl_2 + 2O_2$$

$$ClO_3 \cdot \xrightarrow{\ 4\ } 1/2 Cl_2 + 3/2 O_2$$

The observed kinetics were identified with the initiation step; subsequent reactions of indeterminate nature were considered fast and non-chain producing. The reaction was heterogeneous at $T < 623$ °K.

5. Free Radical Reactions

Reaction: Ethyl radical

$$C_2H_5 \cdot \text{(I)} \longrightarrow H \cdot + C_2H_4 \text{ (II)}$$

	I		H	II
	$V=0$	$V=4$		
$\Delta H^\circ_{f(298)}$	25.7	25.7	52.1	12.5
$S^\circ_{(298)}$	59.6	57.8	27.4	52.5
$C^\circ_{p(298)}$	10.9	12.1	5.0	10.4
$C^\circ_{p(500)}$	16.7	17.7	5.0	15.0

	$V=0$	$V=4$
$\Delta S^\circ =$	20.3	22.1 g/mole
$\Delta H^\circ =$	38.9	38.9 kcal/mole
$\Delta C^\circ_p =$	4.5	3.3 g/mole

log A	E	log k_T (750)	Conditions	System	Surface	References
14.0	40	2.34	673–773 °K $P_T \sim 400$ torr	Hg($^3P_1$)		[1] S. Bywater and E. W. R. Steacie, J. Chem. Phys. **19,** 326 (1951).
11.2	31	2.16	623–778 °K $P_T \sim 10$ torr	(see Experimental)		[2] J. A. Kerr and A. F. Trotman-Dickenson, I. Chem. Soc. 1611 (1960).
13.0	40.0	1.34	693–803 °K 10–150 torr	(see Experimental)		[3] J. H. Purnell and C. P. Quinn, Proc. Roy. Soc. **A270,** 267 (1962).

Preferred:
  log $k_a \simeq 13.5$–$40.7/\theta$.

Comments: Kinetics of the back reaction have been reported by a number of workers: K. R. Jennings and R. J. Cvetanovic, J. Chem. Phys. **35,** 1233 (1961); H. W. Melville and J. C. Robb, Proc. Roy. Soc. (L) **A202,** 181 (1950); Ibid. **A218,** 311 (1953); B. deB. Darwent and R. Roberts, Disc. Faraday Soc. **14,** 15 (1953); K. Yang, J. Am. Chem. Soc. **84,** 3795 (1962). Activation energies range from 2.5 to 5.0 kcal/mole with variations in absolute rates of up to an order of magnitude. We favor k_a(l/mole-sec) $\simeq 10^{10.6-3.0/\theta}$ (K. Yang). From the reaction thermodynamics one then estimates ($T \sim 600$ °K):

  log k_a ($V=0$) $\simeq 13.4$–$40.7/\theta$;
  log k_a ($V=4$) $\simeq 13.7$–$40.7/\theta$.

Experimental

[1] Photosensitized decomposition of ethane at high temperatures. At low temperatures ethyl radicals formed in the reactions ($C_2H_6 + Hg(^3P_1) \longrightarrow Hg(^1S_0) + C_2H_5 + H$; $H + C_2H_6 \longrightarrow H_2 + C_2H_5$) recombine. At higher temperatures the ethyl radical decomposition competes with recombination. Rate constants were based on the H_2 quantum yields at high temperatures.

(Continued)

Ethyl radical *(Continued)*

[2] System — photoinitiated chain decomposition of propionaldehyde in the presence of ethylene. Above 350 °C the rate of ethylene formation increased appreciably, indicating ethyl radical decomposition. The monitoring reaction was the ethyl recombination.

[3] Kinetics deduced from a detailed treatment of the *n*-butane decomposition kinetics. Total product analysis by G.L.C.

Mechanism:

$$C_4H_{10} \xrightarrow{1b} C_3H_7 \cdot + CH_3; \quad C_4H_{10} \xrightarrow{1c} C_2H_5 \cdot + C_2H_5 \cdot$$

$$n\text{-}C_4H_9 \cdot \xrightarrow{2} C_2H_4 + C_2H_5 \cdot$$

$$s\text{-}C_4H_9 \cdot \xrightarrow{3} C_3H_6 + CH_3 \cdot$$

$$C_2H_5 \cdot + C_4H_{10} \xrightarrow{4} C_2H_6 + C_4H_9 \cdot \quad (n \text{ or } s)$$

$$CH_3 \cdot + C_4H_{10} \xrightarrow{5} CH_4 + C_4H_9 \cdot \quad (n \text{ or } s)$$

$$H \cdot + C_4H_{10} \xrightarrow{6} H_2 + C_4H_9 \cdot \quad (n \text{ or } s)$$

$$C_2H_5 \cdot \xrightarrow{7} C_2H_4 + H \cdot$$

$$2C_2H_5 \cdot \xrightarrow{8a} C_4H_{10}$$

$$\xrightarrow{8b} C_2H_4 + C_2H_6$$

Values of k_7 were obtained from the (ethylene/ethane)$=\alpha$ ratio, using the steady state relation $(\alpha-1)\,[C_4H_{10}]=2k_7/k$ and $k_4=5.9\times 10^{8\text{-}15.2/\theta}$ l/mole-sec. The decomposition was shown to be pressure dependent under reaction conditions and was fit to an RRK-pressure falloff curve with $s=7$.

Reaction: *n*-Propyl radical

$$CH_3CH_2CH_2 \cdot (I) \xrightarrow{\ a\ } H \cdot + CH_3CH{=}CH_2 \ (II)$$
$$\xrightarrow{\ b\ } CH_3 \cdot (III) + C_2H_4 \ (IV)$$

	I			H $\cdot$	II	III	IV
	$V=0$	$V=4$	$V=8$				
$\Delta H^\circ_{f(298)}$	$\longleftarrow$	20.7	$\longrightarrow$	52.1	4.9	34.0	12.5
$S^\circ_{(298)}$	69.2	67.2	66.4	27.4	63.8	46.4	52.5
$C^\circ_{p(298)}$	16.4	17.6	17.4	5.0	15.3	8.3	10.4
$C^\circ_{p(500)}$	25.0	26.0	26.1	5.0	24.4	10.1	15.0
$C^\circ_{p(800)}$	34.1	35.1	35.3	5.0	30.8	12.7	20.1

	$a(V=4)$	$b(V=4)$
$\Delta S^\circ =$	24.0	31.7 g/mole
$\Delta H^\circ =$	36.3	25.8 kcal/mole
$\Delta C^\circ_p =$	2.7	1.1 g/mole

Path	log A	E	log k_T (510)	Conditions	System	Surface	References
a	13.6	35.0	$-1.40\,(430)$	298–(737) °K			[1] J. A. Kerr and A. F. Trotman-Dickenson, Trans. Faraday Soc. **55**, 572 (1959).
b	11.7	25.2	-1.11	10–40 mm Hg			
a	14.6	38.0	-1.69	298–723 °K			[2] S. Bywater and E. W. R. Steacie, J. Chem. Phys. **19**, 319 (1951).
	9.2	20.0	-0.97	140–300 mm Hg			
b	....	21.5 ± 1.5		328–630 °K 8–115 mm Hg			[3] C. R. Masson, J. Am. Chem. Soc. **74**, 4731 (1952).
b	....	19		~ 673 °K			[4] R. W. Durham, G. R. Martin, and H. C. Sutton, Nature **164**, 1052 (1949).
b	15.45	34.9	-2.29	471–549 °K $P_T \simeq 80$–100 mm Hg			[5] J. G. Calvert and W. C. Sleppy, J. Am. Chem. Soc. **81**, 1544 (1959).

(Continued)

569

n-Propyl radical *(Continued)*

Path	log A	E	log k_T (510)	Conditions	System	Surface	References
b	15.36	34.5	-2.18	297–564 °K $P_T \simeq 13$–25 mm Hg			[6] J. A. Kerr and J. G. Calvert, J. Am. Chem. Soc. **83**, 3391 (1961).
a	14.1	37.0	-1.76	569–693 °K $P_T \simeq 50$ mm Hg			[7] W. M. Jackson and J. R. McNesby, J. Am. Chem. Soc. **83**, 4891 (1961).
	13.9	31.0	-1.86				

Preferred:
   log $k_a = 13.8 - 38/\theta$;
   log $k_b = 13.6 - 33.1/\theta$.

Comments: A large number of measurements for both back reactions are available. We favor the following:
   log k_{-a} (l/mole-sec) $= 10.6 - 3.0/\theta$ [K. Yang, J. Am. Chem. Soc. **84**, 3795 (1962).]
   log k_{-b} (l/mole-sec) $= 9.07 - 8.66/\theta$ [R. K. Brinton, J. Chem. Phys. **29**, 781 (1958).]
   log k_{-b} (l/mole-sec) $= 8.6 - 7.9/\theta$ [R. J. Cvetanovic and R. S. Irwin, J. Chem. Phys. **46**, 1694 (1967)].

Calculations of the decomposition parameters from the above and the reaction thermodynamics ($V = 2.0$ kcal/mole): $\Delta H_7^\circ(a) = 37.2$ kcal/mole; $\Delta S_7^\circ(a) = 25.6$ g/mole; $\Delta H_7^\circ(b) = 25.7$ kcal/mole; $\Delta S_T^\circ \simeq 31.2$ g/mole, $T = 600$ °K gives
   log $k_a = 14.1 - 39/\theta$.
   log $k_b = 13.8 - 33.2/\theta$.
It is apparent that there is an absolute discrepancy in reaction rates observed and predicted by about a factor of 10, the observed rate constants being the higher. Agreements in activation energies are acceptable with "best" values of $E_a \simeq 38 \pm 2$ kcal/mole and $E_b \simeq 33 \pm 2$ kcal/mole. However, scaled A-factors (observed) for the decompositions do not agree with those calculated.

It is almost impossible to trace the origin of the discrepancy since assumptions regarding other "reference" reactions are involved. The error could be in the forward and reverse A-factors, or in the estimated entropies; however, the former seem more likely. We favor parameters close to those calculated since they are close to what might be predicted by transition state calculations (see section V–10.0).

Experimental

[1] Photolysis of n-butyraldehyde in the presence of ethylene or propionaldehyde. Analysis by G.L.C. Path b decomposition was measured relative to the n-propyl radical recombination ($k_{rec} = 10^{11}$ l/mole-sec-assumed) from both the production of methane and of ethylene. Similar results were obtained from both products. Above 300 °C, propylene production increased markedly and was attributed to path a. The monitoring reaction was again the n-propyl recombination reaction, which was calculated at the higher temperatures from the known relative rate constants for n-propyl radical H-abstraction from the aldehyde and for recombination.

[2] Hg($^3P_1$) photosensitized decomposition of propane. Decompositions (paths a and b) occurred above 300 °C. C_1–C_5 products were separated by fractional sublimation and analyzed with a Blacet-Leighton apparatus. Hexanes were analyzed by M.S. Both paths a and b were calculated from the high-temperature chain production of H_2 and CH_4, respectively, relative to the recombination reaction. Lower pressure experiments led to erratic results. It should be noted that both n-propyl and isopropyl radicals are produced in this reaction and both can decompose to give H_2 as ultimate product.

[3] System — Photolysis of di-n-propyl ketone (3130 Å). Primary processes are:

$$C_3H_7COC_3H_7 \xrightarrow{h\nu} \begin{array}{l} C_2H_4 + CH_3COC_3H_7 \\ 2C_3H_7\cdot + CO\cdot \end{array}$$

(Continued)

The rate of *n*-propyl decomposition was monitored two ways, (1) relative to H-abstraction from the ketone

$$C_3H_7 \longrightarrow C_3H_8 + K_{-H},$$

and (2) relative to the *n*-propyl radical recombination reaction. Insufficient data are provided for an *A*-factor estimate.

[4] System—*n*-propyl radicals produced by the Polanyi sodium flame technique (H. Hartel and M. Polanyi, Z. Physik Chem. **B, 11,** 97 (1930)) were passed through a heated furnace along with radioactive (I_2^{131}). The resulting alkyl iodides were trapped, separated, and analyzed by β-scintillation techniques. Data not amenable to the determination of *A*.

[5] *n*-propyl radicals were produced in the photolysis of azomethane (3660 A) in *n*-butyraldehyde-azomethane mixtures. The $C_3H_7 \cdot$ decomposition was monitored relative to the two radical-radical recombination reactions: $(CH_3 + nC_3H_7 \xrightarrow{5} C_4H_{10}$, and $2CH_3 \cdot \xrightarrow{6} C_2H_6$ with $k_5 = k_6 = 2.2 \times 10^{10}$ l/mole-sec). Analysis by G.L.C.

[6] *n*-propyl radicals were produced in the photolysis of azo-*n*-propane, at 3660 Å. The $C_3H_7 \cdot$ decomposition was monitored relative to the *n*-$C_3H_7 \cdot$ radical recombination reaction. Total product analyses were made, good mass balances were obtained. A total pressure effect on the decomposition was demonstrated. Analysis by G.L.C.

[7] Photolysis of acetone (d_6) in propane-2,2-d_2. The relative rates of the two decomposition paths were determined by the rates of formation CH_4 and CH_3D (i.e., $CH_3CD_2CH_2 \cdot \longrightarrow CH_3 \cdot + CH_2 = CD_2$, the only source of CH_3 radicals), and of HD and D_2 (i.e., $CH_3CD_2CH_2 \longrightarrow \diagup\!\!\!\diagup\!\!\searrow + D \cdot$, the only source of D atoms). Analysis by M.S. Rate constants for D atom elimination (path *a*) were corrected for the deuterium isotope effect. Absolute parameters were obtained on the basis of thermochemical data, assumption regarding the back activation energies (i.e., $E_{-a} = 2$ kcal/mole and $E_{-b} = 7$ kcal/mole), and with the assumption that k_a and k_b were the values determined in reference [1].

NOTE added in proof: Methyl additions to a large number of olefins have been studied recently by R. J. Cvetanovic and R. S. Irwin. Arrhenius parameters are reported based on H-abstraction rates of methyl from isobutane, using $E_{-H} = 7.6$ kcal/mole. Slightly better agreement between the reaction thermodynamics and the observed kinetics of the dissociation and addition reactions are obtained with these addition parameters.

Reaction: 2-Deuteroisopropyl and isopropyl radical

$$CH_3\dot{C}DCH_3 \text{ (I)} \xrightarrow{a} CH_3CD{=}CH_2 \text{ (II)} + H\cdot$$
$$\xrightarrow{b} CH_2{=}CHD \text{ (III)} + CH_3\cdot$$

	I ($V=4$)	II	H·	III	CH₃·
$\Delta H^\circ_{f(298)}$	17.6	4.8	52.1	12.5	34.0
$S^\circ_{(298)}$	65.4	63.7	27.6	52.5	46.4
$C^\circ_{p(298)}$	17.7	15.3	5.0	10.5	8.3
$C^\circ_{p(800)}$	34.7	30.7	5.0	20.2	12.7

	a	b
$\Delta S^\circ =$	25.9	33.5 g/mole
$\Delta H^\circ =$	39.3	28.9 kcal/mole
$\Delta C_p^\circ =$	2.6	1.1 g/mole

Path	log A	E	log k_T (510)	Conditions	System	Surface	References
a	13.1	35 ± 1	−1.90	680–777 °K			[1] C. A. Heller and A. S. Gordon, J. Phys. Chem. **62**, 709 (1958); J. Phys. Chem. **60**, 1315 (1956).
b	12.0	32.5 ± 2	−1.93	$P_T \sim$ 10–20 torr			
a	13.8	36.9	−2.02	673–773 °K			[2] J. A. Kerr and A. F. Trotman-Dickenson, Trans. Faraday Soc. **55**, 921 (1959).
b	19.6	29.5	−2.04	$P_T \sim$ 10–20 torr			
a	14.6	38	−1.69	298–723 °K			[3] S. Bywater and E. W. R. Steacie, J. Chem. Phys. **19**, 319 (1951).
b	9.2	20	0.63	140–300 torr			
b		>45		745–826 °K ~ 50 torr			[4] W. M. Jackson and J. R. McNesby, J. Chem. Phys. **36**, 2272 (1962).

Preferred:
   Reaction a: log k_a 14.3–41.3/θ (from k_{-a} and thermodynamics)
      log k_{-a} (l/mole·sec) = 10.5–2.6/θ (K. Yang, J. Am. Chem. Soc. **84**, 3795 (1962).)
   Reaction b: Suspect.

Comments: It has been argued* that reaction b must involve simultaneous isomerization and decomposition, since in the decomposition of diisopropyl mercury, no n-hexane or 2-methyl pentane (i.e., products of n-propyl radical recombination reactions) were found* and that in the photolysis of diisopropyl ketone, the C₆ hydro-

(Continued)

_____
* B. H. M. Billinge and B. G. Gowenlock, J. Chem. Soc. 3252 (1962).

Deuteroisipropyl and isopropyl radical *(Continued)*

carbon product formed was > 95 percent 2,3-dimethylbutane.** However, it should be noted that since n-propyl radicals decompose about 10^2 times faster than isopropyl radicals at 700 °K, the principal radical in both systems should be isopropyl. Absence of the n-propyl termination products, therefore, does not exclude the possibility of isomerization followed by decomposition homogeneously. However, the displacement reaction $H \cdot + CH_3CD{=}CH_2 \longrightarrow CH_3CHDCH_2 \cdot \longrightarrow CH_3 \cdot + CHD{=}CH_2$ could equally well account for the production of $CHD{=}CH_2$. From reference [4], with isotopically labeled radicals, the minimum activation energy for the isomerization would be 45 kcal and is thus not observable. This seems quite reliable work.

Experimental

[1] Photolysis of diisopropyl ketone. Isopropyl radicals were presumed to be formed photochemically ($I + h\nu \rightarrow i\text{Pr}\cdot + i\text{PrCO}$) and as a result of chain decomposition of the ketone ($R + K \rightarrow RD+$ ⟩-co⟨ (K·); K· → iPr·+· ⟩=c=o). Reaction a was determined from the propylene formed (after correcting for that produced by radical disproportionation and decomposition of $\left(\cdot\rangle\text{-}\overset{\text{O}}{\overset{\|}{\text{C}}}\text{-}\langle \right)$ relative to isopropyl radical-radical recombination. Reaction b was determined by the ethylene and by the methyl radical products. Other secondary reactions capable of producing methane and ethylene were proposed, discussed, and discarded. A-factors reported here are based on an isopropyl radical recombination rate of $k_{(i\text{Pr}\cdot i\text{Pr})} \simeq 10^{10}$ l/mole-sec. Products were analyzed on G.L.C. and M.S.

[2] Photolysis of isobutyraldehyde. A complex but reasonably straightforward Rice-Herzfeld mechanism was proposed. The rate of reaction a was monitored by the recombination reaction ($2i\text{Pr} \rightarrow C_6H_{14}$). The amount of propylene formed in the decomposition was estimated by subtracting from the total amount formed at the higher temperatures of decomposition the amount of propylene produced by disproportionation of isopropyl radicals and that produced in the decomposition of the aldehydic radical ⟩—CHO→ ⟩⟨ + CHO. This latter reaction was assumed to follow rapidly after H-abstraction from the aldehyde and was estimated from the increase in propylene yields in the lower temperature range from 280 to 400 °C. Hexane produced by recombination was also estimated from the measured rate constant ratios of recombination, disproportionation, and H-abstraction involving ($i\text{Pr}\cdot$) radicals at "low" temperatures. Reaction b was estimated relative to the increased methane and ethylene yields at $T > 400$ °C and, as before, monitored by "estimated" yields of hexane via recombination. Both reported rate constants were based on an assumed $i\text{Pr} + i\text{Pr}$ recombination rate constant of $K_{\text{rec}} = 10^{11}$ l/mole-sec with $E_{\text{rec}} = 0$. Analysis of the products was by G.L.C.

[3] (See comments on n-propyl radical decomposition.)

** C. A. Heller and A. S. Gordon. J. Phys. Chem. **60**, 1315 (1956).

Reaction: Cyclobutyl radical

$$\square\!\!\!\!\cdot \;(I)\xrightarrow{\;\;0\;\;}\; {}^{\bullet}CH_2CH_2CH{=}CH_2 \;\;(II)$$

	I	II
$\Delta H^{\circ}_{f(298)}$	49.4	46.0
$S^{\circ}_{(298)}$	65.4	74.9
$C^{\circ}_{p(298)}$	17.0	20.3

$\Delta S^{\circ} = \;\;9.5$ g/mole
$\Delta H^{\circ} = -3.4$ kcal/mole
$\Delta C^{\circ}_p = \;\;3.3$ g/mole

log A	E	log k_T	Conditions	System	Surface	References
———		18.1	456–698 °K $P_T = 75\text{–}115$ torr			[1] A. S. Gordon, S. R. Smith, and C. M. Drew, J. Chem. Phys. **36**, 824 (1962).

Preferred:
   Suspect.

Comments: In a private communication, R. Walsh informs us that an approximate calculation of the A-factor for this reaction from the reported data [1] gives log $A \simeq 7.7$. Using a much more reasonable log $A = 13.5$, he estimates that the activation energy for the cyclobutyl radical decompositions should be about 34 ± 6 kcal/mole; this seems reasonable.

Experimental

   [1] Cyclobutyl radicals were generated by the photolysis of acetone d_6 in cyclobutane. Analysis by M.S. The mechanism assumed was

$$CD_3^{\bullet} + \square \xrightarrow{\;1\;} CD_3H + \square^{\bullet} \qquad CD_3^{\bullet} + CD_3COCD_3 \xrightarrow{\;2\;} CD_4 + {}^{\bullet}CD_2COCD_3$$
$$CD_3^{\bullet} + \square^{\bullet} \xrightarrow{\;3\;} CD_3\text{-}\square \qquad\qquad \square^{\bullet} \xrightarrow{\;4\;} CH_2{=}CHCH_2CH_2^{\bullet}$$

This gives

$$\frac{[\text{yield total CH}_4][\text{yield butenyl products}]}{[Y(\square^{CD_3})][\square + CD_3COCD_3] \times t} = \frac{k_{1,2}k_4}{k_3}$$

The data reported were not sufficient to determine A_3.

Reaction: 1-Buten-4-yl radical

$$\cdot CH_2CH_2CH{=}CH_2 \text{ (I)} \longrightarrow CH_3\overset{\cdot}{C}HCH{=}CH_2 \text{ (II) (resonance stabilized)}$$

	I	II
$\Delta H^\circ_{f(298)}$	46.0	30.5
$S^\circ_{(298)}$	74.9	71.8
$C^\circ_{p(298)}$	20.3	21.1

$\Delta S^\circ = -3.1$ g/mole
$\Delta H^\circ = -15.5$ kcal/mole
$\Delta C^\circ_p = 0.8$ g/mole

log A	E	log k_T	Conditions	System	Surface	References
	20 ± 0.7		456–698 °K $P_T = 75$–115 torr			[1] A. S. Gordon, S. R. Smith, and C. M. Drew, J. Chem. Phys. **36**, 824 (1962).

Preferred:
   Seems unreasonable.

Comments: With a minimum A-factor of 10^{12} for the isomerization, $E = 20$ kcal would lead to 100 percent isomerization compared to the much slower recombination with CH_3. A much more likely process is loss of H-atoms to form butadiene with $k \sim 10^{13.3-34/\theta}$. At 700 °K this should be faster than recombination. Reactions of butadiene with H and CH_3 could then account for the other products. Note that butadiene should also be formed by disproportionation of radicals.

Experimental

[1] Radicals were generated by the photolysis of acetone d_6 in the presence of cyclobutane. (See cyclobutyl decomposition for the mechanism.) Analysis by M.S. The above reaction occurred above 623 °K. The methallyl radical product was monitored by the formation of 3-methyl but-1-ene and pent-2-ene (products of recombination with the dominant CH_3 radicals). By comparing the extent of d label in the products with the d label in 1-butene (i.e., $\cdot CH_2CH_2CH{=}CH_2$ $+ \square$ or $CD_3COCD_3 \longrightarrow$) it was deduced that less than 15 percent of the methallyl products were formed by the reactions

Reaction: *n*-Butyl radical

$$CH_3CH_2CH_2CH_2 \cdot (I) \begin{array}{c} \xrightarrow{a} C_2H_5 \cdot (II) + C_2H_4 (III) \\ \xrightarrow{b} CH_3 \cdot + CH_2=CHCH_3 (IV) \\ \xrightarrow{c} H_2 + (CH_3CHCH=CH_2) \text{ allylic resonance (V)} \end{array}$$

	I	II	III	$CH_3 \cdot$	IV	H_2	V
$\Delta H^\circ_{f(298)}$	15.7	25.7	12.5	34.0	4.8	0	30.5
$S^\circ_{(298)}$	76.6	57.8	52.5	46.4	63.7	31.2	71.8
$C^\circ_{p(298)}$	23.1	12.1	10.5	8.3	15.3	7.0	21.1

	a	b	c
$\Delta S^\circ =$	33.7	33.5	26.4 g/mole
$\Delta H^\circ =$	22.5	23.1	14.8 kcal/mole
$\Delta C^\circ = -$	0.5	0.5	5.0 g/mole

$\langle \Delta C^\circ_p \rangle \simeq -1.0$

Path	log A	E	log k_T (650)	Conditions	System	Surface	References
a	11.2	22.0	3.80	334–689 °K			[1] J. A. Kerr and A. F. Trotman-Dickenson, J. Chem. Soc. 1602 (1960).
b	12.1	27.1	2.99				
a	——	23		523–673 °K 200 torr			[2] S. Bywater and E. W. R. Steacie, J. Chem. Phys. **19**, 172 (1951).
c	——	30		523–673 °K			[3] A. S. Gordon and S. R. Smith, J. Chem. Phys. **34**, 331 (1961).

Preferred:
    log $k_a = 13.6 - 29/\theta$ (from adjusted k_a and the thermodynamics)
    log $k_{-a} = 9.05 - 8.6/\theta$ (J. A. Kerr and A. F. Trotman-Dickenson, J. Chem. Soc. 1611 (1960).)

Comments: Reaction *b*, if valid, must involve isomerization from *n*-butyl to *sec*-butyl radical. The observed rate of decomposition of the *sec*-butyl radical is much faster than reaction *b*, while the calculated rate is about the same. The reported parameters [1] are not unreasonable for a four-center internal H-abstraction and, therefore, could represent the radical isomerization reaction. However, the data seem too inconclusive. Reaction *c* 1, 2-H_2 elimination from molecules appears to proceed with activation energies of the order of 60 kcal/mole (see four-center reactions). The only difference between reaction *c* and such molecular elimination is the resulting allyllic resonance in the radical product (i.e., $R_{allyl} \simeq 12.6$ kcal/mole). Thus it is unlikely that E_c is much less than 45 kcal/mole, plus a low *A*-factor. This would make it too slow to be observable.

Experimental

[1] Radicals were produced in the photolysis of *n*-valeraldehyde and products were analyzed by G.L.C. It was assumed that ethane and ethylene were formed principally from reaction *a*. Corrections for propylene formation from type II elimination from the aldehyde were made in order to calculate the rate of reaction *b*. Both reactions were moni-

(Continued)

tored relative to the *n*-butyl radical recombination which was assigned a rate of 10^{11} l/mole-sec.

[2] $Hg(^3P_1)$ photosensitized decomposition of *n*-butane. Analysis by fractional distillation, Blacet-Leighton micro-analysis apparatus, and M.S. Above 250 °C appreciable additional amounts of methane, ethane, ethylene, and propylene were formed. These were attributed to the *n*-butyl and *sec*-butyl radical decompositions. Activation energy was calculated from the total rate of C_2 production at constant light intensity.

[3] Photolysis of several hydrocarbons (cyclic C_4—C_7, C_2H_6, C_3H_8, and C_4H_{10}) in presence of acetone d_6. Reaction proposed on the basis of the much greater (H_2/HD) ratios as opposed to the (CD_3H/CD_4) ratios. The standard $[(H_2/HD)/(CD_3H/CD_4)]$ ratio was assumed to be that given by C_2H_6 where no such H_2 elimination from the radical is possible. The reported activation energy is an estimate.

Reaction: *sec*-Butyl radical (1-methyl-1-propyl radical)

$$CH_3\dot{C}HCH_2CH_3 \text{ (I)} \xrightarrow{a} CH_3\cdot + CH_3CH=CH_2 \text{ (II)}$$
$$\xrightarrow{b} (n\text{-butyl}\cdot) \longrightarrow C_2H_5\cdot + C_2H_4$$

	I($V=4.0$)	$CH_3\cdot$	II
$\Delta H^\circ_{f(298)}$	12.6	34.0	4.8
S°	76.2	46.4	63.7
$C^\circ_{p(298)}$	23.2	8.3	15.3

a
$\Delta S^\circ = 33.9$ g/mole
$\Delta H^\circ = 26.2$ kcal/mole
$\Delta C^\circ_p = 0.4$ g/mole

Path	log A	E	log k_T (570)	Conditions	System	Surface	References
a	11.81 15.32	24 30.6	2.61 3.59	523–622 °K			[1] *a.* J. T. Gruver and J. G. Calvert, J. Am. Chem. Soc. **78**, 5208 (1956). *b.* J. G. Calvert, Chem. Rev. **59**, 569 (1959).
a	———	23		523–673 °K 200 torr			[2] S. Bywater and E. W. R. Steacie, J. Chem. Phys. **19**, 172 (1951).
b	< 1% of path *a*			638–779 °K ~ 32 torr			[3] J. R. McNesby, C. M. Drew, and A. S. Gordon, J. Chem. Phys. **24**, 1260 (1956).

Preferred:
 log k_a (calc) = 14.16–33.9/θ
 log k_{-a} (l/mole-sec) = 8.88–8.8/θ; M. Mujoski and R. K. Brinton, J. Chem. Phys. **36**, 3019 (1962).

Comments: The reported reaction rate constant is more than two orders of magnitude larger than the calculated value. The *A*-factor discrepancy can be reconciled from the fact that k_{rec} (*sec*-butyl) $\simeq 10^{9.8}$ l/mole-sec is perhaps a better value than the one assumed by Calvert. However, the 4 kcal/mole difference in activation energies is more difficult to explain. Perhaps the secondary butyl radical is less stable than indicated and the activation energy reported should be slightly higher (e.g., $E_b \simeq 32$ kcal/mole).

(Continued)

Experimental

[1a] Radicals were generated by the photolysis of 2-methylbutanol (3130 Å). Primary dissociations were (R = *sec*-butyl)

$$RCHO \xrightarrow{1} R \cdot + \cdot CHO \qquad \Phi_1 = 0.8$$
$$RCHO \xrightarrow{2} C_2H_4 + C_2H_5CHO \qquad \Phi_2 = 0.2$$

Rates were calculated on the basis of methane formation. The recombination reference reaction was assumed to be k_{rec} (*sec*-butyl) $= 10^{11.3}$ l/mole-sec.

[1b] Revised kinetic treatment of ref. [1a] using original data. The rate of propylene formation was equated to the rate of decomposition rather than the rate of methane formation. Methane was believed to be in error due to a possible "down chain" temperature dependent primary process decomposition of the aldehyde

Evidence for similar splits in propionaldehyde and isobutyraldehyde was given.

[2] See comments on *n*-butyl radical (radical produced simultaneously along with *n*-butyl radicals in the $Hg(^3P_1)$ photosensitized decomposition of *n*-butane).

[3] They used photolysis of acetone and $CH_3CD_2CO_2CH_3$ to produce $\cdot CH_2CD_2CO_2CH_3$ and $CH_3\dot{C}DCD_2CH_3$ radicals. They found only normal products from fission without rearrangement, showing absence of H-shifts in the radicals.

Reaction: *t*-Butyl radical

$$(CH_3)_3C \cdot (I) \xrightarrow{a} CH_2=C(CH_3)_2 \ (II) + H \cdot$$
$$\xrightarrow{b} CH_3 \cdot + CH_2=CHCH_3 \ (III)$$

	I($V=4.0$)	II	H·	III	CH$_3$·
$\Delta H^\circ_{f(298)}$	6.8	−4.0	52.1	4.8	34.0
$S^\circ_{(298)}$	70.3	70.2	27.6	63.7	46.4
$C^\circ_{p(298)}$	22.6	21.4	5.0	15.3	8.3

	$a(V=0)$	b
$\Delta S^\circ =$	27.5	39.8 g/mole
$\Delta H^\circ =$	41.3	32.0 kcal/mole
$\Delta C^\circ_p =$	3.8	1.0 g/mole
$< \Delta C^\circ_p > \simeq$	2.5	

Path	log A	E	log k_T (550)	Conditions	System	Surface	References
a	*15.5	43.6	−1.83	300–897 °K			[1] R. N. Birrell and A. F. Trotman-Dickenson, J. Chem. Soc. 4218 (1960).
b	*15.2	46.3	−3.20				
b			<1% of path a	782–857 °K ~ 50 torr			[2] J. R. McNesby and W. M. Jackson, J. Chem. Phys. **38**, 692 (1963).

Preferred:

Path *b*: Unreliable.

Path *a*: Reported [1] and calculated rates are in reasonable agreement.

log $k_a = 14.6 \pm 0.7 - 43.1/\theta$ (from k_{-a} and the reaction thermodynamics).

log k_{-a} (l/mole-sec) 10.5−2.2/θ.

Comments: The path *b* reaction involves radical isomerization (*t*Bu· ⟶ isobutyl·) followed by decomposition. Similar 1,2-H-migration isomerizations are also reported for the isopropyl and *n*-butyl radicals. Reported parameters should apply to the isomerization only, since decomposition of isobutyl is relatively fast. It is more likely that the isomerization does not occur and that the C_3H_6 formation arises from

$$H \cdot + i\text{-butene} \longrightarrow isobutyl \longrightarrow CH_3 \cdot + C_3H_6.$$

Experimental

[1] Radical source was the photolysis of pivaldehyde. Analysis was by G.L.C. Above 663 °K the rate of formation of isobutene increased rapidly. This was attributed to path *a* decomposition. The reference reaction, $2t$Bu ⟶ (tBu)$_2$, was assigned a recombination rate of $k_{rec} \simeq 10^{11.0}$ l/mole-sec.* Above 743 °K the rate of propane formation increased sharply and was accompanied by a corresponding increase in methane. Parameters were based on the propene produced in three runs only, and consequently were not considered particularly reliable.

[2] McNesby and Jackson have shown (see discussion on isobutyl radical) that there is negligible isomerization of *i*-butyl to *t*-butyl. Path *b*, which is the reverse reaction and uphill thermodynamically, is even less likely.

---

* This is too high by 1.5 powers of 10: therefore, the reported *A*-factors have been lowered here by −0.8 log units.

Reaction: Isobutyl radical

$$\xrightarrow{a} CH_2 = CHCH_3 \text{ (II)} + CH_3 \cdot$$

$$(CH_3)_2CHCH_2 \cdot \text{(I)}$$

$$\xrightarrow{b} H \cdot + CH_2 = (CH_3)_2CHCH_2 \cdot \text{(I)}$$

	I($V=4.0$)	II	$CH_3 \cdot$	$H \cdot$	III
$\Delta H^\circ_{f(298)}$	13.7	4.8	34.0	52.1	-4.0
$S^\circ_{(298)}$	73.9	63.7	46.4	27.6	70.2
$C^\circ_{p(298)}$	22.8	15.3	8.3	5.0	21.4

	a	b
$\Delta S^\circ =$	36.2	23.9 g/mole
$\Delta H^\circ =$	25.1	34.4 kcal/mole
$\Delta C^\circ_p =$	0.8	3.6 g/mole

Path	log A	E	log k_T (570) (650)	Conditions	System	Surface	References
a		18.5		523–673 °K			[1] S. Bywater and E. W. R. Steacie, J. Chem. Phys. **19**, 172 (1951).
b		40.0		200 torr			
b	(not an important decomposing mode)			782–857 °K			[2] W. M. Jackson, J. R. McNesby, and B. deB. Darwent, J. Chem. Phys. **37**, 2256 (1962).
a	12.8	26.0	2.83	299–691 °K			[3] E. L. Metcalfe and A. F. Trotman-Dickenson, J. Chem. Soc. 5072 (1960).
b	13.0	31.0	2.58				
b		<1% of path a		782–857 °K ~ 50 torr			[4] J. R. McNesby and W. M. Jackson; J. Chem. Phys. **38**, 692 (1963).
a	12.4	31.0	0.51	540–598 °K 10–50 torr			[5] D. H. Slater, S. S. Collier, and J. G. Calvert, J. Am. Chem. Soc. **90**, 268 (1968).

Preferred:

log $k_a = 14.2 - 32.7/\theta$ (calculated from k_{-a} and the reaction thermodynamics),
log $k_{-a} = 8.4 - 8.8/\theta$, approximately (1/3) addition anti-Markonikov (see *sec*-butyl radical),
log $k_b = 13.7 - 36.6/\theta$,
log $k_{-b} = 10.2 - 2.2/\theta$, same approximation as for k_{-a}.

581

(*Continued*)

Experimental

[1] (See experimental on *n*-butyl radical.)

[2] Relative rates of reactions *a* and *b* were determined in the pyrolysis of deuterium-labeled isobutane $(CH_3)_3CD$. Isotopic analysis of the hydrogen, methane, and isobutene fractions was made by M.S.

$$\cdot CH_2CD(CH_3)_2 \quad \overset{5}{\underset{6}{\xrightarrow{\hspace{1cm}}}} \quad \begin{array}{l} CH_2{=}CDCH_3 + CH_3 \cdot \\ CH_2{=}C(CH_3)_2 + D \cdot \end{array}$$

From the yields of D_2 and HD (from 6 and H-abstraction) relative to CH_3D and CH_4 (from 5 and H-abstraction), the authors concluded that maximum values of (k_5/k_6) were 0.008 (509 °C) and 0.013 (584 °C). These maximum values are about a factor of 10 lower than reported ratios of references [1] and [2]. The conclusion is that the importance of path *b* has been badly overestimated in the prior studies. This conclusion was also confirmed in a similar follow-up study on the pyrolysis of $(CH_3)_2CDCH_3$ (Ref. [4]).

[3] Photolysis of isovaleraldehyde was the source of isobutyl radicals. Analysis of the hydrocarbon products was made by G.L.C. Above 279 °C the rate of formation of propene increased. This was attributed to reaction *a*. Above 329 °C the rate of isobutene increased. This was attributed to path *b*. The reference reaction in both cases was the recombination of isobutyl radicals and assigned a reaction rate of k_{rec}(iso C_4H_9) $= 10^{10\,2}$ l/mole-sec.

[4] See reference [3].

[5] Followed photolysis of azoisobutane. C_3H_6 was formed above 500 °K (G.L.C.). They measured C_3H_6 relative to recombination of *i*-Bu radicals and assumed 10^{11} for recombination. However, these measurements were clearly in the pyrolysis range of the azo compound and may be subject to serious corrections for thermal reactions.

Reaction: Cyclopentyl radical

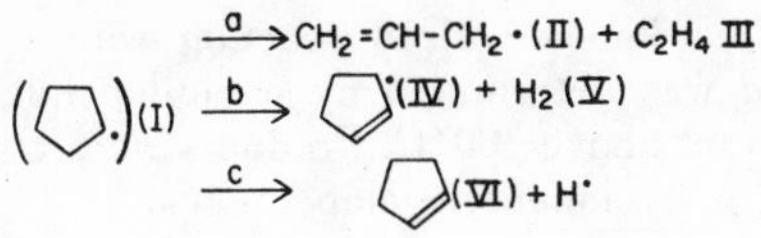

$$\left(\bigcirc\kern-0.4em\cdot\right)_{(I)} \begin{array}{l} \xrightarrow{a} CH_2=CH-CH_2\cdot (II) + C_2H_4\ III \\ \xrightarrow{b} \bigcirc\kern-0.4em\cdot (IV) + H_2\ (V) \\ \xrightarrow{c} \bigcirc (VI) + H\cdot \end{array}$$

	I	II	III	IV	V	VI	H
$\Delta H^\circ_{f(298)}$	24.4	38	12.5	39	0	8.6	52.1
$S^\circ_{(298)}$	72.0	61.4	52.5	68	31.2	69.2	27.4
$C^\circ_{p(298)}$	20	14.1	10.5	44.5	7.0	18.1	5.0

a
$\Delta S^\circ = 41.9$ g/mole
$\Delta H^\circ = 26.1$ kcal/mole
$\Delta C^\circ_p = 4.6$ g/mole

Path	log A	E	log k_T (645)	Conditions	System	Surface	References
a	14.5	37.7	1.72	573–718 °K	static		[1] A. S. Gordon, Can. J.
b	13.5	38	0.62,	$P_T \sim 80$–120			Chem. **43**, 570
c		> 38		torr			(1965).
a	——	36.9 ± 1.2		523–730 °K $P_T \sim 170$ mm Hg	static		[2] H. E. Gunning and R. L. Stock, Can. J. Chem. **42**, 357 (1964).
Relative rates (see Experimental)				473–973 °K $P_T \sim 10^{-3}$ torr			[3] T. F. Palmer and F. P. Lossing, Can. J. Chem. **43**, 565 (1965).

Preferred:

log $k_a = 14.5 - 37.7/\theta$. Reaction b, unreliable; reaction c, like H-atom elimination from n-propyl; log $k_c = 14.2 - 39/\theta$.

Comments: Allyl radicals should add to ethylene with a rate constant of about log k_{-a} (l/mole-sec) $= 7.5 - 10.3/\theta$.

Experimental

[1] Photolysis of acetone d_6 in cyclopentane. Analysis by M.S. Above 300 °C the decomposition to allyl and ethylene was observed. Path a was monitored using the competitive reactions:

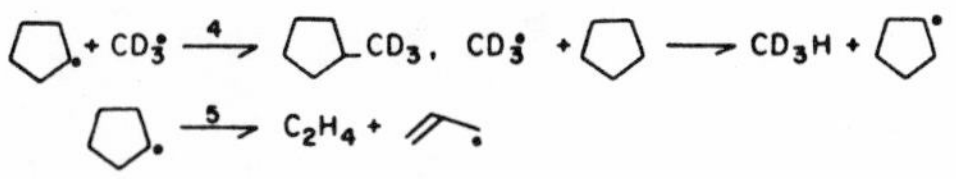

$$\bigcirc\kern-0.4em\cdot + CD_3^\cdot \xrightarrow{4} \bigcirc\kern-0.4em{}_{CD_3}, \quad CD_3^\cdot + \bigcirc \longrightarrow CD_3H + \bigcirc\kern-0.4em\cdot$$
$$\bigcirc\kern-0.4em\cdot \xrightarrow{5} C_2H_4 + \diagup\kern-0.4em\cdot$$

Above 300 °C the rate of total hydrogen ($H_2 + HD$) increased. Since the (H_2/HD) ratios were considerably greater than the (CD_3H/CD_4) ratios (whereas previous results with H and CD_3 indicated abstraction ratios for H and CD_3 of 1.5 (Elimination of molecular H_2 from allyl free radicals, A. S. Gordon and S. R. Smith, J. Chem. Phys. **34**, 331 (1961)), reaction b was proposed. By comparing the yields of H_2 (corrected for radical formation) to the yields of C_2H_4, parameters for path b were deduced. Path c appeared to be important above 300 °C.

(Continued)

Cyclopentyl radical *(Continued)*

[2] Radicals were produced by $Hg(^3P_1)$ photosensitized reaction with cyclopentane. Total products analyzed by G.L.C. The activation energy for path *a* was determined by *five* independent relations with a standard deviation of 1.9 kcal/mole. Path *c* was deemed important above 300 °C. Products were H_2, C_2H_4, ⬠ biallyl, allylcyclopentane, bicyclopentyl, methane, C_2H_6, ↗, ↗, ⬠, cyclopentylcyclopentenes.

[3] Cyclopentyl radicals were generated by the decomposition of cyclopentylmethyl nitrite:

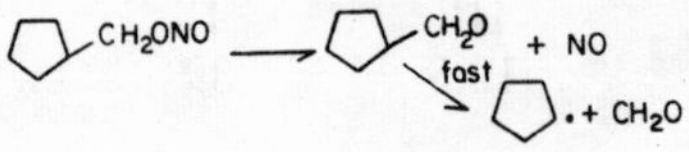

Analysis by M.S. It was estimated that at 700 °C, contributions of the various reaction paths were: path *a*, 66 percent; path *b*, <2 percent; path *c*, 34 percent. Mass balances were good to ±2 percent. Path *c* increased in importance with decreasing temperature.

NOTE: The mechanism involves the steps:

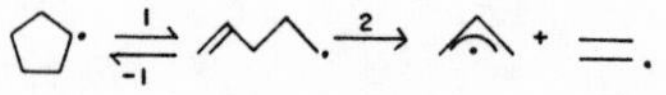

$\Delta H_1 = 16.6$ and $\Delta H_2 = 12.1$ kcal. If $k_2 < k_{-1}$, then $E_{-2} = 9$ kcal, a reasonable result, and $E_{-1} \leqslant 11$ kcal, a not unreasonable result. If, however, $k_2 > k_{-1}$ and step 1 is rate determining, this implies $E_{-1} = 21$ kcal, which seems much too high.

Reaction: Neopentyl radical

$$(CH_3)_3CCH_2 \cdot (I) \xrightarrow{a} CH_3 \cdot + (CH_3)_2C{=}CH_2 \text{ (II)}$$

	I($V=0$)	CH$_3 \cdot$	II
$\Delta H^\circ_{f(298)}$	6.0	34.0	-4.0
$S^\circ_{(298)}$	79.2	46.4	70.2
$C^\circ_{p(298)}$	28.7	8.3	21.4

$\Delta S^\circ = 37.4$ g/mole
$\Delta H^\circ = 24.0$ kcal/mole
$\Delta C^\circ_p = 1.0$ g/mole

log A	E	log k_T (762)	Conditions	System	Surface	References
13 ± 1	34 ± 3.5	3.22	762 °K			[1] K. H. Anderson and S. W. Benson, J. Chem. Phys. **40,** 3747 (1964).

Preferred:
   log $k = 14.0 - 37.5/\theta$.
   Rate constant is reliable.

Comments: In solution, the rate of methyl addition to isobutene has about the same parameters as methyl addition to ethylene. M. Feld and M. Szwarc, J. Am. Chem. Soc. **82,** 3791 (1960). Assuming anti-Markonikov addition to be about one fifth the "normal" rate with equivalent activation energies, therefore, gives k_{-a} (l/mole-sec) $\simeq 8.4-8.3/\theta$. With the reaction thermodynamics one then estimates log $k_a \simeq 14.4-32.3/\theta$. This is so much faster than the observed rate that it appears the assumption on activation energies must be in error and that the activation energy for the reverse step must be closer to 12 kcal.

Experimental

[1] Rates of decomposition of neopentane in the presence and absence of HCl were used to obtain the relative rates of the chain steps:

$$CH_3 \cdot + NP \xrightarrow{2} CH_4 + NP \cdot$$
$$NP \cdot \xrightarrow{3} \text{isobutene} + CH_3 \cdot$$

Thus, $\dfrac{\text{Rate (with HCl)}}{\text{Rate (without HCl)}} = \dfrac{k_3}{k_2} (NP)_0$. Parameters were assigned from the rate constant assuming $A_3 \simeq 10^{13.0}$ sec^{-1}.

Reaction: 1-Methyl-1-pentyl radical (2-hexyl radical)

$$CH_3\dot{C}H(CH_2)_3CH_3 \ (I) \longrightarrow C_3H_6 \ (II) + CH_3CH_2CH_2 \cdot \ (III)$$

	I($V = 4.0$)	II	III($V = 4.0$)
$\Delta H^\circ_{f(298)}$	2.7	4.9	20.7
$S^\circ_{(298)}$	95	63.8	67.2
$C^\circ_{p(298)}$	34.2	15.3	17.6
$C^\circ_{p(800)}$	67.9	30.8	35.1

$\Delta S^\circ = 36$ g/mole
$\Delta H^\circ = 22.9$ kcal/mole
$\Delta C^\circ_p = -1.3$ g/mole

log A	E	log k_T (822)	Conditions	System	Surface	References
13.48	22.4	+7.51	822 °K 92 torr	static		[1] C. P. Quinn, Trans. Faraday Soc. **59**, 2543 (1963).

Preferred:
   $\log k = 14.3 - 27.4/\theta$.

Comments: If one assumes a back reaction rate similar to (CH₃·+⌒) of $\log k_{-a}$(l/mole-sec) $\simeq 9.1 - 8.6/\theta$, then from the reaction thermodynamics, one can calculate $\log k_a \simeq 14.3 - 29/\theta$ (i.e., a factor of 10 slower than the value reported). However, K_8 (800 °K) $\simeq 3$; therefore, the agreement between reported and calculated rates is fairly good (i.e., ~ factor of 3). We prefer the calculated A-factor and an activation energy adjusted to give the proper rate at 800 °K.

Experimental

[1] Pyrolysis of ethane. Analyses of all products as a function of time by G.L.C. The rate of secondary methane formation (i.e., not from the primary free radical chain reactions of the ethane decomposition) was interpreted in terms of the following mechanism involving the isomerization of n-hexyl radicals:

$$C_2H_5 \cdot + C_2H_4 \underset{\longleftarrow}{\overset{6}{\rightleftharpoons}} CH_3CH_2CH_2CH_2 \cdot$$
$$CH_3CH_2CH_2CH_2 \cdot + C_2H_4 \underset{\longleftarrow}{\overset{7}{\rightleftharpoons}} CH_3(CH_2)_4CH_2 \cdot$$
$$CH_3(CH_2)_4CH_2 \cdot \underset{\longleftarrow}{\overset{8}{\rightleftharpoons}} CH_3\dot{C}H(CH_2)_3CH_3$$
$$CH_3\dot{C}H(CH_2)_3CH_3 \overset{9}{\longrightarrow} C_3H_6 + CH_3CH_2CH_2 \cdot$$

A steady-state treatment gave $K_8 k_9 = 3 \times 10^7$ sec^{-1}. On the assumptions that $K_8 \simeq 1$ and $A_9 \simeq 3 \times 10^{13}$ sec^{-1}, the reported parameters were calculated.

Reaction: Formyl radical

$$\overset{\cdot}{H C} O \text{ (I)} \longrightarrow H \cdot + CO \text{ (II)}$$

	I	H	II
$\Delta H^\circ_{f(298)}$	7.2	52.1	-26.4
$S^\circ_{(298)}$	53.7	27.6	47.3
$C^\circ_{p(298)}$	8.3	5.0	7.0
$C^\circ_{p(500)}$	9.2	5.0	7.2

$\Delta S^\circ = 21.2$ g/mole
$\Delta H^\circ = 18.5$ kcal/mole
$\Delta C^\circ_p = 3.7$ g/mole

log A	E	log k_T (298)	Conditions	System	Surface	References
13	14.4	2.51	298 °K $P_T \sim 200$ torr			[1] R. J. Cvetanovic, Can. J. Chem. **33,** 1684 (1955).
———	> 13		423–623 °K $P_T \sim 150$–450 torr			[2] J. G. Calvert and E. W. R. Steacie, J. Chem. Phys. **19,** 176 (1951).
———	14.0		393–498 °K $P_T \sim 130$ torr			[3] F. B. Marcotte, W. A. Noyes, Jr., J. Am. Chem. Soc. **74,** 783 (1952).

Preferred:
   $\log k = 13.7 - 19.0/\theta$.

Comments: This reaction must be pressure-dependent at normal temperature and pressure conditions (J. E. Longfield and W. D. Walters, J. Am. Chem. Soc. **77,** 6098 (1955)). None of the reported parameters are reliable. A reasonable estimate can be made by assuming the following parameters for the back reaction, $k_b = 10^{10.8 - 1.0/\theta}$ l/mole-sec, and using the indicated thermodynamics. One then obtains $\log k_{est} = 13.7 - 19.0/\theta$. Calvert has discussed the experimental data from all sources on this radical (J. Phys. Chem. **61,** 120 (1957)) and has concluded that $D(H-CO) \simeq 15$ kcal/mole. The thermodynamics are based on the reliable measurement of $\Delta H^\circ_f (\cdot CHO)$ by Walsh and S. W. Benson.

Experimental

[1] $Hg(^3P_1)$ photosensitized decomposition of ethylene oxide. The rate of the decomposition reaction was estimated from the observed stoichiometry relative to the radical termination reaction, $CH_3 + HCO \longrightarrow CH_4 + CO$, and $2CH_3 \longrightarrow C_2H_6$. The A-factor of 10^{13} was assumed for this single temperature study.

[2] Vapor phase photolysis of H_2CO. Activation energy was obtained from the Arrhenius plot of the rate of (H_2) production. Prior values of 16.4 (Akeroyd and Norrish, J. Chem. Soc., 890 (1936) and 12 (Style and Summers, Trans. Faraday Soc. **35,** 899 (1939)) obtained in similar systems were quoted.

[3] Photolysis of acetone in the presence of O_2. Formyl radicals were produced by the reaction

$$CH_3 + O_2 \longrightarrow CH_3O + H_2O.$$

The decomposition kinetics were monitored by the competitive trapping reaction:

$$HCO \longrightarrow H + CO$$
$$HCO + O_2 \longrightarrow \text{(other products)}$$

No A-factors could be determined.

Reaction: Hydroxymethyl radical

$$\cdot \, CH_2OH \; (I) \longrightarrow CH_2O \; (II) + H \cdot (III)$$

	I	II	III
$\Delta H^\circ_{f(298)}$	-4	-27.7	52.1
$S^\circ_{(298)}$	58.6	52.3	27.4
$C^\circ_{p(298)}$	10.2	8.5	5.0

$\Delta S^\circ = 21.1$ g/mole
$\Delta H^\circ = 28.4$ kcal/mole
$\Delta C^\circ_p = 3.3$ g/mole

log A	E	log k_T (725)	Conditions	System	Surface	References
13.05	29	4.31	673–773 °K 30–100 torr	static		[1] M. K. Phibbs and B. deB. Darwent, J. Chem. Phys. **18**, 495 (1950).

Preferred:
   $\log k_a = 13.05 - 29/\theta$.

Comments: A back reaction similar to $H + C_2H_4$ is reasonable. If one assumes, therefore, $\log k_{-a}$ (l/mole-sec) $= 10.6 - 3.0/\theta$, then from the reaction thermodynamics, $\log k_a(\text{est}) \simeq 13.3 - 31/\theta$. The agreement is good. It is probable, however, that the measured rate was in a pressure-dependent region.

Experimental

[1] $Hg(^3P_1)$ photosensitized decomposition of methyl alcohol. The decomposition rate was determined relative to the recombination reaction (calculated)

$$2\dot{C}H_2OH \xrightarrow{3} (CH_2OH)_2$$
$$\dot{C}H_2OH \xrightarrow{4} CH_2O + H$$

$$\frac{k_1}{k_3^{1/2}} = 10^{8.05-29/\theta} \left(\frac{\text{moles}}{\text{l. sec}}\right)^{1/2}$$

Analysis was performed on the noncondensible products by standard gas techniques and formaldehyde was titrated. The A-factor reported here assumes $k_3 \simeq 10^{10}$ l/mole-sec.

Reaction: Acetyl radical

$$CH_3\dot{C}O\ (I) \longrightarrow CH_3\cdot\ (II) + CO\ (III)$$

	I	II	III
$\Delta H^\circ_{f(298)}$	-5.4	34.0	-26.4
$S^\circ_{(298)}$	64.5	46.4	47.3
$C^\circ_{p(298)}$	12.7	8.3	7.0
$C^\circ_{p(500)}$	16.4	10.1	7.2

$\Delta S^\circ = 29.2$ g/mole
$\Delta H^\circ = 13.0$ kcal/mole
$\Delta C^\circ_p = 2.6$ g/mole

$\log A$	E	$\log k_T$ (520)	Conditions	System	Surface	References
10.22	13.5	4.55	296–400 °K $P_T \sim 25$–65 torr			[1] J. G. Calvert and J. T. Gruver, J. Am. Chem. Soc. **80**, 1313 (1958).
10.3	15.0±1	3.99	473–568 °K $P_T \sim 12$–150 mm Hg			[2] E. O'Neal and S. W. Benson, J. Chem. Phys. **36**, 2196 (1962) .
_____	16.0±2		393–498 °K $P_T \sim 130$ torr			[3] F. B. Marcotte and W. A. Noyes, Jr., J. Am. Chem. Soc. **74**, 783 (1952).
_____	13.5±2		300–390 °K			[4] D. H. Volman and W. M. Graven, J. Am. Chem. Soc. **75**, 3111 (1953).

Preferred:

log $k = 10.3 - 15.0/\theta$. These parameters are in reasonably good agreement with the thermodynamics and the back reaction kinetics. However, the low A-factor is in serious disagreement with unimolecular rate theory and poses a problem which needs more study.

Comments: Measurements on the back reaction: $CH_3 \cdot + CO \longrightarrow CH_3CO$

$k_{-a} = 1.41 \times 10^5 \times 10^{-3.84/\theta}$ l/mole-sec (ref. [1]).
$k_{-a} = 10^{5.56 - 3.9/\theta}$ l/mole-sec (J. A. Kerr and J. G. Calvert, J. Phys. Chem. **69**, 1922 (1965)).

The reaction thermodynamics ($\Delta S^\circ_T \simeq 30.1$ g/mole, $\Delta H^\circ_T \simeq 13.4$ kcal/mole) and the back reaction kinetics predict $k_a = 10^{10.1 - 16.3/\theta}$ sec^{-1}, in reasonably good agreement with references [2] and [3]. Note that the A-factor is abnormally low. The reaction is pressure-dependent at normal experimental pressures.

Experimental

[1] Photolysis of azomethane in the presence of acetaldehyde. Analysis by M.S. and G.L.C. The mechanism was

(Continued)

589

$$CH_3 \cdot + CH_3CHO \xrightarrow{\ 3\ } CH_4 + CH_3\dot{C}O$$

$$CH_3\dot{C}O \underset{}{\overset{1}{\rightleftharpoons}} CH_3 \cdot + CO$$

$$CH_3 \cdot + CH_3\dot{C}O \xrightarrow{\ 2\ } CH_3COCH_3$$

$$2CH_3 \cdot \xrightarrow{\ 5\ } C_2\dot{H}_6$$

This gives $R_{CO}R_{C_2H_6}^{1/2}/R_{acetone} = k_1 k_5^{1/2}/k_4$.

The back reaction rate was also determined through photolysis of azomethane in CO with the result k^2(1/mole-sec) $= 10^{5.15-3.8/\theta}$.

[2] Photolysis of acetone in the presence of (HI). The decomposition was studied as a function of pressure relative to the radical trapping reaction with HI.

$$CH_3\dot{C}O + (M) \xrightarrow{\ d\ } CH_3 \cdot + CO + (M)$$

$$CH_3\dot{C}O + HI \xrightarrow{\ 3\ } CH_3CHO + I.$$

The parameters are based on an assumed trapping reaction constant of $k_3 = 10^{9.2-1.5/\theta}$ l/mole-sec, a value supported by other kinetic studies on the reaction of $HI + CH_3COI \longrightarrow CH_3CHO + I_2$. Analysis by G.L.C. ($CH_3CHO$) and standard methods for CH_4 and CO.

[3] Photolysis of acetone in the presence of O_2. The decomposition was monitored relative to the trapping reaction with O_2.

$$CH_3\dot{C}O \xrightarrow{\ 2\ } CH_3 \cdot + CO$$

$$CH_3\dot{C}O + O_2 \xrightarrow{\ 3\ } \text{(other products)}$$

The Arrhenius *A*-factor was not determined and it was assumed that $E_3 \simeq 0$. Analysis on the noncondensible gas products by standard methods.

[4] Photolysis of acetone in the presence of butadiene. Decomposition was measured relative to the acetyl addition to butadiene.

$$CH_3\dot{C}O + \diagup\!\!\!\diagdown\!\!\!\diagup \xrightarrow{\ 12\ } \text{addn product}$$

$$CH_3\dot{C}O \xrightarrow{\ 8\ } CH_3^* + CO$$

$k_{12}/k_8 \simeq 720$, $E_8 - E_{12} = 8.1$ kcal/mole. The activation energy $E_{12} \simeq 5.4$ was also measured in the study by following the rate of butadiene polymerization with ΔP measurements.

Reaction: Epoxyethyl radical

$$CH_2\text{—}CH \cdot (I) \longrightarrow CH_3 \cdot (II) + CO\ (III)$$
$$\diagdown O \diagup$$

	I	II	III
$\Delta H^\circ_{f(298)}$	(36.2)	34.0	-26.4
$S^\circ_{(298)}$	59.4	46.4	47.3
$C^\circ_{p(298)}$	12.1	8.3	7.0

$\Delta S^\circ = 34.3$ g/mole
$\Delta H^\circ = -28.6$ kcal/mole
$\Delta C^\circ_p = 3.2$ g/mole

log A	E	log k_T (1050)	Conditions	System	Surface	References
13	25	780	900–1200 °K (Ar, CO$_2$, and N$_2$ carriers)	flow		[1] L. Cracco, I. Glassmann, and I. E. Smith, J. Chem. Phys. **31**, 506 (1959).

Preferred:

   Not reliable.

Comments: Kinetic scheme is oversimplified and k_3 is assigned at least 100-fold too fast compared to known rate. Reaction involves hot molecules and hot radicals. k_3 (measured) $= 10^{8.1-10/\theta}$.

Experimental

[1] Nitrogen carrier flow decomposition of ethylene oxide at high temperatures. Rate of reaction based on the temperature profile in the reaction zone (a unique system). Above parameters were based on an assumed mechanism fit to observed kinetics:

$$\triangledown \xrightarrow{1} \text{radicals} \quad k_1 \sim 10^{13-5.5/\theta}\ \text{sec}^{-1}$$
$$\triangledown^\circ \xrightarrow{2} CH_3^\cdot + CO$$
$$\triangledown + CH_3^\cdot \xrightarrow{3} CH_4 + \triangledown^\circ \quad k_3 \sim 6 \times 10^{9-5/\theta}\ \text{l/mole-sec}$$
$$CH_3^\cdot + \triangledown^\cdot \xrightarrow{4} \text{termination} \quad k_4 \sim 6 \times 10^{10}\ \text{l/mole-sec}$$

Reaction: Ethoxy radical

$$C_2H_5O \cdot (I) \longrightarrow CH_3 \cdot (II) + CH_2O \, (III)$$

	I	II	III
$\Delta H^\circ_{f(298)}$	(−4.9)	34.0	−27.7
$S^\circ_{(298)}$	65.9	46.1	52.3
$C^\circ_{p(298)}$	14.0	8.3	8.5

$\Delta S^\circ = 32.5$ g/mole
$\Delta H^\circ = 11.2$ kcal/mole
$\Delta C^\circ_p = 2.8$ g/mole

log A	E	log k_T (375)	Conditions	System	Surface	References
10.45	13	2.87	488–468 °K			[1] M. H. J. Wijnen, J. Am. Chem. Soc. **82**, 3034 (1960)*; M. H. J. Wijnen, J. Am. Chem. Soc. **80**, 2394 (1958)**.
10.1	12.5	2.82				

Preferred:
  $\log k = 13.4 - 17.5/\theta$.

Comments: Kinetics of the back reaction are not known; however, one might guess that methyl addition to formaldehyde will have parameters intermediate between those for $CH_3 + CO \longrightarrow CH_3CO$ and $CH_3 + C_2H_4 \longrightarrow C_3H_7$. From the kinetics of the former (see acetyl radical), one obtains $\log k_a \simeq 10.9 - 13.5/\theta$, while those of the latter give $\log k_a = 14.4 - 19.2/\theta$. The isopropoxy and t-butoxy radical decompositions have both been shown to have some pressure dependence. One would therefore also expect the above reaction to be in its pressure falloff region and thus account for the low experimental parameters.

Experimental

*Reinvestigation of ethyl propionate photolysis. Same conditions, but analysis was complete (except for CH_2O) by G.L.C. Products were CO, CO_2, CH_2O, CH_4, C_2H_6, C_2H_4, C_3H_8, C_4H_{10}, C_2H_5OH, CH_3CHO, and $C_2H_5OC_2H_5$. Decomposition was again measured relative to ethoxy H-abstraction from the parent ester, and the kinetics of the H-abstraction were determined relative to the radical recombination reactions:

$$2C_2H_5 \cdot \xrightarrow{2} C_4H_{10}$$
$$C_2H_5 \cdot + C_2H_5O \cdot \xrightarrow{4} C_2H_5OC_2H_5$$
$$C_2H_5O \cdot + P \xrightarrow{16} C_2H_5OH + P_{-H}$$

at 19 °C, $k_{16}k_2^{1/2}/k_4 = 31 \times 10^{-12} \left(\dfrac{cc}{molec}\right)^{1/2}$ sec$^{-1/2}$. Assuming that $k_2 = 3 \times 10^{10}$ l/mole-sec and $k_4 = 10^{10}$ l/mole-sec, one then obtains $k_{16}(19\ ^\circ\mathrm{C}) = 4.42 \times 10^4$ l/mole-sec. The Arrhenius plot of $(k_{16}k_2^{1/2}/k_4)$ gave $E \simeq E_{16} = 5.5$ kcal/mole; one obtains $k_{16} = 10^{8.75 - 5.5/\theta}$ l/mole-sec. Also, for the decomposition reaction (8 below), the data gave $k_{16}/k_8 = 10^{-1.7} \times 10^{7.5/\theta}$ (l/moles).

**The photolysis of ethyl propionate. Analysis of gaseous products by M.S. A usual Rice-Herzfeld scheme was proposed. The decomposition reaction was estimated relative to the H-abstraction reaction:

$$C_2H_5O \cdot \xrightarrow{8} CH_3 \cdot + CH_2O$$
$$C_2H_5O \cdot + A \xrightarrow{15} C_2H_5OH + A_{-H}$$
$$2C_2H_5O \cdot \xrightarrow{7} C_2H_5OH + CH_3CHO$$

Results were:

$$\frac{k_8}{k_{15}} = 10^{1.34 - 7/\theta}; \ k_8/k_7^{1/2} \simeq 2.3 \times 10^{-5} \left(\frac{mole}{l\text{-sec}}\right)^{1/2} \text{ at 30 °C.}$$

Reaction: 2-Oxo-1-propyl radical (acetonyl radical)

$$\cdot CH_2COCH_3 \ (I) \longrightarrow CH_3 \cdot \ (II) + CH_2CO \ (III)$$

	I	II	III
$\Delta H^\circ_{f(298)}$	-6	34.0	-14.6
$S^\circ_{(298)}$	72.5	46.4	57.1
$C^\circ_{p(298)}$	17.8	8.3	11.4

$\Delta S^\circ = 31.0$ g/mole
$\Delta H^\circ = 25.6$ kcal/mole
$\Delta C^\circ_p = 1.9$ g/mole

log A	E	log k_T	Conditions	System	Surface	References
_____	41		365–435 °K $P_T \simeq 50$ torr			[1] R. K. Brinton, J. Am. Chem. Soc. **83**, 1541 (1961).

Preferred:

$$\log k_a \simeq 12.5 - 40/\theta$$

This assumes a back reaction with parameters $\log k_{-a}$ (l/mole-sec) $= 7.7 - 15/\theta$.

Experimental

[1] High-temperature photolysis of acetone. The decomposition was monitored relative to the acetonyl radical recombination reaction.

$$\cdot CH_2COCH_3 \xrightarrow{7} CH_2CO + CH_3$$
$$2 \cdot CH_2COCH_3 \xrightarrow{6} (CH_3COCH_2)_2$$

Analysis was by a variety of methods including M.S., G.L.C., and chemicals. The rate constant ratios $(k_7/k_6^{1/2})$ were found to increase with increasing pressure. The A-factor reported above has been calculated, assuming $k_6 \simeq 10^{10}$ l/mole sec.

Reaction: Isopropoxy radical

$$(CH_3)_2CHO \cdot \text{(I)} \longrightarrow CH_3CHO \text{ (II)} + CH_3 \cdot \text{(III)}$$

	I	II	III
$\Delta H^\circ_{f(298)}$	(-12.4)	-39.8	34.0
$S^\circ_{(298)}$	72.2	63.2	46.4
$C^\circ_{p(298)}$	20.0	13.1	8.3

$\Delta S^\circ = 37.4$ g/mole
$\Delta H^\circ = (6.6)$ kcal/mole
$\Delta C^\circ_p = 1.4$ g/mole

$\log A$	E	$\log k_T$ (460)	Conditions	System	Surface	References
10.65	16.0	3.05	448–473 °K $P \sim 35$ mm Hg			[1] J. M. Ferguson and L. Phillips, J. Chem. Soc., 4416 (1965).
11.8	17.3	3.58	433–473 °K $P \sim 20$–230 torr			[2] D. L. Cox, R. A. Livermore, and L. Phillips, J. Chem. Soc. **B**, 245 (1966).
9.32	11.5	3.86	301–338 °K 15–30 mm Hg			[3] M. J. H. Wijnen, J. Am. Chem. Soc. **82**, 1847 (1960).

Preferred:
All results are suspect.

Comments: The kinetics and thermodynamics for this reaction are incompatible. Thus

$$A_a \simeq A_{-a} \text{ (atm}^{-1} \text{ sec}^{-1}) \times 10 \, \frac{\Delta S^\circ}{4.575}$$

and from [2], using $A_a = 10^{11.8}$ sec^{-1}, one obtains $A_{-a} \simeq 10^{5.5}$ l/mole-sec, which compares to the "abnormally" low value found for $CH_3 + CO$ addition. However, $E_{-a} \simeq E_a - \Delta E^\circ = 17.3 - 5.7 = 11.6$ kcal/mole, which is appreciably higher than the "normal" value for $CH_3 + C_2H_4$ addition. Such a low A-factor and high activation energy for the back reaction $(-a)$ are particularly unreasonable. There also exists a rather uncomfortable trend in absolute decomposition rate constants in the series C_2H_5O, i-C_3H_7O, and t-C_4H_9O. Thus $1/10 \, k_{t\text{-BuO}} \simeq 10 \, k_{i\text{PrO}} \simeq k_{\text{EtO}}$ at $T \sim 400$ °K. The above reported decomposition appears to be much too slow. It is very likely pressure dependent.

Experimental

[1] Pyrolysis of isopropyl nitrite in static system. The decomposition was measured relative to the rate of reaction with NO.

$$NO + i\text{PrO} \xrightarrow{2} CH_3COCH_3 + HNO$$

$$k_2 \simeq 10^7 \text{ l/mole-sec}$$

$$i\text{PrO} \xrightarrow{4} CH_3 + CH_3CHO$$

Continuous analysis of reaction was by I.R. The NO was determined by M.S.

(Continued)

594

[2] Decomposition of isopropyl nitrite in NO. The decomposition was found to be total-pressure dependent. By employing a classical Hinshelwood-Lindemann treatment of the data (i.e., $k_{uni} = k_0 M/(1 + k_0 M/k_\infty)$), the high- and low-pressure limiting rate constants were estimated. The low-pressure constant reported was $k_0 = 10^{10.1-8.3\theta}$ l/mole-sec, giving an RRK$-s \sim 20$. Energy transfer efficiencies of various third bodies were studied.

[3] Photolysis of isopropylpropionate. $iPrOCOC_2H_5 \xrightarrow{h\nu} C_2H_5CO + iPrO$. The rate of decomposition was monitored relative to the H-abstraction from the parent molecule $(E_7 - E_6) = 7$ kcal/mole

$$iPrO\cdot + A \xrightarrow{\ 6\ } iPrOH + R_{-H}$$
$$iPrO\cdot \xrightarrow{\ 7\ } CH_3CHO + CH_3$$

Production of acetaldehyde via spontaneous decomposition of "hot" $iPrO\cdot$ radicals was proposed and an appropriate correction made. Formation of $iPrOH$ via radical disproportionation was believed to be unimportant. The relative rate constant ratios reported were $k_7/k_6 = 1.0 \times 10^{17}$ (molec/cc) 28 °C, and 5×10^{17} molec/cc (65 °C), from which one obtains k_7/k_6 (moles/1) $= 3.7 \times 10^{-6/\theta}$. The parameters reported here are for an assumed rate of H-abstraction of $k_6 = 10^{8.75-5.5/\theta}$ l/mole-sec (same as observed for H-abstraction by $C_2H_5O\cdot$ from ethyl propionate; see ethoxy radical decomposition).

Reaction:_sec_-Butoxy radical

$$CH_3CHOCH_2CH_3 \text{ (I)} \xrightarrow{\quad 1 \quad} CH_3CHO \text{ (II)} + C_2H_5 \cdot \text{ (III)}$$

	I	II	III
$\Delta H^\circ_{f(298)}$	-20	-39.8	$+26$
$S^\circ_{(298)}$	83.9	63.2	59.6
$C^\circ_{p(298)}$	25.0	13.1	10.9

$\Delta S^\circ = 38.9$ g/mole
$\Delta H^\circ = 6.2$ kcal/mole
$\Delta C^\circ_p = -1.0$ g/mole

$\log A$	E	$\log k_T$ (460)	Conditions	System	Surface	References
~ 14	~ 17.5	5.69	$423\text{–}463\,^\circ K$	static	very little effect	[1] R. L. East and L. Phillips, J. Chem. Soc. A, 1939 (1967).

Preferred:
Reported values are estimates and very likely lower limits to correct high-pressure values.

Experimental
[1] _sec_-BuȮ radicals were generated by pyrolysis of the nitrite in NO. Relative rates of radical decomposition (1) to disproportionation (2) were followed in terms of the yield ratios of CH_3CHO and $CH_3COC_2H_5$. The latter were total pressure dependent. High-pressure parameters reported here were obtained from a simple Hinshelwood-Lindemann treatment assuming $E_2 = 0$ and $A_1 = 10^{14}$ sec^{-1}.

$$(M) + CH_3CHOCH_2CH_3 \xrightarrow{\quad 1 \quad} CH_3CHO + C_2H_5 \cdot + (M)$$

$$NO + sec\text{-BuO} \cdot \xrightarrow{\quad 2 \quad} HNO + CH_3COC_2H_5$$

Reaction: *t*-Butoxy radical

$$(CH_3)_3CO \cdot (I) \longrightarrow CH_3COCH_3 \ (II) + CH_3 \cdot (III)$$

	I	II	III
$\Delta H^\circ_{f(298)}$	(-21.5)	-51.7	34.0
$S^\circ_{(298)}$	76.5	70.5	46.4
$C^\circ_{p(298)}$	25.7	17.9	8.3

$\Delta S^\circ = 40.4$ g/mole
$\Delta H^\circ = (3.8)$ kcal/mole
$\Delta C^\circ_p = 0.5$ g/mole

log A	E	log k$_T$ (425)	Conditions	System	Surface	References
9.7	13.2	2.91	400–440 °K $P_T \sim 150$–550 torr			[1] F. W. Birss, C. J. Danby, and C. N. Hinshelwood, Proc. Roy. Soc. (L) **A239**, 154(1957).
11.2	11.0	5.54	298–352 °K $P \sim 20$ torr			[2] G. R. McMillan, J. Am. Chem. Soc. **82**, 2422 (1960).
13.71	17.0	4.97	403–427 °K Pinene 0–200 torr $P \sim 15$–20 torr			[3] R. K. Brinton and D. H. Volman, J. Chem. Phys. **20**, 25 (1952).
————	11.2		300–390 °K $P_T \sim 55$ torr			[4] D. H. Volman and W. M Graven, J. Am. Chem. Soc. **75**, 3111 (1953).
10.17	9	5.54	298–352 °K $P_T \sim 15$ torr			[5] G. McMillan and M. H. J. Wijnen, Can. J. Chem. **36**, 1227 (1958)
13.5	16.5±1	5.01	393–453 °K $P_T \sim 100$ torr			[6] L. Batt and F. R. Cruickshank, J. Phys. Chem. **71**, 1836 (1967).
14.7	22.8		398–436 °K 10–60 torr			[7] M. Y. Quee and J. C. J. Thynne, Trans. Faraday Soc **63**, 2970 (1967).

Preferred:
Tentatively, $\log k = 13.5 - 16.5/\theta$.

Comments: As in the isopropoxy radical decomposition, there is an apparent serious discrepancy between the kinetics and the reaction thermodynamics. If one accepts the most intuitively appealing parameters (ref. [6] or [3]), then one calculates $\log k_{-a}$ (l/mole-sec) $= 6.6 - 13.5/\theta$. The back reaction kinetics have been measured by O'Neal and Lubin (to be published), who found $\log_{-a}$ (l/mole·sec) $= 6.17 - 5.0/\theta$. Clearly there is a serious error in k_{-a}, k_a, ΔH°, or all three.

(Continued)

t-Butoxy radical *(Continued)*

The pressure dependence of this decomposition and an analysis of earlier results have been given b
H. Hershenson and S. W. Benson, J. Chem. Phys. **37**, 1889 (1962). See also D. J. Williams and M. F. R. Ma
cahy, Aus. J. Chem. **17**, 1291 (1964) with regard to the experimental verification of the pressure dependenc

Experimental

[1] Decomposition of di-*t*-butyl peroxide in the presence of NO. Rates of reaction were measured by ΔP and analys
of products by M.S. The decomposition was measured relative to the trapping reaction, $t\mathrm{BuO}\cdot + \mathrm{NO} \longrightarrow t\mathrm{BuONC}$
The rate of the trapping reaction was assumed to be the same as the rate of $\mathrm{CH_3O + NO}$, which was measured relativ
to the methyl radical recombination reaction to be k_4(l/mole-sec)$\simeq 10^{9.08}$.

[2] Photolysis (full Hg arc) of di-*t*-butyl peroxide with azomethane. The important steps in the mechanism assume
were:

$$\mathrm{ROOR} \xrightarrow{h\nu} 2t\mathrm{BuO}\cdot; \quad \mathrm{CH_3N{=}NCH_3} \xrightarrow{h\nu} 2\mathrm{CH_3}\cdot + \mathrm{N_2}$$

$$t\text{-}\mathrm{BuO}\cdot \xrightarrow{\ 2\ } \mathrm{CH_3COCH_3 + CH_3}\cdot$$

$$\mathrm{CH_3}\cdot + t\mathrm{BuO}\cdot \xrightarrow{\ 5\ } \mathrm{CH_3O}{-}t\mathrm{Bu}$$

$$\mathrm{CH_3}\cdot + \mathrm{CH_3}\cdot \xrightarrow{\ 8\ } \mathrm{C_2H_6}$$

Recombination rate constants for 5 and 8 were taken as $k_{rec} \simeq 2.2 \times 10^{10}$ l/mole-sec. The relative rates of decompos
tion (2) and H-abstraction of *t*-BuO from isobutane ($t\mathrm{BuO} + \mathrm{(CH_3)_3CH} \xrightarrow{16} t\mathrm{BuOH} + t\mathrm{Bu}\cdot$) were also determined
the photolysis of mixtures of the peroxide with isobutane. The result was $k_{16}/k_2 = 10^{-3.4+7/\theta}$ (l/moles) with $E_2 - E_{16} \simeq$
kcal/mole, which implies a 4 kcal/mole activation energy for tertiary hydrogen H-abstraction by $t\mathrm{BuO}\cdot$. Analysis b
G.L.C.

[3] Thermal decomposition of di-*t*-butyl peroxide in presence of ethylenimine. The relative rates of H-abstracti
from the imine and decomposition were determined.

$$t\mathrm{BuO}\cdot \xrightarrow{\ 2\ } \mathrm{CH_3COCH_3 + CH_3}\cdot$$

$$t\mathrm{BuO}\cdot + \mathrm{(CH_3)_2NH} \xrightarrow{\ 5\ } t\mathrm{BuOH} + \mathrm{(CH_3)_2N}.$$

$k_2/k_5 = 10^{+6.05-12/\theta}$ (moles/l). The parameters reported have been calculated assuming k_5 (l/mole-sec) $= 10^{7.66-5/\theta}$.

[4] Photolysis of di-*t*-butyl peroxide in butadiene. Analysis of products (acetone, ethane, CO, $\mathrm{CH_4}$ $\mathrm{(CH_3CO)_2}$, a
*t*BuOH) by M.S. Yields were corrected for the subsequent decomposition of acetone to $\mathrm{C_2H_6 + CO}$. Rate of decomp
sition was measured relative to the rate of addition to butadiene.

The data give $k_2/k_{10} = 23 \times 10^{-5.8/\theta}$ (moles/l). The reported activation energy is based on $E_{10} \simeq 5.4$ kcal/mole (measure
in the study).

[5] Photolysis of di-*t*-butyl peroxide. Pertinent reactions were

$$t\mathrm{BuO}\cdot \xrightarrow{\ 2\ } \mathrm{acetone} + \mathrm{CH_3}\cdot$$

$$t\mathrm{BuO}\cdot + \mathrm{CH_3}\cdot \xrightarrow{\ 5\ } t\mathrm{BuOCH_3}$$

$$t\mathrm{BuO}\cdot + \mathrm{P} \xrightarrow{\ 6\ } t\mathrm{BuOH} + \mathrm{P_{-H}}$$

$$\mathrm{CH_3}\cdot + \mathrm{CH_3}\cdot \xrightarrow{\ 8\ } 2\mathrm{C_2H_6}$$

Analysis of products by M.S. and G.L.C. The results were $k_2 k_8^{1/2}/k_5 = 2.44 \times 10^{-2}$ (moles/l-sec)$^{1/2} = 10^{4.99-9/\theta}$. (Indicat
parameters and based on $k_5 \simeq k_8 = 2.2 \times 10^{10}$ l/mole-sec.) In addition, $k_2/k_6 = 3.6 \times 10^{-3/\theta}$ (moles/l). If H-abstraction
given the same parameters as found for ethoxy, adjusting for the different numbers of abstractable hydrogens, $k_6 \simeq 10^{9.4}$
l/mole-sec, one obtains $k_2 = 10^{9.56-9/\theta}$ sec^{-1}.

(Continue

[6] Decomposition of di-*t*-butyl peroxide in the presence of HBr. The radical decomposition was measure relative to its H-abstraction from HBr. Parameters of the trapping reaction with HBr (tBuO + HBr $\xrightarrow{t}$ tBuOH + Br) were assumed to be $k_t = 10^{8.95-2/\theta}$ l/mole-sec and the A-factor for decomposition was also assumed (i.e., $10^{13.5}$ sec^{-1}, as reported).

[7] Thermal decomposition of di-*t*-butyl peroxide in the presence of NO. Reaction was found to be pressure dependent and the high-pressure Arrhenius parameters were estimated by a Hinshelwood-Lindemann treatment. $M_{1/2} \simeq 112$ torr at 436 °K, and $n \simeq 23$.

Reaction: 1-Ethoxy-1-ethyl radical

$$CH_3\dot{C}HOCH_2CH_3 \text{ (I)} \longrightarrow CH_3CHO \text{ (II)} + C_2H_5 \cdot \text{ (III)}$$

	I	II	III
$\Delta H^\circ_{f(298)}$	(−17.8)	−39.8	25.7
$S^\circ_{(298)}$	88.1	63.2	59.8
$C^\circ_{p(298)}$	25.4	13.1	11.1

$\Delta S^\circ = 34.9$ g/mole
$\Delta H^\circ = 3.7$ kcal/mole
$\Delta C^\circ_p = -1.2$ g/mole

log A	E	log k_T (435)	Conditions	System	Surface	References
10.91	23.5±2	−0.89	418–453 °K			[1] J. Long and G. Skirrow, Trans. Faraday Soc. **58**, 1403 (1962).
6.35	17.0	−2.19	540–638 °K $P_T \simeq 6$–25 torr			[2] M. H. Wijnen and E. W. R. Steacie, Can. J. Chem. **29**, 1092 (1951).

Preferred:
log $k_a = 10.91 - 23.5/\theta$, although the A-factor seems too low.

Comments: The reaction thermodynamics and k_a predict

$$\log [k_{-a} \text{ (l/mole-sec)}] \simeq 5.6 - 20/\theta.$$

Experimental

[1] Decomposition of di-t-butyl peroxide in the presence of diethyl ether. Analysis of all products (CO, CH$_4$, C$_2$H$_6$, C$_3$H$_8$, CH$_3$CHO) by G.L.C.
Mechanism:

$$CH_3 + (C_2H_5)_2O \xrightarrow{\;1\;} CH_4 + CH_3\dot{C}HOCH_2CH_3(R\cdot)$$
$$R\cdot + CH_3\cdot \xrightarrow{\;4\;} i\text{PrOEt}$$
$$R\cdot \xrightarrow{\;3\;} CH_3CHO + C_2H_5\cdot$$
$$CH_3 + C_2H_5 \xrightarrow{\;5\;} C_3H_8$$
$$CH_3 + CH_3 \xrightarrow{\;2\;} C_2H_6$$

The decomposition was followed relative to reactions (2) and (4), giving

$$\frac{k_3 k_2^{1/2}}{k_4} \left(\frac{\text{moles}}{\text{cc-sec}}\right)^{1/2} = 10^{7.11 - 23.5 \pm 2/\theta}.$$

The A-factor given above was reestimated, using $A_2 = 2 \times 10^{10}$ l/mole-sec and $k_4 = 10^{10}$ l/mole-sec.

[2] Photolysis of 2,2',4,4'-tetradeuterodiethyl ketone. Analysis for CO, C$_2$H$_4$, and C$_2$H$_6$, using fractional distillation,

(Continued)

1-Ethoxy-1-ethyl radical *(Continued)*

M.S., and a Blacet-Leighton apparatus. The decomposition reaction was monitored relative to the pentanonyl radical recombination with ethyl d_2 radicals and the D-abstraction of ethyl d_2 radicals from the ketone:

$$(k_6 k_4 / k_9) \simeq 10^{4.05 - 25.7/\theta} \ \text{sec}^{-1}$$

$$CH_3 CD_2 + K \xrightarrow{\ 9\ } X$$

$$CH_3 CD_2 + K \xrightarrow{\ 4\ } C_2 H_3 D_3 + K_{-D}$$

$$CH_3 CDCOCD_3 CH_3 \xrightarrow{\ 6\ } C_2 H_3 D + CO + CD_2 CH_3$$

The reported *A*-factor was obtained by assuming $k_9 \simeq 10^{10}$ l/mole-sec and using the calculated $k_4 = 10^{7.73 - 8.7/\theta}$ l/mole-sec.

Reaction: 4-Oxo-2-heptyl radical

$$CH_3CHCH_2COC_3H_7 \text{ (I)} \longrightarrow C_3H_6 \text{ (II)} + C_3H_7\dot{C}O \text{ (III)}$$

	I	II	III
$\Delta H^\circ_{f(298)}$	-27.7	4.9	-15.4
$S^\circ_{(298)}$	110.7	63.8	83.5
$C^\circ_{p(298)}$	41.1	15.3	24.4

$\Delta S^\circ = 56.6$ g/mole
$\Delta H^\circ = 17.2$ kcal/mole
$\Delta C^\circ_p = -1.4$ g/mole

log A	E	log k_T	Conditions	System	Surface	References
———	10		328–630 °K $P_T = 8$–115 torr			[1] C. R. Masson, J. Am. Chem. Soc. **74**, 4731 (1952).

Preferred:
Unreliable.

Comments: The thermodynamics cannot be greatly in error, and they show that the above decomposition must have an activation energy greater than 17 kcal/mole. $\Delta H^\circ_f(C_3H_7\dot{C}O)$ is based on $\Delta H^\circ_f(CH_3CO)$ and group additives; ΔH°_f (reactant) has been calculated assuming $DH^\circ(C-H) = 95$ kcal/mole in the di-*n*-propyl ketone.

Experimental

[1] Photolysis of di-*n*-propyl ketone (3130Å). Above 160 °C a chain reaction became important and was attributed to the above reaction. The decomposition was measured relative to the heptanonyl radical recombination reaction, which, in turn, was estimated from mass balances. Products were CO, CH_4, C_2H_6, C_2H_4, C_3H_6, C_3H_8, *n*-C_6H_{14}, and a C_4-hydrocarbon. Data are insufficient to calculate the A-factor. Products were separated by low-temperature distillation and analyses were performed by a variety of techniques including oxidation over CuO, M.S., and absorption of unsaturates, using a Blacet-Leighton apparatus.

Reaction: Methyl peroxymethyl radical

$$CH_3OOCH_2 \cdot (I) \longrightarrow CH_2O \ (II) + CH_3O \cdot (III)$$

	I	II	III
$\Delta H^\circ_{f(298)}$	13.5	−27.7	3.9
$S^\circ_{(298)}$	77.3	52.3	54.6
$C^\circ_{p(298)}$	17.3	8.5	8.4

$\Delta S^\circ = 29.6$ g/mole
$\Delta H^\circ = -37.3$ kcal/mole
$\Delta C^\circ_p = -0.4$ g/mole

log A	E	log k_T	Conditions	System	Surface	References
————	5.8		394–453 °K $P_T \sim 9$–150 torr			[1] Y. Takezake, T. Mizazaki, and N. Nakohara, J. Chem. Phys. **25**, 536 (1956).

Preferred:
Unreliable, because of implausible mechanism.

Comments: In view of the reaction exothermicity, the activation energy would be expected to be quite low.

Experimental

[1] Photolysis of dimethylperoxide (2537Å). Major products were CO, CH₃OH, and CH₂O. A complete and detailed treatment of the photochemically induced decomposition is presented. The overall rate, measured manometrically, was related to the reaction mechanism from which the activation energy relation, $E_2 + E_3 - E_4$, was deduced. Thus,

$$CH_3O + P \xrightarrow{\ 2\ } CH_3OH + \cdot CH_2OOCH_3$$

$$CH_3OOCH_2 \cdot \xrightarrow{\ 3\ } CH_2O + CH_3O\cdot$$

$$CH_3O + CH_3OOCH_2 \xrightarrow{\ 4\ } 2CH_2O + CH_3OH \cdot$$

From the nature of the reactions, it is likely that $E_2 \simeq E_4$. The A-factor could not be obtained from the data. Reaction 4 is not a likely one.

Reaction: Perfluoro-*t*-butoxy radical

$$
\begin{array}{c}
\overset{\displaystyle O \,\cdot}{\underset{\displaystyle |}{}} \\
(CF_3)_2CCF_3 \text{ (I)} \longrightarrow CF_3COCF_3 \text{ (II)} + CF_3 \cdot \text{ (III)}
\end{array}
$$

	I	II	III
$\Delta H^\circ_{f(298)}$			
$S^\circ_{(298)}$			
$C^\circ_{p(298)}$			

$\Delta S^\circ =$
$\Delta H^\circ =$
$\Delta C^\circ_p =$

log A	E	log k_T	Conditions	System	Surface	References
————	30.6		323–610 °K 25–180 torr			[1] A. S. Gordon, J. Chem. Phys. **36,** 1330 (1962).

Preferred:
   Reasonable.

Comments: ΔH° estimated by author was 21 kcal from E_{act} for forward and reverse rate. This is a significantl
stronger bond than in the H-analog.

Experimental
   [1] Photolysis of perfluoroacetone.
Mechanism:

$$
CF_3COCF_3 \xrightarrow{h\nu} 2CF_3 \cdot + CO
$$

$$
CF_3 \cdot + A \underset{-1}{\overset{1}{\rightleftharpoons}} (CF_3)_2COCF_3
$$

$$
\begin{array}{c}
\overset{\displaystyle O \,\cdot}{\underset{\displaystyle |}{}} \\
CF_3 \cdot + (CF_3)_2CCF_3 \xrightarrow{\ 2\ } (CF_3)_3COCF_3
\end{array}
$$

$$
2CF_3 \cdot \xrightarrow{\ 3\ } C_2F_6
$$

Rates of addition (1) were obtained at low temperatures from the yields of ether and perfluoroethane. Rates of the decom
position reaction (−1) were obtained from the high-temperature data where decomposition becomes important. $E_1 \simeq 9.$
kcal/mole. Analysis of the products was by G.L.C. Note radical structure is not certain.

Reaction: 2-Chloro-1-ethyl radical

$$\cdot CH_2CH_2Cl \; (I) \longrightarrow C_2H_4 \; (II) + Cl \; (III)$$

	I	II	III
$\Delta H^\circ_{f(298)}$	20.2	12.5	29.0
$S^\circ_{(298)}$	68.2	52.5	39.5
$C^\circ_{p(298)}$	14.8	10.4	5.2

$\Delta S^\circ = 23.8$ g/mole
$\Delta H^\circ = 21.3$ kcal/mole
$\Delta C^\circ_p = 0.8$ g/mole

log A	E	log k_T	Conditions	System	Surface	References
13	23.9		(*)			[1] R. Eckling, P. Goldfinger, G. Huybrechts, G. Martens, L. Meyers, and S. Smoes, Chem. Ber. **93**, 3014 (1960).

Preferred:
   $\log k_a = 13.6 - 22.2/\theta$.

Comments: Photochlorination study made by F. S. Dainton, D. A. Lomax, and M. Weston, Trans. Faraday Soc. **58**, 308 (1962). If $\log k_{-a}$ (l/mole-sec) $= 10.3 - 1.5/\theta$, as suggested by P. B. Ayscough, A. J. Cocker, F. S. Dainton, and S. Hirst, Trans. Faraday Soc. **58**, 318 (1962), then from the reaction thermodynamics, one obtains the preferred parameters.

Experimental

*[1] Calculated from various data sources.

Reaction: 1,2-Dichloro-1-ethyl radical

$$CH_2ClCHCl\cdot \text{ (I)} \longrightarrow CH_2\!\!=\!\!CHCl \text{ (II)} + Cl \text{ (III)}$$

	I	II	III
$\Delta H^\circ_{f(298)}$	(14.7)	8.4	29.0
$S^\circ_{(298)}$	76.9	63.0	39.5
$C^\circ_{p(298)}$	17.5	13.0	5.2

$\Delta S^\circ = 25.6$ g/mole
$\Delta H^\circ = (22.7)$ kcal/mole
$\Delta C^\circ_p = 0.7$ g/mole

log A	E	log k_T (315)	Conditions	System	Surface	References
10	22	−5.27	703–741 °K $P_T \sim 1$–80 mm Hg	static		[1] K. E. Howlett, Trans. Faraday Soc. **48,** 25 (1952).
13	23.8	−3.52	(*)			[2] R. Eckling, P. Goldfinger, G. Huybrechts, G. Martens, L. Meyers, and S. Smoes, Chem. Ber. **93,** 3014 (1960).

Preferred:
    log $k = 13.5 - 24.5/\theta$.

Comments:
    log $k_{-a} = 9.4 - 0.9/\theta$. P. B. Ayscough, A. J. Cocker, F. S. Dainton, S. Hirst, and M. Weston, Proc. Chem. Soc., 244 (1961).
    log k_a (est) $= 13.1 - 23.0/\theta$.
$\Delta H^\circ_f(R\cdot)$ based on $DH^\circ(C\!-\!H) = 98$ kcal/mole (see $C_2Cl_5\cdot$ decomposition). This puts the Pi bond strengt in $CHCl\!\!=\!\!CHCl$ at 1 kcal less than butene-2.

Experimental

    [1] Pyrolysis of 1,2-dichloroethylene. Rate was followed by pressure change with stoichiometry ($C_2H_4Cl_2 \longrightarrow C_2H_3Cl + HCl$). The mechanism proposed was

$$C_2H_4Cl_2 \xrightarrow{\ 1\ } \cdot C_2H_4Cl + Cl$$
$$Cl + C_2H_4Cl_2 \xrightarrow{\ 2\ } \cdot C_2H_3Cl_2 + HCl$$
$$\cdot C_2H_3Cl_2 \xrightarrow{\ 3\ } C_2H_3Cl + Cl$$
$$Cl + \cdot C_2H_3Cl \xrightarrow{\ 4\ } C_2H_3Cl + HCl$$

From the above, $k = \left(\dfrac{k_1 k_2 k_3}{k_4}\right)^{1/2} = 10^{10.8 - 47.0/\theta}$ sec^{-1}. An induction period was also observed and accounted for quantitatively. A pressure falloff of the rate was attributed to the unimolecular falloff of k_1, occurring at $P < 20$ torr. Variation of S/V had no effect.
    [2] Calculated from a number of data sources, photochlorination studies of vinylchloride performed by F. S. Dainton, P. A. Lomax, and M. Weston, Trans. Faraday Soc. 58, 308 (1962).

---

*Temperature range was 25–55 °C. Rotating sector technique employed.

Reaction: 1,2,2-Trichloro-1-ethyl radical

$$CHCl_2CHCl \cdot (I) \longrightarrow CHCl{=}CHCl\ (II) + Cl\ (III)$$

	I	II	III
$\Delta H^\circ_{f(298)}$	13.1	4.2	29.0
$S^\circ_{(298)}$	83.9	69.4	39.5
$C^\circ_{p(298)}$	20.7	15.8	5.2

$\Delta S^\circ = 25.0$ g/mole
$\Delta H^\circ = 20.1$ kcal/mole
$\Delta C^\circ_p = \ \ 0.3$ g/mole

log A	E	log k_T (325)	Conditions	System	Surface	References
12	20.3	-0.65	313–335 °K Rotating sector	static		[1] R. Eckling, P. Goldfinger, G. Huybrechts, G. Martins, L. Meyer, and S. Smoes, Chem. Ber. **93**, 3014 (1960).

Preferred:

log k_a (est) $\simeq 13.1 - 20.4/\theta$.

log $k_{-a} = 9.5 - 1.0/\theta$. P. B. Ayscough, A. J. Cocker, F. S. Dainton, S. Hirst, and M. Weston, Proc. Chem. Soc., 244 (1961).

Experimental

[1] Calculated from data of various sources. Photochlorination study made by P. B. Ayscough, A. J. Cocker, F. S. Dainton, and S. Hirst, Trans. Faraday Soc. **58**, 295 (1962). Rotating sector technique employed.

Reaction: 1,1,2,2-Tetrachloro-1-ethyl radical

$$CHCl_2CCl_2 \cdot \; (I) \longrightarrow Cl \; (II) + CHCl = CCl_2 \; (III)$$

	I	II	III
$\Delta H^\circ_{f(298)}$	9.5	29.0	0.3
$S^\circ_{(298)}$	89.3	39.5	77.5
$C^\circ_{p(298)}$	23.9	5.2	19.3

$\Delta S^\circ = 27.7$ g/mole
$\Delta H^\circ = 19.8$ kcal/mole
$\Delta C^\circ_p = 0.6$ g/mole

log A	E	log k_T (468)	Conditions	System	Surface	References
13.7	20.4	4.11	433–497 °K $P_T \simeq 60$–110 mm Hg	static		[1] G. Huybrechts, L. Meyers, and G. Verbeke, Trans. Faraday Soc. **58**, 1128 (1962).

Preferred:
Parameters are reasonable. $\log k = 13.7 - 20.4/\theta$.

Comments: Kinetics are in reasonable agreement with the estimated thermodynamics. The back-reaction kinetics have also been determined by Dainton et al., Proc. Chem. Soc., 244 (1961), to be $\log k_{-a}$ (l/mole-sec)$= 9.6 - 0.7/\theta$. See also F. S. Dainton, D. A. Lomax, and M. Weston, Trans. Faraday Soc. **53**, 460 (1947) for earlier work on the photochlorination of C_2HCl_3.
$\Delta H^\circ_f(R \cdot)$ based on DH(C—H) $= 98$ kcal/mole (see $C_2Cl_5 \cdot$ decomposition).

Experimental

[1] Photochlorination of trichloroethylene. Analysis of the chlorinated products was made by M.S. as a function of time. The kinetics for the chlorination mechanism gave a measure of the reverse addition reaction, $\log k_2$ (l/mole-sec)$= 9.75$, and the equilibrium constant for dissociation, $(k_4/k_2) = 10^{3.97-20.4/\theta}$ moles/l, from which the decomposition kinetics were calculated.

Mechanism:

$$Cl_2 \underset{}{\overset{h\nu}{\rightleftharpoons}} 2Cl$$

$$Cl + C_2HCl_3 \underset{4}{\overset{2}{\rightleftharpoons}} \cdot C_2HCl_4$$

$$\cdot C_2HCl_4 + Cl_2 \underset{5}{\overset{3}{\rightleftharpoons}} C_2HCl_5 + Cl$$

$$2Cl + M \overset{6}{\longrightarrow} Cl_2 + M$$

$$\cdot C_2HCl_4 + Cl \overset{7}{\longrightarrow} \text{termination products}$$

$$2 \cdot C_2HCl_4 \overset{8}{\longrightarrow} \text{termination products}$$

Reaction: Pentachloroethyl radical

$$C_2Cl_5 \cdot (I) \longrightarrow C_2Cl_4 (II) + Cl (III)$$

	I	II	III
$\Delta H^\circ_{f(298)}$	7.9	−3.6	29.0
$S^\circ_{(298)}$	94.5	81.4	39.5
$C^\circ_{p(298)}$	28.1	22.8	5.2

$\Delta S^\circ = 26.4$ g/mole
$\Delta H^\circ = 17.5$ kcal/mole
$\Delta C^\circ_p = -0.1$ g/mole

log A	E	log k_T (345)	Conditions	System	Surface	References
12.8	16.8	2.15	30–388 °K	static		[1] (a) J. Adam, P. Goldfinger, and P. A. Gosselain, Bull. Soc. Chim. Belges **65**, 549 (1956); (b) P. Goldfinger, M. Jeunehomme, and G. Martens, J. Chem. Phys. **29**, 456 (1958); (c) R. Eckling, P. Goldfinger, G. Huybrechts, G. Martens, L. Meyers, and S. Smoes, Chem. Ber. **93**, 3014 (1960).

Preferred:
 log $k_a = 13.5 - 17.8/\theta$.

Comments: The reaction enthalpy and radical heat of formation have been obtained from the kinetics. This also gives DH°(C—H) in $C_2HCl_5 \simeq 98.9$ kcal/mole and suggests that the DH°(C—H) in chlorinated ethanes is not appreciably affected by the chlorine substitution. The back reaction rate, log k_{-a} (l/mole·sec) $= 9.4$, has been measured by P. Goldfinger, G. Huybrechts, and G. Martens, Trans. Faraday Soc. **58**, 2210 (1961). See also reference [1c] above. This gives $A_{a(est)} = 10^{13.4}$ sec^{-1} (using the estimated ΔS° reaction), in reasonable agreement with the value reported.

Experimental

[1] Photochemical chlorination of tetrachloroethylene.
Mechanism:

$$Cl_2 \xrightarrow{h\nu} 2Cl \cdot \qquad \text{(Deduced rate constants)}$$

$$Cl + C_2Cl_4 \underset{-2}{\overset{2}{\rightleftarrows}} C_2Cl_5 \cdot \qquad \log k_{-2} \simeq 9.6$$

$$\cdot C_2Cl_5 + Cl_2 \underset{-3}{\overset{3}{\rightleftarrows}} C_2Cl_6 + Cl \cdot \qquad \log k_3 \simeq 8.31 - 5.4/\theta$$

$$Cl \cdot + C_2Cl_5 \cdot \xrightarrow{4} C_2Cl_6 \qquad \log k_{-3} \simeq 11.6 - 19.5/\theta$$

$$2Cl \cdot + M \xrightarrow{5} Cl_2 + M \qquad \log k_4 \simeq 11.31$$

$$2C_2Cl_5 \cdot \xrightarrow{6} C_2Cl_4 + C_2Cl_6 \qquad \log k_6 \simeq 8.66$$

(Continued)

For a complete summary of references to photochlorinated studies and a discussion of mechanisms for these reactions under varied conditions, see R. J. Cvetanovic, *Advances in Photochemistry*, Vol. 1, p. 115 (Interscience Publ., New York, 1963).

Reaction: 4-Chlorodifluoromethyl-2,5-cyclohexadienyl radical (resonance stabilized)

$$I \qquad II \qquad III$$

$\Delta H^\circ_{f(298)}$

$S^\circ_{(298)}$

$C^\circ_{p(298)}$

$\Delta S^\circ =$
$\Delta H^\circ =$
$\Delta C^\circ_p =$

log A	E	log k_T	Conditions	System	Surface	References
———	11.4		300–520 °K $P_T \sim 38$–100 mm Hg	static		[1] J. R. Majer, D. Phillips, and J. C. Robb, Trans. Faraday Soc. **61**, 110 (1965).

Preferred:
   Suspect.

Comments: The value is only slightly larger than the estimated endothermicity of 10 ± 2 kcal and suggests too low an activation energy for the reverse reaction.

Experimental

   [1] Photodecomposition of (CF₂ClCOCF₂Cl) in the presence of benzene. Products analyzed (M.S. and G.L.C.) were $C_2F_4Cl_2$, CF_2Cl_2, $C_3F_6Cl_2$, CF_2ClH, and CO. Higher molecular weight products were believed to be too involatile. The rate of addition (reverse of above) was measured from the decrease in rate of the (CF₂Cl) radical products (R_f) relative to CO formation caused by the addition of benzene compared to the pure ketone system. At higher temperatures (above 120 °C), the (R_f/CO) ratios reached a minimum and then increased with increasing temperature. This was interpreted in terms of the above decomposition. An Arrhenius plot of the (R_f/CO) ratios gave at low temperatures, $E_{addn} \sim 5.3$ kcal/mole, and at high temperatures, $E_{dec} \simeq 11.4$, as reported. In a similar study, $E_{dec} \simeq 10.7$ kcal/mole for $CF_2Cl$$_{d_6}$ (Trans. Faraday Soc. **61**, 122 (1965).

610

Reaction: 2-Bromo-1-ethyl radical

$$\cdot CH_2CH_2Br \text{ (I)} \longrightarrow C_2H_4 \text{ (II)} + Br \text{ (III)}$$

	I	II	III
$\Delta H^\circ_{f(298)}$	30.4	12.5	26.7
$S^\circ_{(298)}$	70.2	52.5	41.8
$C^\circ_{p(298)}$	15.0	10.4	5.0

$\Delta S^\circ = 24.1$ g/mole
$\Delta H^\circ = 8.8$ kcal/mole
$\Delta C^\circ_p = 0.4$ g/mole

log A	E	log k_T (310)	Conditions	System	Surface	References
	13 ± 2		333–353 °K $P_T \sim 200$ torr $(Br_2/=) \sim 1.0$	static		[1] H. Schmitz, H. J. Schumacher, and A. Jager, Chem. Ber. **B51**, 281 (1942).
	14 ± 2		298–327 °K	static		[2] D. A. Armstrong and J. W. T. Spinkes, Can. J. Chem. **37**, 1210 (1959).
	$\geqslant 7.4$		423–573 °K $P_T \sim 50$–600 torr	static		[3] R. Barker and A. Maccoll, J. Chem. Soc., 2839 (1963).
12.9	11.1	5.07	(ref. [2])			(4) E. O'Neal and S. W. Benson (unpublished calculations).

Preferred:
$\log k_a = 12.9 - 11.1/\theta$.

Comments: The back reaction rate has been measured at 60 °C (R. J. Cvetanovic, *Advances in Photochemistry*, Vol. **1**, p. 173, Interscience Publ., New York, 1963) to be k_{-a}(l/mole-sec) $\simeq 4 \times 10^7$. Assuming $A_{-a} \simeq 10^{9.5}$, one then calculates $E_{-a} \simeq 2.9$ kcal/mole, and $\log k_a \simeq 12.9 - 11.1/\theta$.

Experimental
[1] Photolysis of ethylene with bromine. The rate was followed manometrically.

Mechanism:

$$Br_2 \xrightarrow{h\nu} 2Br$$
$$C_2H_4 + Br \underset{3}{\overset{2}{\rightleftharpoons}} C_2H_4Br$$
$$C_2H_4Br + Br_2 \xrightarrow{4} C_2H_4Br_2 + Br$$
$$2Br + M \xrightarrow{5} Br_2 + M$$

[2] Gas phase addition of HBr to ethylene induced by Co^{60} γ-rays. Relative rates of the decomposition and trapping
(Continued)

2-Bromo-1-ethyl radical *(Continued)*

reaction were obtained.

$$\cdot C_2H_4Br \xrightarrow{\ 1\ } C_2H_4 + Br$$

$$\cdot C_2H_4Br + HBr \xrightarrow{\ 2\ } C_2H_5Br + Br$$

[3] Photolysis of ethylbromide. Products were C_2H_4 and HBr. Reaction rate was followed by ΔP and checked by HBr titration.

Mechanism proposed:

$$C_2H_5Br + h\nu \xrightarrow{\ 1\ } C_2H_5 + Br$$

$$Br + C_2H_5Br \xrightarrow{\ 2\ } HBr + \cdot C_2H_4Br$$

$$\cdot C_2H_4Br \xrightarrow{\ 3\ } C_2H_4 + Br$$

$$\cdot C_2H_4Br + Br \xrightarrow{\ 4\ } \text{chain ending}$$

$$C_2H_5 + Br \xrightarrow{\ 5\ } \text{chain ending}$$

$$2Br + M \xrightarrow{\ 6\ } Br_2 + M$$

$$Br + W \xrightarrow{\ 7\ } 1/2Br_2 + W$$

From the mechanism at high pressures, rate $= \left(\dfrac{k_1 k_2 k_3}{2k_4}\right)^{1/2} (C_2H_5Br)_0 I_o^{1/2}$, from which $E = 1/2(E_1 + E_2 + E_3 - E_4) = 10.5$; The reported activation energy follows from $E_2 = 13.6$ kcal/mole (Anderson and Van Artsdalen, J. Chem. Phys. **12**, 479 (1944)).

[4] Reanalysis of data of reference [2] on basis of "the wrong radical" mechanism.

Mechanism:

$$C_2H_5Br + h\nu \xrightarrow{\ 1\ } C_2H_5 \cdot + Br$$

$$Br + C_2H_5Br \underset{-2}{\overset{2}{\rightleftharpoons}} \cdot CH_2CH_2Br + HBr$$

$$M + C_2H_4Br \xrightarrow{\ 3\ } C_2H_4 + Br + M$$

$$Br + C_2H_5Br \underset{-4}{\overset{4}{\rightleftharpoons}} HBr + CH_3 \cdot CHBr$$

$$Br + CH_3CHBr \xrightarrow{\ t\ } CH_3CHBr_2$$

The decomposition is pressure dependent (low-pressure region).

Reaction: *p*-(Bromomethyl) benzyl radical

$$\cdot CH_2 \diagup \!\!\! \diagdown \!\!\! -CH_2Br \,(I) \longrightarrow CH_2 \!\! = \!\! \diagup \!\!\! \diagdown \!\! = \!\! CH_2 \,(II) + Br\,(III)$$

	I	II	III
$\Delta H^\circ_{f(298)}$	40.3		26.7
$S^\circ_{(298)}$	97		41.8
$C^\circ_{p(298)}$	34.2		5.0

$\Delta S^\circ =$
$\Delta H^\circ =$
$\Delta C^\circ_p =$

log A	E	log k_T (780)	Conditions	System	Surface	References
13	40	1.79	748–814 °K $\delta P \simeq 0.03$–0.06 torr	flow		[1] M. Levy, M. Szwarc, and J. Throssell, J. Chem. Phys. **22**, 1904 (1954).

Preferred:

log $k = 13 - 40/\theta$ (however, see comments).

Comments: Parameters are not unreasonable, but E_{act} could well be about 10 kcal too low.

Experimental

[1] Toluene carrier technique in the pyrolysis of w,w'-dibromo *para*-xylene.
Mechanism:

$$BrCH_2 \emptyset CH_2 - Br \xrightarrow{\;2\;} Br + \cdot CH_2 \emptyset CH_2Br \,(R\cdot)$$
$$R\cdot + \emptyset CH_3 \xrightarrow{\;3\;} \emptyset CH_2 \cdot + CH_3 \emptyset CH_2 Br \,(P)$$
$$P \xrightarrow{\;1\;} CH_3 \emptyset CH_2 \cdot + Br$$
$$R\cdot \xrightarrow{\;4\;} Br + CH_2 = \diagup\!\!\!\diagdown = CH_2$$

termination by benzyl and paramethylbenzyl radicals.

Rates were based on the rate of HBr production. By equating the rates of reactions (2) and (1), it was possible to deduce the rate of reaction (4) relative to (3) from the steady-state relations. Parameters reported are for an assumed A_4 and an assigned $E_3 = 10$ kcal/mole.

Reaction: Dimethylgallium radical

$$\cdot Ga(CH_3)_2 \text{ (I)} \longrightarrow \cdot Ga(CH_3) \text{ (II)} + CH_3 \cdot \text{ (III)}$$

	I	II	III
$\Delta H^\circ_{f(298)}$			
$S^\circ_{(298)}$			
$C^\circ_{p(298)}$			

$\Delta S^\circ =$
$\Delta H^\circ =$
$\Delta C^\circ_p =$

log A	E	log k_T (835)	Conditions	System	Surface	References
7.94	35.4	−1.33	(see Ga(CH$_3$)$_3$) 686–983 °K $P_T \simeq 13$ torr	flow		[1] M. G. Jacko and S. W. Price, Can. J. Chem. **41**, 1560 (1963).

Preferred:
   Suspect.

Comments: In order for such a low *A*-factor to be valid, this decomposition must not only be in the falloff region, but it also must be non-adiabatic (i.e., require electronic state crossing).

Experimental

[1] See Ga(CH$_3$)$_3$ for experimental details. From the methyl balance relative to decomposed Ga(CH$_3$)$_3$, it was proposed that at low temperatures only the first methyl group is eliminated. At much higher temperatures (above 830 °K), the above reaction was postulated. Treatment of the data using the theory of successive reactions gave the parameters reported. The reaction was found to be pressure-dependent and extremely sensitive to the nature of the surface.

Reaction: Methylindium diradical

$$:In(CH_3) \text{ (I)} \longrightarrow In \text{ (II)} + CH_3 \text{ (III)}$$

	I	II	III
$\Delta H^\circ_{f(298)}$			
$S^\circ_{(298)}$			
$C^\circ_{p(298)}$			

$\Delta S^\circ =$
$\Delta H^\circ =$
$\Delta C^\circ_p =$

log A	E	log k_T (665)	Conditions	System	Surface	References
10.91	38.7	-1.81	(see In(CH$_3$)$_3$) 550–781 °K $P_T \simeq 13$ torr	flow		[1] M. G. Jacko and S. J. W. Price, Can. J. Chem. **42**, 1198 (1963).

Preferred:
Reasonable.

Comments: The A-factor is in the region anticipated for a pressure-dependent unimolecular decomposition.

Experimental

[1] See In(CH$_3$)$_3$ for experimental details. At temperatures below 670 °K, two methyls were released. At higher temperatures, the above decomposition became important. Method of successive reactions was used to determine the Arrhenius parameters. From (S/V) effects, the reaction was judged 97 percent homogeneous. The rate constant was also strongly pressure-dependent, indicating a unimolecular reaction well into its second-order region.

Reaction: Methylzinc radical

$$CH_3Zn \cdot (I) \longrightarrow CH_3 \cdot (II) + Zn \ (III)$$

	I	II	III
$\Delta H^{\circ}_{f(298)}$			
$S^{\circ}_{(298)}$			
$C^{\circ}_{p(298)}$			

$\Delta S^{\circ} =$
$\Delta H^{\circ} =$
$\Delta C^{\circ}_p =$

log A	E	log k_T (920)	Conditions	System	Surface	References
6.8	35.0	−1.52	(see Zn(CH$_3$)$_2$) 843−1000 °K $P_T = 16$ torr	flow		[1] S. J. W. Price and A. F. Trotman-Dickenson, Trans. Faraday Soc. **53**, 1208 (1957).

Preferred:

Pressure-dependent; not reliable.

See comments on the (CH$_3$)$_2$Ga$\cdot$ decomposition.

Experimental

[1] See (CH$_3$)$_2$Zn for details. Above reaction was observed at $T > 1000$ °K. The method of successive reactions was applied to the data in order to determine the above parameters. The rate was directly proportional to pressure, and therefore was in its second-order region.

Index to Reactants

C

D

619

Index by Formula

Index by Formula—Continued

Index by Formula—Continued

THE NATIONAL ECONOMIC GOAL
Sustained maximum growth in a free market economy, without inflation, under conditions of full employment and equal opportunity

THE DEPARTMENT OF COMMERCE
The historic mission of the Department is "to foster, promote and develop the foreign and domestic commerce" of the United States. This has evolved, as a result of legislative and administrative additions, to encompass broadly the responsibility to foster, serve and promote the nation's economic development and technological advancement. The Department seeks to fulfill this mission through these activities:

MISSION AND FUNCTIONS OF THE DEPARTMENT OF COMMERCE

"to foster, serve and promote the nation's economic development and technological advancement"

Participating with other government agencies in the creation of national policy, through the President's Cabinet and its subdivisions.

- Cabinet Committee on Economic Policy
- Urban Affairs Council
- Environmental Quality Council

Promoting progressive business policies and growth.

- Business and Defense Services Administration
- Office of Field Services

Assisting states, communities and individuals toward economic progress.

- Economic Development Administration
- Regional Planning Commissions
- Office of Minority Business Enterprise

Strengthening the international economic position of the United States.

- Bureau of International Commerce
- Office of Foreign Commercial Services
- Office of Foreign Direct Investments
- United States Travel Service
- Maritime Administration

Assuring effective use and growth of the nation's scientific and technical resources.

- Environmental Science Services Administration
- Patent Office
- National Bureau of Standards
- Office of Telecommunications
- Office of State Technical Services

Acquiring, analyzing and disseminating information concerning the nation and the economy to help achieve increased social and economic benefit.

- Bureau of the Census
- Office of Business Economics

NOTE: This schematic is neither an organization chart nor a program outline for budget purposes. It is a general statement of the Department's mission in relation to the national goal of economic development.

JULY 1969

NATIONAL BUREAU OF STANDARDS

The National Bureau of Standards [1] was established by an act of Congress March 3, 1901. Today, in addition to serving as the Nation's central measurement laboratory, the Bureau is a principal focal point in the Federal Government for assuring maximum application of the physical and engineering sciences to the advancement of technology in industry and commerce. To this end the Bureau conducts research and provides central national services in four broad program areas. These are: (1) basic measurements and standards, (2) materials measurements and standards, (3) technological measurements and standards, and (4) transfer of technology.

The Bureau comprises the Institute for Basic Standards, the Institute for Materials Research, the Institute for Applied Technology, the Center for Radiation Research, the Center for Computer Sciences and Technology, and the Office for Information Programs.

THE INSTITUTE FOR BASIC STANDARDS provides the central basis within the United States of a complete and consistent system of physical measurement; coordinates that system with measurement systems of other nations; and furnishes essential services leading to accurate and uniform physical measurements throughout the Nation's scientific community, industry, and commerce. The Institute consists of an Office of Measurement Services and the following technical divisions:

> Applied Mathematics—Electricity—Metrology—Mechanics—Heat—Atomic and Molecular Physics—Radio Physics [2]—Radio Engineering [2]—Time and Frequency [2]—Astrophysics [2]—Cryogenics. [2]

THE INSTITUTE FOR MATERIALS RESEARCH conducts materials research leading to improved methods of measurement standards, and data on the properties of well-characterized materials needed by industry, commerce, educational institutions, and Government; develops, produces, and distributes standard reference materials; relates the physical and chemical properties of materials to their behavior and their interaction with their environments; and provides advisory and research services to other Government agencies. The Institute consists of an Office of Standard Reference Materials and the following divisions:

> Analytical Chemistry—Polymers—Metallurgy—Inorganic Materials—Physical Chemistry.

THE INSTITUTE FOR APPLIED TECHNOLOGY provides technical services to promote the use of available technology and to facilitate technological innovation in industry and Government; cooperates with public and private organizations in the development of technological standards, and test methodologies; and provides advisory and research services for Federal, state, and local government agencies. The Institute consists of the following technical divisions and offices:

> Engineering Standards—Weights and Measures — Invention and Innovation — Vehicle Systems Research—Product Evaluation—Building Research—Instrument Shops—Measurement Engineering—Electronic Technology—Technical Analysis.

THE CENTER FOR RADIATION RESEARCH engages in research, measurement, and application of radiation to the solution of Bureau mission problems and the problems of other agencies and institutions. The Center consists of the following divisions:

> Reactor Radiation—Linac Radiation—Nuclear Radiation—Applied Radiation.

THE CENTER FOR COMPUTER SCIENCES AND TECHNOLOGY conducts research and provides technical services designed to aid Government agencies in the selection, acquisition, and effective use of automatic data processing equipment; and serves as the principal focus for the development of Federal standards for automatic data processing equipment, techniques, and computer languages. The Center consists of the following offices and divisions:

> Information Processing Standards—Computer Information — Computer Services — Systems Development—Information Processing Technology.

THE OFFICE FOR INFORMATION PROGRAMS promotes optimum dissemination and accessibility of scientific information generated within NBS and other agencies of the Federal government; promotes the development of the National Standard Reference Data System and a system of information analysis centers dealing with the broader aspects of the National Measurement System, and provides appropriate services to ensure that the NBS staff has optimum accessibility to the scientific information of the world. The Office consists of the following organizational units:

> Office of Standard Reference Data—Clearinghouse for Federal Scientific and Technical Information [3]—Office of Technical Information and Publications—Library—Office of Public Information—Office of International Relations.

---

[1] Headquarters and Laboratories at Gaithersburg, Maryland, unless otherwise noted; mailing address Washington, D.C. 20234.
[2] Located at Boulder, Colorado 80302.
[3] Located at 5285 Port Royal Road, Springfield, Virginia 22151.

NBS TECHNICAL PUBLICATIONS

PERIODICALS

JOURNAL OF RESEARCH reports National Bureau of Standards research and development in physics, mathematics, chemistry, and engineering. Comprehensive scientific papers give complete details of the work, including laboratory data, experimental procedures, and theoretical and mathematical analyses. Illustrated with photographs, drawings, and charts.

Published in three sections, available separately:

● Physics and Chemistry

Papers of interest primarily to scientists working in these fields. This section covers a broad range of physical and chemical research, with major emphasis on standards of physical measurement, fundamental constants, and properties of matter. Issued six times a year. Annual subscription: Domestic, $9.50; foreign, $11.75*.

● Mathematical Sciences

Studies and compilations designed mainly for the mathematician and theoretical physicist. Topics in mathematical statistics, theory of experiment design, numerical analysis, theoretical physics and chemistry, logical design and programming of computers and computer systems. Short numerical tables. Issued quarterly. Annual subscription: Domestic, $5.00; foreign, $6.25*.

● Engineering and Instrumentation

Reporting results of interest chiefly to the engineer and the applied scientist. This section includes many of the new developments in instrumentation resulting from the Bureau's work in physical measurement, data processing, and development of test methods. It will also cover some of the work in acoustics, applied mechanics, building research, and cryogenic engineering. Issued quarterly. Annual subscription: Domestic, $5.00; foreign, $6.25*.

TECHNICAL NEWS BULLETIN

The best single source of information concerning the Bureau's research, developmental, cooperative and publication activities, this monthly publication is designed for the industry-oriented individual whose daily work involves intimate contact with science and technology—*for engineers, chemists, physicists, research managers, product-development managers, and company executives.* Annual subscription: Domestic, $3.00; foreign, $4.00*.

* Difference in price is due to extra cost of foreign mailing.

Order NBS publications from: Superintendent of Documents
Government Printing Office
Washington, D.C. 20402

NONPERIODICALS

Applied Mathematics Series. Mathematical tables, manuals, and studies.

Building Science Series. Research results, test methods, and performance criteria of building materials, components, systems, and structures.

Handbooks. Recommended codes of engineering and industrial practice (including safety codes) developed in cooperation with interested industries, professional organizations, and regulatory bodies.

Special Publications. Proceedings of NBS conferences, bibliographies, annual reports, wall charts, pamphlets, etc.

Monographs. Major contributions to the technical literature on various subjects related to the Bureau's scientific and technical activities.

National Standard Reference Data Series. NSRDS provides quantitive data on the physical and chemical properties of materials, compiled from the world's literature and critically evaluated.

Product Standards. Provide requirements for sizes, types, quality and methods for testing various industrial products. These standards are developed cooperatively with interested Government and industry groups and provide the basis for common understanding of product characteristics for both buyers and sellers. Their use is voluntary.

Technical Notes. This series consists of communications and reports (covering both other agency and NBS-sponsored work) of limited or transitory interest.

Federal Information Processing Standards Publications. This series is the official publication within the Federal Government for information on standards adopted and promulgated under the Public Law 89–306, and Bureau of the Budget Circular A–86 entitled, Standardization of Data Elements and Codes in Data Systems.

CLEARINGHOUSE

The Clearinghouse for Federal Scientific and Technical Information, operated by NBS, supplies unclassified information related to Government-generated science and technology in defense, space, atomic energy, and other national programs. For further information on Clearinghouse services, write:

Clearinghouse
U.S. Department of Commerce
Springfield, Virginia 22151

Announcement of New Publications in
National Standard Reference Data Series

Superintendent of Documents,
U.S. Government Printing Office,
Washington, D.C. 20402

Dear Sir:

Please add my name to the announcement list of new publications to be issued in the series: National Standard Reference Data Series — National Bureau of Standards.

Name...

Company...

Address...

City..State................Zip Code...................

(Notification key N−337)

Publications in the National Standard Reference Data Series
National Bureau of Standards

You may use this listing as your order form by checking the proper box of the publication(s) you desire or by providing the full identification of the publication you wish to purchase. The full letter symbols with each publications number and full title of the publication and author must be given in your order, e.g. NSRDS–NBS–17, Tables of Molecular Vibrational Frequencies, Part 3, by T. Shimanouchi.

Pay for publications by check, money order, or Superintendent of Documents coupons or deposit account. Make checks and money orders payable to Superintendent of Documents. Foreign remit-tances should be made either by international money order or draft on an American bank. Post-age stamps are not acceptable.

No charge is made for postage to destinations in the United States and possessions, Canada, Mexico, and certain Central and South American countries. To other countries, payments for docu-ments must cover postage. Therefore, one-fourth of the price of the publication should be added for postage.

Send your order together with remittance to Superintendent of Documents, Government Print-ing Office, Washington, D.C. 20402.

☐ NSRDS-NBS 1, **National Standard Reference Data System—Plan of Operation,** by E. L. Brady and M. B. Wallenstein, 1964 (15 cents).

☐ NSRDS-NBS 2, **Thermal Properties of Aqueous Uni-univalent Electrolytes,** by V. B. Parker, 1965 (45 cents).

☐ NSRDS-NBS 3, Sec. 1, **Selected Tables of Atomic Spectra, Atomic Energy Levels and Multiplet Tables, Si II, Si III, Si IV,** by C. E. Moore, 1965 (35 cents).

☐ NSRDS-NBS 3, Sec. 2, **Selected Tables of Atomic Spectra, Atomic Energy Levels and Multiplet Tables, Si I,** by C. E. Moore, 1967 (20 cents).

☐ NSRDS-NBS 4, **Atomic Transition Probabilities, Volume 1, Hydrogen Through Neon,** by W. L. Wiese, M. W. Smith and B. M. Glennon, 1966 ($2.50).

☐ NSRDS-NBS 5, **The Band Spectrum of Carbon Monoxide,** by P. H. Krupenie, 1966 (70 cents).

☐ NSRDS-NBS 6, **Tables of Molecular Vibrational Frequencies, Part 1,** by T. Shimanouchi, 1967 (40 cents).

☐ NSRDS-NBS 7, **High Temperature Properties and Decomposition of Inorganic Salts, Part 1, Sulfates,** by K. H. Stern and E. L. Weise, 1966 (35 cents).

☐ NSRDS-NBS 8, **Thermal Conductivity of Selected Materials,** by R. W. Powell, C. Y. Ho, and P. E. Liley, 1966 ($1).

☐ NSRDS-NBS 9, **Bimolecular Gas Phase Reactions (rate co-efficients),** by A. F. Trotman-Dickenson and G. S. Milne, 1967 ($2).

☐ NSRDS-NBS 10, **Selected Values of Electric Dipole Moments for Molecules in the Gas Phase,** by R. D. Nelson, Jr., D. R. Lide, Jr., and A. A. Maryott, 1967 (40 cents).

☐ NSRDS-NBS 11, **Tables of Molecular Vibrational Frequencies, Part 2,** by T. Shimanouchi, 1967 (30 cents).

☐ NSRDS-NBS 12, **Tables for the Rigid Asymmetric Roto: Trans-formation Coefficients from Symmetric to Asymmetric Bases and Expectation Values of P_z^2, P_z^4, and P_z^6,** by R. H. Schwende-man, 1968 (60 cents).

☐ NSRDS-NBS 13, **Hydrogenation of Ethylene on Metallic Cata-lysts,** by J. Horiuti and K. Miyahara, 1968 ($1).

☐ NSRDS-NBS 14, **X-Ray Wavelengths and X-Ray Atomic Energy Levels,** by J. A. Bearden, 1967 (40 cents).

☐ NSRDS-NBS 15, **Molten Salts, Vol. 1, Electrical Conductance, Density, and Viscosity Data,** by G. Janz, F. W. Dampier, G. R. Lakshminarayanan, P. K. Lorenz, and R. P. T. Tomkins, 1968 ($3).

☐ NSRDS-NBS 16, **Thermal Conductivity of Selected Materials, Part 2,** by C. Y. Ho, R. W. Powell, and P. E. Liley, 1968 ($2).

☐ NSRDS-NBS 17, **Tables of Molecular Vibration Frequencies, Part 3,** by T. Shimanouchi, 1968 (30 cents).

☐ NSRDS-NBS 18, **Critical Analysis of the Heat-Capacity Data of the Literature and Evaluation of Thermodynamic Prop-erties of Copper, Silver, and Gold From 0 to 300 K,** by G. T. Furukawa, W. G. Saba, and M. L. Reilly, 1968 (40 cents).

☐ NSRDS-NBS 19, **Thermodynamic Properties of Ammonia as an Ideal Gas,** by L. Haar, 1968 (20 cents).

☐ NSRDS-NBS 20, **Gas Phase Reaction Kinetics of Neutral Oxygen Species,** by H. S. Johnson, 1968 (45 cents).

☐ NSRDS-NBS 22, **Atomic Transition Probabilities, Vol. II, Sodium Through Calcium, A Critical Data Compilation,** by W. L. Wiese, M. W. Smith, and B. M. Miles ($4.50).

☐ NSRDS-NBS 23, **Partial Grotrian Diagrams of Astrophysical Interest,** by C. E. Moore and P. W. Merrill, 1968 (55 cents).

☐ NSRDS-NBS 24, **Theoretical Mean Activity Coefficients of Strong Electrolytes in Aqueous Solutions from 0 to 100° C,** by Walter J. Hamer, 1968 ($4.25).

☐ NSRDS-NBS 25, **Electron Impact Excitation of Atoms,** by B. L. Moiseiwitsch and S. J. Smith, 1968 ($2).

☐ NSRDS-NBS 26, **Ionization Potentials, Appearance Potentials, and Heats of Formation of Positive Ions,** by J. L. Franklin, J. G. Dillard, H. M. Rosenstock, J. T. Herron, K. Draxl, and F. H. Field ($4).

☐ NSRDS-NBS 27, **Thermodynamic Properties of Argon from the Triple Point to 300 K at Presures to 1000 Atmospheres,** by A. L. Gosman, R. D. McCarty, and J. G. Hust ($1.25).

☐ NSRDS-NBS 28, **Molten Salts, Vol. 2, Section 1, Electro-chemistry of Molten Salts: Gibbs Free Energies and Excess Free Energies From Equilibrium-Type Cells,** by G. J. Janz and C. G. M. Dijkhuis. **Section 2, Surface Tension Data,** by G. J. Janz, G. R. Lakshminarayanan, R. P. T. Tomkins, and J. Wong ($2.75).

☐ NSRDS-NBS 29, **Photon Cross Sections, Attenuation Coeffic-cients and Energy Absorption Coefficients From 10 keV to 100 GeV,** J. H. Hubbell (75 cents).

☐ NSRDS-NBS 30, **High Temperature Properties and Decomposi-tion of Inorganic Salts. Part 2. Carbonates,** by K. H. Stern and E. L. Weise, 1969 (45 cents).

(cut here)